EARTH

DK

EARTH

Editors-in-Chief

James F. Luhr and Jeffrey E. Post

Senior Editor Peter Frances

Senior Art Editor Caroline Buckingham

Project Editors Sophie Bevan, Kim Dennis-Bryan, Sean O'connor, Gill Pitts, David Summers, Miezan van Zyl

Art Editors Clare Joyce, David Ball, Kirsten Cashman, Kenny Grant, Thomas Keenes, Helen Taylor, Duncan Turner

Editors Dharini Ganesh, Georgina Garner, Ben Hoare, Giles Sparrow, Nikky Twyman

Designers Paul Drislane, Lee Riches, Vanessa Thompson

Indexer John Noble

DTP Designers Rajen Shah, Simon Longstaff, Martin Nilsson

Pre-Production Producer Adam Stoneham
Picture Researchers Louise Thomas, Aditya Katyal
Illustrators Tom Coulson (Encompass Graphics Limited), Arran Lewis (ecorche), Peter Bull (Peter Bull Art Studio) John Plumer, Planetary Visions Limited
Cartographers David Roberts, Iorwerth Watkins
Production Controllers Elizabeth Cherry, Sarah Dodd
Producer Mary Slater
Jacket Designer Natasha Rees
Jacket Editor Manisha Majithia
Jacket Design Development Manager Sophia MTT

Managing Art Editor Michelle Baxter
Managing Editor Angeles Gavira Guerrero
Publisher Sarah Larter
Art Directors Philip Ormerod, Bryn Walls
Associate Publishing Director Liz Wheeler
Publishing Director Jonathan Metcalf

COOLING BROWN
(Rocks, Minerals, Environmental Issues)
Art Editor Philip Lord
Project Editor Joanna Chisholm
Creative Director Arthur Brown
Managing Editor Amanda Lebentz

SMITHSONIAN PROJECT CO-ORDINATOR
Kealy Wilson

Content previously published as *Illustrated Encyclopedia of Earth* in 2011 and as *Earth* in 2003 and 2013 by Dorling Kindersley Limited 80 Strand, London, WC2R 0RL

Copyright © 2003, 2011, 2013, 2015 Dorling Kindersley Limited

A Penguin Random House Company

2 4 6 8 10 9 7 5 3 1
001-289941-September/2015

A CIP catalogue record for this book is available from the British Library.

ISBN 978-0-2412-4311-4

Printed in China

A WORLD OF IDEAS:
SEE ALL THERE IS TO KNOW

www.dk.com

CONTENTS

PLANET EARTH

LAND

OCEAN

ATMOSPHERE

ABOUT THIS BOOK

Earth is divided into four main sections. The first section, PLANET EARTH, is an introduction to the Earth as a whole. The next three sections are about the planet's main environments – the LAND, OCEAN, and ATMOSPHERE. Within these sections, the Earth's features are divided into categories, such as Rivers and Lakes. Introductory pages describe typical features found in each category and explain how they are formed. On the succeeding pages, major features in that category are profiled individually. Thematic panels (see right) appear throughout.

Planet Earth

This overview of our planet is divided into three parts. The History of the Earth is a narrative account of how our planet and the Universe as a whole came to be the way they are now. The Anatomy of the Earth looks at the Earth's structure and materials, while The Changing Earth explains those processes that operate on a global scale.

HISTORY OF THE EARTH
These pages contain a summary of the history of our planet, beginning with the formation of the Universe.

text explains key concepts to support later sections

ANATOMY OF THE EARTH
This section contains an explanation of the complex structure of Earth and its layers.

three-dimensional artworks reveal structural detail

Land, Ocean, and Atmosphere

These three sections focus on specific features – on the Earth's landmasses, in the five great oceans, and in the layer of gases separating the Earth from space. Within each section, features are grouped by type into smaller sections, and then explained in general and individually profiled. Most profiles describe actual features (such as particular volcanoes), while others characterize general kinds of phenomena (such as types of clouds). Profiles of actual features are presented according to the continent on which they are found, in the following order: the Arctic, North America, Central America, South America, Europe, Africa, north and west Asia, south and east Asia, Australasia, and Antarctica. Within continents, features are arranged approximately in north–south order.

◀ MAIN SECTIONS
The three main domains of the Earth's exterior are described in separate sections.

GROUP INTRODUCTIONS ▶
The main sections are subdivided so that particular types of feature are grouped together. Some sections are divided again to create a further level of detail.

colour-coded panel contains references to other relevant sections

EXPLANATORY PAGES ▶
Throughout the book, these pages contain explanations of forces and processes, as well as descriptions of typical features. Most of these pages are followed by profiles of actual features.

compass direction indicates position within continent (locations within Australasia are identified by name of country)

name of continent on which feature is found

NORTH AMERICA *north*

North American boreal forest

name of feature being profiled

LOCATION Extending from central Alaska, USA, in the west to central Labrador, Canada, in the east

description of detailed location, including name of country (or countries) in which feature is found

location of feature identified on world map by red dot (or red rectangle for larger features)

detailed map shows feature in regional context

Anchorage

ATLANTIC OCEAN

Hudson Bay

purple shading shows extent of larger features

PACIFIC OCEAN

Vancouver

Montréal

table of summary information (categories vary between sections)

TYPE Boreal forest

AREA 6.25 million square km (2.4 million square miles)

scale bar divided into blocks, each representing 100km (60 miles)

LOCATION AND DATA ▲

Thematic Panels

FOREST SIZES
The technology of satellite imaging has had an enormous impact on ecological monitoring. The comparison of satellite photographs with existing ground surveys allows detailed interpretation and analysis of such images, and enables the accurate mapping of the size of existing forests. The satellite image below, for example, clearly shows the current extent of forest in the Black Hills of South Dakota, USA. It is vital to build up such snapshots of vegetation cover if the effects of factors such as deforestation are to be accurately monitored. Satellite imaging is also used to to their pai control n

◀ SCIENCE
These features reveal how scientists have learned about different aspects of the workings of our planet.

JOSEPH BANKS
Englishman Joseph Banks (1743–1820) was one of the great botanical explorers and collectors. Aged 25, he joined James Cook's expedition to the South Pacific on the *Endeavour*. In 1770, they landed in eastern Australia, where Banks amassed a vast collection of botanical specimens then unknown to Europeans. Appropriately, Captain Cook named their landing place Botany Bay.

▲ BIOGRAPHY
Notable earth scientists, explorers, and others are profiled in this type of feature.

RAINFOREST FIRES
Fires are a major threat, even to moist rainforest, and Indonesia has suffered badly, both from natural fires and from those started deliberately as an aid to logging operations or for clearing trees to make way for alternative land-use. Once a forest fire has taken hold, particularly in dry conditions, such as those of the drought in 1997, the proximity of the trees allows it to spread rapidly, destroying not only the trees themselves but virtually all the associated wildlife.

◀▲ ENVIRONMENT
The ways in which humans are changing the Earth – and how the Earth, in turn, affects humans – are described in double-page features (above) and smaller panels (left) throughout the book. Each double-page article takes a global view of a particular subject.

FIGHTING THE FIRE
This village is attempting to douse a brush fire in Kalimantan, the Indonesian part of Borneo, in 1997.

thematic panels (see above) on explanatory pages describe general trends or issues; panels in feature profiles cover localized effects

in most sections, a world map shows global distribution of features being described

introductory panel defines terms and measurements given in the feature profiles that follow

▼ FEATURE PROFILES
All profiles contain a text description and a locator or distribution map. Most profiles are also illustrated with a colour photograph.

profiles are arranged on page in geographical order

CONTRIBUTORS AND CONSULTANTS

Earth is the product of a collaboration between Dorling Kindersley, several contributors (listed below), and staff members of the Smithsonian (listed at the bottom of this panel).

CONTRIBUTORS

Michael Allaby Atmosphere
David Burnie Agricultural Areas, Environment features
Robert Dinwiddie The History of the Earth, Glaciers, Ocean
John Farndon The Changing Earth, Fault Systems, Urban Areas, Industrial Areas, Tectonic Atlas
Douglas Palmer The History of the Earth, The Anatomy of the Earth, The Changing Earth, Mountains, Volcanoes, Hot Springs and Geysers
Clint Twist Rivers, Lakes, Underground Rivers and Caves, Urban Areas, Industrial Areas, Atmosphere
Martin Walters The Changing Earth, Deserts, Forests, Wetlands, Grasslands and Tundra
Tony Waltham Igneous Intrusions, Underground Rivers and Caves
Richard Beatty Glossary

SMITHSONIAN CONSULTANTS

ORIGINAL EDITION
James F. Luhr Editor-in-Chief
Bruce B. Collette Ocean
Douglas H. Erwin The History of the Earth
Richard S. Fiske Igneous Intrusions, Hot Springs and Geysers
Bevan M. French Meteorite Impacts
Andrew K. Johnston Urban Areas, Industrial Areas
Ian G. MacIntyre Ocean
Timothy McCoy The History of the Earth, Rocks, Meteorite Impacts
J. Patrick Megonigal Water, Rivers and Lakes, Wetlands, Atmosphere
William G. Melson Ocean
Jeffrey E. Post Minerals
Richard Potts The History of the Earth
Stanwyn G. Shetler Life, Deserts, Forests, Grasslands and Tundra, Agricultural Areas
Lee Siebert Volcanoes, Mass Movement
Timothy Rose Underground Rivers and Caves
Tom Simkin Tectonic Plates, Plate Boundaries, Volcanoes
Sorena S. Sorensen Rocks, Mountains, Glaciers
Edward P. Vicenzi Mountains
Scott L. Wing The History of the Earth

REVISED EDITION
The revised edition was prepared with the help of the following staff of the National Museum of National History:

Dr. Jeffrey E. Post, Curator-in-Charge, National Gem Collection, **Editor-in-Chief**
Dr. Benjamin J. Andrews, Research Geologist, Department of Mineral Sciences
Dr Doug Erwin, Curator for Paleozoic Invertebrates, Department of Paleobiology
Brian T. Huber, Chair and Curator of Foraminifera, Department of Paleobiology
Gene Hunt, Curator, Department of Paleobiology
Dr. Briana Pobiner, Research Scientist and Educator, Human Origins Program
Nicholas D. Pyenson, Ph.D., Curator of Fossil Marine Mammals, Department of Paleobiology
Hans-Dieter Sues, Curator of Vertebrate Paleontology

PLANET EARTH

ANCIENT LIFE-FORMS
Some of the first organisms to inhabit the Earth can still be seen. Over 3 billion years ago, bacteria in shallow seas began to form mounds called stromatolites. Such structures are still forming at Shark Bay, Australia.

THE HISTORY OF THE EARTH

OVER THE LAST 200 YEARS, scientists have carefully studied the Earth's rocks and recovered the remains of past animals and plants in order to piece together the history of our planet. The Earth came into existence about 4,560 million (4.56 billion) years ago, as a hot, rocky body in our Solar System. Primitive life first appeared in the oceans about 3,500 million years ago and has been spreading and diversifying ever since, but its evolutionary path has been far from smooth. The Earth's environments have always been subject to change, as volcanic activity, meteorite impacts, and climate changes have produced often life-threatening and sometimes catastrophic effects. The development of our planet has turned out to be remarkably eventful – and, from the evidence of history, it will continue to be so.

The Earth's Past

Rocks 46–49

Tectonic plates 52–53

GEOLOGISTS USE INFORMATION from many sources to help them reconstruct the Earth's long history within the even longer evolution of the Universe. Valuable information about the Earth's early history can be gathered from extra-terrestrial sources, such as meteorites. Analysis of rocks, minerals, and fossils found at the surface tells us directly about the crust and provides some clues about the interior. However, new techniques and analyses are revealing a more detailed view of the Earth's interior, its evolution, and its interaction with the crust. They also provide information about the interaction of these geological processes and events with the atmosphere and the evolution of life.

The Rock Record

Natural processes of deposition lay down successive layers of rock and mineral material as sedimentary strata (or layers), with relatively young strata lying on top of older ones. Geologists have matched (or correlated) strata from around the world using distinctive fossils and rock types to produce what is known as a stratigraphical column, stretching over the Earth's entire history. However, the process is complicated by many breaks in the record through plate movement and lack of deposition.

ROCK LAYERS
The angular relationship of strata at Siccar Point in Scotland represents a break in the record.

Geological Time

The Universe formed about 13–14,000 million years ago and, according to radiometric dating (see panel, opposite), the history of the Earth spans the last 4,560 million years. To make sense of the immensity of the Earth's history, it has been subdivided by geologists into a hierarchical scheme. The largest divisions are eons, many hundreds of millions of years long, including the Phanerozoic Eon, which extends from 541 million years ago to the present day. Within the Phanerozoic, there are three eras, based on the history of life. Eras are divided into smaller segments called periods, which in turn are divided into epochs. Decisions about where boundaries between the main periods of time should be are ongoing. Evidence from fossils plays an important part in positioning these boundaries. However, international correlation between rock strata can be very difficult because the original sediments may have been deposited in different environments and climatic conditions and therefore contain different fossils.

AFRICAN SHIELD
Diamond-rich sands of the Namibian diamond field cover the Precambrian shield of southern Africa, one of the world's most ancient landmasses.

THE DIVISION OF GEOLOGIC TIME
Just 250 years ago, the Earth was generally thought to be a few thousand years old. It was not until the 1950s that a near-accurate age of 4,550 million years was determined. It took another decade to establish that the Universe is 13,000–14,000 million years old.

GRAND CANYON
Rocks revealed in the Grand Canyon, USA, were laid down over a period of almost 1,500 million years. The oldest are 1,700 million years old.

The Big Bang   first galaxies   Milky Way forms

13,000 million years ago (mya)   12,000 mya   11,000 mya

9,000 mya   10,000 mya

8,000 mya   7,000 mya

5,000 mya   6,000 mya

4,500 mya   4,000 mya   3,000 mya

formation of the Earth   first evidence of life   first landmasses

PLANET EARTH

Fossils

Fossils are the remains of past life that have been entombed by geological processes in rock strata. They range from pollen grains to the skeletons of giant dinosaurs or whales. Life can be preserved in many ways, and fossils vary from vague traces of past activity (such as burrows or footprints) or body chemistry (biomolecules) to encapsulated bodies (such as insects caught in amber). Most processes of preservation involve considerable loss of information about organisms. Nevertheless, the fossil record shows that life began in the seas approximately 3,500 million years ago and that from about 575 million years ago life diversified as it colonized, in succession, fresh water, land, and air. However, the record is highly biased towards marine organisms with hard parts, such as shells. By studying the processes of burial and fossilization, scientists have been able to search out rarer examples of fossils in which soft parts have been preserved. For example, the beautifully preserved fossils from the Cambrian Period found in the Burgess Shale, western Canada (see right), give better insights into the total diversity of past life and its biology.

PLANT FOSSIL
Rosettes of late Carboniferous horsetail (calamite) leaves are preserved here in rock.

PETRIFIED TREE STUMPS
Silica replacement of the woody tissues of these Triassic trees from the Chinle formation in Arizona, USA, has made them resistant to weathering and erosion.

BURGESS SHALE
High in the Canadian Rocky Mountains, the World Heritage Site of the Burgess Shale has yielded a remarkable diversity of late-Cambrian marine fossils.

HOW FOSSILS FORM

Fossilization is a lengthy and complex process. It requires the rapid covering of an organism's remains by sediment, followed by the deep burial, compression, and chemical changes involved in rock formation. Later uplift and erosion – sometimes combined with excavation – re-expose the fossil at the surface.

1. ANIMAL DIES
decomposing body
accumulating sediment

2. SKELETON BURIED
rapidly buried remains

3. ROCK FORMS
compressed rock
skeleton replaced by minerals

4. FOSSIL REVEALED
erosion of rock and excavation
evidence of hard body parts

RADIOMETRIC DATING

Until the advent of radiometric dating at the beginning of the 20th century, there was no reliable method of dating minerals, rocks, and fossils. The discovery of radioisotopes of some elements (such as uranium, carbon, and potassium) and their decay products that occur in minerals, rocks, and some ancient organic material, together with the measurement of their rates of decay, make it possible to calculate the age of these materials. The limits of radiometric dating depend on the element being used – carbon dating (used for most fossils) cannot provide dates for material that is more than 50,000 years old.

PLANET EARTH

KEY TO TIMELINE OF EARTH HISTORY

The pages that follow contain a visual summary of the history of the Earth, beginning with the formation of the Universe. Information is summarized in the following bands:

EON
ERA
PERIOD
EPOCH

Divisions of geological time. (Decisions on boundaries are ongoing.)

CLIMATE — Average temperatures and composition of the atmosphere. The intensity of the colour in this band indicates temperature trends

LIFE — Events and trends in the evolution of flora and fauna

GEOLOGIC EVENTS — Includes maps indicating continental movements

SYMBOL KEY

◆ Event occurs at this time

Trend occurs over this period

Event occurs during this period

◆------------|------------◆

MAP KEY

▨ Siberia/N. Asia ▢ Baltica/N. Europe

▢ Gondwana ▢ Ice-caps

---

first birds | first primates | early human ancestors | *Homo sapiens*

EON	Phanerozoic – age of abundant and evident life													
ERA	Paleozoic – age of ancient life						Mesozoic – age of dominant reptiles				Cenozoic – age of dominant mammals			
PERIOD	Cambrian	Ordovician	Silurian	Devonian	Carboniferous	Permian	Triassic	Jurassic	Cretaceous		Paleogene			Quaternary	
EPOCH					Mississippian Pennsylvanian				Lower	Upper	Eocene	Oligocene	Miocene	Pliocene	Pleistocene Holocene

541.0 | 485.4 | 443.4 | 419.0 | 358.9 | 323.2 | 298.9 | 252.2 | 201.3 | 145.0 | 100.5 | 66.0 | 56.0 | 33.9 | 23.0 | 5.3 | 2.6 | 0.01 | 0

Phanerozoic Eon

2,000 mya — first multi-celled organisms

1,000 mya

541.0 mya — first land plants | first land vertebrates | first dinosaurs

Present day

TIME AFTER BIG BANG	1 FEMTOSECOND (10⁻¹⁵ SECONDS)	1 PICOSECOND (10⁻¹² SECONDS)	1 NANOSECOND (10⁻⁹ SECONDS)	1 MICROSECOND (10⁻⁶ SECONDS)	1 MILLISECOND (10⁻³ SECONDS)	1 SECOND	1 MINUTE	1 HOUR	1 DAY	1 YEAR	1 THOUSAND YEARS	1 MILLION YEARS	1 BILLION YEARS

(The table above presents time after Big Bang with corresponding TEMPERATURE (K), DENSITY (G/CM3), and DIAMETER (M) values across the timeline; values include exponents such as 10^{14}, 10^{16}, 10^{23}, 10^{12}, 10^{11}, 10^{10}, 10^{9}, 10^{8}, 10^{7}, 10^{6}, 10^{5}, 10^{4}, 10^{3}, 10^{2} etc.)

AFTER THE BIG BANG
In its first billionth of a second, the hot, expanding universe was a "soup" of scores of types of particles that varied enormously in their properties.

"up" quark   "down" quark

PROTON   NEUTRON

QUARKS BIND
Quarks started combining to form protons and neutrons. One "down" and two "up" quarks made a proton; one "up" and two "down" quarks made a neutron.

neutron   helium nucleus   energy released by collisions   proton

BIG BANG NUCLEOSYNTHESIS
Between 1 and 180 seconds after the Big Bang, proton and neutron collisions formed the atomic nuclei of some light elements, mainly helium.

electron   electron   proton   nucleus   electron

HYDROGEN ATOM   HELIUM ATOM

FIRST ATOMS
After about 300,000 years, protons and helium nuclei (consisting of protons and neutrons) began to capture electrons, forming hydrogen and helium atoms.

Before the Earth

To understand the origins of the Earth, it is necessary to go back to the origin of the Universe itself, some 13,000–14,000 million years ago in the event described by the Big Bang theory, when matter, time, energy, and space all came into existence. The early Universe was small, hot, and dense. Ever since, it has been expanding and cooling. Within a nanosecond (a billionth of a second), it was hundreds of millions of kilometres in diameter with a temperature of tens of trillions Kelvin (degrees above -273°C or absolute zero).

BUILDING BLOCKS

At this stage, the Universe was a seething "soup" of particles created out of energy, together with vast numbers of photons (little packets of radiant energy). Among the most numerous particles were electrons and quarks, but there were also many other kinds that no longer exist today. Although it contained plenty of electrons, the early Universe held neither of the other main building blocks of atoms: protons and neutrons. However, after just one microsecond (a millionth of a second), it had cooled sufficiently for vast quantities of protons and neutrons to form as two different types of quark combined.

Most of the protons were destined to become the nuclei of hydrogen atoms, but from about one second after the Big Bang, collisions between protons and neutrons started to form the nuclei of some other light elements – helium and tiny amounts of lithium and beryllium. This process, termed Big Bang nucleosynthesis, was completed in three minutes and formed the nuclei of 98 per cent of the helium atoms present in the Universe today. It also mopped up all the neutrons.

PARTICLE TRACKS
Today, scientists try to simulate what happened in the Big Bang by using particle accelerators to smash subatomic particles together. The resulting tracks can then be studied.

THE FIRST ATOMS

For the next few hundred thousand years, the Universe continued to expand and cool, but it was still too energetic for atoms to form. If electrons and atomic nuclei came together momentarily, they were quickly split apart by photons, which were themselves trapped in a process of continual collision with the particles. Eventually, after 300,000 years, when the temperature had dropped to about 3,000 Kelvin, the protons and other atomic nuclei started capturing electrons permanently, forming the first atoms, which were primarily hydrogen and helium. At the same time, the photons were

BACKGROUND EVIDENCE

A crucial piece of evidence supporting the Big Bang theory is the existence of Cosmic Microwave Background Radiation (CMBR). This is a faint heat radiation that emanates uniformly from all points in the sky. The only plausible explanation is that this originated in the hot fireball conditions of the early Universe, as described by the Big Bang theory.

released and streamed freely in all directions. At this stage, the Universe became transparent, as the earlier "fog" of particles and energy cleared.

GALAXIES FORM

Gravity now began to cause gas atoms to come together. Over hundreds of millions of years, swirling clouds of hydrogen and helium gas formed and started to extend into long thin strands. About 13,000 million years ago (or 500 million years after the Big Bang), the strands began to clump together to form the first galaxies. Further concentration of matter within galaxies led to the creation of the first stars. The production of energy (including heat and light) in stars began when hydrogen nuclei in their centres started fusing to form helium.

NEW ELEMENTS

When the first galaxies and stars formed, there were still just four chemical elements in the Universe: hydrogen, helium, lithium, and beryllium. The formation of the first stars was highly significant, because it is within these that heavier chemical elements are created from lighter ones, through various processes of fusion. Many of the most common chemical elements on Earth, such as oxygen, silicon, and iron, were made in this way. The very heaviest elements, such as lead, cannot be created in ordinary stars but form only in

REMNANTS OF A SUPERNOVA
Supernovae are huge star explosions that distribute new elements through galaxies. This is the remnant of Cassiopeia A, which exploded about 10,000 years ago.

supernovae – the massive explosions of giant stars in their final death throes. These explosions also distributed new elements throughout galaxies, where they were incorporated into new stars and planets.

BIRTH OF THE SOLAR SYSTEM

The exact age of our own galaxy, the Milky Way, is not known, but it was probably formed by 10,000–11,000 million years ago. About 4,560 million years ago, within our galaxy, a clump of gas and dust, known as a nebula, began to condense into what became the Solar System.

Within this nebula, matter coalesced into a denser central region (the proto-Sun) and more diffuse outer regions. Eventually the nebula shrank into a spinning, disk-like object, called the proto-planetary disk. Within the disk, dust and ice collided randomly to form ever larger particles. In the centre of the disk, as matter was drawn in by gravity, temperatures rose to the point where hydrogen fused to form helium, and a fully-fledged star – our Sun – was born.

In other parts of the disk, the predominant matter was solid particles. Nearest the Sun, rocky materials became the main component. In the colder outer regions of the disk, ice particles were more common. As particles throughout the disk became larger, gravity drew them into collisions. This process, known as accretion, caused larger

NEBULA
The Solar System condensed out of huge clouds of gas and dust, similar to these of the Lagoon Nebula, a star-forming region in the Milky Way.

and larger bodies to merge, eventually forming planetesimals. These were the size of boulders, or larger, and composed of rock or rock and ice.

As well as heat and light, the new Sun also emitted a stream of energetic particles known as the solar wind. This "wind" blew volatile gases from the inner areas into the outer areas of the disk. Most of the remaining planetesimals collided to form the four rocky inner planets. They also formed the cores of the outer planets, around which the volatile gases collected.

Not all of the planetesimals merged to form planets. Some "leftovers" remain in the Solar System as two types of bodies: asteroids and comets. Most of the asteroids orbit in a belt between Mars and Jupiter, but some follow Jupiter's orbit, and some others have paths that cross the Earth's orbit. Comets formed from icy planetesimals in the outer edge of the disk.

FORMATION OF THE SOLAR SYSTEM
The Solar System formed in several stages. First a huge nebula (cloud) of gas and dust condensed into a spinning, disk-like object. The centre of the disk condensed further to form the Sun, while particles in the outer parts of the disk collided and accreted to form the planets.

NEBULA
gas and dust cloud
dense central region

CONTRACTING NEBULA
flattened and rotating cloud

PROTOPLANETARY DISK
emerging proto-Sun
rings appear

SUN AND PLANETESIMALS
particles collide and accrete
defined rings

THE SOLAR SYSTEM
gaseous outer planets
rocky inner planets
asteroid belt

PRECAMBRIAN

MILLION YEARS AGO	4,600	**4,500**	4,400	4,300	4,200	4,100	**4,000**	3,900	3,800	3,700
EON	PRECAMBRIAN (4,560–541.0 MYA)									
ERA	HADEAN (4,560–4,000 MYA)						ARCHEAN (4,000–2,500 MYA)			
PERIOD										
EPOCH										
CLIMATE				Earth cools; first oceans form ◆		meteorite bombardment vaporizes early oceans				
LIFE						meteorite bombardment destroys any nascent life			first chemical fossils of prokaryotes and eukaryotes ◆	
GEOLOGIC EVENTS	◆ formation of the Earth	◆ oldest Moon rock			oldest minerals (zircons)	heavy meteorite bombardment (150 x present level)			◆ oldest crustal rock and banded iron formation (Isua, Greenland)	
		◆ bombardment by planetesimals								
		◆ differentiation of the Earth's layers							lavas with pillow structures indicate presence of water	
		◆ formation of the Moon								

Precambrian Earth

At one time, the Precambrian Eon was seen as a geological *terra incognita*, of unknown age and without fossil remains. Not until 1956, when the age of the Earth was accurately measured, did the immensity of the Precambrian's 4,000 million years become glaringly obvious. Since then, fossils have been found, rocks dated, and the formation of the Solar System unravelled. The Earth's early history is now known to be a time of cataclysmic change. Early accretion and differentiation of the core and mantle, along with bombardment from space, culminated in the Moon's formation.

FORMATION OF THE MOON

Around 4,500 million years ago, a planetary body the size of Mars collided with the Earth, tearing away a large volume of rock. The debris was held by the Earth's gravity and cooled and coalesced to form the satellite we recognize as the Moon.

ZIRCON CRYSTALS
Crystals from rocks in Western Australia have been dated at 4,400–3,900 million years old.

Continued layering was followed by the formation of a primitive atmosphere, oceans, crust, and possibly life. However, renewed meteorite bombardment, which so scarred the Moon, also devastated the Earth, causing melting of its rocks.

Not until about 3,500 million years ago were oceans and a primitive atmosphere regenerated and the first chemical evidence for photosynthesis by marine micro-organisms preserved. However, these life-forms had to tolerate a lack of oxygen and high ultraviolet radiation because there was no ozone layer to screen it. It took time for the atmosphere and oceans to develop to their present condition. Surface temperatures fell slowly and oxygen levels rose slowly as increasing numbers

THE EARTH'S LAYERS FORM

Early accretion of cosmic material formed a larger, growing body, in which melts formed and migrated. Heavy elements concentrated in the core and lighter ones in the overlying mantle.

small bodies and dust accrete to asteroid size

heavy elements

lighter elements form mantle

melts migrate

core forms

molten core

of photosynthesizing microbes produced oxygen and a protective ozone layer, aided by the emission of water vapour that split to release oxygen and ozone into the upper atmosphere.

The Precambrian Eon is divided into the Hadean, Archean, and Proterozoic eras, during which dynamic processes originating from within the Earth generated new ocean-floor rocks and destroyed them elsewhere, while continents grew and were moved through the processes of plate tectonics (see pp.52–55). Meanwhile, an increasing diversity of marine micro-organisms evolved slowly. Major events continued to perturb evolving ecosystems, with large-scale volcanism, impact events, and climate change culminating in runaway glaciations. Although often catastrophic, these upheavals may have stimulated evolution.

BOMBARDMENT OF THE EARTH

Mars-sized impactor

Earth

coalescing rock debris

DEBRIS ORBITS THE EARTH

ACCRETION OF THE MOON

debris melts and forms the Moon

high surface temperatures falling gradually   temperatures falling rapidly to well below present average ◆

◆ oldest stromatolites (Warrawoona Group, Australia)
◆ microscopic filaments and spheroids   oldest lake with microbial life ◆
◆ first carbonaceous microfossils   first chemical biomarker evidence for an oxygenated atmosphere ◆

METEORITE BOMBARDMENT

Dating of the Moon's rocks and the appearance of its heavily cratered surface provide evidence that for some 600 million years after their formation, both the Moon and Earth were subject to intense bombardment from space. The Moon has impact craters, such as the Aitken Basin, up to 2,500km (1,500 miles) across, and because of its greater size and gravity, the Earth underwent greater bombardment than the Moon. The results were melting of rock and destruction of any nascent life and atmosphere.

A LIFE-SUSTAINING ATMOSPHERE

The Earth's first atmosphere was blasted away by impacts and the solar wind. Volcanism built up a secondary atmosphere by releasing nitrogen, carbon dioxide, and water vapour. The latter was split by ultraviolet light into hydrogen, oxygen, and ozone. The lightest gas, hydrogen, was released into space.

solar wind
hydrogen
debris from space
helium

FIRST ATMOSPHERE

hydrogen
UV light
water
nitrogen
carbon dioxide
oxygen and ozone

SECOND ATMOSPHERE

OCEANS AND CONTINENTS

The Hadean Era, as its name suggests, was hellish: the early Earth's turmoil destroyed any primary atmosphere, oceans, and life. The Archean times that followed saw the water vapour released from volcanoes collecting to form oceans, where salts dissolved to increase salinity gradually. Low-density silicate minerals accumulated to form the Earth's outer crust. But continuing volcanic eruptions resulted in the constant formation of new surface rocks. As the Earth was no longer expanding through accretion, the cooler and denser rocks, which had been formed previously, sank into the interior to accommodate the new crustal rocks. The Earth's crust was fragmented into a number of plates, with both convergent and divergent margins (see pp.54–55). Low-density rocks accreted into continents and higher density rocks formed the ocean floor.

EARLY LIFE

Fossil evidence for early life is rare in ancient sedimentary rocks, which were altered by heat and pressure. The oldest fossils are the degraded remains of organic carbon isotopes from 3,700-million-year-old seabed muds found in Western Greenland. They derived from photosynthesizing prokaryote micro-organisms that used light energy from the Sun. Within 250 million years, such marine microbes were interacting with seabed

PROKARYOTES
These single-celled organisms have a simple cell that lacks structures (such as a nucleus) found in advanced cells.

sedimentary processes and producing distinctive structures known as stromatolites. The oldest stromatolites date from around 3,430 million years ago and they become increasingly common, but the most ancient do not preserve fossils of the microbes that made them.

Although the first carbonaceous microfossils date from 3,500 million years ago, the first well-defined microfossils from South Africa, known as acritachs, date from 3,200 million years ago and formed microbial mats in sunlit nearshore waters. There is some chemical biomarker evidence for the production of oxygen by photosynthesis by 2,700 million years ago. There is geochemical evidence (from biomarkers) for oxygen in the atmosphere by 2,400 million years ago.

hydrogen atom
carbon atom

METHANE (CH$_4$)
The simplest organic compound is one carbon atom combined with four hydrogen atoms.

CLAIRE PATTERSON

After working on the first atomic bomb and studying radioactivity, American physicist Claire Patterson became interested in calculating the age of the Earth. In 1956, he compared measurements from meteorites and Earth minerals to obtain the age of 4,550 million years. This was the first accurate estimate.

MILLION YEARS AGO	**2,500**	2,400	2,300	2,200	2,100	**2,000**	1,900	1,800	1,700	1,
EON	PRECAMBRIAN (4,560–541.0 MYA)									
ERA	PROTEROZOIC (2,500–541.0 MYA)									
PERIOD										
EPOCH										
CLIMATE	◆ Great Oxygenation Event				O₂ levels rising; temperatures well above present average		◆ O₂ at 15% of present level			
	glaciation ◆			◆ ◆						
LIFE	◆ photosynthetic prokaryotes and eukaryotes cause rising O₂ levels			earliest eukaryote fossil ◆		◆ oil and gas hydrocarbons suggest microbial life widespread in seas				
	◆ chemical evidence for first micro-organisms on land					◆ multicellular algae contribute to rise in oxygen levels				
GEOLOGIC EVENTS				increasing O₂ levels curtail large-scale banded iron formation		◆ Sudbury meteorite impact, Canada				
			Vredefort meteorite impact, South Africa ◆							

early continents formed from low-density rocks

OXYGENATING THE ATMOSPHERE

About 2,700 million years ago, primitive photo-synthesizing micro-organisms released increasing volumes of oxygen into the early atmosphere. This oxygen was initially used up oxidizing iron in the oceans, and little entered the atmosphere. By 2,200 million years ago, oxygen levels were still only about 1 per cent of present levels (oxygen comprises 21 per cent by volume of today's atmosphere), but by 1,900 million years ago oxygen levels were about 15 per cent of present levels. Micro-organisms preferring the anoxic (low-oxygen) conditions were forced to adapt by retreating within sediments and below ground.

An important development for evolving life was the formation of the protective ozone layer above the atmosphere to filter out incoming ultraviolet rays that are particularly harmful to

CHEMICAL FOSSILS

Even when organisms die and their tissues decay, the organic chemicals (hydrocarbons) of which they are made may survive in sediments, albeit in a degraded form. These are known as chemical fossils. Commonly, these hydrocarbons form mobile oil and gas, but some residues can persist within the rock record. Chemical analysis of these residues can differentiate the organic molecules present, their structural complexity and, broadly, what kind of organisms they are derived from.

MODERN STROMATOLITES
Known as stromatolites, these mounds of layered sediment with surface films of bacteria are identical to those found in Precambrian sedimentary rocks.

BANDED IRON
These layered iron deposits were formed by oxidation reactions in the oceans before the formation of the atmosphere.

DNA. Above a 2-per-cent oxygen level, an ozone layer will begin to form, so it should have been well established by 1,900 million years ago. An oxygen-rich atmosphere, protected by an ozone shield, permitted new life-forms to evolve and thrive. Oxygen-tolerant photosynthesizers inherited the Earth.

MULTICELLULAR LIFE

Coiled filamentous microfossils from Michigan, USA, called *Grypania*, are 2,100 million years old and provide the first direct fossil evidence for eukaryotes. These organisms may have had multiple eukaryote cells, but the oldest convincing direct fossil evidence for multicells comes in the form of 1,200-million-year-old fossils of a red alga called *Bangiomorpha* from arctic Canada. The many cells of these microscopic filaments show some specialization, including structures indicating that they reproduced sexually.

By 1,000 million years ago, towards the end of the Proterozoic Era and following a prolonged evolutionary gestation, the "big bang" of eukaryotic evolution had started. The evolution of multicellular organisms with sexual reproduction paved the way for larger and more diverse organisms. It used to be thought that it was the development of sexual reproduction, with its exchange of genetic material, that was the key to this diversification. However, it is now known that this innovation alone did not promote eukaryotic diversification of life, as

glaciation ◆ first snowball Earth event second snowball Earth event glaciation
glaciation ◆ Earth event

◆ first multicellular algae fossils (*Bangiomorpha*), ◆ decline in stromatolites oldest multicellular (metazoan) body fossils
showing evidence of sexual reproduction first skeletons (silica) in unicell algae ◆ first evidence for fossil sponges

◆ major spread of eukaryote population ◆ oldest Ediacarans

amalgamation of supercontinent of Rodinia, followed by break up banded iron formation ◆ banded iron formation ◆ banded iron formation ◆

completion of Rodinian break up ◆ low sea-floor spreading rate ◆

clustering to form Rodinian supercontinent

formation of Gondwanan supercontinent

even bacteria exchange genetic material. More important perhaps is the ability of multicellular organisms to increase in size beyond the microscopic, with specialization of certain cells for certain tasks within the organism. By 720 million years ago, the first fossil sponges from Australia and the traces they left behind in Oman, provide evidence for the increasing complexity of marine animals. They are followed by Ediacaran fossils from 579 million years ago and the first shelled animals, such as *Cloudina*, from 548 million years ago.

COMPLEX CELLS EVOLVE

Unlike the more primitive prokaryotes, eukaryotes have their nuclear material enclosed in a membrane. Eukaryote cells are sometimes part of a larger, multicellular organism, while prokaryotes are exclusively single-celled organisms and often incorporate a flagellum for mobility in a watery environment.

PROKARYOTE CELL
EUKARYOTE CELL
nucleus contains DNA
nuclear membrane
nucleoid contains DNA
flagellum

GRYPANIA
Coiled ribbons, at least 20cm (8in) long, called Grypania *may be the oldest multicellular eukaryote algae.*

SNOWBALL EARTH

There is evidence that the Earth suffered extensive glaciation in Late Proterozoic times, with ice-caps that extended from the poles to the tropics. Depending on whether most of the Earth's surface was covered, or just a large part of it, they have been interpreted snowball or slushball events. The occurrence of glacial deposits known as diamictites close to sea-level in the tropics provides evidence for low latitude glaciation. Measurements of magnetically orientated minerals within Precambrian glacial sediments indicate that 750 and 635 million years ago there were were two snowball events (with glacial retreat in between), and a glacial event between 2,450 and 2,220 million years ago, whose extent is not yet well established. Important support for the theory comes from the presence of carbonate sediments, which are typical of low latitudes, immediately above glacially related ones. The appearance of sedimentary iron formations in the oceans suggests that conditions were anoxic, which is consistent with glacial events. The cause of such events is not fully understood but is thought to be related to the clustering of the continents within the tropics, raising the amount of light reflected from the planet and cooling global climates.

SNOWBALL EARTH
Geological evidence shows that low-latitude continents were glaciated; the extent of sea-ice cover is less clear.

SOFT-BODIED ANOMALIES

The Ediacarans are among the most intriguing Precambrian fossils. A group of sea-dwelling organisms that lived 580–543 million years ago, they are the first known animals. Their bodies were up to 2m (6ft) long, which were entirely soft without any hard skeletal parts (see below) but often ribbed or quilted. Their relationship to to living animal groups is unclear. They had a variety of body shapes, including a flat disc or a frond, while some had attachment discs and curiously quilted or serially divided surfaces. About 100 species are known, all entirely soft-bodied and preserved as sediment moulds and infills, suggesting that some lived within the sediment and that their body tissues were tougher than those of jellyfish, which are rarely preserved as fossils. Their first known appearance follows the last glacial event and their evolution may have been stimulated by its meltdown.

EDIACARAN FOSSIL
Spriggina, an Ediacaran fossil with a head-like structure, is named after Australian geologist Reg Sprigg, who found the Ediacarans in Australia.

MILLION YEARS AGO	**550**	**540**	**530**	**520**	**510**	**500**	**490**	**480**	**470**
EON	PRECAMBRIAN	PHANEROZOIC (541.0 MYA–PRESENT DAY)							
ERA	PROTEROZOIC	PALEOZOIC (541.0–252.2 MYA)							
PERIOD		CAMBRIAN (541.0–485.4 MYA)						ORDOVICIAN (485.4–443.4 MYA)	
EPOCH									

CLIMATE — rising O₂ levels linked to increasing biodiversification; temperature high — temperature falling; carbon dioxide (CO₂) to high of over 16 x present level — CO₂ at less than 16 x present level; temperature low, then fluctuating above present average

LIFE — maximum Ediacaran diversity ◆ decline in Ediacarans — ◆ increasing trace fossils; diverse small shelly fossils — ◆ Cambrian explosion: unarmoured vertebrates, graptolites, arthropods including trilobites, and first chordates (animals with a notochord) — ◆ Burgess Shale: conodonts (eel-like marine chordates) and jawless fish — first complete armoured jawless fish — ◆ first metazoan skeletal reefs: archaeocyathan sponges, cyanobacteria — first terrestrial bryophyte (moss-type) fossils ◆

GEOLOGIC EVENTS — ◆ brief assembly of Pannotia supercontinent — ◆ Gondwanan continental assembly stretches from pole to pole — ◆ North America separated from Gondwana by the Iapetus ocean — ◆ maximum sea-floor spreading rate

rotation of Gondwana towards south pole

The Paleozoic Era

Paleozoic means "ancient life", and this era saw the appearance of abundant shelly fossils and the development of land plants. It ended with life's biggest ever extinction event, at the end of the Permian Period, when 90 per cent of all life on the Earth was wiped out.

PLATE TECTONICS

The Earth's continents are constantly reconfigured by movements of crustal plates, with new oceans opening and the subduction of the old ocean floor (see p.55). During the Paleozoic, amalgamation of the southern continents formed the Gondwanan supercontinent, which drifted north over time to form the even larger supercontinent of Pangea. By the end of the Paleozoic, Pangea stretched from pole to pole.

MOLECULAR CLOCKS

The molecular clock uses genetic difference between living groups and assumptions of constant rates of evolution to estimate the origin and divergence of groups of organisms. However, it needs to be calibrated by appropriate fossils of known age. For instance, according to the molecular clock, sharks evolved 528 million years ago, yet fossils first occur in 385 million-year-old strata. The discrepancy may reflect a lack of fossils, or a misunderstanding about rates of evolution.

THE CAMBRIAN EXPLOSION

In the mid-19th century, fossil evidence seemed to indicate that life began in the earliest Cambrian with the appearance of a variety of sea-dwelling organisms, such as sponges and trilobites, with mineralized shells and skeletons. We now know that life is much more ancient and that shelled animals first appear in late Proterozoic rocks. However, it still seems that a large variety of fossil shells appear suddenly at the beginning of the Cambrian. Many of these fossils are very small and represent several different kinds of molluscs and armoured arthropods (creatures with paired and jointed limbs) – it is as if there was an explosion in the diversity of life.

Some scientists have argued from early molecular clock estimates that there was no great explosion of life. Rather, it was the rapid acquisition of readily fossilizable hard part, such as shells and skeletons that produces the appearance of an explosion. However, the overwhelming empirical evidence is that while animal lineages did begin to diversify during the late Neoproterozoic, as suggested by recent molecular clock estimates, the Cambrian explosion of fossils does accurately reflect the acquisition of new body plans and larger

SILURIAN TRILOBITE
Marine arthropods called trilobites, with mineralized exoskeletons, evolved in Cambrian times.

CHARLES WALCOTT

The American paleontologist Charles Walcott (1850–1927) quarried some 70,000 mid-Cambrian fossils from the Burgess Shale in the Canadian Rocky Mountains, which is now a World Heritage Site. The soft-part preservation of its fossils provides insights into marine life of the time. Walcott became director of the US Geological Survey, then secretary of the Smithsonian Institution in Washington D.C., USA.

body size. Within Cambrian times there is fossil evidence for the appearance of most of the major groups of marine invertebrates (those animals that lack a backbone), including a number of groups that subsequently became extinct, such as the trilobites, conodonts, and graptolites. Importantly, from the evolutionary point of view, a recent discovery from China shows that the first fish-like animals with the beginnings of a backbone (a stiffening rod called a

SILURIAN (443.4–419.2 MYA)   DEVONIAN (419.2–358.9 MYA)

◆ temperature below present average
◆ temperature low
◆ falling CO₂ levels; temperature rising
◆ temperature high, just above present average
◆ CO₂ at 17 x present level
CO₂ at 12 x present level; O₂ at 15% of atmosphere ◆
◆ extinction event (50% of marine genera extinct) ◆ spread of early fish, including jawed fish
◆ first wingless insects: mites, pseudoscorpions, spiders
◆ first freshwater animals (millipedes)
◆ first truly terrestrial animals: trigonotarbids (arthropods)
first tree-like plants (2–3m/6–9ft high) ◆
◆ first vascular land plants: *Cooksonia*, *Eohostimella*
◆ jawless fish enter fresh waters
◆ glaciation and lowered sea-level
◆ all-time high sea-level and maximum flooding of continents with shallow seas
◆ most of continents clustered in southern hemisphere
◆ closure of Iapetus Ocean and amalgamation of Laurentia, Avalonia, and Baltica to form Laurussia

Laurentia and Baltica converge   *Iapetus Ocean closing*   *Avalonia moves north*

notochord) also evolved in the Cambrian. The vast majority of this life was confined to the oceans and seas. However, recent discoveries indicate that shallow water, fresh water, and the land were invaded back in the early Proterozoic by microbial life.

MARINE LIFE
Because the fossil record mostly preserves mineralized hard parts such as shells, skeletons, and teeth, it tends to be highly biased. The fossil record from the Cambrian preserves the first appearances of hardparts belonging to a number of groups of organisms, which must have originated in late Proterozoic times. Initially, the most common fossils were the remains of seabed sponges; various arthropods, such as the extinct trilobites; molluscs, especially cephalopods; and brachiopods, which look like molluscan clams but are anatomically different. Additionally, there were numerous soft-bodied groups, especially worms, such as the priapulids. Other important groups soon evolved, such as the echinoderms and the vertebrates along with the corals, whose reef growth provided new environments for life ranging from calcareous algae and bryozoans (moss-animals) to crinoids (sealilies) and fish.

DEVONIAN JAWLESS FISH
Strange-looking fish without jaws or teeth, such as this Devonian cephalaspid, were among the first animals with backbones.

ICE AGE
The discovery of ice-scratched rock surfaces, ice-rafted boulders, and other glacial deposits in the late Ordovician strata of North Africa might seem hard to explain in relation to today's climate. However, measurement of iron-rich grains orientated by the Earth's Ordovician magnetic field shows that these rocks were clustered near the South Pole at the time of their formation and have since been moved by the processes of plate tectonics. Africa and South America, both part of the supercontinent of Gondwana, were glaciated by the growth of a polar ice-cap. The resulting drastic climate and sea-level change caused the end-Ordovician mass extinction, which wiped out about 50 per cent of the genera of marine organisms.

COOKSONIA
The tiny forked, leafless stems of Cooksonia *from Silurian strata are among the earliest upright-growing land plants.*

LIFE ON LAND
Evidence for macroscopic life on land begins with rare fossil footprints of freshwater arthropods and spores of primitive moss-like plants, both in Ordovician strata. The Silurian saw upright-growing (vascular) plants, such as *Cooksonia*, still dependent on watery environments for reproduction, and tiny arthropods that fed on their decaying remains.

GREENING OF THE LAND
The earliest fossil record of land-plant evolution comprises mainly spores and pollen. Plant fossils are increasingly common from the Devonian onwards, reflecting the development of woodlands.

ORDOVICIAN PERIOD
first land plants — moss-like bryophytes

SILURIAN PERIOD
tiny, upright-growing land plants

DEVONIAN PERIOD

first tree-sized land plants

CARBONIFEROUS PERIOD
extensive forests, which formed coal deposits

EON	PHANEROZOIC (541.0 MYA–PRESENT DAY)								
ERA	PALEOZOIC (541.0–252.2 MYA)								
PERIOD	DEVONIAN (419.2–358.9 MYA)		CARBONIFEROUS (358.9–298.9 MYA)						PERMIAN (298.9–252.2 MYA)
EPOCH			MISSISSIPPIAN (354.0–323.0 MYA)			PENNSYLVANIAN (323.0–290.0 MYA)			
CLIMATE	◆ CO₂ at 10 × present level; O₂ rising; temperature falling to present average				◆ temperature high (20°C/68°F average)		◆ temperature falling to below present average	◆ temperature low (10°C/50°F average); O₂ at all-time high	
LIFE	◆ oldest tetrapod ◆ oldest terrestrial tetrapod	◆ first forests; first ferns ◆ extinction event	◆ *Tulerpeton* (closest relative of the amniotes)		◆ first temnospondyl amphibians and anthracosaur amniotes ◆ first extensive tropical coal-measure forests ◆ first cockroaches		◆ first beetles ◆ first land snails ◆ earliest certain reptile amniotes ◆ first pelycosaurs (mammal-like reptiles)		
GEOLOGIC EVENTS		◆ low sea-level (associated with glaciation)			Laurentia straddles equator (coinciding with development of coal-measure forests) ◆	◆ Gondwana rotates clockwise; low sea-floor spreading rate	maximum deposition of coal-bearing shales ◆ Gondwana converges with Laurentia and Baltica ◆		

Gondwana moves north

The early Devonian brought a rapid diversification of land plants, with accompanying fauna, and by the late Devonian, the first forests covered low-lying wetlands, which were full of fish. Some of these fish evolved four limbs (making them the earliest tetrapods) and ventured on land to feed, but they had to return to water to breed.

CLIMATE CHANGE

Today the sequence of rock strata preserved within individual continents, such as North America, shows a Paleozoic history of drastic climate change, from the cool marine waters of Ordovician

FOSSILIZED TREE STUMP
Fossil trees from Antarctica indicate times when the climate of the continent was much warmer than it is today.

PERMIAN SANDSTONE
Thick piles of sandstone strata were deposited within the vast arid deserts of the Pangean supercontinent. Structures in the beds show that these were once part of sand dunes.

times through Devonian deserts to Carboniferous tropical seas (during the Mississippian Epoch), tropical rain forests (during the Pennsylvanian Epoch), and back to deserts again in the Permian Period. However, this sequence of changes is not, as might be expected, due to dramatic changes in global climates but to the movement of continents through the Earth's climate zones due to plate tectonics.

From Ordovician to Permian times, North America (on the Laurentian Plate) moved from the southern hemisphere across the equator into the northern hemisphere.

LAND VERTEBRATES

Early land tetrapods were salamander-like animals about 1m (3ft) in length. Little is known of their biology except that they had to return to water to breed. By the mid-Carboniferous, both amphibian and more reptile-like groups had evolved. The amphibians were 2–3m (6–10ft) long and resembled crocodilians. However, the critical reptilian feature – the ability to lay a shelled (amniote) egg on dry land – is difficult to recognize in the fossils.

From the late Carboniferous into the Permian Period, however, true reptiles were diversifying. The Pangean supercontinent was occupied by many short-lived

CARNIVOROUS AMPHIBIAN
These early Triassic fossil remains of several meat-eating amphibians were found in South Africa, clustered around those of a plant-eating animal called Lystrosaurus.

reptile groups, some of which were to eventually evolve into the dinosaurs, others into turtles, and yet others into mammals.

EXTINCTION

At the end of the Permian, an estimated 90 per cent of all living organisms (60 per cent of genera), died out in the biggest mass extinction known. Groups that died out include the Paleozoic corals, trilobites, and water scorpions, while the echinoderm crinoids (sea-lilies), brachiopods and clams suffered serious losses, as did 60–70 per cent of life on land.

Geologists have searched for a single cause, especially a major meteorite impact like that which brought about the end-Cretaceous extinction event (see pp.24–25), but without success. There is evidence for widespread anoxia in the oceans, which may have disrupted food chains, causing many marine organisms to die out. The source of this anoxia was thought to have been a sudden release of methane from gas hydrates buried in ocean-bed deposits. However, since sea-level was rising during the extinction, this is unlikely. Instead, it is much more likely that the extinction coincided with a vast outpouring of lavas and volcanic gasses in Siberia (known as the Siberian Traps), which may well have altered global climates.

280	270	260	**250**	240	230	220	210	**200**

MESOZOIC (252.2–66.0 MYA)
TRIASSIC (252.2–201.3 MYA)

◆ rising CO₂; temperature rising above present average — ◆ CO₂ at 5 x present level; O₂ low, less than 15% of atmosphere — ◆ temperature low, but well above present level

temperature high (19°C/66°F) ◆ ◆ falling CO₂ levels; O₂ rising to 19%, then falling

◆ first cynodonts (warm-blooded vertebrates) ◆ first modern (scleractinian) corals — ◆ first dinosaurs — ◆ first flying pterosaur reptiles ◆ first primitive mammals — ◆ extinction event

◆ largest ever extinction event (60% of genera, both marine and terrestrial) — ◆ first turtles — ◆ first modern sharks

◆ first flies — ◆ first teleost fish — land plants become dominated by conifers, ginkgos and cycads ◆

Siberia collides with Baltica, building the Ural Mountains ◆ — ◆ extensive deserts form in Laurentia — ◆ initial breakup of Pangea, extensive rifting, rising sea-levels — ◆ opening of Tethys Ocean between Baltica and Gondwana

◆ rising sea-level

◆ eruption of Siberian Traps

The Mesozoic Era

Spanning the 187 million years of the Triassic, Jurassic, and Cretaceous periods, the Mesozoic (or "middle life") Era lies between two major extinction events, the second one known as the end-Cretaceous extinction. It is often characterized the Age of the Reptiles, because many major reptile groups, such as the land-living dinosaurs and the marine ichthyosaurs and turtles all diversified.

MARINE LIFE

The end-Permian extinction and collapse of the Paleozoic reefs caused a major turnover in marine life. Eventually modern reef corals evolved and marine diversity and food chains were re-established. The more adaptable molluscan clams and snails gradually took over from brachiopods. Both bony and cartilaginous fish diversified, with some sharks becoming top predators. But the waters were also occupied by new marine reptiles, along with the now extinct plesiosaurs, dolphin-like ichthyosaurs, and mosasaurs.

SEA REPTILES
New predators occupied the seas, such as the fast-swimming ichthyosaurs. Shaped like dolphins with toothed, beak-like jaws, these reptiles lived from the Triassic to the Cretaceous.

PLANT LIFE

During the late Permian and early Triassic, the dominant Paleozoic plants – such as ferns, clubmosses, and horsetails – declined. Newly diversifying groups included conifers, which reproduce by means of seeds borne in cones. They became particularly important in Jurassic and Cretaceous times, along with cycads and cycad-like bennettitaleans. Most of the cycads also had seed-bearing cones and were distributed worldwide, even in polar regions when they were free of ice. Flowering plants (angiosperms) evolved through the Cretaceous. They combined a number of features found in other plants of the Mesozoic, such

as flower-type reproductive structures (also found in the bennettitaleans), with the one unique feature that distinguishes flowering plants – unfertilized seeds enclosed in a carpel.

DINOSAURS

For 150 million years, from the late Triassic to the end of the Cretaceous, terrestrial life was dominated by reptiles. One very varied group, known as the dinosaurs, with around 1,000 genera, diversified from crow-sized bipedal forms to the largest land-living animals ever known – the four-limbed sauropods at up to 34m (110ft) long.

Dinosaurs were first recognized as a distinct group of reptiles in 1842, their distinguishing characteristic being that they walked with their legs tucked under their bodies, unlike living reptiles, which have splayed legs. Most very large dinosaurs were plant-eaters with long necks. However, there were also very large carnivorous predators such as the Jurassic allosaurs, which were up to 12m (40ft) long.

MARINE TURTLES
The first turtles evolved during the Triassic, although it is uncertain whether they did so on land or in the sea.

SURVIVING CYCADS
The few living cycads are survivors of a far larger group of seed-bearing plants that were key members of Jurassic and Cretaceous forests.

PLACERIAS
This late Triassic 3m- (10ft-) long giant from North America was one of last surviving therapsids.

MILLION YEARS AGO	190	180	170	160	150	140	130	120	110
EON	PHANEROZOIC (541.0 MYA–PRESENT DAY)								
ERA	MESOZOIC (252.2–66.0 MYA)								
PERIOD	JURASSIC (201.3–145.0 MYA)					CRETACEOUS (145.0–66.0 MYA)			
EPOCH						LOWER CRETACEOUS (145.0–100.5 MYA)			

CLIMATE
- O₂ at 15% present level
- CO₂ at 3.5 x present level
- O₂ at 22% present level
- CO₂ at 4 x present level; temperature well above present average
- CO₂ at 3 x present level
- O₂ at 24% present level
- CO₂ at 4 x present level; temperature average of 17.5°C/63.5°F

O_2 at 15% present level; CO_2 at 3.5 x present level; O_2 at 22% present level; CO_2 at 4 x present level; CO_2 at 3 x present level; O_2 at 24% present level; CO_2 at 4 x present level

LIFE
- first primitive mammal jaws
- first birds (*Archaeopteryx*)
- first flowering-plant pollen
- early flowering plants (*Archaefructus*); feathered dinosaurs; first placental mammals (*Eomaia*)

GEOLOGIC EVENTS
- Gulf of Mexico and mid-Atlantic begin to open
- southern Atlantic begins to open
- Madagascar rifts from Africa
- India rifts from Australia and Antarctica
- first flowering-plant leaves
- Parana and Etendeka flood-basalt eruption; rifting of South America and Africa begins; rising sea-floor spreading rate
- first egg-laying monotreme mammals
- maximum sea-floor spreading rate

Pangean supercontinent begins to break up

Tethys Ocean

The dinosaurs filled most available habitats of the Mesozoic. There are two distinct types of dinosaur: one with a bird-like pelvis and the other reptile-like. The latter type included a group called the maniraptoran dinosaurs, a number of which were feathered, and one Cretaceous group of these small predators was probably the ancestors of the birds.

DINOSAUR FOOTPRINTS
These three-toed footprints of dinosaurs, initially mistaken for those of giant birds, are now used to estimate how fast dinosaurs could run.

MAMMALS AND BIRDS
Mammals (5,500 living species) and birds (10,000 living species) are the two groups of warm-blooded vertebrates that came to dominate Cenozoic landscapes. Although reptiles were still abundant (9,000 living species), they were mostly smaller than mammals. Fossils show that the reptile origins of mammals and birds lie deep within the Mesozoic, the former in the late Triassic and the latter in the Jurassic. According to the fossil record, a significant spread of both groups did not occur until after the end-Cretaceous extinction event, which wiped out most of the evolving bird groups and some of the early mammals. However, so many different bird and mammal groups appear immediately after the Mesozoic Era in the Paleocene Period that there were probably more late-Cretaceous ancestral groups than the fossil record preserves.

Primitive Mesozoic mammal groups ranged in size from that of a shrew to a large rat, and most died out. However, the marsupials and egg-laying monotremes have survived, especially in Australasia and the Americas.

MEGAZOSTRODON
Morganucodontids, such as the insect-eating Megazostrodon, *were among the first primitive shrew-like mammals.*

ARCHAEOPTERYX
The first fossil bird was first found in 1861 complete with impressions of flight feathers.

CLIMATE CHANGE
There were no polar ice-caps during the Mesozoic, and global temperatures were generally high, averaging 19°C (66°F), but carbon-dioxide levels fluctuated on a downward trend throughout the Mesozoic and the Cenozoic Era, that followed. During the end-Cretaceous extinction event 66 million years ago, climates were disturbed on a global scale. The details are still debated, but fossil charcoal indicates there was a short period of global wildfire that devastated life and perhaps longer-term warming, enhanced by greenhouse gasses derived from a massive outpouring of lava known as the Deccan eruptions, which formed the upland region of India known as the Deccan Plateau.

EXTINCTION
More than 75 per cent of all species died out at the end of the Cretaceous, in an event known as the K-PG extinction event. Victims included the dinosaurs (apart from the birds), the remaining marine and flying reptiles, and ammonites (shelled, squid-like animals). The extinction coincided with the impact of a large meteorite in the Caribbean Sea, off the Yucatan Peninsula at Chicxulub, Mexico, and the Deccan lava eruptions. Both had a significant effect on the global climate, but the several effects of the meteorite impact probably caused the extinctions.

CENOZOIC (66.0 MYA–PRESENT DAY)
TERTIARY SUB-ERA: PALEOGENE (66.0–23.0 MYA)
PALEOCENE (66.0–56.0) **EOCENE** (56.0–33.9 MYA)

NEOGENE
MIOCENE

UPPER CRETACEOUS (100.5–66.0 MYA)

OLIGOCENE (33.9–23.0)

CO_2 at 2 x present level; ◆
temperature average of 16°C/61°F

average temperature of 17°C/63°F; CO_2 at
2 x present level; O_2 at 27% of present level

average temperature of 16°C/61°F ◆
initial growth of Antarctic ice sheet ◆

O_2 at 23% of present level; ◆
temperatures fluctuate around present level

◆ first snakes
◆ first bees
◆ extinction of ichthyosaurs
extinction of large marine reptiles ◆
◆ K-PG extinction event
◆ first relative of primates (*Purgatorius*)
◆ spread of mammals ◆ first horses
◆ first bats and rhinoceros
◆ first primitive whale relative (*Pakicetus*)
◆ first grasslands and grazing mammals
◆ spread of songbirds
earliest anthropoid (*Eosimia*)

◆ Australia and Antarctica begin to rift;
widespread chalk deposition in Tethys Ocean
◆ India begins to move rapidly north
break up of Laurasia
◆ opening of North Atlantic
building of central Rocky Mountains ◆ rifting of the North Atlantic continues with intense volcanic activity
◆ Chicxulub impact
eruption of Deccan Traps, India
collision of India with Asia begins building of Himalayas ◆
Tethys Ocean begins to close ◆ building of Alps begins
Arabia and Africa rift along Red Sea; Ethiopian flood-basalt eruption

*formation of Atlantic
and Southern oceans*

India moves towards Asia

The Cenozoic Era

The Cenozoic Era extends from 66 million years
ago to the present day (Cenozoic means "recent
life"). The era is characterized by a diversification
of modern bony fish, flowering plants, pollinating
insects, birds, and mammals, including our
primate relatives.

RIFTING AND VOLCANISM

Cenozoic movements of the Earth's plates had a
considerable influence on the evolution of life.
Mountain building and large-scale uplift down
the western flank of the Americas transformed
regional climates, while the formation of the
Himalayas (see pp.128–29) and the Tibetan
Plateau generated the Southeast Asian monsoon.
Rifting and volcanism opened up the North
Atlantic (see pp.320–21) and created the Great
Rift Valley of east Africa (see pp.108–09), where
many of our primate ancestors flourished.

Cenozoic volcanism, associated with rising
plumes of heat from within the Earth, led to
doming and rifting at the surface (see p.116). The
early Cenozoic saw a region 2,000km (1,250 miles)
wide, from Greenland to Norway, domed by up
to 2km (1¼ miles), leading to rifting and the

PRESERVED LAVAS AT GIANT'S CAUSEWAY
*As early Cenozoic lavas erupted in the rift between Norway,
Britain, and Greenland, the North Atlantic widened. Evidence
of this outpouring can still be seen in Ireland (shown here).*

outpouring of lava, with the Atlantic Ocean
flooding north through the rift, a process
continuing today in Iceland. Similar doming in
Africa led to rifting and the outpouring of the
Ethiopian flood basaltic lava (31–28 million years
ago) and outpouring of the Columbia River lava
in North America (15 million years ago).

LUIS AND WALTER ALVAREZ

Walter Alvarez (b.1940), an American geologist,
found high concentrations of the rare element
iridium in a marine clay dated to the Cretaceous–
Cenozoic boundary. From this finding, in 1980
he developed the hypothesis with his father Luis
(1911–88), a Nobel physicist, that the iridium
concentration is best explained by an extra-terrestrial
body, such as a very large meteorite, impacting upon
the Earth. They further speculated that a global
catastrophe accompanying the impact caused the
demise of the dinosaurs.

CHICXULUB IMPACT
*Sixty-six million years ago, a meteorite
crashed into shallow seas, which are
now part of the Yucatan Peninsula,
Mexico (see p.83). The impact blasted
huge volumes of carbonate rock through
the atmosphere, blocking out sunlight
and shutting down photosynthesis.*

EXTRA-TERRESTRIAL IMPACTOR
*10km- (6 mile-)
wide impactor*

EXPLOSION ON IMPACT
*back of impactor
continues forward*
*front of impactor
collapses*

CRATER FORMATION
*rocks blast into
atmosphere*
*crater 100km
(60 miles) wide
and 12km (7½
miles) deep*

CRATER COLLAPSE
*steep sides
fall in*
*crater up to
240km (150
miles) wide*

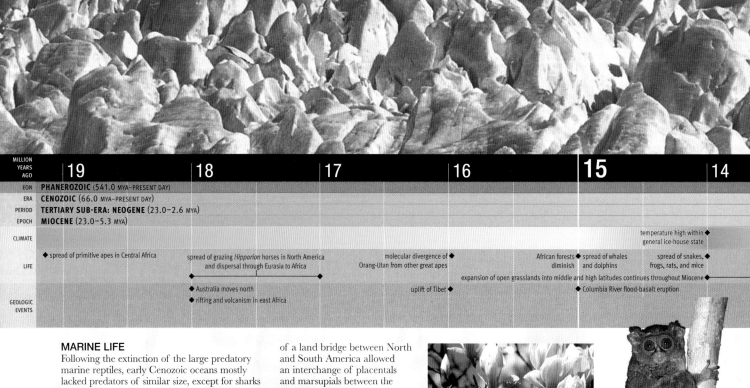

MILLION YEARS AGO	**19**		**18**		**17**		**16**		**15**		**14**
EON	PHANEROZOIC (541.0 MYA–PRESENT DAY)										
ERA	CENOZOIC (66.0 MYA–PRESENT DAY)										
PERIOD	TERTIARY SUB-ERA: NEOGENE (23.0–2.6 MYA)										
EPOCH	MIOCENE (23.0–5.3 MYA)										

CLIMATE — temperature high within ◆ general ice-house state

LIFE — ◆ spread of primitive apes in Central Africa · spread of grazing *Hipparion* horses in North America and dispersal through Eurasia to Africa · molecular divergence of ◆ Orang-Utan from other great apes · African forests ◆ spread of whales diminish and dolphins · spread of snakes, ◆ frogs, rats, and mice · expansion of open grasslands into middle and high latitudes continues throughout Miocene ◆

GEOLOGIC EVENTS — ◆ Australia moves north · ◆ rifting and volcanism in east Africa · uplift of Tibet ◆ · ◆ Columbia River flood-basalt eruption

MARINE LIFE

Following the extinction of the large predatory marine reptiles, early Cenozoic oceans mostly lacked predators of similar size, except for sharks and some bony fish. By the Early Eocene, the appearance of the earliest whales and sea cows heralded the start of several different mammalian groups that returned to the seas. These marine mammals diversified into large predators that inhabited the open sea from 35 million years ago to the present day.

LIFE ON LAND

In early Cenozoic times, mammals took over the habitats that had previously been occupied by terrestrial dinosaurs. However, there were major differences between the emerging mammals, with Australia and South America inheriting the pouched marsupials and egg-laying monotreme mammals, while the rest of the world was soon dominated by placental mammals. The latter give birth to bigger, more advanced young, nurtured for longer within the mother's body via a placenta.

Initially marsupials thrived, evolving both plant-eaters and carnivorous predators, which diversified into forms that were subsequently mimicked by the placental rodents, hippopotamuses, horses, dogs, and big cats. However, as the more advanced placentals evolved and diversified, they tended to diplace the marsupials. Formation of a land bridge between North and South America allowed an interchange of placentals and marsupials between the continents. Today the surviving marsupials of the Americas are the opossums, which are still represented by 63 species. But even more marsupials held out for longer on the isolated continent of Australia.

The earliest Cenozoic placental mammals were mostly shrew-like insect-eaters, but soon bigger (sheep-sized) browsing and rooting plant-eaters evolved. By the late Paleocene, there were rhinoceros-sized browsers and some dog-sized carnivores. The number of placental families more than quadrupled from the Cretaceous to the Eocene. The Earth's habitats were soon filled by placental mammals, from otters, seals, and whales in the seas, through the vast range of land mammals – from shrews to giant plant-eaters, such as the extinct 8m- (26ft-) long giant rhinoceros *Indricotherium*, and numerous carnivores – to bats

FLOWERING TREES
By earliest Cenozoic times flowering plants had evolved into a diverse range, including the magnolia (above) and laurels that formed the woodlands.

TARSIER
Today's tiny insect-eating tarsiers are thought to be descended from a primitive Cenozoic primate group.

in the air. Environmental and climatic changes also affected mammal evolution, especially decreasing forest cover and increasing grasslands, with the co-evolution of pollinating insects, song-birds, and grazing mammals. These changes are also thought to have affected the evolution of hominoids (higher apes and humans).

MOUNTAIN BUILDING

Cenozoic times saw the formation of four major mountain belts around the world: the Andes (see pp.140–41), the Rocky Mountains (see p.139), the European Alps (see pp.144–45), and the Himalayas (see pp.150–51). The Andes

MAMMALS OF LAKE MESSEL
Fifty million years ago, the oil-rich muds of a German lake bed preserved an astonishing diversity of its inhabitants, such as this Ailuravus, a rodent slightly larger than a squirrel.

AMBER LIFE
Since Cretaceous times, amber from some resin-producing trees has trapped and preserved small animals, especially insects.

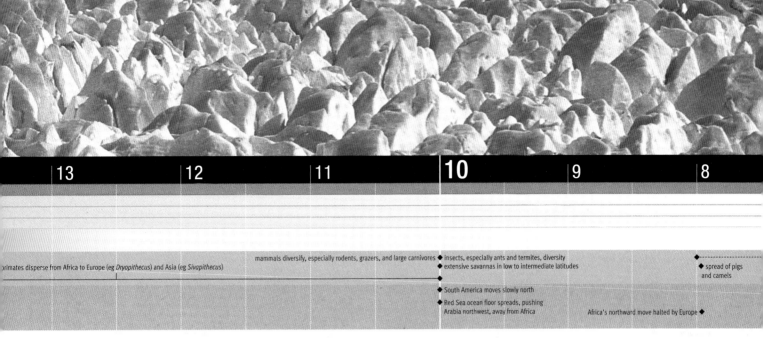

primates disperse from Africa to Europe (eg *Dryopithecus*) and Asia (eg *Sivapithecus*)

mammals diversify, especially rodents, grazers, and large carnivores ◆ insects, especially ants and termites, diversity
◆ extensive savannas in low to intermediate latitudes

◆ spread of pigs
and camels

◆ South America moves slowly north

◆ Red Sea ocean floor spreads, pushing
Arabia northwest, away from Africa

Africa's northward move halted by Europe ◆

are a classic example of mountain building,
resulting from the convergence of an oceanic
(Pacific) plate with a continental plate (South
America), combined with the subduction of the
oceanic plate (see p.55) and frequent earthquakes
and volcanoes. By contrast, the Alpine–Himalayan
belt resulted from the convergence of the African
and Indian plates with Europe and Asia
respectively. Africa's northward movement
subducted a body of water known as the Tethys
Ocean; the intervening rocks were compressed,
thickened, and elevated with intense folding and
faulting, leading to the formation of the Alps. The
breakaway of India from Africa and Antarctica,
which began in the Mesozoic, eventually caused
the subduction of the eastern Tethys and its

SPREADING GRASSLANDS

*By the Miocene, cooling climates and greater aridity
caused forests to break up and grasslands to expand,
along with fleet-footed grazing mammals and their
predators, such as big cats.*

HIMALAYAS

*The spectacular mountain belt
of the Himalayas, with the
high plateau of Tibet to the
north and low sediment-filled
floodplains to the south, is the
result of the convergence of
the Indian and Asian plates.*

convergence with Asia,
beginning 20 million
years ago. Again, the
intervening rocks were compressed, thickened,
and elevated with intense folding and faulting,
resulting in the formation of the Himalayas. The
continuing northward drive of India is thought to
have pushed the deeper part of the Indian plate
beneath Tibet, thickening and elevating it without
folding. The formation of this high and elongated
physical barrier caused significant change in the
regional climate, with the development of the
Southeast Asian monsoon.

The Origin of Humans

Humans, apes, lemurs, and
monkeys are all mammals and
were first grouped together as
primates in 1758 by the Swedish
naturalist Carolus Linnaeus
(1707–78). The fossil record shows
that the earliest primate-like
mammals originated as small insect-
eating animals, such as the shrew-like
Purgatorius in the early Paleocene.
In the early Cenozoic, a group
of tree-climbing, squirrel-like
animals (the plesiadapiforms)
had evolved in North
America and Europe.
They were followed by
tarsier- and lemur-like
primates, which spread
into Africa and Asia along
with two groups of higher
primates, the New World
monkeys and the Old
World monkeys and apes.

BIPEDAL BEGINNINGS

*It seems likely that our
ape–human ancestor was a
knuckle-walker, like today's
apes. However, fossil
hominids from 6–7 million
years ago, appear already
to have walked on two feet.*

It was from the latter group that hominoids
evolved in Africa. These included the 25- to
23-million-year-old (early Miocene) tail-less and
monkey-like *Proconsul*, which could climb trees
and walk on all fours. By the late Miocene Epoch,
the apes diversified and separated into African,
European, and Asian branches, some of whose
members increased in size.

MILLION YEARS AGO	**7**	6.5	**6**	5.5	**5**	4.5

EON	**PHANEROZOIC** (541.0 MYA–PRESENT DAY)
ERA	**CENOZOIC** (66.0 MYA–PRESENT DAY)
PERIOD	**TERTIARY SUB-ERA: NEOGENE** (23.0–2.6 MYA)
EPOCH	**MIOCENE** (24.0–5.3 MYA) **PLIOCENE** (5.3–2.6 MYA)

CLIMATE
◆ strengthening of Asian monsoon due to uplift of Tibet
◆ falling and fluctuating temperatures

LIFE
◆ molecular divergence of gorillas and humans
spread of African grassy woodland; Afro–Asian faunal interchange
◆ first hippopotamuses; first mammoths
earliest human relatives; molecular divergence of chimps and humans
Sahelanthropus tchadensis ◆
Ardipithecus ramidus ◆

GEOLOGIC EVENTS
◆ uplift of Tibet
◆ volcanic eruptions and release of ice-rafted debris and dust layers in Pacific
◆ initiation of uplift and rifting in northeast Africa
uplift, cooling, and aridification of Africa; evaporation of Mediterranean
◆ closure of Tethys Ocean complete

It was the great apes of Africa that evolved into gorillas, chimpanzees, and humans. Gorillas diverged first, about 10 million years ago, while the chimpanzees and humans share a common ancestor who, according to the molecular clock (see p.30), lived 5–7 million years ago.

THE SPREAD OF HOMINIDS

The fossil record of our extinct human relatives (the hominids) is sparse, but there are certain hotspots with relatively abundant remains, such as the sediments of the Great Rift Valley of East Africa and caves in South Africa, Europe, and Asia. This preservational bias has distorted our view of human evolution but important finds have been made elsewhere – such as a skull of the 6–7 million year old *Sahelanthropus* found in Chad. It combines features of a chimp-sized, small-brained ape with human features, suggesting that it may have been able to walk upright. Fossil remains of *Orrorin*

SKULL RECORD

By examining the skulls, it is clear that brain size increases significantly from Australopithecus *to the large-brained* Homo *species:* H. neanderthalensis *and* H. sapiens.

AUSTRALOPITHECUS

HOMO NEANDERTHALENSIS

HOMO SAPIENS

CHARLES LYELL

A Scottish-born barrister, Charles Lyell (1797–1875) took up geology and wrote the *Principles of Geology* (1830–33), an important synthesis of geological ideas that greatly influenced the naturalist Charles Darwin. Lyell believed that the interpretation of the past must be based on an understanding of present processes. He also divided the Tertiary into epochs. Lyell initially disagreed with the theory of evolution proposed by Charles Darwin and Alfred Wallace, but finally, if reluctantly, came to accept it.

(6.2–5.8 million years old), *Ardipithecus* (4.4 million years old), and *Australopithecus afarensis* (3.85–2.95 million years old) support the early evolution of upright walking among hominids and also an African base for early human evolution. From 4 million years ago, evolution of the small, ape-like australopithecines and their relatives gave rise to the first more human-like *Homo habilis* by 2.4 million years ago.

LAETOLI FOOTPRINTS

Some 3.6 million years ago in Laetoli, east Africa, two upright-walking human-related adults and a juvenile walked on wet volcanic ash, leaving the oldest known footprints.

HUMAN ATTRIBUTES

The attributes that distinguish human species (members of the genus *Homo*) from other extinct human relatives have become less definite in recent decades. Traits that were once attributed to human species are now known to be more ancient. Upright walking originated some 6 million years ago. The use and manufacture of tools began at least 2.6 million years ago, slightly before the earliest known *Homo* remains, whose body and brain size (are not as different from that of the australopithecines as once thought. However, the earliest known human species, *Homo habilis* can be distinguished by its smaller cheek teeth and enlarged incisors, which indicate a change from the australopithecine diet including tough plant materials to a more varied and nutritious one that included animal tissues, perhaps scavenged from carcasses.

By 1.9 million years ago, at least one other tool-making species of *Homo* had evolved in Africa. *Homo erectus* had an even more human anatomy. It was taller (145–185 cm/4ft 9in–6ft 1in), more slender, more mobile, and had a larger brain (600–910 cubic cm/37–56 cubic in). These were the first human relatives to spread beyond Africa, reaching

DEVELOPING SKILLS

The fossil record tends to preserve only stone and bone tools, but some of the most primitive tools were probably digging sticks.

QUATERNARY (2.6 MYA–PRESENT DAY)
PLEISTOCENE (2.6–0.01 MYA)

increasing aridity in Asia, northern hemisphere cooling   onset of northern hemisphere glaciation   intensified glaciation in Europe, Asia, and North America ◆

◆ Arctic ice-cap established, temperatures same as present

◆ Australopithecus anamensis, first australopithecine
◆ oldest human footprints (Laetoli)
Australopithecus africanus   earliest stone ◆ tools in Africa
◆ earliest Homo habilis fossil
oldest human remains in Europe H. antecessor/H. erectus ◆

Australopithecus afarensis – "Lucy"
◆ H. erectus spreads out of Africa to Europe and Asia   H. erectus ◆ in China

◆ first robust australopithecines
◆ stone tools in China

◆ eruption of La Pacana, Chile
◆ uplift of Tibetan plateau
◆ volcanic eruptions (Kamchatka/Aleutians) and release of ice-rafted debris in Pacific
◆ opening of Red Sea straits, breaking Africa–Arabia land bridge

◆ flooding of Mediterranean basin
◆ eruption in Yellowstone, Wyoming, USA
eruption of Valles, New Mexico, USA ◆

closing gap between North and South America changes ocean circulation
◆ widespread loess deposition in China

◆ eruption of Cerro Galan, Argentina   eruption in Yellowstone, Wyoming, USA ◆

CAVE ART
Representations of animals, some extinct and others no longer living in the same region, point to the antiquity of much rock art, which is otherwise very difficult to date.

Georgia in western Asia by 1.8 million years ago and Southeast Asia (Java) by at least 1.6 million years ago.

In Europe, the earliest human relatives date from around 1.2 million years ago. Found in Spain, *Homo antecessor* has evolutionary links to the older *Homo erectus* and the younger *Homo heidelbergensis*. The latter dates from around 700,000 years ago and was widespread from southern Africa, Eastern Asia, and Europe. It was well built, with males averaging 1.57m (5ft 2 in) in height and females 1.75m (5ft 9in). *Homo heidelbergensis* was probably ancestral to the extinct Eurasian species *Homo neanderthalensis*, around 300,000 years ago, and the African *Homo sapiens* from around 200,000 years ago. *Homo heidelbergensis* is also ancestral to another species from western Asia called the Denisovans, from 80,000–30,000 years ago, which is known only from its DNA and a few fossil bones. All three species may have met up in western Asia, but only *Homo sapiens* survived the rigours of the Quaternary Ice Ages.

The evolution of sophisticated tools and culture allowed *Homo sapiens* to expand globally with a population of more than 7 billion. Recent discoveries include a strange, chimp-sized human species, *Homo floresiensis*, which lived on the Indonesian island of Flores between 95,000 and 17,000 years ago and whose ancestry is still unclear.

The Ice Ages
The recent geological past has seen the Earth plunge into an ice-house phase of alternating cold and warm climates known as Ice Ages. Global climate cooled after the mid-Miocene, around 16 million years ago. From around 3 million years ago, the acceleration of cooling led to the onset of glaciation in the northern hemisphere and the formation of the Arctic ice cap around 2.5 million years ago.

HUMAN EVOLUTION
Recent discoveries, mostly in Africa, show that human ancestry extends further back than previously thought. The result is a shrub-like evolutionary tree with about 20 known species of extinct human relatives, arranged in seven genera.

Homo rudolfensis
Homo erectus
Homo ergaster   Homo heidelbergensis
Australopithecus garhi
Homo neanderthalensis
Australopithecus rudolfensis
Homo floresiensis
Homo habilis
Homo sapiens
Paranthropus boisei
Australopithecus afarensis
Australopithecus sediba
Orrorin tugenensis
Australopithecus anamensis   Paranthropus aethiopicus
Sahelanthropus tchadensis
Ardipithecus kadabba
Ardipithecus ramidus   Australopithecus africanus   Paranthropus robustus   Chimpanzee

7 million years ago   6 mya   5 mya   4 mya   3 mya   2 mya   1 mya   present day

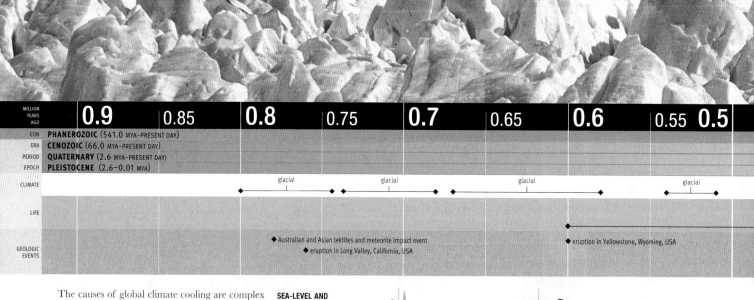

EON **PHANEROZOIC** (541.0 MYA–PRESENT DAY)
ERA **CENOZOIC** (66.0 MYA–PRESENT DAY)
PERIOD **QUATERNARY** (2.6 MYA–PRESENT DAY)
EPOCH **PLEISTOCENE** (2.6–0.01 MYA)

CLIMATE   glacial   glacial   glacial   glacial

LIFE

GEOLOGIC EVENTS   ◆ Australian and Asian tektites and meteorite impact event   ◆ eruption in Yellowstone, Wyoming, USA
◆ eruption in Long Valley, California, USA

The causes of global climate cooling are complex (see pp.368–71) but include the interplay of astronomical cycles related to fluctuations in the Earth's orbit around the Sun, which produces a 100,000-year cycle, and variation in the tilt of the Earth's axis of rotation, which produces a 41,000-year cycle. Other factors include changes to the circulation of ocean currents brought about by plate movement. The Quaternary Ice Ages began around 2.6 million years ago and have been marked by 50 cycles of alternating colder glacial and warmer interglacial climates.

ADVANCING GLACIERS

Extensive ice-sheets and glaciers first developed in the northern hemisphere about 2.6 million years ago. An ice-cap formed over the Arctic Ocean, which eventually extended as far south as today's

FORAMINIFERANS

The shell composition of tiny, sea-dwelling single-celled animals called foraminiferans records changes in the chemistry of ocean waters. By recovering such fossil shells from ocean-floor sediments and analysing their chemistry over successive generations, the changes in ocean chemistry can be reconstructed. Oxygen-isotope ratios in the calcium carbonate of the shells are measured, and from this information past fluctuations in ocean temperature, ice volume, and hence climate change can be recovered.

SEA-LEVEL AND TEMPERATURE
Changes in global average temperatures over the latter part of the Quaternary ice ages, with their fluctuating cold and warm spells, are closely tracked by related sea-level changes.

 Temperature

 Sea-level

POST-GLACIAL TEMPERATURE
Global temperatures over the last 10,000 years, since the end of the last glacial advance, have been unusually stable, but may not remain so for long.

New York in North America, close to London, England, and St Petersburg in Russia. Beyond the ice, permafrost extended as far south as the Black and Mediterranean seas. Mountain glaciers developed globally, even in the tropics. Landscapes were dramatically altered with upland glacial erosion and lowland deposition of glacial debris.

From such extremes of cold, the numerous ice-age cycles saw interglacial climates, which were occasionally warmer than those of today. For instance, 125,000 years ago elephants and hippos flourished in England, where previously there had been mammoths and giant deer. The climate cycles were accompanied by changes in sea-level, allowing migration of animals and peoples and then isolating them on offshore islands.

QUATERNARY ICE-CAPS
Polar ice-caps grew and retreated several times during the Quaternary, reaching the maximum extent shown here.

LIFE ADAPTS TO CHANGE

Climate chage, such as that of the ice ages, has a considerable impact on life. In the face of climate change, some species evolve in response to the new conditions, others shift their geographic ranges to track suitable conditions, and still others go extinct. As climate cooled, some animals adapted to conserve heat better through improved insulation (provided by fatty tissues, hair, feathers or clothing)

PURPLE SAXIFRAGE
Some flowering plants, such as the Arctic bog cotton and purple saxifrage, are well adapted to tundra conditions.

HOLOCENE (0.01 MYA–PRESENT DAY)

glacial   glacial   glacial   penultimate glaciation   ◆ cooling event followed rapid temperature rise

last glacial ◆

Homo heidelbergensis ◆ oldest preserved wooden spears   ◆ early *H. neanderthalensis*   modern humans leave Africa ◆   *Homo floresiensis*   ◆ arrival of modern humans in Europe

◆ simple stone tools   ◆ origin of *H. sapiens* in Africa   ◆ last Neanderthals

◆ eruption of Mount Shasta, California, USA   release of icebergs in North Atlantic every 2–3,000 years

eruption of Toba, Indonesia ◆

◆ eruption of Kos, Greece

Africa and India still moving north

MAMMOTH
Well adapted to the cold, the woolly mammoth had insulating hair, a thick layer of fat, and tusks to clear snow from vegetation.

and more compact bodies in which surface area was lower in relation to volume. The mobility of many animals allows them to migrate towards their preferred climates but rooted plants have more of a problem. They have to rely upon reproduction and dispersal for survival of successive generations. Cold-adapted plants have to be able to withstand freezing air and soils with short growing seasons. As a result they tend to have small leaves, shallow roots, and ground-hugging form.

CARIBOU MIGRATION
Reindeer, also known as Caribou, are cold-adapted herd animals that survive in polar regions by migrating over long distances between winter and summer feeding grounds.

MIGRATION OF HOMO SAPIENS
Through the collection of fossil records, the pathways by which modern humans (Homo sapiens) are thought to have achieved global distribution have been reconstructed. The journey is believed to have begun in east Africa about 120,000 years ago.

HUMAN MIGRATION

Both archaeological and biomolecular evidence show that the first migration of modern humans (*Homo sapiens*) from Africa was initiated about 100,000 years ago. The migration reached the western shores of the Mediterranean Sea by around 90,000 years ago, but then went no further. Around 60,000 years ago, another wave of migration left the African continent, reaching China 68,000 years ago, Australia 50,000 years ago, and then Eurasia 40,000 years ago. With the lowered sea-level at the time, the existence of the Bering landbridge from Siberia to North America allowed humans to reach South America by 11,500 years ago.

Newly discovered fossil remains from the remote Denisova Cave in Siberia, Russia, and biomolecular data have revealed previously unknown human species whose existence indicates that human migration was a lot more complex than once thought, especially within Eurasia.

RECENT EXTINCTIONS

Over the last 50,000 years, there has been continuing global extinction of the megafauna – animals over 45kg (100lb) in weight, such as the mammoth. Another victim was the Neanderthals, whose demise followed the arrival of modern humans about 40,000 years ago. They co-existed for more than 10,000 years in western Europe, but eventually died out. Comparison of Neanderthal and modern human DNA suggests that in people of western Eurasian origin some 1–4 per cent of their genetic makeup results from past interbreeding with the Neanderthals. The exact cause of the megafauna extinction, whether climatic and environmental change, human hunting, or a combination of the two, is still debated. However, recent accurate dating, especially in Australasia, which suffered little climate change, shows that extinctions closely follow the arrival of modern human hunters. The exception is Africa, where modern humans co-existed with large mammals for much longer, but now rising populations are threatening even Africa's big game.

Of course, human influence on the Earth goes far beyond that of hunter. The encroachment on almost all natural habitats, from the rainforests to the polar wastes, along with the effects of human-enhanced global warming, pose a far greater threat to the planet's flora and fauna.

RAW MATERIAL
Lava pouring across the Pacific island of Hawaii is a vivid demonstration of Earth's hot interior, and the processes that formed the diverse minerals and rocks at the surface.

THE ANATOMY OF THE EARTH

PLANET EARTH IS A COMPLEX structure that is made up of three primary layers: the core, the mantle, and the crust. The density and temperature of the materials that make up the Earth increase approaching the metallic iron core, which has a solid interior and a molten exterior. The brittle outer layer of the planet, however, is made of many different kinds of rock, some up to 4 billion years old. Rocks consist of combinations of minerals, and are formed by various geological processes. These include internal forces, such as the movement of tectonic plates and volcanic eruptions, layering and compression of sediment, and interaction with living organisms and the atmosphere.

The Earth's Structure

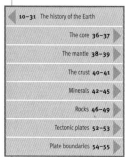

EVERYDAY EXPERIENCE ON THE EARTH might suggest that our planet is remarkably varied – its materials range from water and ice to atmospheric gases and a host of rocks and minerals. However, the thin surface biosphere we occupy is not typical of the Earth as a whole. Overall, the planet is much less varied – within a few tens of kilometres below the surface, it consists only of rocks, minerals, and metallic compounds. Measurements of earthquake waves passing through the Earth allow us to probe its structure, since different layers propagate the waves at different speeds. They reveal the existence of a hot, dense core, surrounded by a mantle and a thin, rocky outer crust. The crust and a thin layer of mantle together form the jigsaw of tectonic plates that make up the Earth's outer shell.

INSIDE THE EARTH
The Earth has a layered internal structure, with each layer increasing in density and temperature. It is heated internally mainly by radioactive decay and by heat left over from its formation. Heat flows from the top of the core through the mantle, until it eventually reaches the cooler crust and escapes.

North-American Plate
Under Yellowstone Park, on the North American plate, lies a huge reservoir of magma (hot, melted rock) possibly originating from the mantle.

Shape and Form

The overall shape of the Earth, called the geoid, is determined by the effects of gravity and rotation on the materials that make up our planet. Gravity will pull any sufficiently massive object into a sphere – only smaller Solar System objects have non-spherical shapes. The Earth is an almost perfect sphere, but its rapid rotation every 24 hours – equivalent to the surface at the Equator moving at more than 1,600kph (1,000mph) – reduces the effect of gravity around the Equator, and means that equatorial regions bulge outwards by about 21km (13 miles) compared to the poles. The Earth's surface topography varies by about 20km (12½ miles) from the highest mountains to the deepest ocean trenches, and variations in surface elevation reflect two fundamentally different types of surface crust: continental crust with average elevation of less than 1km (⅗ mile) above sea-level; and oceanic crust with average depth about 4.5km (2⅔ miles) below sea-level. Gravity, coupled with processes such as tectonics (see pp.52–53) and erosion (see pp.58–59), make larger variations in elevation unsustainable over long periods.

Cascadia subduction zone
This marks where the small Juan de Fuca tectonic plate dips below the North American plate.

Gorda Ridge
This spreading ridge is formed by a shallow magma upwelling.

Hawaiian Island chain
These islands have formed during the past 30 million years from movement of the Pacific plate over a "hotspot" currently under the Big Island of Hawaii.

The hotspot under Hawaii is possibly caused by a plume of hot material rising from the mantle.

GREAT RIFT VALLEY
Tectonic processes have pushed up these mountains in east Africa, but erosion over millions of years will reduce them to insignificant hills.

EARTH IN SPACE
Seen from space, Earth is a blue planet. Two-thirds of the surface is covered by sea, and much of the land is often obscured by cloud.

direction of rotation (1,600kph/1,000mph at Equator)

Earth bulges at the Equator

CHANGING SHAPE
The Earth's high rotation rate slightly distorts its structure so that it bulges at the Equator and is flattened at the poles.

flattened pole

Tonga Trench
Up to 10,880m (35,702ft) deep, this marks where the Pacific plate dips below the small neighbouring Tonga plate.

Top layer of upper mantle
Together with overlying crust, this forms the lithosphere, the sole component of tectonic plates.

Asthenosphere
The semi-solid, deformable layer on which the lithosphere floats.

Transition zone
A distinct layer that lies just below, and is slightly denser than, the upper mantle.

D' layer
A deep, apparently uniform layer that makes up most of the lower mantle.

D" layer
A distinct, somewhat denser layer, of variable thickness, at the bottom of the lower mantle.

CONTINENTAL CRUST
STATE Solid **DENSITY** 2.7g/cm³
DEPTH 9km (5½ miles) above to 70km (45 miles) below surface
TEMPERATURE -90–900°C (-130–1,650°F)

OCEANIC CRUST
STATE Solid
DENSITY 2.9g/cm³
DEPTH 3–11km (2–7 miles) below surface
TEMPERATURE 0–400°C (30–750°F)

ATMOSPHERE
STATE Gaseous
DENSITY 0.0012g/cm³ (at sea level)
DEPTH Up to 1,000km (600 miles) above sea level
TEMPERATURE -90–15,000°C (-130–2,700°F)

← *ocean water*

← *lithosphere*

subducting plate

INNER CORE
STATE Solid **DENSITY** 13g/cm³
DEPTH 5,100–6,375km (3,170–3,965 miles) below surface
TEMPERATURE 5,000–6,500°C (9,000–11,700°F)

OUTER CORE
STATE Liquid **DENSITY** 10–12g/cm³
DEPTH 2,900–5,100km (18,000–3,170 miles) below surface
TEMPERATURE 4,000–6,000°C (7,200–10,800°F)

LOWER MANTLE
STATE Solid **DENSITY** 4–6g/cm³
DEPTH 410–2,900km (255–18,000 miles) below surface
TEMPERATURE 2,200–4,000°C (4,000–7,2000°F)

UPPER MANTLE
STATE Solid **DENSITY** 3.5g/cm³
DEPTH 11–410km (7–255 miles) below surface
TEMPERATURE 400–2,300°C (750–4,150°F)

Chile Rise
This ridge marks the divergence of two lithospheric (tectonic) plates, associated with upwelling of magma.

Chemical Composition

Analysis of rocks in the Earth's crust shows that most are rich in silicon dioxide. The basalts of the oceanic crust have proportionally more calcium, iron, and magnesium, whereas the less dense continents are richer in aluminium. Beneath the Earth's crust, the layers become progressively denser, and this is reflected in differences in mineral composition. Rock samples from the mantle, occasionally brought to the surface by volcanism, show that this region is made of silicate minerals rich in magnesium and iron. The composition of the core is thought to be similar to that of iron meteorites formed in the early Solar System, consisting mainly of iron with some nickel.

SILICON DIOXIDE
ALUMINIUM OXIDE
IRON AND IRON OXIDES
CALCIUM OXIDE
MAGNESIUM OXIDE
NICKEL OXIDE
OTHERS

CONTINENTAL CRUST
OCEANIC CRUST
MANTLE
CORE

CHEMICAL COMPOSITION
The proportions of different chemical compounds vary between the Earth's different layers. At the centre, the core is almost entirely metallic iron and nickel.

PLANET EARTH

The Core

THE EARTH'S CORE IS FAR TOO DEEP to be studied by direct sampling, so our understanding of it depends on indirect investigations. Comparing the Earth's overall mass with the density of rocks close to its surface shows that parts of the Earth's interior must be much denser than its crustal rocks. Confirmation of a distinct core comes mainly from studies of earthquake waves travelling through the planet. These not only reveal the size of the core, they also show it has solid inner and liquid outer parts. Density calculations and the examination of meteorites formed at the same time and from the same materials as the Earth itself, have helped to establish that the core must consist mainly of iron, together with some nickel and small amounts of other elements. The nature of the Earth's magnetic field has also provided evidence of the core's structure and composition.

P-WAVES
Also known as primary or compressional waves, P-waves produce alternate stretching and compression in the material they pass through.

rock moves up and down

rock is stretched

rock is compressed

direction of wave

S-WAVES
Also known as secondary or shear waves, S-waves shake rocky material from side to side or up and down as they pass. Unlike P-waves, they cannot pass through liquids.

Evidence for the Core

An earthquake produces shock waves, some of which travel through the Earth's interior. Seismometers can be used to detect these planet-penetrating waves, where they arrive back at the surface. There are two different types of waves: P-waves and S-waves. P-waves passing straight through the Earth are significantly slowed down within a central region, indicating that this region must have a fundamentally different composition from the rest of the planet. There are "shadow zones" on Earth's surface where no P-waves are detectable following an earthquake, an effect of the core refracting P-waves. For every earthquake, there is also a large shadow zone for S-waves on the opposite side of the Earth. Since S-waves cannot pass through liquids, this implies that at least part of the core is liquid.

The Inner Core

The inner core was discovered in the 1930s, when Danish seismologist Inge Lehmann detected some weak P-waves (which she called P'-waves) in the P-wave shadow zone. She suggested that these must have reflected off a boundary between inner and outer regions within the core. It is now known that the inner core is a solid ball, consisting mainly of a crystalline iron-nickel alloy. Over the past decade, evidence has been found that it may rotate within the outer core at a slightly different rate from the Earth as a whole, and that it may be gradually growing, or is possibly growing on one side and melting on the other.

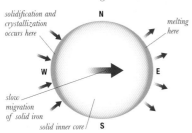

solidification and crystallization occurs here

N

melting here

W

E

slow migration of solid iron

solid inner core

S

CORE MELT AND FORMATION
Some evidence indicates that the Earth's inner core may be growing on one side, by solidification of outer core material onto it, and melting on the other.

P-wave shadow zone

P-wave

S-wave

waves can be detected with seismometers where they arrive back at surface, which can be anything from a few seconds to more than 20 minutes after earthquake

waves refract (change direction) sharply when they encounter sudden changes in density

waves follow curved paths due to gradual changes in density with depth through the interior

S-waves are blocked where they encounter the liquid outer core

earthquake focus is point of origin of both P- and S-waves that travel through Earth's interior

SHOCK WAVE PATTERN
The pattern in which P- and S-type waves from an earthquake are detected around the surface of the world, and the time it takes them to reach various points, has proved that the Earth has a core that is partly liquid and partly solid.

Earth's Magnetic Field

An important effect of the Earth having an outer core of liquid iron (see below) is the generation of a substantial magnetic field. The lines of the field converge at two points on Earth's surface called the magnetic poles. The magnetic field extends far into space and creates a protective bubble that deflects high-speed streams of charged particles from the Sun, called the solar wind. Without this field, the solar wind would likely have stripped away Earth's atmosphere long ago and life on Earth would be very different. Studies of iron-rich materials in the Earth's crust have shown that at variable time intervals – from less than 100,000 to millions of years – the Earth's north and south magnetic poles have switched. These reversals are recorded in iron-containing minerals in sedimentary rocks and have proved important in deciphering Earth's history.

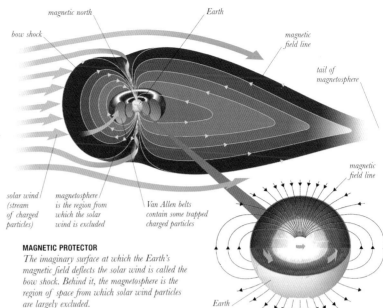

magnetic north   Earth

bow shock   magnetic field line

tail of magnetosphere

magnetic field line

solar wind (stream of charged particles)   magnetosphere is the region from which the solar wind is excluded   Van Allen belts contain some trapped charged particles   Earth

AURORAE
Electrically charged particles from the Sun, funnelled into the Earth's magnetic field above the poles, collide with atoms in the upper atmosphere to produce luminous streams of light known as aurorae.

MAGNETIC PROTECTOR
The imaginary surface at which the Earth's magnetic field deflects the solar wind is called the bow shock. Behind it, the magnetosphere is the region of space from which solar wind particles are largely excluded.

The Outer Core

The Earth's outer core is about 2,200km (1,370 miles) deep and makes up 95 per cent of the volume of the whole core. It is thought to consist mainly of iron with some nickel, and its temperature ranges from around 4,000°C (7,200°F) at the boundary with the mantle up to about 6,000°C (10,800°F) at its interface with the inner core. At these temperatures, the pressure in the outer core is insufficient to keep it solid; instead it is a low-viscosity liquid. An overall flow of heat occurs through the outer core. This heat is generated principally by solidification of molten metal onto the inner core (releasing latent heat). The heat flow sets up convection currents, which combined with the Earth's rotation sets up spiralling motions in the liquid metal, creating a magnetic field. The inner core may act to stabilize this magnetic field.

MOLTEN IRON
Metallic iron (seen here being poured in a foundry) has a high density and strongly magnetic character. It probably forms most of the Earth's core, along with a small percentage of nickel and some other lighter element, perhaps sulphur.

S-wave shadow zone, where no S-waves can be detected, provides evidence that the core is partly liquid

arrival of P-waves that have passed right through the planet is appreciably delayed because they have been slowed during their journey through the core

P-wave shadow zone, where no strong, direct, P-waves can be detected, provides evidence of a core that refracts P-waves

P'-wave (weak P-wave) within P-wave shadow zone provides evidence of an inner core that reflects some P-waves

Earth's rotational axis

spiralling convection currents influenced by rotation of the Earth

SPIRALLING CONVECTION
Acting like the spinning conductor in a bicycle dynamo, the liquid iron and nickel in the outer core continuously churns under the combined influence of the Earth's rotation and heat fluxes.

outer core   inner core

The Mantle

THE EARTH'S MANTLE IS KNOWN to be basically solid, but seismic studies indicate that it is not of uniform composition. Instead, it contains layers that increase in density with depth. Despite being solid, the rocks of the mantle appear to slowly deform, producing heat transfer by convection. Over the past 20 years, imaging of the mantle by means of earthquake waves, called seismic tomography, and other investigations have shown that the pattern of this convection is more complex than originally thought, and the exact nature of it is still being debated.

ANDRIJA MOHOROVICIC

The boundary between the crust and mantle was first detected and described by Croatian geophysicist Andrija Mohorovicic (1857–1936). By studying records of seismic waves generated by an earthquake near Zagreb in 1909, Mohorovicic noticed that some waves seemed to arrive earlier than others. He reasoned that they were affected by a density change within the Earth, around 30km (18 miles) deep. Now known as the Mohorovicic discontinuity, or Moho, its depth changes from 25–70km (16–45 miles) beneath the continents to 7–11km (4–7 miles) below the ocean floor. The discontinuity marks the compositional change between the crust and the underlying mantle.

The Upper Mantle and Transition Zone

From the base of the Earth's crust down to a depth of about 660km (410 miles) is a region now considered to have two main parts: the upper mantle down to about 410km (255 miles); and a denser region, the transition zone, forming the rest. Earthquake waves passing across the boundary at 410km suddenly speed up due to a change in density. Within the upper mantle are two distinct zones. The top layer is fused to the crust, forming the Earth's rigid outer shell (lithosphere), which is split into tectonic plates. Beneath this is a warmer, slightly more plastic layer, about 200km (120 miles) deep, called the asthenosphere. The predominant rock type in the upper mantle is peridotite, which consists mainly of the minerals olivine and pyroxene. In the transition zone, the increase in pressure alters the crystal structure or arrangement of atoms within olivine to produce denser versions of it.

MANTLE XENOLITHS
A xenolith is a rock fragment of different origin from the igneous rock in which it is embedded. The dark xenolith here has come from the upper mantle.

PERIDOTITE
These igneous rocks in Newfoundland, Canada, are the remains of ancient ocean floor. They include coarse-grained, olivine-rich rocks called peridotites, thought to have similar composition to upper mantle rocks.

LOCATION OF SLICE THROUGH THE EARTH

Mid-oceanic ridge
The magma erupted at divergent plate boundaries, such as the Mid-Atlantic Ridge, is thought to come from the upper mantle

Magma upwelling
Africa is starting to rift apart as a result of an upwelling of magma underneath the continent

Incipient mantle plume
This model allows that there may be some plumes formed of hot material rising from the core–mantle boundary

Trindade hotspot

Rising current
Heat is transferred outwards from interior by rising currents

lithosphere

asthenosphere

transition zone

D" layer

Subducting plate
In this model, cold slabs of subducting plate may penetrate as far as the core–mantle boundary

Descending current
Cold, dense mantle descends into interior, often coinciding with zones of plate subduction

South America

Colombian trench

blue indicates slow-moving waves

red indicates fast-moving waves

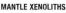

Depth in kilometres: 0, 100, 200, 300, 400, 500, 600, 700, 800

Transition zone

Lower mantle

Distance in kilometres: 0, 500, 1,000, 1,500

SEISMIC TOMOGRAPHY
This technique is used to generate images of the Earth's interior from measurements of seismic wave velocity, which varies with the temperature and composition of rocks.

The Lower Mantle

Earthquake waves reaching a depth of around 660km (410 miles) in the mantle significantly speed up, indicating a change in rock density. The region of Earth's interior that extends from this boundary down to the core–mantle boundary, at around 2,900km (1,800 miles), is known as the lower mantle. It is of mostly uniform composition, but at its base is a distinct sublayer, varying from about 50 to 200km (30 to 125 miles) deep, called the D" layer. This appears to have a complex structure, involving local layering and regions of partial melt, possibly reflecting processes occurring at the core–mantle boundary. The D" layer may be the site from which upwelling mantle plumes originate, as well as a repository for material from subducted plates. The most abundant minerals in the lower mantle contain magnesium, iron, or calcium in combination with silicate (silicon and oxygen). Of these, a substance called magnesium silicate perovskite is probably the most abundant mineral on Earth.

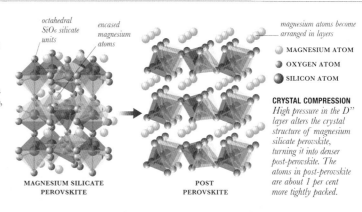

octahedral SiO6 silicate units

encased magnesium atoms

magnesium atoms become arranged in layers

○ MAGNESIUM ATOM
○ OXYGEN ATOM
● SILICON ATOM

MAGNESIUM SILICATE PEROVSKITE

POST PEROVSKITE

CRYSTAL COMPRESSION
High pressure in the D" layer alters the crystal structure of magnesium silicate perovskite, turning it into denser post-perovskite. The atoms in post-perovskite are about 1 per cent more tightly packed.

WHOLE-MANTLE CONVECTION MODEL
In this "single layer" model of mantle convection, which is partly speculative, a series of convection cells gradually carry material from the bottom of the mantle to the top and vice versa.

Madagascar

Volcanic hotspot
Thought to have been intermittently active for 65 million years, this hotspot has most recently created the volcanic island of Réunion

Mantle plume
Some scientists think the Réunion hotspot is caused by a rising plume of hot material from deep in the lower mantle

FIRES WITHIN
Investigation of the chemistry of magma that reaches the Earth's surface in various volcanic settings, including hotspots and spreading ocean ridges, has provided some clues to the pattern of mantle convection.

Mohorovicic discontinuity

Sunda trench

Sumatra

Subduction zone
Volcanism in these regions results from magma produced by relatively shallow, upper-mantle processes

Borneo

Philippines

Philippines trench

Mariana Islands

Mariana trench

Mantle Convection

At the base of the mantle, heat continuously flows out of the Earth's core. This rising heat causes the mantle to slowly circulate, its rocks shifting a few centimetres a year, carrying heat outwards by convection. At the top of the mantle, convection plays a part in driving the movement of tectonic plates. However, the overall pattern of convection in the mantle is not fully understood – a point of debate, for example, is whether it occurs in a single layer, as in the whole mantle convection model (see left) or in two layers, as in the deep layer model (below). In formulating different models, geophysicists strive to explain findings obtained from studies such as seismic tomography and chemical analysis of magma (presumed to come from the mantle) erupted in different settings at the Earth's surface. For example, any model has to explain why magmas erupted at volcanic hotspots in the middle of plates are different from those erupted at mid-ocean ridges. Some scientists think that the former are in many cases the result of streams of hot material, called mantle plumes, coming from the core–mantle boundary, whereas the latter are caused by shallow, upper mantle processes. Another point to be settled is whether slabs of plate subducted in zones such as the Sunda trench penetrate all the way down to the core–mantle boundary as part of mantle convection cells, or disintegrate at a shallower depth.

Hotspot volcanism
Some deep layer material flows upwards as mantle plumes, creating hotspots

Deep layer
Convection of material here is largely separate from that in the rest of the mantle

Descending slabs
Lithosphere slabs do not penetrate as far as the core–mantle boundary

DEEP LAYER CONVECTION MODEL
In this "two layer" model, heat from the Earth's interior causes two distinct layers to slowly swell and shrink in complex patterns, without much mixing.

PLANET EARTH

The Crust

THE THINNEST AND OUTERMOST LAYER of the Earth is the crust, with an average thickness of about 30km (18 miles) below the land surface and about 7.5km (4½ miles) below the seafloor. The crust and the uppermost layer of the mantle, to which the crust is fused, constitute Earth's lithosphere, which is split up into plates (see pp.62–63). In general, the rocks of the crust are less dense than mantle rocks, because they are richer in minerals containing relatively light elements. However, there are two distinctly different different types of crust – oceanic and continental. Variations in their composition, density, and thickness help to account for differences in their topography, relative age, and history of formation.

OCEAN
The Earth is the only planet in the Solar System with persistent oceans of liquid water that cycle moisture through the atmosphere to the land and back to the oceans.

ATMOSPHERE
Above the crust lies the Earth's gaseous atmosphere. Its interaction with oceans and landmasses, and the protection it offers from damaging radiation, are vital for the survival of life.

Oceanic Crust

The oceanic crust forms over two-thirds of the Earth's surface, but even the oldest parts of the ocean floor are no more than 200 million years old and covered only by a thin veneer of sediment. Composed of relatively dense basaltic lavas and related rocks, oceanic crust varies from 7–8km (4–5 miles) thick. Because of its density, it is less elevated than the lighter continental crustal rocks, with an average depth about 3km (2 miles) below sea-level. Oceanic crust is continually formed from mantle material within the long rifts known as spreading ridges (see p.54). Here, the mantle is rising, heating, and expanding the overlying rocks to form an elevated submarine mountain chain, where oceanic plates on either side of the rift are carried apart like two opposing conveyor belts. Basaltic lavas erupt from fissures and cones, and cool to form new oceanic floor that is also punctuated by numerous individual volcanoes. These can grow large enough to rise above sea-level, and where the crust is moving above a semi-permanent mantle hotspot plume (see p.53), they may form chains of volcanic islands. Elsewhere, in areas called subduction zones, oceanic crust descends into the mantle at the same rate that it is created at the ridges (see p.55).

ANDESITE CONES, JAVA
When the energy released by subduction of oceanic crust partially melts mantle rocks, it can trigger the formation of curved chains of island volcanoes.

Basalt makes up much of the upper part of oceanic crust.

Sediments

Oceanic crust
This consists mainly of gabbro and basalt rock.

Mohorovicic discontinuity
The boundary between crust and mantle.

Uppermost mantle layer
This consists mainly of the coarse-grained igneous rock peridotite.

Asthenosphere
This deformable mantle layer lies just below the lithosphere.

OCEANIC LITHOSPHERE

ICELANDIC RIDGE
Because of the density of their basaltic rocks, oceanic crust and mid-ocean ridges do not usually appear above sea-level. Iceland is an exception, raised above the waters by exceptional heat flow.

OCEANIC LITHOSPHERE
This consists of a top layer of oceanic crust, about 7 to 8km (4 to 5 miles) thick, underlain by about 40 to 100km (25 to 60 miles) of the uppermost mantle layer. On top of the oceanic crust is a thin layer of sediments.

PLANET EARTH

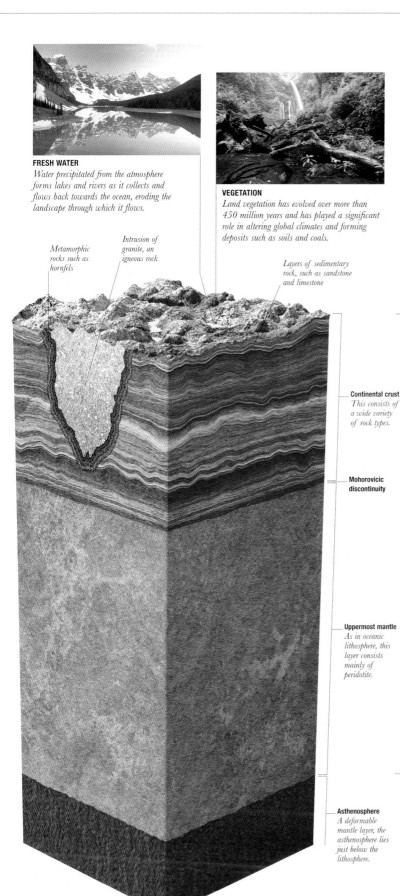

FRESH WATER
Water precipitated from the atmosphere forms lakes and rivers as it collects and flows back towards the ocean, eroding the landscape through which it flows.

VEGETATION
Land vegetation has evolved over more than 450 million years and has played a significant role in altering global climates and forming deposits such as soils and coals.

Metamorphic rocks such as hornfels

Intrusion of granite, an igneous rock

Layers of sedimentary rock, such as sandstone and limestone

Continental crust
This consists of a wide variety of rock types.

Mohorovicic discontinuity

CONTINENTAL LITHOSPHERE

Uppermost mantle
As in oceanic lithosphere, this layer consists mainly of peridotite.

Asthenosphere
A deformable mantle layer, the asthenosphere lies just below the lithosphere.

Continental Crust

The continental crust accounts for only about one-third of the Earth's global surface, but it forms all the major landmasses and their fringing shallow seas. Its thickness ranges from 25 to 70km (16 to 45 miles), with the thickest portions underlying young mountain belts, and it has huge variations in composition – from sedimentary rocks such as sandstone, coal, and limestone through metamorphic rocks such as marble and slate to igneous rocks such as granite and gabbro. This variety of rock types has come about mainly because light continental crust is not recycled within the Earth to the same extent as denser oceanic crust. As a result, some continental rocks are up to 4 billion years old, and much of the material now above sea-level has been through repeated cycles of erosion, formation into sedimentary rocks, and metamorphosis. Tectonic forces have also subjected the continents to phases of fragmentation, amalgamation, and long-term movement, resulting in the formation of new oceans, mountain building, widespread volcanism, and occasional coalescence into single landmasses called supercontinents. Throughout all this, new layers of rock have constantly been added to the surfaces and margins of the continents, forming the strata that are the basis for much of our understanding of the geological history of the Earth and, through the fossil record, its life.

TIBETAN PLATEAU
Regions of high elevation such as this windswept plateau are underlain with continental crust that is far thicker than average.

ARAL BASIN
Low-lying areas of continental crust are also the thinnest. When surrounded by more elevated regions, they form natural drainage basins.

Isostasy

The continental crust is at its thickest beneath young mountain belts, where deep roots of crust stretch down to depths of about 70km (45 miles) – well into the underlying mantle. Crustal blocks can be thought of as floating on the mantle – a concept known as isostasy. Because the continental crust has a much lower density than the mantle, it is buoyant, in the same way that an iceberg is buoyant in seawater. But the greater the mass of rock above sea-level, the more buoyancy is required to support it, and the deeper its roots must go. By comparison, thinner, denser oceanic crust is less buoyant, and so reaches an equilibrium point well below sea-level which is why it is rarely seen as dry land.

SEA-LEVEL CHANGE
Old beaches and cliffs raised above present sea-level attest to past changes in the levels of both sea and land.

CONTINENTAL LITHOSPHERE
This consists of a top layer of about 25 to 80km (16 to 50 miles) of continental crust underlain by about 80km (50 miles) of uppermost mantle layer. As in oceanic lithosphere, a change in chemical composition occurs at the Mohorovicic discontinuity.

Minerals

MINERALS ARE THE NATURAL building blocks of the rock materials of the Earth and all the solid bodies of the Universe. Studying minerals helps us to understand the origin and evolution of the Earth and planets. Most minerals are solid crystalline substances composed of atoms, which are generally arranged in orderly, repeating patterns, giving the mineral its crystalline structure and shape. A few minerals, however, have no such orderly crystalline structure but are amorphous solids similar to glass. Although more than 4,000 minerals have been discovered, only about 30 (known as rock-forming minerals) are common at the Earth's surface.

REGULAR MATRIX
Gold atoms grown on a carbon substrate naturally bond and pack together in an orderly cubic structure.

Mineral Formation

Individual minerals are distinguished by unique combinations of chemical elements and the arrangement of their atoms. This is determined when a gas or liquid crystallizes into a solid. Generally, the resulting structure is a regular, repeating three-dimensional array, or lattice, of atoms. The lattice grows by the ordered addition of atoms and usually maintains the same shape and composition. Some minerals have well-developed crystal form, but most are aggregates with other textures and habits. Similarly sized mineral grains have a granular texture, while a mineral lacking crystal faces is called massive. Primary minerals are formed at the same time as the host rock; later changes from, for example, erosion or metamorphism, produce secondary minerals.

Crystal Structure and Shape

A crystal is a solid such as a mineral with an orderly, repeating atomic structure. With unrestricted growth, it forms a geometric shape with naturally flat planes, called faces, which are often arranged symmetrically. Faces are the external expression of a mineral's internal atomic regularity of structure, and they lie at specific angles one to another, depending on the crystal system to which the mineral belongs. Six main crystal systems – cubic, hexagonal/trigonal, monoclinic, orthorhombic, tetragonal, and triclinic – are defined by their geometric symmetry. Slight misalignment of the structure during growth often produces twinned crystals that are the mirror image of one another. Crystal shape is described using terms such as platy for thin, flat forms and prismatic for columnar crystals.

CRYSTAL SHAPES
Crystal systems are defined by the proportions of their axes and the angles between them (see open figures below). Crystals in any one system can assume various shapes (one of which is represented by a solid figure below).

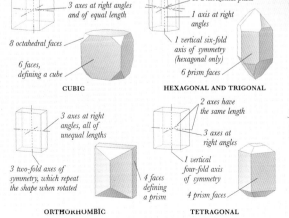

CUBIC
- 3 four-fold axes of symmetry
- 3 axes at right angles and of equal length
- 8 octahedral faces
- 6 faces, defining a cube

HEXAGONAL AND TRIGONAL
- 3 axes of equal length in a horizontal plane
- 1 axis at right angles
- 1 vertical six-fold axis of symmetry (hexagonal only)
- 6 prism faces

MONOCLINIC
- 3 axes of unequal lengths
- 2 axes not at right angles
- 1 two-fold axis of symmetry
- 4 prism faces

ORTHORHOMBIC
- 3 axes at right angles, all of unequal lengths
- 3 two-fold axes of symmetry, which repeat the shape when rotated

TETRAGONAL
- 2 axes have the same length
- 3 axes at right angles
- 1 vertical four-fold axis of symmetry
- 4 faces defining a prism
- 4 prism faces

TRICLINIC
- 3 axes of unequal length
- no axes at right angles
- parallel faces in repeated pairs have same shape and angular relationship to the crystal axis

- sodium atom
- chlorine atom
- axis of symmetry

SALT CRYSTAL
Sodium and chlorine atoms pack together to give the mineral halite (salt) a cubic form. Its crystals growing as perfect cubes with six square faces at right angles to one another, as can be seen here.

SALT CRYSTAL

Mineral Identification Tests

For 2.6 million years, humans and their extinct relatives have exploited particular minerals, and rocks for a variety of purposes, from making stone tools to swords, ploughshares, space shuttles, and exquisite jewellery. To use minerals to their best advantage, it is first necessary to identify their individual characteristics. Over the millennia, many minerals have been discovered to possess unique combinations of physical properties, such as colour, hardness, and specific gravity, which allow them to be picked out even when surrounded by other minerals in a rock. Several of these properties, such as crystal shape, hardness, specific gravity, and cleavage, can be related to actual crystal structures, and are thus predictable. The specific gravity of an open-structured mineral such as graphite, for example, is low, while diamond, with the same composition but a more closely packed structure, has a higher specific gravity. Expert mineralogists can recognize hundreds of different minerals largely on the basis of their appearance and a few tests with a steel point and a hand lens. The identification of other minerals, however, needs optical, chemical, X-ray, or other kinds of analysis.

CALCITE **MUSCOVITE**

CLEAVAGE
This describes a plane of weak bonding between atoms in a crystal, along which the crystal may split. Calcite has three cleavage planes, which meet to form rhomb-shaped cleavage fragments, while muscovite mica has well-developed and distinct cleavage in just one plane.

cleavage plane

FRACTURE
Resulting from mineral breakage other than along cleavage planes, fracture frequently shows characteristic forms, such as opal's glass-like, conchoidal (rounded) fracture or kaolinite's irregular one.

curved fracture plane

OPAL **KAOLINITE**

HARDNESS
The strength of a mineral's chemical bonds determines its hardness. This is measured by its resistance to scratching on a 1–10 scale, which was invented by Friedrich Mohs in 1822; soft (talc) is 1 and hard (diamond) is 10.

TALC **DIAMOND**

SPECIFIC GRAVITY
This is determined by the structure and composition of a mineral. The weight of a mineral's atoms relate to its specific gravity. Gold has a higher specific gravity than halite because its atoms are heavier. Specific gravity is measured by comparing the weight of the mineral with an equal volume of water.

HALITE **GOLD**

COLOUR
The composition of a mineral, its atomic structure, often the presence of certain trace elements, and selective light absorption combine to generate the colour of a mineral. The element copper in azurite produces its typical blue colour. Other minerals are uncoloured or white, because no light is absorbed, as in milky quartz.

AZURITE **MILKY QUARTZ**

LUSTRE
The way in which light is absorbed or reflected off the surface of a mineral determines its lustre, which is independent of a mineral's colour. It may be diagnostic, as in smoky quartz, which shows a vitreous or glassy lustre, and galena, which has a metallic one.

glassy lustre

metallic lustre

SMOKY QUARTZ **GALENA**

TRANSPARENCY
This is the extent to which light can pass through a mineral. It ranges from the water-clear transparency of the rock crystal form of quartz, to the complete opacity of many metal ore minerals, such as magnetite.

ROCK CRYSTAL **MAGNETITE**

STREAK
The colour of a mineral when crushed to a powder provides its streak, which often differs from the mineral's surface colour, especially in certain ore minerals. For example, hematite varies in its colour, but its streak is always red.

red streak

HEMATITE

LIGHT STUDIES

As light passes through many minerals, it is altered by the optical properties of the structure and chemistry of the mineral. By using polarizing microscopes and extremely thin slices of a rock, which transmit light, mineralogists can distinguish the minerals present. Some minerals, however, are opaque and appear black – such as spinel (shown here).

GEODE INTERIOR
Natural rock cavities, or geodes, often become infilled with concentric or radial crystal growths when permeated by mineral-rich solutions. Here, an agate geode has quartz minerals growing in its centre.

Classifying Minerals

Many of the 4,000 or more known natural minerals have similarities in their properties. These have led to them being grouped according to whether they are chemical compounds, such as oxides or silicates, rather than minerals of particular elements, for example, copper or calcium. These groupings are reinforced by their occurrence in similar geological settings. Minerals are chemical compounds with a stability based on an electrical balance between two parts. One positively charged (cationic) part is balanced by a negatively charged (anionic) part, and this is reflected in their chemical formula. The positive part is usually a metal, such as iron (Fe), and is written first. After it comes the negative part, usually a non-metallic ion, such as oxygen (O) or sulphur (S), or a combination of negatively charged elements, such as sulphate (SO_4). Minerals are classified by their anionic groupings, and are commonly divided into the ten groups shown here. Each grouping contains many minerals: for example, the carbonates include over 200 minerals ranging from calcite to azurite.

NATIVE ELEMENTS

A group of about 20 elements, of which 10 are geologically significant. Native elements include minerals such as gold (Au) and platinum (Pt). In each of these, the single element is free and uncombined. Metallic native elements with relatively low melting-points, such as copper, formed the historical basis for metal technology. The non-metals sulphur and carbon (especially as diamond) are also economically important.

GOLD

SULPHIDES

A group of about 600 minerals, such as stibnite (Sb_2S_3) and galena (PbS), in which sulphur (S) combines with metallic and metal-like elements. Most sulphides are opaque, with distinctive colours and characteristic streaks.

STIBNITE

OXIDES AND HYDROXIDES

Two closely related groups of about 400 minerals, in which metallic elements combine with oxygen (O_2) or hydroxyl (OH). Oxides and hydroxides contain some important ore minerals, such as chromite ($FeCr_2O_4$) and goethite (FeO(OH)).

CHROMITE

HALIDES AND FLUORIDES

Two closely related groups of about 140 minerals, in which fluorine (F), chlorine (Cl), bromine (Br), or iodine (I) combines with elements, such as calcium (Ca) or sodium (Na). Fluorite (CaF_2) is an example.

FLUORITE

CARBONATES

A group of more than 200 minerals, in which a metal combines with strongly bonded carbonate (CO_3) units. Most do not contain water (H_2O), but a few do, such as azurite. Calcite ($CaCO_3$) is an important carbonate.

CALCITE

BORATES

A group of 125 minerals in which metal elements combine with borate (BO_3), for example borax ($Na_2B_4O_5(OH)_4.8H_2O$). Borate units form chains and sheets that are similar to those found in SiO_4 groups in silicates.

BORAX

SULPHATES

A group of about 300 minerals in which metallic elements combine with sulphate (SO_4), for example anhydrite ($CaSO_4$). Sulphate forms a fundamental structural unit, because sulphur has a strong bond with oxygen.

ANHYDRITE

MOLYBDATES AND TUNGSTATES

Two closely related groups of minerals, in which metallic elements combine with molybdate (MoO_4) or tungstate (WO_4), such as in wulfenite ($PbMoO_4$) and wolframite $(Fe,Mn)WO_4$.

WULFENITE

PHOSPHATES AND VANADATES

Two closely related groups of more than 400 minerals, in which elements combine with phosphate (PO_4) or vanadate (VO_4); examples include apatite $Ca_5(PO_4)_3(F,Cl,OH)$ and carnotite ($K_2(UO_2)2(VO_4)_2.3H_2O$).

APATITE

SILICATES

A group of about 500 minerals in which metallic elements combine with silicon and oxygen (SiO_4) to form structural units known as tetrahedra, for example olivine (($Mg,Fe)_2SiO_4$). These can link singly, in sheets, in chains, or three-dimensionally.

OLIVINE

ABRAHAM GOTTLOB WERNER

Abraham Werner (1749–1817) was a German mineralogist and teacher, who attracted students from all over Europe, even the Americas, to the Freiberg Mining Academy. He produced one of the earliest classification systems for minerals, and was a leading proponent of the Neptunist theory, which claimed that all rocks were laid down sequentially in an ocean created by the Flood described in the Bible. Igneous and metamorphic rocks were deposited, then sedimentary rocks, and finally surface sediments.

Rock-Forming Minerals

By far the most abundant elements in the Earth's crust are oxygen and silicon, respectively 46.6 and 27.7 per cent by weight, then aluminium at 8.3 per cent and iron at 5.0 per cent. Together these elements account for 87.6 per cent by weight of the crust. Therefore, silicate minerals, such as olivine, pyroxene, amphibole, feldspar, and quartz, which combine silicon with oxygen, make up more than 90 per cent of the rocks of the Earth's surface. They are the main constituents of the commonest rocks, especially igneous ones, many metamorphic rocks, and clay-rich sedimentary ones. The non-silicate minerals contain different groups of chemicals, such as oxygen combined with carbon to form carbonates (as in limestone), which are important sedimentary rocks. Oxygen can also combine with metals to form oxides such as hematite. Most rocks are comprised of just a few essential minerals, but may also contain small quantities of various other – so-called accessory – minerals.

RIVER MUD
This deposit of river mud (below) is largely made of silicate clay minerals derived from the weathering or alteration and erosion of other silicate minerals such as feldspars.

KAOLINITE
Many silicate clay minerals, such as kaolinite (above), form minute platy crystals. These produce a single, well-defined cleavage that is parallel to the sheet-like, platy surfaces.

Ore Deposits

Mineral deposits from which valuable metals can be extracted profitably are known as ores. Market conditions determine whether a naturally occurring concentration of a mineral can be regarded as an ore: the cost of extraction is justified only if it is outweighed by the deposit's market value. Platinum, for example, is so valuable that it need only have a concentration of more than 0.1 parts per million to be exploitable, whereas iron is less valuable and so the ore needs to contain a much higher iron content, perhaps 50 per cent, if extracting it from the ground is to be a viable proposition.

IRON DEPOSITS
The sedimentary iron ore deposits of the Hamersley Range in Australia contain about 40 billion tonnes of ore with a lucrative 55 per cent iron concentration. They date from the Precambrian Eon.

PLACER DEPOSITS
Many valuable ore minerals are concentrated in river and shallow-sea sediments, and these can be extracted by panning, washing, and sieving. Here, diamond-rich gravel is being worked in the Moa River, Sierra Leone.

HYDROTHERMAL VEINS
Many ore deposits are derived from hot, mineral-enriched solutions, which invade the surrounding rocks through any available cracks, cavities, or pores, where they form hydrothermal veins.

surface water seeps down through the strata

fluids can reach the surface as geysers or hot springs

hydrothermal fluids rise through fractures or fissures and migrate along bedding planes

hot groundwater enriched with minerals

hot, mineral-rich liquid left from crystallization of granite pluton

weathering turns ore minerals at surface into different minerals

mineral deposits form in small cracks or permeable zones adjacent to veins

Gems

Minerals that have been fashioned for use as personal adornment are known as gems. The most ancient known decorations, some 30,000 years old, were made of bone, shell, and amber, but, since stone cutting and polishing technology has developed, most materials selected as gems today are natural, inorganic minerals and commonly crystalline. They are valued as such because they are beautiful, rare, and durable. Out of the 4,000 or more different minerals in the Earth, only 50 or so are typically used as gems. Such is the value of many gems that there has been a very successful technological drive to manufacture synthetic ones, generally using the same chemical compounds as the natural stones themselves.

amethyst quartz

fluorite

OVAL STEP CUT

OCTAGONAL STEP CUT

sphalerite

TYPES OF CUT
Brilliant cuts are best for delicately coloured gems such as sphalerite, to give brightness and "fire", whereas step cuts show deeply coloured stones to best advantage.

BRILLIANT CUT

uncut Burmese ruby crystal

cushioned mix cut ruby

CUTTING STONES
Gem cutting is designed to enhance a stone's colour and beauty. For each gem mineral, selected and angled flat faces (facets) are cut or ground and polished to help reflect light from the stone.

MAMMOTH MINERAL GROWTH
One of the most accessible processes of mineral formation is to be seen around hot springs, here at Yellowstone, USA. Evaporation of hot, mineral-enriched water leads to the formation of minerals, especially carbonates.

Rocks

THE EARTH'S CRUST IS made of solid materials known as rocks, most of which are naturally occurring assemblages of minerals. The Earth's rocks are largely concealed beneath soil and vegetation, but in some places they are exposed at the surface, where they may form features such as rocky cliffs and mountains. The huge diversity of the Earth's rocks has developed over thousands of millions of years through the geological processes of igneous activity, changes in form known as metamorphism, and the formation of sediments and sedimentary rocks (including organic materials such as coal). Although most of the Earth's rocks are formed within the planet, meteorites derived from outer space are also found on its surface.

Minerals and Rocks

Rocks are made of minerals, and although they vary enormously across the Earth, rocks all form from three basic processes. Igneous rocks solidify from a hot, molten state. Some cool slowly underground and produce the relatively large crystals of plutonic rocks, such as granite. Others erupt at the surface to form volcanic rocks such as obsidian. Metamorphic rocks are transformed from older rocks of any type by heat and pressure within the Earth. Surface processes, such as erosion, transport, and deposition form sediments and, with burial and compaction, sedimentary rocks.

HOW ROCKS ARE MADE
Igneous, metamorphic, and sedimentary rocks form in a self-perpetuating cycle. Volcanic activity creates rocks at the Earth's surface. Rock is broken down by weathering and erosion, and fragments are carried away, settling in lakes, at coasts, and on seabeds. Burial transforms sediments into sedimentary rocks. Metamorphism induces further changes, and uplift and erosion expose them all.

River erosion
Rivers transport silt and rock fragments created by weathering.

Marine sedimentation
Tiny rock particles carried into the sea by rivers slowly settle at the bottom of the sea.

Coastal deposition
Rock particles settle as sand, mud, or pebbles on the coast.

MAGNIFIED IGNIMBRITE
This rock formed as magma cooled rapidly after a volcanic eruption. It consists of crystals, rock fragments, and glass shards welded together.

mica crystal

glass shard

PLUTONIC IGNEOUS ROCK FORMATION
In a plutonic igneous rock, the first minerals to grow form large crystals. Crystals that form later are smaller and less distinct.

remaining magma

large, first-formed crystals

crystalline matrix

quartz grain

SEDIMENTARY ROCK AGGREGATIONS
When mineral grains are deposited by wind or water, they form loose sediments. Over time, these are compacted to form solid rock strata.

rock fragment

water

substrate

MAGNIFIED SANDSTONE
Sedimentary sand grains of different shapes, sizes, and minerals are held together by a fine-grained matrix, or mineral groundmass, in this sandstone.

settling grains

sediment grains

matrix (or cement)

Sediment
Layers of fine sand or silt are deposited on the seabed or at the bottom of a lake.

Burial and compaction
As new layers of sediment form, deeper layers are pressed together, forming solid sedimentary rock.

Transport
Streams and winds carry particles that have been weathered by rain, frost, heat, chemical action, and living things.

Precipitation
Snow and rain feed glaciers and streams, which erode rocks.

Glacial erosion and deposition
When advancing, a glacier transports rocks beneath and around it.

Extrusion
Magma escapes from a volcano in the form of ash and lava, which cool to form solid rock or ash deposits.

Volcano
Typically consists of many layers of solidified lava, with some ash and cinders.

IGNEOUS ROCK
Rock that forms when magma cools and solidifies is called igneous rock.

Crystallization
When magma cools inside the Earth, it solidifies slowly, forming rocks with large crystals, such as granite.

Intrusion
An intrusion is a mass of magma within the Earth.

Magma
This hot, liquid rock contains dissolved gas.

METAMORPHIC ROCK
Heat and pressure can make any rock change into another type, called metamorphic rock.

Melting
When lithosphere is subducted, water escapes from it. Water combined with heat and pressure make the nearby rock melt.

Uplift
The upward movement of rock masses is called uplift.

Subducted rock
Formerly seafloor, rock near the top of a subducting plate has a high water content.

Subduction
When two tectonic plates converge, one plate can be pushed under the edge of the other.

SEDIMENTARY ROCK
This type of rock forms when pressure and cementation bind particles of sediment together.

VOLCANIC DEBRIS
Igneous rock material erupted from the Novarupta volcano in Alaska, USA, is here being transported and redeposited to form river sediments.

Types of Rocks

Earth's numerous rock types can be grouped according to the way they formed into igneous, metamorphic, and sedimentary rocks, plus a small number of meteorites. Igneous rocks, which were once molten, are divided into extrusive (or volcanic) rocks, such as lavas, formed on the Earth's surface and intrusive (or plutonic) rocks, such as granite, formed beneath the surface. Metamorphic rocks form from any pre-existing rocks transformed by heat and pressure. They vary from low-grade metamorphic rocks such as slate (derived from shale) to high-grade schist and gneiss (from shale and sandstone). Metamorphic rocks often have distinctive planar textures called schistosity, in which platy minerals are aligned in parallel. Sedimentary rocks are formed from sediment through weathering, erosion, dissolution, transport of particles, biochemical precipitation, and deposition. They can broadly be divided into those transported by water, wind, or gravity. Land-based (terrestrial) sediments include deposits in rivers, lakes, and on floodplains, along with coal-forming organic materials, soils, and other residual deposits from weathering and volcanic eruptions. Marine deposits include granular sediments and biochemical deposits such as carbonates.

PLANET EARTH

Igneous Rocks

Rocks that solidify from a hot, molten state are known as igneous and are broadly divided into extrusive rocks, such as those produced by volcanoes, and intrusive bodies, such as plutons and dykes. They vary in composition from basalt to granite and in texture from rapidly cooled glasses and tiny crystals to slowly cooled coarse grains. Igneous rocks include the basalts (volcanic) and underlying gabbros (plutonic) that create all of the oceanic crust, plateau basalts (such as the Deccan Traps), basaltic island volcanoes (such as those of Iceland), many hazardous subduction-zone volcanoes (such as Fuji, see p.134), and expansive plutons of granite (such as the Sierra Nevada, USA) and gabbro (such as the Skaergaard, see p.140). Plutonic rocks also form smaller bodies, which are classified (in decreasing size) as plutons, stocks, sills (roughly horizontal), and dykes (roughly vertical). The term pegmatite refers to silica-rich (granitic) plutonic bodies with giant crystals, which are sources of both gems and industrial minerals rich in rare elements.

IGNEOUS INTRUSION
This vertical intrusive dolerite dyke in the Cuillin Hills, UK, acted as a feeder for the extrusive basaltic lavas that form the cliffs at top left.

IGNEOUS ROCK FORMATION
Molten rock (magma) collects in underground chambers within the Earth's crust. It may solidify in place to form an intrusion, or it may erupt at the surface to form an extrusive igneous rock.

cinders and ash

extrusive rock, with quick-cooling, glassy to fine-grained matrix

rock forms from cooling lava

igneous intrusion

intrusive rock, made of large, slow-cooling crystals

magma chamber

IGNEOUS EXTRUSION
Large volcanic outpourings of basaltic magma shrink as they cool and develop roughly 5-sided columns that are perpendicular to the cooling surfaces, such as these near Aldeyarfoss, Iceland.

Metamorphic Rocks

All rocks can be changed by heat and pressure. Such changes are called metamorphism. The most significant transformations occur at depth within the Earth, but local changes can be produced nearer the surface. Strong pressure creates dynamic metamorphism, typified by the compression of mud-rocks into slates. On a smaller scale, such pressure may be localized, for example along fault planes, where rocks are distorted by the Earth's movements. Intense heat produces thermal metamorphism, which ranges from localized heating of rocks around a small igneous body to more widespread heating that produces kilometre-wide zones of recrystallization, called thermal aureoles, around major, deep-seated plutonic intrusions. Together, heat and pressure on a large scale create regional metamorphism, which is graded from low to high, with increasing pressure and temperature triggering the formation of assemblages of new minerals, and so converting the original rock texture into a metamorphic texture, often dominated by planar foliation.

SPECTACULAR FOLDING
Intense folding of sedimentary rocks, seen here in the Ugab valley, Namibia, also initiates dynamic metamorphism through compression and recrystallization.

CREATION OF SLATE
Clay minerals of sea-bed muds at Ingleton quarry, England, have been changed by dynamic metamorphism into a slaty cleavage.

THERMAL METAMORPHISM
Where large bodies of igneous rock such as granite are formed, they radiate sufficient heat into the surrounding rocks to alter their mineralogy, a process known as thermal metamorphism.

existing rock changed by hot intrusion

eroded landscape

CHANGE OF ROCK TYPE
This tilted and frost-shattered layer of sandstone in Shropshire, England, was originally quartz sand on a sea bed, but it has since been cemented and recrystallized, and ultimately metamorphosed into quartzite.

granite intrusion

zones of decreasing thermal metamorphism

DYNAMIC METAMORPHISM
The Earth's movements can apply pressure to sedimentary rocks and transform them through dynamic metamorphism by orientating mica minerals to form slaty cleavage.

section of rock deep in the Earth's crust

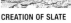

tectonic compression

folded strata

tectonic compression

vertical, slaty cleavage forms at right angles to forces of compression

Sedimentary Rocks

For at least 3,800 million years of the Earth's history, sediments have accumulated on the surface of the planet. Laid down layer upon layer and separated by bedding planes, they accumulate in sequences with the oldest layer at the bottom. With deep burial, they are compacted (lithified) into sedimentary rock, occasionally disturbed by folding or faulting, and returned to the surface again. These processes were first demonstrated by Nicolaus Steno (see panel, below). The Earth's depositional environments vary greatly, producing many kinds of sediments and sedimentary structures, such as ripples. The sands and muds from ancient rivers, deserts, and seas, along with the deposits associated with glaciers and volcanoes, are all preserved in the Earth's stratigraphic record. The original sediment is mainly mineral and rock debris from weathering, erosion, and transport by water (for example, sandstone), wind (loess), glacial and mass movement (tillite), biochemical activity (limestone), or evaporation (salt deposits). Once laid down, sediments may be altered by a variety of processes. Water is driven off, mainly due to compaction, and further changes over time transform the soft sediment into hard and brittle, layered rocks such as sandstone, limestone, and shale.

QUARTZ SANDSTONE
At a magnification of x 25, the individual quartz grains of this sandstone can be seen to be held together by tiny but well-formed crystals of a quartz cement – the small, angular, surface protrusions.

WATER-LAID SEDIMENTARY ROCKS
The alternation of limestone and shale deposits at Lyme Regis, in southern England, show that conditions of sedimentation kept changing from carbonate to that of fine-grained mud deposition.

weathering
and erosion

transport by
water, wind,
and ice

inland
evaporite
deposits

transport by
ocean current

sea bed

burial and
lithification

ocean current

particles in ocean
water settle to form
sea-floor sediments

uplift

different kinds of
sediment accumulate
in distinct layers

ANCIENT FRESHWATER DEPOSITS
Many old sedimentary rocks (such as these ones in Bryce Canyon, Utah, USA) are derived from sediments originally deposited in rivers and lakes.

SEDIMENTARY ROCK FORMATION
The creation of sedimentary rocks occurs in overlapping stages. Rocks are weathered and eroded on land to create sediments that ultimately are transported to the sea. There, further transport may occur before deposition, burial, and lithification, the process that turns loose sediment into hard sedimentary rock.

Meteorites

Natural objects from space made of iron and stone crash through the Earth's atmosphere all the time. They range from dust-sized particles to massive lumps weighing many tonnes. Such meteorites have fallen throughout the history of the Earth, and they are important as they record the birth of the Solar System 4,560 million years ago and its subsequent history. Records of meteorite falls first appear in cuneiform writings, in about 1900 BCE, while fossilized meteorites recently found in Sweden fell to the Earth more than 450 million years ago. Meteorites are made of the same elements as the Earth and Sun. These elements combine to form more than 300 different minerals, including many not found on the Earth. The abundance and types of minerals found in the meteorites are used to classify them into stones (both chondrites and achondrites), stony-irons (such as pallasites), and irons.

ANTARCTIC FIND
In recent decades, a large number of extremely well-preserved meteorites (right) have been collected from the surface of the Antarctic ice-sheet, where they have accumulated over hundreds of years.

alloy of
nickel
and iron
metal

METEORITE SECTION
Cut in half, this spindle-shaped meteorite (above) with its black surface shows a grey metallic interior made entirely of intergrown crystals of nickel-iron alloy typical of iron meteorites.

NICOLAUS STENO

Although Danish, Nicolaus Steno (1638–86) studied in Italy and became physician to the Grand Duke of Tuscany. While there, he demonstrated the principle of superposition and showed that sedimentary rock strata were originally laid horizontally on top of one another by the deposition of particles from a fluid. Consequently, in any series of strata younger layers lie on older ones. He also ascertained that tilted and deformed strata result from displacement by the Earth's movements after deposition, and proved that fossils are the remains of once-living organisms.

RIVER FLOW
Water is a powerful force of change.
Rivers such as the Thjorsá in Iceland
(shown here) move rock fragments and
organic material from land to the sea,
where it may eventually form new rock.

THE CHANGING EARTH

THE SURFACE OF THE EARTH is constantly changing under the influence of forces within the planet, and surface processes, and even the impact of objects from outer space. The effects of such change are often discernible only after many thousands of years, although some changes such as landslides and meteorite impacts have an instant effect. The relentless movement of the tectonic plates, which form the Earth's surface, can open new oceans, create mountains, and change continents. Wherever the Earth's materials are exposed at the surface, they are subjected to the processes of weathering, erosion, and transport by wind, water, and ice. These processes can sculpt rock and create sediment, which is deposited on land and beneath the sea. Water covers most of the Earth's surface and is a significant agent of change. The Earth is also the only planet known to support life. Living things both adapt to the conditions on the surface and shape the environment around them.

Tectonic Plates

THE COOL, BRITTLE outer rock layer of the Earth is called the lithosphere, and it is broken into seven large, continent-sized tectonic plates and about a dozen much smaller plates. These irregularly shaped segments fit together like a jigsaw puzzle and cover the entire surface of the Earth. Tectonic plates have an outer layer of crustal rocks that is inseparable from an underlying layer of upper-mantle rocks. Throughout geological time, the growth and reduction of plate size has also moved them across the Earth's surface. Oceans have opened and closed, forming mountain ranges and volcanoes, and shuffled the positions and orientations of the continents.

ALFRED WEGENER

The German meteorologist and geophysicist Alfred Wegener (1880–1930) was responsible for the theory of continental drift, which was the forerunner of current ideas about plate tectonics. Impressed by the complementary shapes of the coastlines of Africa and South America, he believed that all the continents once joined together in a supercontinent called Pangea, which split in the Mesozoic Era.

The Earth's Plates

Seven major plates, which are up to 100km (60 miles) thick, cover 94 per cent of the Earth. They carry the major continents, most of which were once part of the ancient landmass of Pangea (see p.20). The Pacific Plate is by far the largest in area at 108 million square kilometres (42 million square miles). It is followed in size by the African Plate; the Eurasian Plate, which includes Europe and Asia; the Australian Plate; the North American Plate; Antarctica; and the South American Plate. The remaining surface area is accounted for by about a dozen much smaller plates, such as the Juan de Fuca Plate, which is located off the coast of the northwest USA. The Pacific Plate is constructed entirely of oceanic crust and mantle, while, at present, the rest of the major plates contain both continental and oceanic material. Plate size is constantly changing as some expand and others get smaller. These processes occur at plate boundaries (see pp.54–55). A balance between the two processes is maintained as the size of the Earth is constant. Most plate boundaries occur within the oceans or adjacent to continents, but some are marked on land by mountain belts, such as the Himalayas, which is where the Eurasian and Indian plates meet, or volcanic island arcs, such as the Aleutians in Alaska, which marks the subduction of the Pacific Plate beneath the North American Plate.

Eurasian Plate

Okhotsk Plate

boundary between plates (exaggerated on this model)

Philippine Plate

Indian Plate

TECTONIC PLATES TODAY
At present the Earth's surface is broken into seven major tectonic plates and about a dozen minor ones. The boundaries of the plates are marked by features such as mountains, ocean ridges, and deep-sea trenches.

WESTERN AUSTRALIA
The Precambrian rocks of Western Australia (right) are more than 3,400 million years old. They form a stable continental mass that is part of the Australian Plate.

CASCADE RANGE, USA
When two plates converge, mountains rise. Subduction of the Juan de Fuca Plate beneath the North American Plate has generated the Cascade Range in northwestern USA, including Mount Adams on the horizon.

THE EUROPEAN ALPS
The division between the African and Eurasian plates is marked by the high peaks of the European Alps.

How Plates Move

The Earth's tectonic plates are known to be in constant motion, shifting by up to 15cm (6in) each year. However, the mechanism that causes them to move has been hotly debated. Some scientists have argued that organized convection cells in the mantle move the tectonic plates. The relatively cool lithospheric plates are underlain by mantle rock that is hot enough to flow, and this rock is thought to churn in three-dimensional cells, similar to the much more rapid convective cells in a pan of boiling soup. At their upper margins, mantle convection cells are thought to act like conveyer belts, dragging along the overlying plates. Other scientists discount the idea of organized three-dimensional convection cells in the mantle, and instead argue that gravity pushes actively growing plates down and away from high, thermally buoyant spreading ridges. Furthermore, once an oceanic plate segment enters a subduction zone, gravity acts to pull the cool and relatively dense plate downwards into the hot mantle.

PLATE MOTION
Convection currents within the Earth's mantle are one possible explanation for the movement of the Earth's lithospheric plates. Hot mantle is thought to rise, cool, and then sink again in a circular motion, moving the plates along as it does so.

upper mantle

lower mantle

lithospheric tectonic plate

subduction zone where tectonic plate descends into mantle

core

mantle plume rises from lower mantle to form hotspot

plate dragged along by convection current

circular motion of convection current

Past Plate Movement

Several scientific breakthroughs have led to the reconstruction of past movements of the Earth's tectonic plates. Mapping of plate boundaries, the discovery of sea-floor spreading (see p.54), and measurement of the direction and rate of movement of the plates has enabled scientists to recreate their history. There is also much geological evidence to give clues to the positions of the plates in the past. For instance, the distribution of ancient mountains, such as the Caledonian belt – which today has remnants on either side of the Atlantic (see pp.100 and 102), and unusual deposits and fossils, have helped to pin down past plate positions. Fossils of the marine reptile *Mesosaurus* have been found in both Africa and South America, suggesting that the two continents were once joined. Mapping and drilling of the ocean floor beginning in the 1950s and 1960s provided further evidence of plate movement, as it was discovered that the oldest-known sea-floor rocks were just 180 million years old. Thus the ocean floor is relatively young, and any older rocks have disappeared, swallowed back within the Earth. Plate movements from the present back to the Permian Period show that over the course of about 200 million years, today's continents evolved from a continental cluster called Pangea, which stretched from pole to pole (see p.20). Late Precambrian models have also been reconstructed, and include a group of continents called Rodinia. Little information exists for earlier tectonic distributions.

FOSSIL FOUNDATIONS
Fossils are a key to past plate reconstructions. Identical fossils have been found on either side of the Atlantic. Other species, such as this Gasosaurus, *are isolated within stable continents.*

MADAGASCAN PRIMATE
The lemurs of Madagascar, including this Ring-Tailed Lemur, were isolated as a species when the island split from Africa in the late Cretaceous Period.

MEASURING PLATE MOVEMENT

Radio telescope arrays are helping to provide data about the movement of tectonic plates that is accurate to a few millimetres. The radio telescopes of the Very Long Baseline Array, including this one at Mauna Kea Observatory on Hawaii, provide accurate measurements of their location by measuring radio signals from distant quasars. When compared with data from other radio telescopes on other plates around the world, the relative plate motions can be determined.

Plate Boundaries

THERE ARE THREE MAIN TYPES of boundary between the Earth's tectonic plates. At two of these types of boundary, plates change in size. Plate growth occurs at divergent boundaries along sea-floor spreading ridges, while plate consumption occurs at convergent boundaries, which are marked by deep ocean trenches and subduction zones. Divergent and convergent zones form 80 per cent of plate boundaries; the remaining 20 per cent are known as transform boundaries, where two plates slide past one another with no significant change in the size of either plate.

VOLCANIC CHAIN
Iceland is split by the divergent plate boundary between the North American and Eurasian plates. Volcanoes have formed parallel to the boundary.

Divergent Boundaries

Where plates move apart, they form divergent (or constructive) boundaries. An example of a divergent boundary is the Mid-Atlantic Ridge, which stretches beneath the ocean between the North and South Poles, although it rises above sea-level in Iceland. Divergent boundaries are marked by slowly spreading rift valleys (see p.98). As two plates move away from each other, the mantle rises and partially melts to form basaltic magma. When the molten basalt erupts on the sea floor, it solidifies as it comes into contact with ocean water, forming oceanic crust, a process that is repeated as the plates continue to diverge. New oceanic crust is created at divergent boundaries at a rate of a few centimetres a year, a process called sea-floor spreading. Over many millions of years, this widening process can lead to the opening of new oceans. Because the Earth remains the same size, lithosphere is consumed by subduction (see opposite page) at the same rate that it is created. The straight lines of divergent boundaries are disrupted by the Earth's curvature, and transform boundaries (where two plates slide past each other) form. These are neither constructive nor destructive boundaries.

direction of plate movement

spreading ridge

mid-ocean rift, where molten basalt reaches the sea-floor

divergent plate boundary

plates move past each other at transform boundaries like trains on opposite tracks

lithosphere

asthenosphere

rising magma from mantle

diverging ocean plate

oceanic crust formed when magma cools and solidifies

DIVERGENT AND TRANSFORM BOUNDARIES
Divergent plate boundaries are offset by transform boundaries. Plates slide past one another along transform boundaries, and, since the lithosphere is neither destroyed nor created, they are also known as conservative plate boundaries.

MAGNETIC REVERSALS

The rate at which new crust is created along a spreading ridge can be measured by studying the magnetic properties of the rocks on either side. As upwelling magma cools, iron-rich minerals within it, orientated by the Earth's magnetic field, are set in position. These reflect the direction and inclination of the magnetic poles at the time the rocks formed. Their magnetism can be mapped by magnetometers, and these reveal symmetrical patterns on either side of a ridge, which show the periodic reversals of the Earth's magnetic field. In this image, bands of colour identify rocks of normal and reversed magnetization.

VOLCANIC ACTIVITY
At Geysir in Iceland (left), groundwater, superheated by hot rocks below the Mid-Atlantic Ridge, regularly blasts out at the surface in the form of a steam geyser.

TRANSFORM FAULT
Horizontal sliding movement along the boundary between the North American and Pacific plates occurs either side of the San Andreas fault.

PLANET EARTH

Convergent Boundaries

Convergent boundaries (also known as destructive boundaries) occur where plates move towards one another. Continental crust is thicker and less dense than oceanic crust. If continental and oceanic plate boundaries converge, for example, as is happening off the coast of South America, a subduction zone forms, at which the denser oceanic crust descends beneath the continental margin. This leads to uplift of the continental plate, and the formation of volcanic mountains, such as the Andes. Where two oceanic plates converge (see p.97), the older of the two will be subducted beneath the younger, as it is cooler and denser. At these boundaries, volcanic island arcs form (see p.305). Convergent boundaries involving oceanic plates are marked by deep-sea trenches, where the ocean floor reaches depths of up to 11km (7 miles). At subduction zones, earthquakes occur deep within the Earth as the tectonic slab descends into the mantle. The plate also begins to bleed fluids, which trigger partial melting in the mantle. The resulting magma can ascend to the surface in a volcanic eruption. When two continental plates converge, no subduction occurs as the plates are of a similar density. Instead the pressure leads to the formation of mountain ranges such as the Himalayas (see pp.196–97).

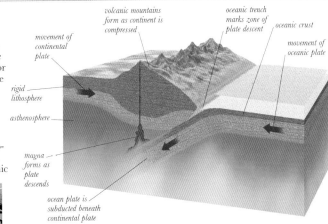

volcanic mountains form as continent is compressed

oceanic trench marks zone of plate descent

oceanic crust

movement of continental plate

movement of oceanic plate

rigid lithosphere

asthenosphere

magma forms as plate descends

ocean plate is subducted beneath continental plate

VALLE DE LA LUNA, ANDES
The Andes have been formed by crustal compression as a result of the convergence of the Nazca and South American plates.

SUBDUCTION ZONE
When an oceanic plate collides with a continental plate, it sinks into the mantle and eventually melts. The collision leads to the formation of an ocean trench and a chain of volcanic mountains on land.

World Boundaries

Six of the seven largest tectonic plates are predominantly continental, but the largest of all, the Pacific Plate, is oceanic. Asia and North America, in particular, have grown by the addition of numerous smaller plates, and are known as accretionary terranes. These are geologically welded to the main plates. Well-defined zones of seismic and volcanic activity are distributed along the current plate boundaries, as shown here.

Divergent or transform plate boundary

Convergent plate boundary

Deep-sea trenches

JOHN TUZO WILSON

In 1965, the Canadian geophysicist John Tuzo Wilson (1908–93) demonstrated that sea-floor spreading ridges are segmented and offset by what he called transform-fault boundaries. Wilson also put forward the theory of hotspots (see p.305) and their part in the formation of volcanic island chains such as Hawaii. His discoveries were a key contribution to the acceptance of the theory of plate tectonics.

Weathering

WHEN ROCKS ARE EXPOSED at the Earth's surface they are subjected to a group of physical, chemical, and biological processes collectively known as weathering. Over long periods – sometimes millions of years – weathering can lead to the disintegration of rocks, making them susceptible to later transport and erosion. Many rocks are formed in conditions that are very different to those on the Earth's surface. When rocks are exposed, they react in various ways with the atmosphere, water, and living organisms, depending on their structure and composition. The speed at which weathering occurs also depends on climatic conditions – rocks in warm, humid environments tend to weather more quickly than those in arid or cold conditions.

SHATTERED ROCK
Exactly how desert boulders, such as this one in Arizona, shatter is debated. Cycles of heat expansion and contraction and frost shattering may play a role in this type of weathering.

Physical Weathering

The process whereby rocks break apart without substantial change to their chemical structure is known as physical or mechanical weathering, and is largely due to changes in pressure or temperature. All rocks have natural areas of weakness, along which cracks can appear. During the processes of uplift (see p.47) and erosion (see pp.58–59), which expose rocks at the surface, much of the heat and pressure that surrounded them is removed, so they cool and shrink, causing them to fracture. Water invades the resulting cracks and when it freezes, it expands by almost one-tenth of its volume. This exerts immense pressure on the surrounding rock and enlarges the fracture. If a cycle of freezing and thawing is established, the rock eventually breaks up. Called frost shattering or heaving, such freeze–thaw processes are particularly visible on exposed mountainsides. Similar processes of expansion and contraction may also occur in deserts, where the fluctuation between daytime rock surface temperatures, which can reach up to 60°C (140°F), and night-time temperatures, which can be freezing, may result in rock fracture.

FROST-SHATTERED ROCK
The fracture of rocks by freeze–thaw action in exposed mountain areas, such as this one in Wales, UK, is a physical weathering process.

Chemical Weathering

Physical weathering exposes rock surfaces to other processes, including chemical weathering. This type of weathering can lead to the breakdown of some minerals within the rock, and the formation of new ones. In warm, wet climates, chemical weathering occurs far more rapidly than in arid conditions. The process is enhanced by rainfall, which combines with carbon dioxide in the atmosphere to form an acidic solution. As this oozes through soils it takes some minerals, particularly calcium carbonate, into solution in a chemical reaction that is reversible. For example, limestone readily dissolves in acidic water, which can hollow out underground passages in the rock. Inside these passages, the limestone may be redeposited from solution to create rock formations such as stalactites or flowstone (see pp.200–01). The chemical weathering of limestone produces a distinctive type of landscape called karst. Groundwater and seawater can also lead to reactions with other minerals. For instance, many rock-forming silicate minerals, such as olivine, combine with water. At or just below the Earth's surface, micas, feldspars, and some amphiboles may also combine with water to form clay minerals, such as kaolinite (china clay). These are a principal component of the Earth's soil and sediment, so chemical weathering is a hugely important geological process. Many rocks also contain iron-rich minerals, which react in the atmosphere to form iron oxide residues that are characterized by their rust colour.

SALT WEATHERING
Seawater has lashed against this rock, penetrated it, and then evaporated to leave behind salt crystals, which have expanded to produce holes in the surface.

KARST LANDSCAPE
Extensive weathering of limestone has led to the creation of spectacular scenery in Guilin, China. The hills and towers are all that remain of the original rock.

ACID RAIN

Chemical weathering by acid rain, which is so effective in forming cave systems, also attacks limestone buildings and sculptures (see below). Since the Industrial Revolution, the process has accelerated, particularly in areas of atmospheric pollution. Nitrogen oxides and sulphur dioxide are released as a result of burning fossil fuels and vehicle emissions, and compounds react in the atmosphere to form acid rain. Damage is also caused by acid-rain run-off into groundwater, rivers, and lakes.

LICHEN
In the soil-free Antarctic landscape, primitive lichens obtain nutrients from rock surfaces. Acids within the lichens dissolve the outer parts of the rock.

Biological Weathering

Organisms, especially micro-organisms, play an important role in the weathering of rocks, reacting with them to cause biochemical decay. Lichens tolerate extreme environmental conditions, and were probably the first organisms to colonize the land. Their acids dissolved the minerals within rocks, breaking them down to form soil. This addition of organic material to inorganic rock debris was an important stage in the formation of materials that could support the growth of the first land plants. In recent years it has been discovered that microbial life exists far below the ground, living on the surface of mineral grains. This evidence suggests that biological weathering may play a far more important role in the alteration of rock-forming minerals than has been recognized previously. Macroscopic plants, such as trees, also play a significant role in the formation of soils as they release organic acids that attack rocks. They also contribute to physical weathering as their roots and seeds penetrate and grow within the cracks in rocks, forcing them to open further. It could also be argued that humans have been one of the most influential organisms to have brought about weathering of landscapes, by clearing land for agriculture and construction.

PLANT COLONIZATION
Even recent lava flows, such as this example in Hawaii, can be colonized by plants. These succulents derive nutrition from their harsh environment.

TREE INVASION
Angkor Wat, the 12th-century capital of the Khmer kingdom (present-day Cambodia), was abandoned in 1443. Since then it has been overtaken by the growth of the encroaching jungle.

Erosion

THE PROCESSES BY WHICH soil and rock material are loosened, dissolved, and removed from any part of the Earth's surface are known collectively as erosion (from the latin *erodere*, which means "to gnaw"). They include corrasion, which is the mechanical erosion of rocks by materials carried within water, wind, and ice, and the movement of rock material as sediment or in solution. Erosion follows vertical uplift of rocks. Together with gravity, the processes of erosion combine to lower and flatten the Earth's surface. Without erosion and sediment transport, the rock debris that results from weathering (see pp.56–57) would accumulate where it formed. There are two primary ways in which material is transported: by the movement of air, water, or ice; and by the forces of gravity.

W. M. DAVIS

The American physical geographer William Morris Davis (1850–1934) was a pioneering student of landscape erosion and erosive cycles. He envisioned a cycle in which juvenile landscapes evolved to maturity and old age, with characteristic landforms for each stage. Davis's model saw rivers cutting steep V-shaped valleys, which matured into broader valleys with meandering rivers and floodplains, which then became more prolonged "old-age" lowland landscapes close to sea-level. Over the last few decades, the reality has been shown to be more complex.

Water Erosion

Flowing water is continually reshaping the landscape, and the effects of its erosive power are evident all around us. Water is capable of lifting and transporting loose rock fragments (sediment), which then act abrasively on rock, wearing it away. It can also wash away soil and dissolve minerals, carrying them downstream before depositing them elsewhere (see pp.60–61). When rainwater falls on slopes, it runs downhill, cutting small channels called rills, which can deepen with further rainfall to form gullies. These channels can eventually join up with streams and rivers. Rivers are important erosive agents, carving their way through the Earth's surface to create valleys and canyons, and carrying sediment towards the sea. The volume of sediment, and the distance that it is transported, depends upon the size of the particles a river carries and the energy of the flow. A major flood has huge erosive potential. Seawater is also a powerful erosive force, as waves constantly bombard coastlines, re-shaping them and creating dramatic rock formations, such as caves and stacks (see p.354).

AUSABLE RIVER
A powerful, fast-flowing river, such as this one in New York State, USA, transports abrasive particles, and can quickly cut a steep gorge through rock. In other settings, rivers may erode the rock more slowly.

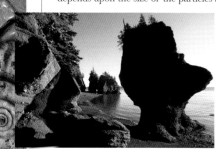

CLIFF EROSION
Exceptionally high tidal ranges in the Bay of Fundy, Canada, and sediment-laden attack by waves, have cut through the cliff face to produce these free-standing rocks.

ACCELERATED EROSION

High winds, the shifting course of the Yellow River (see p.181), and overcultivation of land in northwest China's arid interior have led to the erosion of the vast layer of fertile loess (silt) that blankets the landscape. The loess was deposited by winds from the arid Arctic regions of northern Asia during the last ice age. Today, lack of vegetation to bind the surface allows strong winds to lift these light particles into the air, where they are carried in suspension as dust storms over large distances. Millions of tonnes of China's loess are stripped away by wind and water erosion every year.

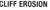

Wind Erosion

Moving air has the power to carry huge volumes of sediment, especially under arid conditions. When there is a lack of vegetation or moisture to hold surface deposits together, the wind picks up loose grains and transports them. Wind carried material is itself an effective agent of erosion, sculpting rocks into a variety of shapes. These include ventifacts, which are rocks that have been blasted by particles carried within the air flow, and yardangs, which are wind-shaped desert ridges (see p.236). By removing loose material, the wind exposes rock to further weathering and erosion, with the result that land surfaces are actively transformed by these two processes. Until the Earth's landscapes were covered by vegetation in the Permian Period, wind was probably as significant an agent of erosion as water. Today, wind erosion occurs primarily in arid or desert regions. Only the tiniest grains, about the size of a particle of silt or clay, are lifted high into the wind flow. The transport of larger grains takes place in a process called saltation, in which grains are lifted up to 1m (3ft) into the air, and carried along briefly, before landing back on the ground. As each particle bounces back to the surface, it collides with other fragments that are too large to be lifted, and shunts them along in a creeping motion. This results in the build up of ripples and dunes.

VENTIFACT
Grains carried by wind have sand-blasted this erratic Antarctic boulder. Known as ventifacts, such structures are normally associated with hot deserts.

ERODED ROCK
Wind erosion has stripped away the softer strata of this sedimentary rock in the Sahara Desert, emphasizing its constituent layers.

Glacial Erosion

Glaciers form in areas where ice and snow remain all year round and where, over the course of a year, more accumulates in winter than melts in summer. At present, 10 per cent of the Earth's land surface, about 14.9 million square km (5.75 million square miles), is covered by diminishing amounts of glacial ice as global climates continue to warm. However, 18,000 years ago, during the last ice age, this proportion was closer to 30 per cent. Rock-laden ice is one of the most effective abrasive forces in the natural world. The ice removes loose rock debris and incorporates it into its flow, which then carves, scours, and scrapes the surfaces it creeps over, dramatically modifying landscapes. These effects become visible only when the ice melts. The classic land-forms of glacial erosion include pyramid-shaped mountain peaks with steep rock walls called glacial horns – one of the best examples of which is Switzerland's Matterhorn (see p.105); scooped-out cirques separated by sharp rock ridges called arêtes (see p.215); and broad U-shaped valleys (see p.215). Many rock surfaces are covered with tell-tale traces of glacial erosion in the form of scratches and grooves.

GLACIAL VALLEY
This broad valley in northern England's Lake District, surrounded by steep, bare rock walls that contain a flat valley floor without a major river, is a typical result of glacial erosion.

DELICATE ARCH
The flow of seawater millions of years ago, ice wedging, and collapse along joints, contributed to the formation of this remarkable stone arch in Utah, USA.

GLACIAL GROOVE
Smooth, rounded rock outcrops covered in parallel scratches and grooves, such as these in northern Norway, are typical of erosion by rocks embedded in glacial ice.

Deposition

THE SOLID PRODUCT OF THE PROCESSES of weathering and erosion is sediment, which is moved across the Earth's surface by the fluid motion of water, wind, ice, or mass movement (see pp.62–63). As this movement slows down – for example, if a river reaches flatter ground – particles carried within the flow are deposited, with denser fragments falling out first. Sediment is deposited in layers in natural "traps", such as river deltas, or basins on land or in the sea. This accumulation of layers of sediment represents the initial stage of sedimentary rock formation (see p.49). Deposition is also an important process in the formation of fertile land for cultivation.

Water-Borne Deposition

Water plays a major role in the transportation and deposition of sediment. The particles carried by water can range from tiny grains of clay to boulders, depending on the speed and depth of the flow. Water is also capable of dissolving certain minerals and rocks, especially limestones, and transporting the mineral constituents in solution. Some minerals may subsequently come out of solution to form new minerals. Rivers carry sediment from the steeper parts of their courses, depositing it within lakes and on floodplains or in deltas. Floodplains are important sites of deposition: for instance, the Mississippi floodplain in the USA (see p.165) is 15km (9 miles) wide, and is characterized by fertile deposits of sand, silt, and mud. Much river-borne material is also carried towards the sea and deposited in deltas (see p.161). The deltas of large rivers, such as the Nile (see p.177) and the Ganges (see p.182), are sites of significant deposition. As it enters the sea, river-borne sediment is redistributed, contributing to the formation of continental shelves. Sediment can also be transported into the ocean by a high-energy flow called a turbidity current (see p.310).

RIVER TRANSPORT
Pebbles and boulders of various sizes are transported downstream by high-energy waters that also smoothe their shape.

ANCIENT SANDFLATS
Washed by waves and currents, layers of sand were deposited on an ancient beach. The layers were buried and compacted to form this sandstone in Utah, USA.

SEDIMENT SAMPLING

By taking samples of the layers of sediment at a deposition site, scientists can reconstruct the conditions that prevailed in the past. From these samples, it is possible to determine the structure of the deposits. This is done by measuring the thickness of each layer of sediment, identifying fossils, measuring the size and shape of grains, and analysing mineral composition, all of which can be used to track the site's geological history.

LAND RECLAMATION

Where land is at a premium for human habitation, such as around Hong Kong Harbour, materials are removed from other locations and deposited to form new land. In Hong Kong, material has been removed from mountain tops and deposited in the sea, supplemented by rock that has been transported from elsewhere in the world. Land reclamation has increased the space for building in Hong Kong, but has also narrowed one of the world's finest natural harbours.

WHITEHAVEN BEACH, AUSTRALIA
These white sands are constantly shifting in the shallow tropical sea, but some will eventually be deposited on continental shelves.

Wind-Borne Deposition

Air cannot transport large particles of sediment. However, atmospheric wind and storm systems can be so energetic that they carry enormous volumes of dust, silt, and fine sand. As wind subsides, it deposits the material it is carrying. A strong wind can carry sediment over vast distances – particles from the Sahara Desert in Africa have been found deposited on the opposite side of the Atlantic, in Barbados. Most wind-formed landscapes are situated within the world's hot, arid equatorial deserts, although there are significant mid-latitude deserts, such as the Gobi in Asia (see p.252). The most striking desert landforms caused by wind-borne deposition are dunes, which are usually between 5 and 30m (15 and 100ft) high. Some dunes are concentrated in huge sand seas called ergs, which have an area of more than 32,000 square km (12,000 square miles). Dunes vary in shape, and include ripples and ridges, which are transverse and parallel to wind direction, crescent-shaped barchans, domes, and star-shaped formations (see p.237). Narrow zones of sand dunes also form along coastlines, as beach sands are blown inland and deposited. One of the Earth's most significant wind deposits is a thick layer of fine, fertile silt called loess. It covers large areas of the Earth's surface, particularly in China, and was deposited during the last ice age (see p.58).

LAYERED SANDSTONE
Distinctive layers of large-scale dune deposits, dating back to the Jurassic Period, are evident in these sandstones in Utah, USA.

AFRICAN SANDSTORM
Wind-driven sandstorms, such as this massive system over Chad in central Africa, can transport and deposit desert particles over many thousands of kilometres.

Glacial Deposition

Rock material eroded by mountain glaciers and ice sheets is called till, and consists of particles that range from tiny fragments to boulders. This detritus is carried downhill by the glacier, and then deposited over surrounding landscapes. The features produced by till deposits are called moraines, which range from linear trains of debris to wide sheets of rock that can be moulded into many different shapes (see p.215). Till that is deposited at the sides of glaciers is known as a lateral moraine, and creates ridges that are parallel to ice flow. If two glaciers merge, a medial moraine is formed from the till, while ridges formed at right angles to the front edge of a glacier are called terminal moraines. These deposits remain as distinctive landforms when glaciers recede. Melt-waters re-shape till and generate sediments called fluvioglacial deposits that consist primarily of sand and gravel. Rivers that flow beneath glaciers channel these deposits into sinuous ridges called eskers.

MEDIAL MORAINE
A medial moraine, such as this one in Switzerland, is formed when two glaciers merge. Their lateral moraines combine to form a central band of till deposits.

Volcanic Deposition

Material ejected by volcanoes into the atmosphere includes ash and aerosol particles, which are deposited in layers over surrounding landscapes. The finest material can be spewed high into the atmosphere and distributed over great distances before it is finally deposited. The longest-lasting and most widely dispersed volcanic particles are droplets of sulphuric acid. Clouds of these droplets absorb incoming solar radiation, preventing it from reaching the Earth's surface, which then affects climate (see p.373). Ultimately, these droplets fall out of the atmosphere at the poles, where they are buried by snow. These deposits have been detected within cores drilled from polar ice sheets.

DEPOSITS IN THE ATMOSPHERE
The left-hand image, taken from the Space Shuttle in 1984, shows a clear atmosphere. The right-hand image was taken less than two months after the eruption of Mount Pinatubo in 1991, which released nearly 20 million tonnes of aerosol particles into the atmosphere. Two distinct dark layers of aerosol particles are visible, some of which eventually fell to Earth.

Mass Movement

ROCK MATERIALS MAY APPEAR TO BE STRONG and capable of maintaining mountains and cliffs high above their surroundings. However, all rocks have finite strengths, and the pull of gravity, combined with the processes of weathering (see pp.56–57) and erosion (see pp.58–59), alters the shape of the Earth's surface. A steep cliff may survive for millennia, but can quickly collapse if it is undercut by a river. A hillside may seem to have stable, shallow slopes, but will fail suddenly and collapse, sometimes with disastrous results, if the forces that bind it are altered by rain, vegetation clearance, or a geological event such as an earthquake (see pp.64–65). Known as mass movement, the speed of the motion depends on the angle of the slope and the material involved.

Slope Stability

The slope of a pile of material has a natural angle of repose that is maintained by friction between the individual particles. This is true both of slopes that are consolidated (in which the particles are joined) and those that are unconsolidated (in which they are loose). If the angle is steepened or disturbed, the pile will collapse until it reaches a more stable position. Masses of material will also start to move, under the influence of gravity, if the cohesive strength is altered by the presence of water, additional weight, or sudden movement such as an earthquake. Any of these factors can drastically alter the equilibrium of the mass, and cause it to collapse. Vast amounts of unstable unconsolidated and consolidated material are found all over the Earth's surface both on land and beneath the sea. Much of this is in slopes that are close to their maximum angle of repose and, if triggered, will fail. The inhabitants of high mountains and coasts with steep cliffs are only too familiar with the processes of mass movement and the potential instability of slopes.

SAND DUNES
If disturbed, sand grains will roll down the slope of a sand dune until they reach their natural angle of repose.

slope is stable at 35°

FINE SAND

slope is stable at 40°

COARSE SAND

slope is stable at 45°

ANGULAR PEBBLES

ANGLES OF STABILITY
When loose materials are poured, they form natural piles. Large particles form slopes with higher angles of repose than those made of fine particles.

Rock Mass Movement

Several factors and processes contribute to the downward movement of rock material under the force of gravity. Rock that is weakened by weathering, particularly the process of frost shattering (see p.56), can break away from a slope and tumble down it. Weathering can decrease the strength of a rock mass, until it, too, becomes unstable and moves down a slope. A rock slide occurs when a block breaks off and moves along a bedding plane or a joint. The most devastating rock mass movement is a rock avalanche, which can be triggered by an earthquake or torrential rain. This type of mass movement is violent, sudden, and rapid, moving at speeds of up to 320kph (200mph), and contains many pieces of rock. The largest rock avalanches are the result of the collapse of volcanoes, such as the one that occurred during the eruption of Mount St. Helens in 1980 (see p.119). Evidence of rock mass movement can be seen in talus or scree slopes, which accumulate at the bottom of cliffs or mountains. Rocks can also form part of unconsolidated mass movement (see opposite page).

ROCK FALL
Avalanches of rock debris, such as this one above the Hood River in Oregon, USA, are common in steep, hilly areas prone to heavy rainfall.

CLIFF SLIDE
Cliffs that are weakened by the bombardment of waves are prone to rock falls, especially in areas where movement along active faults can trigger them, such as the coast of California, USA.

PLANET EARTH

Unconsolidated Mass Movement

Soil and sediment consisting of uncemented grains can move downhill in various ways. The addition of water further affects this movement. Unconsolidated mass movements include creep, earth-flows, mudflows, and debris avalanches. Soil creep and solifluction (see below) are slow movements (a few millimetres a year) that usually occur over gentle slopes. These processes are common in permanently frozen ground (permafrost), particularly during the seasonal thaws, when saturated debris moves downhill over surfaces lubricated by water, fine sediment, or a combination of the two. Debris flows and mudflows containing soil, rocks, and water, can occur suddenly and move very rapidly. Lahars occur on the sides of volcanoes, and can be triggered by an eruption or rainfall that remobilizes ash and volcanic debris to create a fast-moving and often catastrophic flow. Such rapid movements can pose substantial threat to life, as they have the potential to envelop everything in their path. Mass movements of unconsolidated material can include simple, unconfined hillside flows, those that are confined by valleys and eventually spread out on to open ground, and highly destructive large-scale flows with enough energy to over-ride topography.

MUDFLOW
Heavy rainfall on this cliff on the Isle of Wight, UK, has saturated and liquefied the clay within it, causing it to collapse and resulting in a mudflow that has spread across this beach.

SOLIFLUCTION
The slow flow of water-saturated soil from higher to lower ground is known as solifluction. The tilt of these old building piles in Svalbard, in the Arctic, is evidence that solifluction has occurred.

SUBMARINE MASS MOVEMENT

The large blocks of rock detected on the submarine slopes of oceanic volcanoes (such as those of the Hawaiian Islands in the Pacific and the Canary Islands in the Atlantic) suggest that these unstable edifices have repeatedly collapsed and swept down their submarine slopes. Imagery of the ocean floor surrounding the Canary Islands has revealed blocks of rock 1km (2/3 mile) wide on the underwater slopes, extending 80km (50 miles) out from the islands. Geologists have suggested that the Cumbre Vieja volcano on La Palma in the Canary Islands (see right), which is the most active volcano in the group, could collapse and cause a huge submarine mass movement, triggering a tsunami with the potential to devastate the eastern seaboard of the USA.

PLANET EARTH

Types of Slope

The development, form, and decline of slopes is a fundamental feature of landscape evolution and depends on a number of elements. These include the relative hardness of the materials forming the slope, and the elements that impact upon it such as wind and rain. For example, resistant rocks such as granite can form perpendicular cliffs, while softer rock such as shale forms slopes that are more gradual. Free-standing cliffs may form as a result of undercutting by waves or stream erosion, glacial excavation, differential weathering, or collapse along vertical joints. Then, sloping pediments of debris build up and protect the lower parts of the cliffs from further weathering or erosion. In arid and semi-arid environments, prominent rock cliffs such as mesas (see p.237) are common, but in areas where the climate is more varied and there is more rainfall, fragmented debris may dominate the slope – unless another geological process, such as glaciation, removes it.

BUTTES
Vertical-faced mesas or smaller buttes, such as these at Monument Valley, USA, rising above gently sloping pediments, are typical of slope development under arid conditions.

SCREE
Rock debris that has been loosened by freeze–thaw action (see p.56) tumbles down a hillside, piling up to form scree slopes on the sides of valleys, such as this one in England.

AVALANCHES
An avalanche is a downwards movement of snow, ice, or debris in a mountainous area, such as Alaska (seen here). It can be triggered by sudden noises or thawing.

LANDSLIDES

On 8 August 2010, nearly two million cubic metres (70 million cubic ft) of mud and rocks tore through the city of Zhugqu in Gansu province, China, in a surge up to five storeys high. The landslide began when heavy rain piled up water behind a dam of debris that had built up in a small river – then suddenly swept it away. Many landslides have entirely natural causes, but excessive tree-felling and dam construction may well create the instability that triggers landslides too.

Slopes That Fail

Landslides are mass movements (see p.62) that occur when gravity overcomes friction and pulls soil or rock downhill. During a landslide, part of a slope shears away along a basal failure plane, and initially moves as a coherent block. In some landslides, the moving material breaks up, but in others it stays more or less intact as it shifts. An example of this occurred on the coast of Dorset, England, in 1839. Coastal cliffs gave way, carrying clifftop farmland with them, but the fields remained usable, and crops were grown on them for several years.

One of the most common causes of landslides is heavy rainfall, which saturates the ground. Earthquakes and volcanic eruptions are much more violent triggers. Human activities can increase both the risk of landslides and the danger that they present.

In mountainous regions, forest clearance is a frequent cause of landslides, because it increases water run-off and accelerates erosion. Road construction is another hazard, because it cuts into hillsides, destabilizing rock. Urbanization also causes problems. In Malaysia, a landslide demolished a 12-storey apartment block in 1994, while, in Hong Kong, landslides have killed nearly 500 people in the last 50 years. Most of these fatalities have been due to poor construction techniques on steep slopes, aggravated by the region's heavy summer rainfall.

Although some landslides strike without any warning, in many cases ground movements show that an area is at risk. During the early 1960s, several small landslips occurred during the construction of the Vaiont Dam, in the Italian Alps. During the autumn of 1963, rising water levels saturated a clay layer, triggering a massive landslide that plunged into the reservoir below. The dam held, but displaced water surged over its

VAIONT DAM DISASTER
Following a landslide, water from the Vaiont reservoir destroyed the town of Longarone, in 1963. A second overspill – also caused by a landslide – occurred in 1966.

crest, devastating a town in its path. Altogether, more than 2,000 people lost their lives.

The most catastrophic landslides in recorded history took place during a major earthquake in the Gansu region of China in 1920, which triggered collapses of steep cliffs of fine-grained loess soils. Ten large cities and many villages were buried, and an estimated 200,000 people lost their lives during a single day.

Mud on the Move

Landslides move at speeds ranging from a slow, barely perceptible creep to more than 100kph (60mph) on steep slopes. Both debris avalanches and water-saturated mass movements (mudflows) can travel many tens of kilometres, causing widespread devastation and smothering everything in their paths. Mudflows are common in the western USA during El Niño years (see p.371), and they were responsible for many of the fatalities caused by Hurricane Mitch, when it stalled over Central America in 1998, shedding considerable quantities of rain.

Mudflows in volcanic terrain, called lahars, can occur in association with eruptions, or later, as rains remobilize loose ash deposits. Fine ash is particularly dangerous, because it easily forms a fluid mass. When a lahar comes to a halt, the transported mud or ash sets like cement, making escape almost impossible. In 1985, a lahar poured down the flanks of Nevado del Ruiz, a volcano in Colombia (see p.122), and struck the town of Armero, 50km (30 miles) to the east. Most of its 29,000 inhabitants were asleep, and fewer than a third survived.

Mudflows on this scale are impossible to prevent, but, in the future, improved communications may reduce the cost in human lives. A satellite-based system, now under trial in the Caribbean, will gather rainfall data and flash warnings to home computers, or even mobile phones.

EXPOSED TO THE ELEMENTS
Completely clearing a forested area aggravates natural erosion, leading to frequent landslides, as has happened here in Cabin Creek, in the Cascade Range, USA.

LARGEST LANDSLIDES			
Most of the largest landslides and debris flows in the last 100 years (listed below) have occurred in tectonically active zones.			
Location	Date	Cause	Fatalities
Gansu, China	1920	Earthquake	200,000+
Vaiont, Italy	1963	Dam construction	2,600
Mount Huascarán, Peru	1970	Earthquake	18,000
Mount St Helens, USA	1980	Volcanic eruption	60
Nevado del Ruiz, Colombia	1985	Volcanic eruption	23,000
Huaraz, Peru	1991	Lake drainage	5,000
Honduras and Nicaragua	1998	Hurricane	2,000+
Gansu, China	2010	Rainfall	1,471
Glacier Bay, USA	2013	Snowmelt	0

TRAIL OF DESTRUCTION
The mudslides that swept through Zhugqu in China covered 300 homes, including an entire village, and claimed over 1,400 lives.

Meteorite Impacts

THE EARTH IS regularly struck by debris from space. In the last billion years, it has been hit by about 130,000 meteorites large enough to produce a crater at least 1km (²/₃ mile) wide. Although this kind of impact site is visible on the Moon, the surface of the Earth is so geologically active that evidence of many impacts has disappeared. Until recently, it was believed that the Earth was hit by large meteorites only very early in its history. However, scientists now realize that the Earth is being struck continually, and that a number of giant craters have been preserved. So far, more than 180 impact sites have been confirmed worldwide, with new craters discovered every year.

WOLFE CREEK CRATER, AUSTRALIA
This Australian impact structure shows features typical of meteorite craters: the near-circular depression is surrounded by a well-preserved blanket of debris.

Causes of Impacts

Most meteorites are fragments of asteroids, although some were produced when asteroids hit the surfaces of the Moon or Mars, flinging debris into space. While they are outside the Earth's atmosphere, these rocks are called meteoroids; those that enter the atmosphere are known as meteors. These are usually so small that they burn up as they plunge towards the Earth, leaving a bright trail in the night sky. Meteor showers are caused when the Earth passes through the tail of a comet. Meteorites are objects large enough to travel through the atmosphere and hit the ground. Impacts may also be caused by debris from comets. If a meteorite is the size of a house, or even larger, the force of the impact blasts out a crater.

METEOR TRAIL
Meteors, which are also called shooting stars, are visible in the night sky when their trails burn up as they travel through the Earth's atmosphere.

NAMIBIAN METEORITE
This 60-tonne rock discovered at Hoba West, Namibia, is the largest meteorite to have been found on Earth.

EUGENE SHOEMAKER

American scientist Eugene Shoemaker (1928–97) was an expert on meteorites. His work confirmed the first identification of an impact crater on the Earth: Meteor Crater in Arizona, USA (see p.69). In the process, he and Edward Chao discovered coesite, a silica mineral produced under the extreme pressure and temperature of an impact. The presence of coesite is now taken as a key indicator of an impact. With his wife Carolyn and friend David Levy, he discovered the Shoemaker-Levy 9 comet, which hit Jupiter in 1994.

Identifying Impact Sites

The most obvious indication of a meteorite impact is a large, circular crater, and geologists may begin their search for new sites by scouring satellite images of the Earth's surface for such features. Although craters erode over time, scars called astroblemes ("star wounds") remain. Once spotted, each site is investigated for evidence to confirm impact. Usually a meteorite vaporizes on impact, but shattered or melted remnants may still exist. These fragments can resemble ordinary rock, but if rich in iridium, osmium, or platinum they probably originate from a meteorite. Geologists also look for damage to rocks around the impact site. These effects are called shock metamorphism, and include shatter cones, tektites, diaplectic glass (a natural glass formed during a meteorite impact), and high-pressure silica minerals such as stishovite and coesite.

TEKTITE
Tektites are beads of glass that are formed when droplets of silica-rich molten material are expelled from a crater during a meteorite impact.

SHOCKED QUARTZ
This image of a quartz grain reveals a key sign of a meteorite impact – shock lamellae. These are deformed layers within the quartz, indicated by bright colours.

METEOR CRATER, ARIZONA
With its distinctive simple bowl shape, Meteor Crater is the result of the most recent significant meteorite impact on Earth, about 50,000 years ago. It was the first major impact structure to be identified (see p.69).

Impact Craters

When a meteorite strikes the Earth, the impact sends shock waves through the ground, squeezing the surrounding rock to two or three times its usual density. The compressed rock then springs back and shatters into fragments, hurling chunks upwards and outwards, along with pieces of the meteorite that have not vapourized. The result is a bowl-shaped crater that is much larger than the meteorite. Rock fragments called ejecta are blasted far beyond the crater. Other fragments fall back into the hollow to form rocks called breccia. Small craters form in just a few seconds, and even giant ones form in a few minutes. Meteorite craters vary widely in appearance from small, cup-shaped bowls to giant depressions filled with multiple ridges and mounds. They are divided into two groups: simple and complex (see below).

impact ejecta   breccia   smooth crater   fractured rock

SIMPLE CRATER
Typically no more than 4km (2½ miles) in diameter, simple craters are smooth bowls that are wider than they are deep. They often have a steep, well-defined rim, and there may be a layer of breccia at the bottom of the crater that is thicker at the centre.

impact ejecta   breccia   domed central peak   fractured rock   ridges around crater

COMPLEX CRATER
Complex craters are larger than simple craters and they are usually shallower. This type of crater often has rings of ridges. Many also have a domed central peak, which was raised as the compressed rock sprang back after impact.

After Impact

The potential energy of a significant meteorite impact on the Earth is over 100 million megatons – more than the world's entire nuclear arsenal. Studying nuclear explosions has given scientists some idea of what might happen after the impact of a large meteorite about 10km (6 miles) in diameter. At the moment of collision, an immense wave of heat and pressure roars outwards, flattening and incinerating everything over a vast area.

Massive amounts of debris are blasted high into the atmosphere and blown around the world by strong winds. Hot ash rains down, starting forest fires, while dust clouds linger in the atmosphere for months, blocking out the Sun and turning the Earth into a dark and frozen planet. When the sky finally clears, the carbon dioxide that has flooded the atmosphere creates a greenhouse effect, warming the global climate by an average of 15°C (27°F).

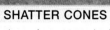

SHATTER CONES

Among the most persuasive signs of a meteorite impact are shatter cones. These are rock structures that have distinctive fractures resembling horsetails. The fractures converge in a cone shape, which can range in size from 2.5cm (1in) to over 2m (6ft) in length. Fractures such as these are only caused by sudden, intense pressure on existing rock. In impact craters, most shatter cones point upwards, which indicates that the impact on the rock came from above.

DINOSAUR EXTINCTION
The global effects of a large meteorite may be so devastating that scientists suspect they are the cause of many of the mass extinctions that have occurred in the Earth's history, including the death of the dinosaurs 65 million years ago.

METEORITE IMPACT PROFILES ▶

The pages that follow contain profiles of the most significant impact craters in the world. Each profile begins with the following summary information:

DATE OF IMPACT Approximate date at which the meteorite hit the Earth

TYPE Simple or complex

DIAMETER Width across the crater

ARCTIC
Haughton

LOCATION On Devon Island, Nunavut Territory, in the Arctic region of northwest Canada

DATE OF IMPACT 23 million years ago

TYPE Complex

DIAMETER 24km (15 miles)

Most craters that are as old as the Haughton impact site have undergone significant erosion. However, because it lies within the Arctic Circle where much of the water is frozen solid, Haughton has escaped the worst effects of weathering. The lack of vegetation covering the site makes it easy for geologists to study the crater both on the ground and from space using satellites. Studies have shown that the giant meteorite that struck

ARCTIC IMPACT
The Haughton meteorite struck within the hilly landscape of Devon Island in Arctic Canada.

MARS TEST

Rocky, arid, and icy cold, Haughton Crater resembles conditions found on the surface of Mars. Scientists have been studying the crater to see what it can tell them about the geology of the Red Planet and also how astronauts could survive on Mars.

here penetrated 1.7km (1 mile) into the ground – as far as the buried ancient rocks of the continental crust. As it crashed into the Earth, it threw a huge shower of shattered fragments of this ancient crust into the air, which can now be found on the surface.

NORTH AMERICA *northeast*
Manicouagan

LOCATION Within Réservoir Manicouagan, near the Laurentian Mountains, Quebec, Canada

DATE OF IMPACT 212 million years ago

TYPE Complex

DIAMETER 100km (60 miles)

The Manicouagan Crater is one of the largest and most intact impact structures on the Earth's surface. Its width is exceeded by only four other craters in the world and matches that of the Popigai Crater in Russia (see p.71). It also one of the Earth's oldest craters, caused by the impact of a huge meteorite in the Triassic Period. The site is notable for its circular central plateau, which is surrounded by the ring-shaped Lake Manicouagan. The crater has been the subject of a great deal of speculation about whether the

RIVERS AND LAKE
Manicouagan Crater has become a focus for numerous surrounding rivers and streams, which flow into its lake.

impact caused a wave of global extinction. Paleontologists identify the boundary of the Triassic and Jurassic periods as one of the times in the Earth's history when vast numbers of species disappeared in a short span of time, an incident known as the TJ extinction. One theory to explain this is that the Manicouagan meteorite impact threw so much rock and dust into the atmosphere that its effect on the planet's climate destroyed many living organisms. However, some scientists believe that the impact happened too early to be responsible for this, and that other cataclysmic events caused the mass extinctions.

NORTH AMERICA *northeast*
Sudbury

LOCATION North of Lake Huron and the town of Sudbury, Ontario, eastern Canada

DATE OF IMPACT 1,840 million years ago

TYPE Complex

DIAMETER 200km (125 miles)

The Sudbury Crater is such an unusual shape that it took geologists a long time to identify it as a meteorite crater. The area is one of the Earth's richest sources of nickel-copper

sulphide minerals, and was initially thought to be of volcanic origin. Now, however, scientists are certain that it is an impact site. The object that smashed into the Earth here produced a crater about 20km (12 miles) deep. What makes the crater so unusual is the fact that it is elliptical and is nearly twice as long as it is wide. The crater is now believed originally to have been circular – its elliptical shape was produced by post-impact deformation of the Canadian Shield, the stable continental rocks in which the impact took place.

NICKEL MINING
The highly productive mines that lie within the Sudbury Crater yield over 1,000 tons of nickel and copper ores every day.

NORTH AMERICA *central*
Manson

LOCATION Around the town of Manson, northwest of Des Moines, Iowa, midwestern USA

DATE OF IMPACT 74 million years ago

TYPE Complex

DIAMETER 37km (23 miles)

Completely buried up to 90m (295ft) beneath glacial deposits, the Manson impact site was thought to be a volcanic structure, but studies in the 1960s revealed its true origin. Initially, the crater was dated at about 66 million years old, so scientists began to wonder if it might be linked to the extinction of the dinosaurs, which occurred at a similar time. In the 1990s, scientists drilled about a dozen research cores to find out more about Manson. They discovered the structure consists of a ring-shaped moat around a central peak. They also revised the date of impact to 74 million years ago, well before the demise of the dinosaurs. The effects of the impact must been enormously destructive, killing most wildlife within 1,000km (620 miles).

NORTH AMERICA *east*
Chesapeake Bay

LOCATION On the Atlantic coast of the USA, beneath Chesapeake Bay, Maryland, and Virginia

DATE OF IMPACT 35 million years ago

TYPE Complex

DIAMETER 85km (53 miles)

One of the largest impact craters on Earth, Chesapeake Bay was identified by chance in the 1980s when teams drilling the sea bed for water sources found samples of jumbled rocks, and an ocean survey ship found shattered quartz and microtektites. Subsequent seismic and gravity surveys then revealed the huge extent of the crater.

SATELLITE IMAGE OF CHESAPEAKE BAY

Meteor Crater

LOCATION East of Flagstaff and west of Winslow, in the Painted Desert, Arizona, USA

DATE OF IMPACT 50,000 years ago

TYPE Simple

DIAMETER 1.2km (¾ mile)

A vast dish carved into the Arizona desert, Meteor Crater is perhaps the Earth's most famous meteorite crater. Its shape has been remarkably well preserved, and it is comparatively young for an impact site. Scientists estimate that the meteorite that crashed here was about 50m (150ft)

across and weighed about 300,000 tonnes. It probably hurtled into the ground at a speed of 65,000kph (40,000mph), creating an immense force as it hit the surface – the equivalent of 20 million tonnes of TNT exploding. Fragments of the nickel-iron meteorite that impacted are scattered all around the crater, as are tiny metallic balls, which were created as the meteorite vaporized on impact. It was the presence of nickel-

CRATER AND CANYON
The Colorado Plateau is scarred by two dramatic geological structures: Meteor Crater (left) and the Grand Canyon (right).

iron that led Daniel Moreau Barringer (see panel, right) to conclude that the crater was the result of a meteorite impact. Further crucial evidence was discovered in 1960 by Eugene Shoemaker, Edward Chao, and Daniel Milton, who found coesite and stishovite at the site. These minerals form only under enormous pressure and at high temperatures, and are key signs of an extra-terrestrial impact. Shoemaker's demonstration three years later of the similarities between Meteor Crater and craters made by nuclear tests in Nevada clinched the argument.

DANIEL MOREAU BARRINGER

Meteor Crater is also called Barringer Crater after the mining engineer who was determined to prove its impact origin, Daniel Moreau Barringer (1860–1929). He found it hard to convince geologists of his theory, which he put forward in 1902, and lost a fortune searching for the meteorite he was convinced was buried there. It was later realized that the meteorite had vaporized on impact.

ARIZONA'S GIANT IMPACT SITE
Meteor Crater is a dramatic, cup-shaped bowl in the Arizona desert. It was the first meteorite impact site on the Earth's surface to be positively identified.

Chicxulub

LOCATION Centred on the town of Chicxulub, beneath the Yucatan Peninsula, Mexico

DATE OF IMPACT 65 million years ago

TYPE Complex

DIAMETER 160–240km (100–150 miles)

Buried deep beneath the limestone of Mexico's Yucatan Peninsula, Chicxulub is one of the largest meteorite craters yet found on the Earth. Some estimates put its width at over 300km (185 miles). At the end of the Cretaceous Period, 65 million years ago, a comet or an asteroid that may have been more than 10km (6 miles) wide crashed into the Earth at this site. The impact was cataclysmic: fires raged over the surface, giant tsunamis radiated across the oceans, and the planet was rocked by massive earthquakes. Many scientists believe that the devastating

global effects of the Chicxulub impact caused the extinction of the dinosaurs (see p.24) and two-thirds of other animal species. Both the size of the catastrophe and its timing are right, and the evidence is very convincing. The Chicxulub Crater is a complex crater with several ring-

CATASTROPHIC CHICXULUB
Magnetic and gravity surveys were used to create this vertically exaggerated computer image of the crater hidden about 1km (⅔ mile) beneath the Yucatan Peninsula. The top of the image represents north.

shaped ridges and a central mound like that of the Manicouagan Crater (see opposite page). To explain its shape scientists have suggested that the impact deformed the solid rock of the Yucatan Peninsula rapidly, almost like a fluid. Rings rippled out from the point of impact, and at the centre a towering mound, at least twice the height of Mount Everest, piled up and then subsided gradually. Because it is buried so deep beneath the surface, Chicxulub was discovered almost by accident when an oil company was prospecting in the area in the 1980s.

THE K-PG BOUNDARY

About 65 million years ago, two-thirds of the Earth's animal species died out suddenly. Scientists link this event to a thin layer of clay that dates from the same time, which is sandwiched between Cretaceous and Tertiary rocks. Called the K-PG boundary, this clay contains high concentrations of iridium, an element rare on the Earth but abundant in meteorites. It is likely that this layer represents debris from the Chicxulub impact that was suspended in the atmosphere. This would have blocked out the Sun's rays, turning the world ice cold and spelling doom for the dinosaurs.

Bosumtwi

LOCATION Beneath Lake Bosumtwi, northwest of Accra and south of Kumasi, Ghana, west Africa

DATE OF IMPACT
One million years ago

TYPE Complex

DIAMETER
10km (6 miles)

Hidden deep within rainforest, and drowned beneath the waters of the lake that fills its crater, Bosumtwi has been more awkward to study than other impact sites. Moreover, the heat and humidity of the region have resulted in rapid erosion of many of its features. However, scientists have managed to confirm that the crater is complex, with a raised central dome buried beneath the lake floor. Tektites of a similar age found along the Ivory Coast are now thought to have been flung out by the Bosumtwi impact.

LAKE BOSUMTWI

Ries

LOCATION In southern Bavaria, northwest of Munich, western Germany

DATE OF IMPACT
15 million years ago

TYPE Complex

DIAMETER
24km (15 miles)

The Ries Crater is perhaps the most studied impact structure in Europe. It is a flat, circular basin with a narrow rim around the edge. The Ries meteorite is thought to have been about 1km (²⁄₃ mile) across. Like some other impact sites, the Ries

Crater is not alone in the landscape. Just 36km (22 miles) to the southwest is another, less perfectly shaped basin called the Steinheim Crater, which measures only 3.8km (2.4 miles) across. This was created by a much smaller meteorite that was barely 100m (300ft) long. Radioactive dating suggests that both these meteorites struck at the same time. It is possible that they were the result of a single meteorite that disintegrated as it came through the atmosphere, but the craters are so far apart that this seems unlikely. Some scientists think it more probable that two meteorites swept into the atmosphere together. When the larger Ries meteorite struck, it penetrated the limestone and marl sediments at the surface and plunged right through to the crystalline crustal

TOWN BUILT WITHIN A CRATER
Within the Ries Crater lies the medieval walled town of Nördlingen, which was built on the dried sediments of the lake that once filled the impact site.

basement over 600m (2,000ft) below the surface of the Earth. The shock melted surface rocks, which were ejected from the site, cooling into spheres of transparent green glass (tektites) that were scattered across the landscape of Bohemia and Moravia in the Czech Republic. Clear examples of this green glass, called moldavite, are today cut to make semi-precious stones. Soon after the impact, both the Ries and the Steinheim craters filled with water to become lakes, but over the next 2 million years they became choked with sediment and eventually formed dry land.

Vredefort

LOCATION Southwest of Johannesburg, east of the Vaal River, Witwatersrand Basin, South Africa

DATE OF IMPACT
2,020 million years ago

TYPE Complex

DIAMETER
300km (180 miles)

The Vredefort impact site is marked by the oldest and largest known crater on the Earth's surface It is also one of the few multi-ringed craters in the world. Such structures are common on the Moon but are rare on the Earth, as most would have formed in the early days of the planet's history and have been destroyed by geological processes. It was initially thought that the dome in the centre of the Vredefort Crater was the result of a volcanic explosion. However, since the mid-1990s, mounting mineralogical evidence, accompanied by the discovery of dramatic distortion of rocks within the dome, has convinced scientists that it is the site

MINING CRATERS

Many impact sites are also the locations of valuable mineral ores, which have been subsequently exploited by mining companies. At Sudbury Crater in Canada (see p.68), the rich nickel and copper ores were formed by the heat of the meteorite's impact. The older sediments beneath Vredefort are rich in gold, which is preserved beneath the crater. Meteorite craters also make very good traps for oil, as it works its way towards the surface through cracks formed by an impact.

GOLD MINING IN VREDEFORT
These mines yield over 7 billion dollars' worth of gold annually, and contain the largest concentration of the precious metal in the world.

of a meteorite impact. Shatter cones are found frequently in the bed of the nearby Vaal River, while rocks that lie flat outside the crater have been forced into almost vertical positions within the basin. The extra-terrestrial body that hit Vredefort was one of the biggest meteorites ever to have hit the Earth, measuring about 10km (6 miles) across.

EARTH'S OLDEST CRATER
This image taken by a satellite over southwestern South Africa clearly reveals the circular wrinkles at the edge of the giant Vredefort structure.

Kara and Ust Kara

LOCATION Close to the mouth of the Kara River, near the coast of the Kara Sea, northwest Siberia, Russia

DATE OF IMPACT
70 million years ago

TYPE Complex

DIAMETER
65–120km (40–75 miles)

Discovered in the 1970s, the Kara Crater is situated in an area of bleak, barely inhabited tundra. It was initially believed that there was just one crater here, about 65km (40 miles) wide. Then more impact outcrops were spotted to the west by the coast of the Kara Sea (see p.322). Some geologists suggested that this was another crater, named Ust Kara, which formed at the same time. However, the results of scientific expeditions in 2001 concluded that the two sites probably form one vast crater. Its age once led scientists to suggest the crater as an alternative candidate to Chicxulub (see p.69) for the K-PG event that might have wiped out the dinosaurs, but it is too old.

ASIA *west*

Tunguska

LOCATION Near the Tunguska River in the forests of eastern Siberia, north of Lake Baikal, Russia

DATE OF IMPACT 1908

TYPE No crater has been discovered

DIAMETER Unknown

Tunguska is one of the Earth's great mysteries. On 30 June 1908, local people witnessed a fireball streaking through the sky before vanishing below the horizon. A huge explosion followed, felling trees over an area of 2,200 square km (850 square miles). There have been several expeditions to the Siberian site to try and discover the cause of the explosion; one theory is that it was due to a comet vaporizing before it hit the surface.

DEVASTATION AT TUNGUSKA

ASIA *northeast*

Popigai

LOCATION Near the town of Popigai, east of the Popigai River, northern Siberia, Russia

DATE OF IMPACT 35 million years ago

TYPE Complex

DIAMETER 100km (62 miles)

ASIA *southwest*

Lonar

LOCATION Northeast of Mumbai, in the Buldana district of Maharashtra, western India

DATE OF IMPACT 50,000 years ago

TYPE Simple

DIAMETER 1.8km (1¼ mile)

The vast Popigai Crater is one of the Earth's largest impact sites, and was probably caused by a 5km- (3-mile-) wide meteorite. The force of the impact was sufficient to turn graphite into microscopic diamonds, and ejecta discovered as far away as Massignano, Italy, may have originated there. The timing of the Popigai collision coincides closely with the impact at Chesapeake Bay (see p.82). This has led to the conjecture that at the time of the impact the Earth may have been subjected to a comet shower.

POPIGAI IMPACT SITE SEEN FROM SPACE

Filled with a lake and surrounded by temples and dense woodland, Lonar is undoubtedly one of the world's most spectacular meteorite impact sites. According to Hindu legend, the crater was created by Lord Vishnu when he destroyed the demon Lavanasur. The site was first recognized as a meteorite impact crater by the American geologist G.K. Gilbert, in 1896. The crater is about 170m (560ft) deep, with a rim that is 20m (65ft) high. Estimates

suggest the meteorite that struck here was about 60m (200ft) long. The Lonar Crater is remarkable in that the impact occurred in hard basalt, therefore the shape of the crater is exceptionally well preserved. The salty, alkaline chemistry of the lake means that it is inhabited by unique species of flora and fauna.

SALT LAKE
Surrounded by a rim produced by the meteorite's impact, Lonar's lake is one of the most saline on Earth, and is an almost perfect circle.

AUSTRALASIA *Australia*

Woodleigh

LOCATION South of Shark Bay and the town of Denham, Western Australia

DATE OF IMPACT 250–364 million years ago

TYPE Complex

DIAMETER 60km (37 miles)

Woodleigh was discovered by mining prospectors in the 1970s, but it wasn't until a 1997 survey revealed a tell-tale dome that a meteorite impact was suspected. Shocked quartz, which was drilled from the dome in 1999, confirmed the site's origins. An impact this large, from a meteorite about 3km (2 miles) wide, probably caused major devastation to the planet's living organisms.

COMPUTER IMAGE OF WOODLEIGH CRATER

AUSTRALASIA *Australia*

Gosses Bluff

LOCATION Near Hermannsburg, west of Alice Springs, Northern Territory, Australia

DATE OF IMPACT 142 million years ago

TYPE Complex

DIAMETER 22km (14 miles)

One of the best-preserved meteorite craters in the world, Gosses Bluff is an imposing sandstone ring in the northern Australian desert. The site is very important to the Western Arrernt Aboriginal people, featuring in some of their Dreamtime stories. The crater formed when an asteroid 1km (⅔ mile) wide smashed into the surface of the Earth. The meteorite is thought to have penetrated 5km (3 miles) into the ground and vaporized. The ground then recoiled to produce the crater's central dome. Over millions of years, some of the crater's original features have eroded

CENTRAL UPLIFT
The true shape of the Gosses Bluff Crater, with its ring of sandstone hills and its slightly raised central area, becomes clearly visible in this photograph from space.

and weathered, and the entire land surface of the region is about 2km (1¼ miles) lower than it was at the time of impact. However, in addition to the striking outer ring, there remains a 4.5km- (2¾-mile-) wide inner ring, which is overlain with breccias and the remnants of the central dome.

SANDSTONE CIRCLE
Rearing out of the desert like a castellated wall, the outer ring of the Gosses Bluff Crater is a striking reminder of the massive asteroid impact millions of years ago.

PLANET EARTH

Water

THE EARTH'S OUTER LAYERS are dominated by water. More than two-thirds of its surface is covered with liquid water; if frozen water, in the form of ice, is also included, this proportion rises to more than four-fifths. Water is essential to life because it is an excellent solvent and it can move or flow easily. Living organisms require not merely the presence of water, but a continuing supply for the maintenance of life. Humans are typical of most animals, being 62 per cent water; soft-bodied aquatic creatures such as jellyfish are more than 98 per cent water.

PLANET EARTH

SURFACE TENSION
The film that forms on water is strong enough to support the weight of insects such as the Common Back-swimmer. This predatory bug can hang down from the surface of ponds.

Properties of Water

Pure water has no colour, taste, or smell. Its freezing point, at which it turns into solid ice, is 0°C (32°F), and its boiling point, when it changes into water vapour, is 100°C (212°F). Water's density, or mass per volume, is 1kg per litre (1¼lb per pint). This is high for a liquid – that is, water is relatively heavy – and the figure is used as a standard for comparing densities of other substances. Each molecule, of water is made of two hydrogen atoms and one oxygen atom (written H_2O). A pinhead-sized drop of water contains about one billion billion molecules. These attract each other powerfully, especially at the surface of the water, where their mutual attraction forms a strong "skin", known as surface tension. As water is difficult to break by tension, it can "creep" into small holes and along narrow cracks. Its ability to change state easily, and to spread or flow even through rock, means that water is always on the move through global and local cycles (see p.75).

Salt Water

Salt water is found in seas and oceans, coastal lagoons, and inland lakes with little or no outlet, such as the Dead Sea (see p.199). In the latter, minerals are washed into drainage basins, where they accumulate at high concentrations because pure water evaporates relatively quickly. The main dissolved minerals in seawater are sodium (10.8 parts per thousand) and chloride (19.35ppt), with smaller amounts of other salts (see p.302). The freezing point of salt water is -1.9°C (28.6°F) at 35ppt. Overall salinity (or salt concentration) is highest in the tropics (above 35ppt), where evaporation occurs fastest, and lowest near the poles (below 30ppt), where there is slower evaporation and melting ice. Seawater is slightly less saline than the body fluids of most marine invertebrates, so water tends to enter their bodies by osmosis; to counteract the inflow, they have body structures such as gills and nephridia (tiny tubes) that are able to pump water out. Marine vertebrates, including most fish, face the opposite problem. Seawater is two to three times more concentrated than their body fluids, so they lose water through their gills and other surfaces. To counteract this, they drink seawater and rapidly filter out the salts, mainly through the kidneys and other specialized organs, to produce small volumes of highly concentrated urine.

SOCKEYE SALMON
Salmon hatch in fresh water, migrate to the sea to mature, then return to their home river to breed. Their physiology changes to enable them to cope with varying salinity.

HIGH-SALINITY SEA
In the landlocked Dead Sea (above) between Israel and Jordan, fluctuating water levels and rapid evaporation lead to the deposition of minerals in pillar-like shapes.

LOW-SALINITY PACK ICE
Pack ice is a typical feature of low-salinity seas, such as the Beaufort Sea off northern Canada (left). In winter, the seawater freezes easily to form a solid sheet, which breaks up in summer.

RJUKANDI WATERFALL
A mass of water flows over this Icelandic waterfall. As water moves in this way, it releases a large amount of erosive energy.

ACIDIC WATER
Bogs are isolated from alkaline groundwater and depend entirely on rainwater, which is relatively mineral poor. As a result, they are naturally acidic, a condition that favours the growth of sphagnum moss, but few other plant species.

Fresh Water

Of all the water on Earth, about 3 per cent is fresh – that is, it contains far lower concentrations of dissolved minerals than salt water. Almost four-fifths of this fresh water is locked up in polar regions as glacier ice; the other fifth lies under the surface, as groundwater in rocks. Only 0.3 per cent of fresh water is in liquid form at the surface, in rivers, lakes, and wetlands, yet this is the form most useful for land animals and many aquatic creatures and plants. Although it may look pure, natural fresh water usually holds measurable amounts of at least 25 dissolved minerals, such as silica, calcium, potassium, magnesium, and iron. The relative terms "hard" and "soft" are used to describe water with higher or lower levels of these minerals, respectively. Rainwater is naturally slightly acidic. It absorbs carbon dioxide gas from the air and from the soil, and becomes a weak form of carbonic acid. This is almost insignificant compared to acid rain formed by atmospheric pollution (see p.57), but it is enough to dissolve chemically rocks such as limestones, where cracks gradually widen to form potholes and caverns (see p.200). The temperature of fresh water varies hugely. Far underground, it may be warmed by hot rocks until it is superheated. It may then burst forth as a geyser.

MINERAL TERRACE
At Pamukkale in southwest Turkey, hard water reaches the surface as hot springs. Minerals in the water precipitate out, or become solid, forming terraces (below).

HOT WATER
The temperature of hot springs (above) may exceed boiling point. Yet life survives here, especially in the form of thermophilic, or heat-loving, micro-organisms such as blue-green algae.

Ice

At any one time, almost four-fifths of all fresh water is frozen solid as ice. Ice exists in numerous forms, including mountain glaciers, polar ice-sheets, icebergs, periglacial landforms (see p.306), and mountain-top coverings. The mass of floating ice in the Arctic Ocean is, on average, 5–7m (16–23ft) thick. The ice covering the landmass of Antarctica has accumulated over thousands of years to become more than 4.5km (2.8 miles) thick in places. Ice is slightly less dense than liquid water, so that icebergs and ice cubes float (although only one-eighth to one-tenth of their bulk is exposed above the surface). As water cools towards its freezing point, it becomes most dense at 4°C (39°F). Below this temperature, it starts to expand again. This property is helpful to aquatic life. In a pond or lake, the densest water at 4°C (39°F) sinks to the bottom, which enables animals to survive beneath the ice that forms at the colder surface.

ICEBERG
As an iceberg warms, chunks break off and it floats at different levels in the water, leaving a vertical series of grooves eroded by the waves.

MELTWATER
Rising temperatures in spring melt ice and snow on higher ground, producing a surge of water along rivers. The tips of glaciers also release meltwater.

Water in the Atmosphere

The proportion of water vapour in the atmosphere is known as absolute humidity. It varies with air temperature and pressure, from almost zero to four per cent by volume. Often a more useful measure is relative humidity. This compares the actual amount of water vapour in a given volume of air to the maximum amount which that air could hold. When relative humidity is 100 per cent, the air is completely saturated and cannot hold any more moisture. At this point, no further evaporation can take place. Water also exists in the atmosphere in both liquid and solid states. When water vapour condenses around particles of dust, it forms either tiny droplets or ice crystals, depending on the air temperature. Large masses of droplets or crystals become visible in the form of clouds (see pp.386–89). Another feature of water droplets and ice crystals is that they float easily in even the weakest air currents, and so are continually colliding and merging. If they grow sufficiently large, they fall as either rain or snow. Sometimes, powerful winds create updraughts that blow raindrops upwards into supercooled clouds, where they rapidly freeze, only to fall again as pellets of frozen rain (or hailstones).

SNOWSTORM
Windblown snow collects on the sides of the Grand Canyon, Arizona, USA, during a storm. In low atmospheric temperatures, for example, in winter in temperate regions or at high altitudes, clouds may be made of ice crystals and precipitation takes the form of snow.

ALTOCUMULUS
These mid-altitude clouds occur when a large air mass is forced to rise, leading to cooling and condensation over a wide area. They can be grey or white or both.

CIRRUS
The wispy strands of cirrus clouds are made of ice crystals blown into shape by the wind. They form when an air mass cools at high altitude and becomes saturated, forming ice instead of water droplets.

RAINSTORM OVER BOHOL SEA
Banks of moisture-laden clouds cause a squall off the southern Philippines. Clouds contain the same mixture of water vapour and droplets as steam,

The Global Water Cycle

Water represents only 0.2 per cent of Earth's weight, but the global water cycle, or hydrological cycle, is one of the world's most important systems. It is responsible for the continuous circulation of water around the planet. The Sun provides a massive input of energy to Earth in the form of solar radiation, especially infrared radiation or heat (see p.364). This warms liquid water, which evaporates into invisible water vapour and then dissipates into the atmosphere. About 22 per cent of the solar radiation that reaches Earth heats oceans, seas, lakes, and rivers, changing liquid water into water vapour. Only pure water evaporates; any dissolved minerals and other substances in it are left behind, mainly as salts in the sea. This process is, in effect, solar-powered distillation (purification) of water. Water vapour is also given off by plants during transpiration, and by animals in exhaled air and perspiration. As water vapour rises into higher, cooler regions of the atmosphere, it condenses to form clouds. Eventually, this returns to the land as precipitation. Here, it is warmed by the Sun – and so the global water cycle continues.

PRECIPITATION
Rain, hail, sleet, snow, frost, and dew form a vital part of the global water cycle. They return water in the atmosphere to the Earth's surface, and in the process release the latent energy stored in water vapour.

water returns to land as rain

loss of water from lakes by evaporation

clouds carry water inland

loss of water from plants by transpiration

water returns to land as snow

frozen water accumulates in glaciers

ice melts to form meltwater streams

water condenses and forms clouds

water seeps into ground and flows to sea

water carried downhill by rivers

BLUE-AND-WHITE PLANET
From space, the Earth appears mainly blue and white. These areas are the visible forms of water, in seas and oceans, and in clouds. Water is the chief weather-determining component of the atmosphere.

loss of water from sea by evaporation

water stored in seas and oceans

water returns to sea via rivers and streams

GLOBAL WATER MOVEMENT
Water is rarely still. It enters the atmosphere mainly through evaporation from the oceans and transpiration by plants. It circulates on air currents as water vapour, condenses to form clouds, and then falls as precipitation. Back on the land, water moves as rivers and glaciers, and it soaks into the soil and rocks; it is also stored in lakes, oceans, and the tissues of living things.

FRESHWATER SPRING
The Ozark Plateau, USA, has many springs, including Greer Springs, Missouri (above), which releases an average flow of a billion litres (222 million gallons) of water each day.

The Local Water Cycle

Many interconnected local water cycles together make up the global water cycle. On a local scale, water movement is determined by factors such as the amount and type of precipitation, the contours of the landscape, and the geology (the composition and layering of soil and rock). Water can percolate through porous or permeable rocks such as chalks, but not through impermeable types such as clay. So regions with porous soils and rocks tend to have less surface drainage, in the form of streams and rivers, because rain and other precipitation soaks straight down. Percolating water accumulates above poorly permeable layers, saturating rocks and creating groundwater deposits. A rock formation that conducts groundwater is known as an aquifer, which people can draw upon for water wells. The upper level of groundwater saturation is called the water table, and usually rises and falls with varying precipitation through the seasons. Where the surface of the land intersects an aquifer, water may escape from it as a spring. Alternatively, the water can percolate unseen below the surface, through to rivers, lakes, and wetlands.

PAVED LANDSCAPE

Today, vast areas of land are covered with waterproof layers, such as tarmac, paving, and concrete, which greatly alter local water cycles. Water can no longer easily percolate into porous soils and rocks to replenish groundwater supplies. Instead it flows into drains and channels and rushes away into larger watercourses. This can lower the water table, cause springs to dry up, and deplete local groundwater supplies needed for irrigation and human use. The sudden rush of surface water after a storm may also cause local flooding.

lake

marsh

stream

zone of aeration

water table (dry-season)

impermeable rock

water table (wet season)

temporarily saturated zone (saturated only in wet season)

permanently saturated zone (saturated in wet and dry seasons)

LOCAL WATER MOVEMENT
In a given area, water may exist at the surface, for example, in a stream, marsh, or lake. Other water is underground. In the zone of aeration, air fills the spaces between particles of soil and rock. Beneath this lie zones of temporary and permanent water saturation, which vary according to the rainfall. The water table is the level below which the ground is saturated.

WATER RESOURCES

Every year, about 40,000 cubic km (9,500 cubic miles) of water evaporates from the oceans and falls on land. This yearly flow is about ten times that of the River Amazon, and – in theory – it is enough to support at least five times the current number of people on Earth. Most of the world's fresh water, however, is difficult to reach, and the remainder is unevenly spread. As demand for water grows, the world's resources are coming under increasing strain.

Surface Water

Water supplies come from two major sources. Some is removed from rivers and lakes (surface water), and some from aquifers – natural reservoirs of water in porous rock (groundwater). A small amount is also produced by desalinization, but this is an expensive procedure that relatively few countries can afford. Surface water has the advantage of being accessible, and, because it is quickly replenished, it can be treated as a renewable resource. Unfortunately, it is also easily polluted – a growing problem in regions with high populations and poor hygiene.

Globally, domestic use accounts for less than a tenth of total water consumption, and industry uses about 25 per cent. The biggest consumer by far is agriculture, which takes about 60 per cent, much of it from rivers. Most of this water is for irrigation, and once it is has been used it often evaporates instead of draining back into natural waterways. In arid parts of the world, from the American West to China, irrigation has – at times – brought major rivers to a halt.

Cutting household consumption helps to conserve water, but cutting agricultural consumption can have an even greater impact. By drip-feeding plants with moisture, micro-irrigation can reduce water consumption by more than 250 per cent. However, this is financially feasible only for high-value cultivation – such as cereal farming – growing drought-resistant varieties can yield much greater savings.

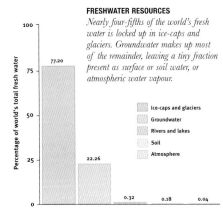

MAN-MADE OASIS
A golf course contrasts with desert scenery near Las Vegas, Nevada, USA. The fairways are irrigated from the Colorado River – an example of recreational water use.

FRESHWATER RESOURCES
Nearly four-fifths of the world's fresh water is locked up in ice-caps and glaciers. Groundwater makes up most of the remainder, leaving a tiny fraction present as surface or soil water, or atmospheric water vapour.

Percentage of world's total fresh water

- Ice-caps and glaciers
- Groundwater
- Rivers and lakes
- Soil
- Atmosphere

77.20
22.26
0.32
0.18
0.04

Groundwater

Some of the world's earliest civilizations depended on groundwater for their survival, and aquifers now underpin life in many dry parts of the world. Groundwater is harder to reach than surface water but is less prone to pollution, and it is often present in places where surface water is scarce. The drawback is that it replenishes itself very slowly. If too much water is used, the water-table sinks and wells run dry. The drop in the water-table can be precipitous: in southern India, falls of more than 25m (82ft) have been recorded in a single year.

In the American Great Plains, declining water-tables threaten some of the most productive farmland in the world. Here, farming relies on the Ogallala Aquifer, an immense reservoir of fossil melt water dating back to the last ice age. Large-scale use of this water began in the 1970s, but, without conservation, it may be depleted within the next 50 years. Australian farmers could face similar problems in the Great Artesian Basin – a huge aquifer where boreholes currently tap about 1.3 billion litres (290 million gallons) a day.

TESTING TIME
In Pakistan, a technician and a farmer check water from a newly sunk artesian well. In such wells, pressurized groundwater flows up to the surface.

Water Wars

When water is in short supply, the potential for conflict grows. Within national borders, this can lead to protracted legal disputes, but when it develops between countries it may even cause wars. More than 250 of the world's largest river basins straddle more than one country, and many experts believe that the threat of "water wars" is likely to increase as the human population grows. According to international law, water cannot be owned outright, but at present there is little to prevent upstream nations from exploiting supplies in ways that harm their neighbours. Likely flash-points for water conflict include the Middle East, southern Africa, and Central Asia – all regions where low rainfall brings about water stress.

In 2003 – the International Year of Fresh Water – a UN report predicted that the average supply of water per person would fall by over a third in 20 years, and that 7 billion people could face a shortage of water by 2050 unless urgent action is taken now. With static water resources, conservation will become increasingly important, but an even bigger challenge will be to make sure that existing supplies are shared fairly.

NATURAL CYCLE
In many parts of India, the monsoon climate means that most of the year's rain falls in a four-month period, after which reservoirs dry out all too quickly.

LAND

MOUNT ST. HELENS, CASCADE RANGE
In May 1980, a violent eruption tore apart the snow-capped peak of Mount St. Helens in Washington State. Such events are a reminder of the hugely powerful, and often devastating, internal workings of the Earth.

MOUNTAINS AND VOLCANOES

THE EARTH'S ROCKY ELEVATIONS, mountains and volcanoes, have an enduring fascination. Mountain belts form imposing barriers and are liable to violent extremes of weather. They are also associated with catastrophic events such as landslides and avalanches. Until recently, some people saw mountains and volcanoes as the homes of wrathful gods, who vent their anger without warning, shaking the ground, and spewing fire, rocks, and ash into the air. But mountains and volcanoes are just the most visible sign of the tectonic forces shaping the Earth – elsewhere fault systems and earthquake zones follow the outlines of the tectonic plates themselves, and igneous intrusions mark areas where molten material has penetrated existing rock. Since scientific investigation of these phenomena began in the 18th century, they have lost many of their superstitious associations, but our fascination with them continues, and they remain impressive reminders of the often spectacular power of Earth's continuing evolution.

Fault Systems

OVER GEOLOGICAL TIME, the relentless movement of the Earth's tectonic plates puts the brittle rock of the crust under so much strain that it buckles, fractures, and is pushed deep down into the mantle. When rock fractures, huge blocks slip past one another. These cracks in the Earth's surface are called faults, and often extend through the crust for many kilometres. Many faults are the result of past movement and are currently inactive. However, many fault systems are still active, and massive amounts of energy can be released in a few seconds as rocks move past each other in an earthquake.

Faults and Joints

Faults are cracks in rocks across which there has been displacement. They range from tiny fissures to sets of interconnecting faults that are many kilometres long. Some active faults move in a slow, continuous manner called creep. More often, they judder in a series of spasmodic jumps, which can release energy in the form of an earthquake (see opposite page). Over millions of years, the cumulative effect of countless small movements along the fault can displace rocks across a fault a substantial distance up, down, or horizontally. Not all rock fractures are faults: joints are cracks along which there is no evidence of movement. These are usually caused by tectonic activity, but may also be the result of erosion (see pp.92–93), which strips away the overlying layer of rock, releasing pressure and allowing the surface of rocks to expand and crack. They can also be formed as igneous rock cools. Joints are exploited by the processes of weathering (see pp.90–91), which may exaggerate the shape of the original fracture. They usually occur close to the surface.

LIMESTONE JOINTS
Sedimentary rocks, such as this limestone in England, have particularly marked joints. When the limestone is exposed at the surface, its strong pattern of criss-cross joints is further etched by acidic rainfall. Such striking formations are called limestone pavements.

CHARLES RICHTER

In 1935, the American seismologist Charles Richter (1900–85) devised the scale for measuring earthquakes that bears his name. Before this, seismologists had been able to compare earthquakes only by using the Mercalli scale, a rule-of-thumb guide to the severity of their effects. The Richter Scale, devised with Beno Gutenberg (1880–1960), measured the magnitude of each earthquake precisely, from the variations in movement it produced on a seismograph (see below). Richter also mapped out the zones in North America that were vulnerable to earthquakes, but he was scathing about the idea of predicting them.

FAULT PLANE
The huge uplift of rock on one side of a fault over a period of thousands of years has created this dramatic precipice in Greece. Scratch marks called slickensides can be seen on the face of the cliff.

MEASURING EARTHQUAKES

Earthquakes are recorded on a seismograph, which charts the magnitude of each vibration. They were traditionally measured on the Richter Scale. Each step in the scale, which begins at 0 and has no upper limit, represents a 30-fold increase in the energy released by an earthquake. The greatest magnitude recorded, 9.5, was from the 1960 Chilean earthquake. Many scientists now use the moment-magnitude scale, which combines seismograph readings with measurements of rock movement.

THINGVELLIR RIFT, ICELAND
This exposure of fault lines parallel to the Thingvellir Rift provides dramatic evidence of tectonic activity. The rift lies on the boundary separating the American and Eurasian plates.

STRIKE-SLIP FAULT, NEVADA, USA
The displacement of the two sides of this right-lateral strike-slip fault can be seen in the white areas on either side of the crack, which were once continuous vertical layers.

FAULT MOVEMENT
Faults are classified by their direction of movement, which reflect surrounding tectonic stresses and whether they shorten or lengthen the original surfaces.

Types of Fault

Faults are created by the compression or extension of the Earth's crust as its tectonic plates move (see pp.54–55). The slope or angle of a fault to the horizontal is called the dip. Faults that show vertical movement are called dip-slip faults, and may be either normal or reverse. Normal faults occur where tension in the Earth's crust pulls the rock apart, and allows a block to slip down the fault plane, which is the surface along which the crack occurs. Parallel sets of normal faults form rift valleys (see p.98), and are associated with divergent plate boundaries. Reverse faults, known as thrust faults if they are at a shallow angle, occur where compression in the crust pushes one block of rock up over another. If two blocks slide past each other horizontally, the fracture is classified as a strike-slip fault, an example of which is the San Andreas Fault (see pp.84–85). If the opposite block in a strike-slip fault moves left, it is left-lateral; if it moves right, it is right-lateral. If a strike-slip fault is combined with compression or tension, the blocks can slide diagonally, creating an oblique-slip fault.

FAULT LINE, UZBEKISTAN
The dramatic effects of fault displacement on the landscape are visible in this escarpment on the outskirts of Tashkent in Uzbekistan, which is the result of ancient earthquakes.

NORMAL DIP-SLIP FAULT
movement along fault plane | fault plane | surface lengthened by faulting | down-faulted block

REVERSE THRUST DIP-SLIP FAULT
upthrust, overhanging block | surface shortened by faulting

STRIKE-SLIP (LEFT-LATERAL)
opposite block (viewed from either side of the fault) moves left | extension of crust

OBLIQUE-SLIP FAULT
vertical movement combines with horizontal movement to create diagonal movement | horizontal movement

Earthquakes

A sudden slip on a fault releases energy in the form of an earthquake, which radiates outwards as seismic waves (see p.36). The Earth's major earthquake zones coincide with faults between tectonic plates. The immense forces generated as these plates grind together trigger most large earthquakes. This happens as the rocks on either side of a fault lock, and stress builds up. The fault eventually ruptures, sending shockwaves shuddering through the planet. The Pacific Ocean's subduction zones are the source of 80 per cent of the world's earthquakes. Almost every day, several hundred minor earthquakes occur around the world. Massive disturbances, such as the 9.1 magnitude Indonesian earthquake of 2004, which triggered tsunamis across the Indian Ocean and killed over 230,000 people, are rare. However, there have been 11 earthquakes of 8.6 and higher magnitude since 1950.

EARTH MOVEMENT
This radar image shows the ground displacement from an earthquake. The closely packed contours near the black line of the fault indicate the greatest movement.

FAULT SYSTEM PROFILES

The pages that follow contain profiles of a selection of the world's most significant fault systems. Each profile begins with the following summary information:

TYPE Normal dip-slip, reverse dip-slip, reverse thrust dip-slip, strike-slip (left-lateral), strike-slip (right-lateral), or oblique slip

LENGTH/AREA Extent of fault line or complex

ACTIVITY Active or inactive

LAND

San Andreas Fault

LOCATION Extending from Cape Mendocino, northern California, to the Gulf of California, western USA

TYPE Strike–slip (right-lateral)

LENGTH 1,200km (800 miles)

ACTIVITY Active

Slicing across California's coastal region, the San Andreas Fault is one of the Earth's most famous faults. It is a strike-slip fault in which the rocks move sideways in opposite directions, although, because it forms a plate boundary, the San Andreas is also a transform fault (see p.54).

To the west of the fault is the Pacific Plate, which extends from the edge of California almost as far as the eastern edge of Asia. To the east is the North American Plate, which forms the bulk of the continent. As the Pacific Plate rotates, coastal California is sliding slowly northwest past the rest of

North America. Over the past 20 million years the Pacific Plate has moved about 560km (350 miles), relative to North America, averaging about 1cm (1/20in) a year. Plate movement seems to be accelerating, and over the past century the fault has shifted almost 5cm (2in) each year. The San Andreas Fault is not one long crack in the Earth's crust, but consists of four major segments and several minor sections. Along some segments of the fault, the strain of the plate movement is released as minor tremors. In major sections, the plates

SLIPPING SIDEWAYS
Images from space reveal the gash across the land created by the San Andreas fault as the Pacific and North American plates move in opposite directions.

BAILEY WILLIS

One of the leading figures in American geology in the early 20th century, Bailey Willis (1857–1949) was a pioneer in the study of California's San Andreas Fault. Willis studied how San Francisco's Golden Gate Bridge might be affected by earthquakes and led the battle for more stringent safety standards for the city's structures.

THE LAST BIG ONE

At 5.12 a.m. on 18 April 1906, the Pacific Plate lurched approximately 6m (20ft) northward along a 430km-(267 mile)- long stretch of the northern San Andreas Fault. In just a few seconds, centuries of pent-up energy were released as a massive earthquake that devastated San Francisco. Although the earthquake destroyed many buildings, the worst damage resulted from the fires that raged through the city in the aftermath.

VISIBLE FAULT LINE
The San Andreas Fault scars the Californian landscape. In addition to the very obvious fault line itself, it is often possible to see hills, valleys, and streams truncated and offset on opposite sides of the fault.

LAND

lock together for many years, allowing stresses to build up that are eventually unleashed as massive earthquakes. These disturbances typically occur in one section of the fault at a time. In 1857, a sudden movement along the segment of the fault in the Transverse Ranges, which separate Central and Southern California, resulted in a severe earthquake that opened a crack 350km (218 miles) long. In 1906, movement in the northern section of the fault caused an earthquake that is estimated to have measured 8.3 on the Richter Scale, and which devastated San Francisco (see panel, left). An earthquake, with its epicentre at Loma Prieta, rocked San Francisco again in 1989. It is feared that pressure is building up in the southern section of the fault, and when it finally unlocks it will unleash an earthquake known as the Big One. This earthquake is now expected to happen before the year 2032. Most of California's population lives close to the San Andreas Fault, and some communities are built right over it.

EARTHQUAKE WATCH

In 1985, the US Geological Survey predicted that an earthquake would strike the small Californian community of Parkfield in 1993. The village was fitted with equipment to monitor the potential disturbance, although it did not happen. However, Parkfield remains the most closely observed earthquake zone in the world, as scientists probe the ground to measure factors such as strain in the rocks, heat flow, and geomagnetism.

FLOODED FAULT
Water exploits the cracks in the landscape created by faults. Rivers flow along them and lakes form in them. In the case of Tomales Bay, the sea has flooded an inlet created by the San Andreas Fault.

Basin and Range

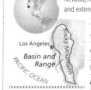

LOCATION Crossing California, Utah, Nevada, Arizona, Oregon, and Texas, and extending deep into Mexico

Los Angeles
Basin and Range
Rocky Mountains
PACIFIC OCEAN

TYPE Complex pattern of normal dip-slip faults

AREA 2.4 million square km (930,000 square miles)

ACTIVITY Active

The Basin and Range country of the southwest USA and northern Mexico has one of the most distinctive landscapes in the world. More than 100 long, roughly parallel mountain ranges run from north to south through the region, each separated from the next by a wide, flat, dry desert basin. On each side, the mountain ranges are bounded by faults that slope into the valleys. This extraordinary landscape is the result of extensive stretching of the North American Plate, which began about 20 million years ago. The crust was pulled, cracked, and thinned, and it is now almost twice its original width. As this happened the crust fractured, and fault after fault opened up. Basins were created as the land dropped down between parallel faults. As the basin blocks slid down, the mountains

DEATH VALLEY, CALIFORNIA
The lowest point in the Basin and Range – and the US – is Death Valley, at 282 ft (86 m) below sea level. Surrounded by sharp mountain peaks, the basin contains several extremely active faults.

were pushed up, reaching heights of 3,500m (11,500ft) in places. Although there are a variety of fault types in the region, the majority of the faults are normal dip-slip faults, created as the Earth's crust was wrenched apart. The faults are all steep, typically descending into the crust at an angle of 60° but flattening at depth. As the mountain ranges rose, they were immediately affected by weathering and erosion (see pp.56–59). Water, wind, and ice have worn down the peaks and deposited debris in the intervening valleys. Sometimes, so much debris has collected in the basins that the solid bedrock is buried thousands of metres below the surface.

SNOW-CAPPED SIERRA NEVADA
The uplifted blocks forming California's Sierra Nevada tower up to 3,300m (11,000ft) above Owens Valley to the east.

LINEAR VALLEYS
In the Great Basin of southern Nevada, the pattern of alternating parallel mountain ridges and deep basins is clearly visible.

EUROPE north
Midland Valley

LOCATION Running from east to west between the Southern Uplands and Scottish Highlands, Scotland

TYPE Strike-slip (right-lateral)

LENGTH 90km (56 miles)

ACTIVITY Inactive

The Midland Valley is bounded on either side by two very ancient strike-slip faults that divide Scotland in two. On the southern side of the valley lies the Southern Upland Fault, while to the north is the Highland Boundary Fault. The origin of these faults dates back more than 540 million years to a time when northern Scotland was part of the ancient continent of Laurentia and was separated from the rest of the British Isles, which were situated on the ancient continent of Avalonia. During the course of the next 200 million years, Laurentia moved gradually towards Avalonia, carrying northern Scotland towards the rest of Britain. As the continents converged, the enormous pressure formed the Scottish mountains in an event called the Caledonian Orogeny (see p.98). About 400 million years ago, Laurentia began to swing away to the southeast, ripping Scotland apart again, and creating not only the two great faults on either side of Midland Valley but also another fault north of the Highlands, Glen Mor (also known as Great Glen), which forms the long basin filled by Loch Ness.

LOCH LOMOND
Seen from Duncryne Hill on its southern shore, Loch Lomond is the largest of Scotland's lochs, and is crossed by the Highland Boundary Fault.

HIGHLAND BOUNDARY
The Scottish Highlands rise along the northwestern margin of the Midland Valley, where the Highland Boundary Fault creates a dramatic shift in the region's geology.

COAL MINING

About 320 million years ago, Scotland sat on the Equator, and had a tropical climate. Swampy forests flourished on the ancient land where the Midland Valley now lies. Over hundreds of millions of years, the remains of the plants from these forests have compressed to form Scotland's richest coal deposits, which have been exploited for over 900 years.

EUROPE north
Moine Thrust

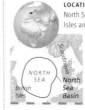

LOCATION Extending northwest from the south of the Isle of Skye to the Moine Peninsula, Scotland

TYPE Reverse thrust dip-slip

LENGTH 180km (112 miles)

ACTIVITY Inactive

NORTHWEST HIGHLAND MOUNTAIN
At 1,062m (3,484ft) high, An Teallach is one of Scotland's many spectacular mountains. It is the site of intense geological study, because layers of the Moine Thrust belt are well-exposed here.

Thrust faults are shallow reverse faults that are created as Earth's upper crust is squeezed, forcing one block up to overhang another. The Moine Thrust is not a single thrust fault, but a formation called a thrust belt. These are created when plate movement forces layers of crust up and over each other, and then pulls them back, a motion that happens again and again. The discovery of the Moine Thrust in 1907 was a milestone in the history of geology, as it was the first thrust belt to be identified. It formed between 410 and 430 million years ago, as Scotland was compressed by tectonic movement. Thrust belts are now recognized as features at the edges of mountain ranges all around the world.

EUROPE north
North Sea Basin

LOCATION Lying beneath the North Sea between the British Isles and Scandinavia

TYPE Normal dip-slip

LENGTH 250km (155 miles)

ACTIVITY Inactive

As geologists prospected the rocks beneath the North Sea for oil in the 1960s, they discovered not only a rift valley but a whole series of faults. Rift valleys form when two normal faults pull in opposite directions, so that as the Earth's crust stretches apart, a block drops down between them (see p.98). The rift valley under the North Sea dates from the Jurassic Period, about 200 million years ago, when the supercontinent of Pangea began to break up, opening up the Atlantic Ocean and the North Sea. It overlies a complex series of much older faults dating from about 50 million years earlier. By studying these structures using seismic surveys that probe into the solid bedrock, geologists are discovering more about how continents diverge, and also the way that rich oil deposits accumulate in down-thrown fault features such as those in the North Sea Basin.

DRILLING FOR OIL
The rich oil fields beneath the North Sea are the largest natural oil and gas deposits in Europe.

EUROPE *eastern*

North Anatolian Fault

LOCATION Extending across northern Turkey and beneath the Sea of Marmara

TYPE Strike-slip (right-lateral)

LENGTH 1,000km (600 miles)

ACTIVITY Active

The North Anatolian Fault is one of the most energetic earthquake zones in the world. Turkey is set on a minor tectonic plate that is being squeezed westwards as the Arabian and Eurasian plates move together. The geological setting is similar to America's San Andreas Fault, with the Anatolian Plate grinding past the Eurasian Plate at 1–20 cm (½–8 in) each year and triggering earthquakes as it moves. Since the 1939 Erzincan earthquake, which killed 33,000 people, there have been seven earthquakes measuring over 7.0 on the Richter Scale and located progressively westwards. Seismologists studying this pattern believe that earthquakes occur in "storms" over a number of decades, and that one earthquake triggers the next. By analysing the stresses caused along the fault by each earthquake, they were able to forecast a disturbance that struck the town of Izmit with such devastating effect in August 1999. It is thought that the chain is not complete and that an earthquake will strike even further west along the fault – perhaps in the heavily populated city of Istanbul.

SEEN FROM SPACE
The great scar across the Turkish landscape made by the North Anatolian Fault is clearly visible when viewed from space.

IZMIT EARTHQUAKE DEVASTATION
In 1999, an earthquake measuring 7.0 on the Richter Scale struck on the North Anatolian Fault. It killed 17,000 people, injured 50,000, and left 500,000 homeless.

EUROPE *central*

Rhine Rift

LOCATION Extending through the middle of northwest Europe, from the Swiss Alps to the North Sea

TYPE Reverse thrust dip-slip

LENGTH 1,320km (820 miles)

ACTIVITY Active

The Rhine Rift is a striking reminder of the tectonic forces that formed the European continent. Rift valleys are usually created when continents diverge, causing land to drop down within the gap as the crust is pulled apart. However, the Rhine Rift is thought to have formed as the two halves of what is now northwestern Europe knitted together between 40 and 50 million years ago. As this happened, a long strip of rock called a graben (from the German word for "ditch") dropped between the two continental massifs: the Vosges in France and the German Black Forest. It was initially assumed that the Rhine Rift was inactive. However, scientists have recently detected signs of movement beneath the surface. Faults within stable continental interiors rarely rupture, but if they do, the subsequent earthquake can be sudden and extremely violent. Northwest Europe's worst earthquake occurred in 1356 in the Upper Rhine Valley, destroying the Swiss city of Basle, and knocking down buildings as far as 200km (125 miles) away. Some geologists believe the cause of the earthquake was not the Rhine Rift, but a fault in the Alps. However, Basle may yet fall victim to an earthquake unleashed by the Rhine Rift,

as an active fault has been found southwest of the city. In 1992 an earthquake along the Peel Fault, which is further down the Rhine, rocked the town of Roermond in the Netherlands.

FAULTED FOREST
Germany's Black Forest lies on a horst block, which is a section of rock that has been left upstanding after the land on either side of it faulted and dropped downwards.

KAISERSTUHL, GERMANY
To the north of Basle is Kaiserstuhl, which is an ancient complex of volcanoes. These were created along the plate margin that also caused the Rhine Rift to form.

AFRICA *east*
Great Rift Valley

LOCATION Extending from the southern Red Sea through East Africa to Beira in Mozambique

TYPE Normal dip-slip

LENGTH 6,400km (4,000 miles)

ACTIVITY Active

One of the longest fault systems in the world, the Great Rift Valley is part of a huge set of fissures in the Earth's crust called the East African Rift System, which threatens to split Africa in two. The Great Rift Valley is the primary branch of the system, which extends from Jordan in the north, through the Dead Sea and the Red Sea (see p.336), and along the length of East Africa to the mouth of the Zambezi River (see p.179). The average width of the valley is 50km (30 miles), although at its widest point in the Danakil Desert it is nearly 480km (300 miles) across. Its

steep walls rise 900m (2,955ft) above the valley floor, but in some places, such as Mau Escarpment, Kenya, the cliffs soar to 2,700m (8,860ft). The valley splits into two branches in Kenya and Tanzania. The western arm extends from the north shore of Lake Nyasa (see p.195) along the western borders of Tanzania, forming an arc that is dominated by Lake Tanganyika (see p.196). The eastern branch includes lakes Manyara (see p.195) and Natron. Most of the lakes in the Rift Valley are extremely deep, with Tanganyika descending to 1,471m (4,800ft). The East African Rift System lies along the boundaries of three tectonic plates, the Arabian, the African–Nubian, and the African–Somalian. It started to form when the plates began to diverge about 100 million years ago. As

RIFT VALLEY WILDLIFE
The Great Rift Valley is home to a huge array of endemic species of African wildlife, among which are leopards.

the Earth's crust stretched, volcanoes erupted; they dot the length of the rift today. About 20 million years ago a series of huge faults opened, and the land dropped between the three plates to form the Great Rift Valley. The plates meet at a triple junction under the Afar Triangle in Ethiopia, where the Red Sea merges with the Gulf of Aden. This may be the beginning of the next major ocean, as hot mantle material doming under the junction splits the plates apart. It is thought that the plates will eventually separate, and that the Horn of Africa will break off from the rest of the continent to form an island. Recent activity includes a magnitude 7.0 earthquake on 22 February 2006, in Mozambique, at the southern end of the rift.

VOLCANIC LANDSCAPE
Where the Great Rift Valley meets the Red Sea, at the Ardoukoba Volcanic Field in Djibouti, the terrain is dominated by volcanoes. A fault-bounded rift extends seaward in the centre of the picture.

RED SEA CORAL REEFS
The Red Sea was formed by the divergence of the African and Arabian plates. Stunning coral reefs have formed in the sea's warm shallows.

STEEP VALLEY CLIFFS
At Losiolo Maralal, Kenya, the valley floor has dropped away to leave sheer escarpments above the Suguta Valley, one of the hottest places on the Earth.

EARLY HUMANS

In 1974, American paleontologist Don Johanson found some of the most important hominid remains ever discovered, an almost complete skeleton of a 3-million-year-old *Australopithecus afarensis*. The skeleton, nicknamed Lucy, is that of a woman drowned. It was preserved in volcanic mud, where minerals from the surrounding liquid slowly replaced the calcium in the bones. The land turned to desert, and the ground was then washed away by rain to reveal the skeleton millions of years later.

THE LEAKEY FAMILY

No name is more closely linked to the wealth of early hominid discoveries in the Great Rift Valley than that of Leakey. Louis Leakey (1903–72) and his wife Mary (1913–96) discovered the first skull of an *Australopithecus* in Olduvai Gorge, Tanzania, in 1959. They also discovered that the remains of the earliest humans *Homo habilis* and *Homo erectus*. Later, Mary Leakey found 3.5-million-year-old footprints in Tanzania proving that these human ancestors walked upright. The couple's son, Richard, has also made significant discoveries in the same field.

GREAT RIFT VALLEY AT THE RED SEA
This image shows the northern edge of the Great Rift Valley and its extension between the African and Arabian plates. The resulting rifts have been filled by the Gulf of Suez (left) and the Gulf of Aqaba (right).

FALLING DOWN
New Zealand's 2011 Christchurch earthquake had a magnitude of 6.3. It caused extensive damage to the city's centre and toppled two bell towers on the Christchurch Catholic cathedral.

LIVING WITH EARTHQUAKES

Earthquakes are the most dangerous of all natural hazards. Unlike storms and volcanic eruptions, they strike within seconds, giving no opportunity for escape. Quite apart from the toll in lives, they cause damage that can take years to repair. Earthquakes cannot be prevented, but current research aims to make life safer in earthquake zones. The chief goal – which still remains elusive – is a reliable way of forecasting exactly when and where future earthquakes will strike.

Predicting Earthquakes

Forecasting earthquakes is notoriously difficult, because they are so complex. Hundreds of variables are involved, and no two fault systems are exactly the same. However, two kinds of data are particularly revealing: the past record of earthquakes in a given area, and the present build-up of stress within a fault system's rocks.

The past record gives average frequencies for earthquakes, which can be used as a guide to future earthquakes. For example, if there has previously been a major earthquake every 100 years, there is a 10 per cent probability of one in any given decade, if earthquakes are randomly spaced. But research into fault-system stress suggests that earthquakes are not random. Far from relieving stress, one earthquake can actually increase the likelihood of another one elsewhere. In 1999, this discovery was successfully used to predict a major aftershock in Turkey, three months after the devastating earthquake at Izmit, which claimed 25,000 lives (see p.87).

SHOCK ABSORBER
The Taipei 101 in Taiwan has a "mass damper" – a swinging, 666-tonne pendulum hanging inside it from the 92nd floor – that absorbs vibrations.

LARGEST EARTHQUAKES

The ten most powerful earthquakes of the last 100 years are here ranked by moment magnitude – a measurement that reflects seismic energy more accurately than the Richter scale.

Location	Date	Magnitude
Chile	22 May 1960	9.5
Prince William Sound, Alaska	28 March 1964	9.2
Off coast of North Sumatra	26 December 2004	9.1
Andreanof Islands, Aleutian Islands	9 March 1957	9.1
Off east coast of Honshu, Japan	11 March 2011	9.0
Kamchatka	4 November 1952	9.0
Offshore Maule, Chile	27 February 2010	8.8
Coastal Ecuador	31 January 1906	8.8
Rat Islands, Aleutian Islands	4 February 1965	8.7
North Sumatra, Indonesia	28 March 2005	8.6

Earthquake Proofing

The Izmit earthquake vividly illustrated a well-established fact: it is not earthquakes that kill, but buildings. Earthquakes have a relatively minor impact in the open – many people even fail to notice them – but when they shake rigid structures, the results can be catastrophic. In Izmit (see right), where the initial shake had a magnitude of 7.4, many new apartment blocks collapsed completely, while older ones nearby were either unaffected or toppled over while remaining intact. Subsequent

SELECTIVE DESTRUCTION
The Izmit 1999 earthquake in Turkey destroyed many new apartments, and reinforced the need for better-designed buildings in earthquake-prone areas.

investigations showed that many of the failures were due to inadequate design or poor building materials.

In California and Japan – two of the world's most populous earthquake zones – strict building codes have saved many lives. Here, high-rise buildings are designed to be slightly elastic, so that the energy from a shock is dissipated harmlessly, instead of fracturing supporting columns and floors. Foundations are fitted with mechanical dampers – structures that function in much the same way as shock-absorbers in cars. Using this kind of technology, skyscrapers such as San Francisco's Transamerica Building have emerged from major shocks unscathed.

Almost as important is the prevention of fire. After San Francisco's 1906 earthquake, fire swept through its central business district (see p.84); similarly, in 1923, thousands of houses were burned in Tokyo, causing almost as much loss of life as the earthquake itself. Although the use of non-flammable building materials greatly reduces this danger, risks still remain. In 1995, more than 5,000 people died when an earthquake hit Kobe (see p.92) – a city widely believed to be one of the most earthquake-proof in the world.

Tsunamis

When earthquakes occur beneath the sea, the sudden slippage of the sea bed can produce tsunamis, or tidal waves. These radiate outwards from the earthquake site, travelling across oceans at speeds of up to 800kph (500mph). In the open ocean, tsunamis are rarely more than 1m (3ft) high, but as they approach coasts their amplitude increases, creating a wall of water that can tower 20m (65ft) above the normal high-tide level.

Like earthquakes, tsunamis cannot be prevented, but monitoring systems can warn when a tsunami is on its way. In the Pacific Basin – by far the world's most tsunami-prone region – an ocean-wide warning system was established in 1948. Based in Hawaii, the system receives information about earthquakes around the Pacific Rim and issues alerts when tsunamis are detected. After the disastrous tsunami on 26 December 2004, a similar system was set up in the Indian Ocean.

ASIA *east*
Nojima Fault

LOCATION Extending the length of Awaji-shima island, Osaka Bay, ending beneath Kobe, Japan

TYPE Strike-slip (right-lateral)

LENGTH 60km (37 miles)

ACTIVITY Active

Early on the morning of 17 January 1995, Kobe, Japan's sixth-largest city, was hit by the worst earthquake to strike the country since the 1923 Tokyo disaster. The earthquake lasted for barely 20 seconds, but it was so powerful, reaching 6.9 on the Richter Scale, and so close to the city, that its effects were devastating. Some 5,500 people were killed, 37,000 were injured, and 300,000 people were left homeless. Scientists began an urgent search for the origins of the earthquake, as the disaster had occurred in a region of the country that was not prone to serious seismic disturbances. The major fault in the region is the Median Tectonic Line (MTL), which extends beneath the sea off the eastern coast of Japan. The Nojima Fault, which is part of the Arima

KOBE EARTHQUAKE

The Kobe earthquake was traced to the Nojima Fault on Awaji-shima island, which is one of a series of faults. Southern Japan sits on the eastern edge of the Eurasian Plate, where the Philippine Plate is being subducted along the Nankai Trough. However, the Eurasian Plate is moving in a different direction. The plate boundary is marked by strike-slip faults that trigger seismic disturbances.

Takatsuki Line, which in turn is a branch of the MTL, was found to be the cause of the Kobe disturbance. The earthquake began 22km (14 miles) beneath the surface of the Earth, and within 20km (12 miles) of the city itself, which is why its effects were so catastrophic. During the earthquake, the ground on the south side of the Nojima Fault moved 1.5m (5ft) to the right, and slipped 1.2m (4ft) downwards.

CRACKED EARTH
The movement along the Nojima Fault during the Kobe earthquake was marked at the surface by a visible rupture and cracks that scarred the surrounding landscape.

REBUILDING

The Kobe earthquake destroyed 100,000 buildings and damaged an equal number. The repair cost for the infrastructure alone was estimated at US$150 billion. Yet rebuilding work began immediately, and within a year all railways and almost all roads had opened again. The people who suffered the most were the poor, who could not afford to rebuild their wooden houses, which were destroyed by the earthquake.

ASIA *east*
Southeast Korea

LOCATION On the southeast edge of the Korean Peninsula, between the Sea of Japan and the Yellow Sea

TYPE Strike-slip (left-lateral)

LENGTH 200km (124 miles)

ACTIVITY Active

Until recently, Korea was not believed to be a major earthquake zone. However, over 30 active faults have now been mapped in the southeast of the peninsula and beneath the surface of the surrounding ocean. Unlike neighbouring Japan, Korea is not located next to any plate boundaries, situated instead within the relatively stable interior of the Eurasian Plate. Nevertheless, there has been at least one minor earthquake here every year for the past 2,000 years. The possibility that Korea may unexpectedly be hit

KOREAN FAULT ZONE
The active fault zone that has recently been discovered in South Korea begins in the heavily populated southeast corner of the peninsula and extends northwest from its edge.

by a major earthquake like the one that devastated Kobe (see Nojima Fault, left) has focused attention on the peninsula's fault network – particularly as many nuclear and industrial facilities are situated in the region. The major fault is the Yangsan, which runs 200km (125 miles) inland in a northeasterly direction from the peninsula's tip. The Yangsan Fault is a strike-slip fault that is moving by up to 1mm (1/50in) every year. Most of the Korean faults were originally opened up by the way the Pacific Plate interacts with the Eurasian Plate and the Okhotsk Plate. The resulting Korean faults were all originally right-lateral strike-slip faults. Yet the way the Pacific Plate is now being subducted under the Okhotsk and Eurasian plates has reversed the movement of the faults, and they are now left-lateral faults.

AUSTRALASIA *New Zealand*
Great Alpine Fault

LOCATION Extending along the west of South Island from Fiordland to Blenheim, New Zealand

TYPE Strike-slip (right-lateral)

LENGTH 500km (310 miles)

ACTIVITY Active

The Great Alpine Fault of New Zealand's South Island is one of the Earth's most remarkable faults; its curving trace is easily visible from space and readily visible on the ground. Over the last 12 million years, the mountains of South Island's Southern Alps have been uplifted about 20km (12.4 miles) along the eastern side of the fault. However, rapid erosion of the mountains, especially by glaciers, has kept their highest point below 4km (2.4 miles). New Zealand is one of the most

FRACTURED EARTH
The activity of the Great Alpine Fault is clearly revealed in this field on South Island, where a large crack has opened across the Earth's surface.

seismically active regions of the world with over 15,000 earthquakes a year, but only a 100 or so are large enough to be felt. However, there have been four major earthquakes of magnitude 8 or more and 15 of magnitude 7.5 or more since 1900. New Zealand straddles the Australian and Pacific plates. At the southern end of South Island, the Australian Plate is subducted (pushed down) below the Pacific Plate. At the other end of the fault system, in North Island, the opposite occurs – the Pacific Plate is subducted over 300km (186.4 miles) below the Australian Plate. This generates deep earthquakes, and the magma that surfaces forms North Island's active volcanic zone. In the middle of the fault system, the two plates shake past one another, with the Pacific Plate rotating anticlockwise and moving south at a rate of 35–45mm (1¼–1¾ in) a year relative to the Australian Plate. This forms South Island's Alpine fault, which is

consequently known as a right-lateral fault. The origins of the fault, and so too those of the Southern Alps, date back about 26 million years to a time geologists call the Kaikoura Orogeny. At this time, New Zealand was barely above sea-level and there were no mountains, but as the Pacific and Australian plates twisted and thrust together, the Southern Alps were forced up and the Great Alpine Fault opened.

HAROLD WELLMAN

Harold Wellman (1908–99) was an English geologist who discovered the Great Alpine Fault. During World War II, the New Zealand Geological Survey sent him to South Island to look for the mineral mica. While there, he discovered a line across the ground where rocks changed from granite to schist. Wellman realized the rocks had been displaced over 500km (310 miles) sideways along this line. He had found one of the Earth's major faults.

MOUNTAIN FAULT
The straight line of the Great Alpine Fault strikes across the landscape of New Zealand's South Island. The line of the fault becomes visible as it emerges in the Southern Alps.

THE DYNAMIC EARTH
In 2011, Japan's largest earthquake since records began in 1900 originated 30km (18 miles) underground. The earthquake's surface expression included this fissure, as well as devastating tsunamis (see pp.308–09).

Mountains

MOUNTAINS ARE ROCK MASSES that have been elevated high above their surroundings, mostly by the Earth's plate-tectonic processes. The origin of a mountain belt can generally be traced to one of the Earth's plate boundaries, past or present. Most mountains can be classified by the type of plate boundary involved in their formation (see pp.54–55). A broad classification can be based on whether the plate boundary is divergent or convergent. The plates involved may be both continental, both oceanic, or of differing types. Once they have been uplifted by tectonic forces, mountains are sculpted into peaks, valleys, and other features by the processes of weathering and erosion.

ANTARCTIC FOLD
Intense folding and metamorphism have transformed the white layers seen in this picture of Antarctica's Royal Society Range from limestone into marble, and deformed them into an overturned anticline.

Folding

Rocks near the Earth's surface are usually hard and brittle, and when subject to pressure they may break, as happens during an earthquake. However, when rocks are deeply buried, heated, and compressed over a long period, they become ductile and can deform, leading to folding, and making them susceptible to the geological processes associated with mountain building. Horizontal sedimentary rock strata buckle and dislocate into a variety of curved shapes. Upfolds, known as anticlines, are separated by downfolds known as synclines. These processes can produce folds from a few millimetres to many kilometres long. The hills and valleys flanking mountain belts are typically symmetrical folds with vertical planes of symmetry. By contrast, deep within mountain belts, where temperatures are greater, folds may become overturned to such an extent that the fold becomes almost flat (recumbent), and the tip may become detached and slide or be forced further along a fault plane.

VERTICAL STRATA, NAMIBIA
The effect of differential stress (unequal pressure in different directions) on rock strata can be powerful enough to rotate them from a horizontal to a vertical position.

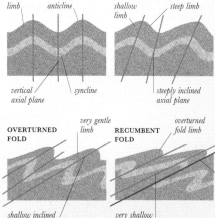

SYMMETRICAL FOLD
limb · anticline
vertical axial plane · syncline

ASYMMETRICAL FOLD
shallow limb · steep limb
steeply inclined axial plane

OVERTURNED FOLD
very gentle limb
shallow inclined axial plane

RECUMBENT FOLD
overturned fold limb
thrust fault
very shallow axial plane

FOLD SHAPES
Folds with limbs (sides) whose axial planes are inclined at the same angle are called symmetrical folds. If the axis of a fold is tilted to one side, and one limb has deformed so that it is steeper than the other, the fold is asymmetrical. When the fold axis is inclined at 45° or less to the horizontal, the fold is overturned. If the fold axis lies at a shallow angle, the fold is known as recumbent and is often accompanied by low-angle thrust faulting.

ANDEAN PEAKS
Although they began forming millions of years ago, the Andes, seen here in Patagonia, are among the Earth's youngest mountains.

Continents in Collision

Some of the Earth's most impressive mountain ranges, such as the Himalayas (see pp.110–11), have been formed by continents colliding directly with each other. Most tectonic plates are a combination of upper mantle rocks with dense oceanic crust and lighter but thicker continental crust. When an ocean basin is consumed by subduction, two continental masses move towards each other and meet, forming a convergence zone. Their similar density means neither will readily subduct into the mantle. Subduction cannot continue, even though the plates carrying the continents continue to converge. Instead the continental margins, with their thick layers of sediments washed off the continents, and then the continents themselves collide to form vast folded and faulted mountain belts in which crustal rocks are thickened, deformed, and metamorphosed. Within such a belt, slivers of oceanic crust and even upper mantle rocks may be preserved, testifying to the earlier subduction.

mountain range formed by continental collision

plateau behind mountain range

overlying plate

plate attached to subducted sea floor

suture zone

major fault

subducted oceanic crust

HIMALAYAN PEAKS
The mass of rock is supported by a root of thickened continental crust below it that floats on the mantle. This balancing act is called isostasy.

PLATE MOVEMENT
As continents come together, sea floor from one plate is subducted beneath the other, creating volcanic mountains. As the continental crust blocks finally collide, a second range is created by compression and uplift, with the previous mountains forming a plateau.

Ocean–Continent Collisions

Where the oceanic part of a plate converges with the edge of a continent, a subduction zone is formed, as the denser oceanic slab of crust and mantle is driven beneath the less dense continental crust. This type of subduction forms a continental volcanic arc, such as the Cascade Range of the western United States. Sediments scraped from the ocean floor by the subduction process are faulted onto the continental margin, which is further compressed and thickened by folding. Such subduction is also responsible for the Ring of Fire around the Pacific Ocean, and contributes to the building of the young mountain belt extending from the South American Andes (see pp.100–101) through the Western Cordillera of North America and the mountains of the Aleutian Islands to Japan and beyond.

LAND

ANDES AND PACIFIC OCEAN
This image, taken from space, shows the Chilean Andes, with the Pacific Ocean to the right of the range.

subducting oceanic plate

deep ocean trench formed

continental plate

mountain range

ANDEAN-STYLE MOUNTAINS
An oceanic plate subducts below the overriding continental plate. The continent's edge thickens, buckles, and is built up further by volcanism.

converging oceanic plate

arc of mountainous volcanic islands

subduction zone

subduction of older and cooler oceanic plate

Ocean–Ocean Collisions

When converging plates are both capped by oceanic crust of similar density, a volcanic island arc (see p.306) can be produced. Typically, this consists of mountainous islands with a parallel trench running offshore along one side of the chain. The trench marks where the plate that is older, cooler, and therefore slightly denser is subducting beneath the other one. Hot, molten rock (magma) rises through the overriding plate to erupt at the surface, building up gradually into a chain or arc of mountainous volcanic islands such as the Marianas, Vanuatu, or Solomon Islands in the Pacific and the Antilles and Scotia arc in the Atlantic. Island arcs and their associated sediments can sometimes become joined or accreted to continental margins, forming so-called exotic terranes. Such terranes are thought to have contributed to new mountains on the Pacific margin of North America's Western Cordillera.

VOLCANIC ISLAND ARC
Subduction of the older plate triggers volcanic activity, creating an island arc and forming new continental crust.

JAPANESE ISLANDS
Plate convergence below Japan generates frequent and often damaging earthquakes, fault movements, and occasional volcanic eruptions.

Rift Mountains

Where continental crust is pulled apart at divergent boundaries, the brittle surface rocks do not stretch very far before fracturing along parallel fault lines. Between the faults, the central block subsides, forming a rift valley flanked by cliff-like escarpments that can reach mountainous dimensions, as in parts of Africa's Great Rift Valley (see pp.88–89). If rifting continues, plates may split in two, with a new ocean between them. Where two oceanic plates diverge, they generate sea-floor spreading (see p.304), leading to the formation of submarine mountain ranges quite different in structure to those on land. As the plates are pulled apart, molten rock rises from the upper mantle to erupt along the axis of the sea-floor spreading ridge. These ridges form the Earth's longest mountain chain.

steep fault scarps

parallel faults

down-faulted central block

magma rises through fractures in crust

young deposits preserved in rift valley

gentle back slopes

plates pull apart

RIFTING
A rift valley, flanked by parallel faults, is formed where rocks are pulled apart on a regional rather than a continental scale.

RIFT VALLEY
The Great Rift Valley is flanked by mountains, including volcanoes, that rise over 2,000m (6,600ft) above the valley floor.

EDUARD SUESS

Austrian geologist Eduard Suess (1831–1914) pioneered studies of the folds, faults, and geological structure of the European Alps. Suess's acclaimed four-volume book *The Face of the Earth (Das Antlitz der Erde, 1885–1909)* was an encyclopedic overview of the Earth's mountains, their structure and formation, and a history of the oceans. He was also the geologist who first put forward the idea – later disproved – that there could have been land bridges that joined the continents of South America, Africa, India, and Australia. Suess named this once-vast continent Gondwanaland – the name is still used for an ancient supercontinent.

Epeirogenic Movements

The Earth's crust can be subjected to large-scale movement without extensive deformation and folding. This movement can be either downwards, which results in the creation of large sedimentary basins, or upwards to form elevated domes or plateaus. Both trends are referred to as epeirogenic movements. These events tend to be gradual, and usually affect large regions, such as the Colorado Plateau in the USA. An area of about 40,000 square km (15,500 square miles), the plateau is cut off from the Great Plains by the Rocky Mountains, and has been stable for at least 500 million years. Epeirogenic uplift in the last 65 million years has led to increased erosion by the Colorado River, excavating deep canyons in the plateau.

UTAH GOOSENECKS
At Goosenecks State Park, Utah, epeirogenic uplift has led to the formation of a deep canyon by the San Juan River.

Orogenic Belts

Over geological time, plate movements have produced innumerable episodes of mountain building around the world, a process known as orogenesis. The resulting linear arrays of mountains, shown below, are called orogenic belts, with the events that form them known as orogenies. They are usually identified by a geographical name, such as the Caledonian orogeny, which was first identified in Scotland (known as Caledonia to the Romans). Due to later plate movements, most ancient orogenic belts are no longer located where they formed; for instance, the Caledonian belt was originally an extension of the North American Appalachians.

ANCIENT MOUNTAIN ROOTS
The Scottish hills now barely qualify as mountains, but they are the eroded remnants of once higher mountains.

MOUNTAIN PROFILES

The pages that follow contain profiles of some of the world's mountain belts. Each profile includes the following summary information.

HIGHEST PEAK Name and height above sea-level

LENGTH Distance along the belt's longest axis

AGE Geological era within which the mountain belt formed

FORMATION TYPE Continent–continent, ocean–continent, ocean–ocean, or rift

NORTH AMERICA *west*
Rocky Mountains

LOCATION Stretching along the western side of North America from Alaska to New Mexico

HIGHEST PEAK Mount Elbert, USA 4,400m (14,400ft)

LENGTH 4,800km (3,000 miles)

AGE Mesozoic–Cenozoic

FORMATION TYPE Ocean–continent

The Rocky Mountains are part of one of the largest mountain belts on Earth, the great Western Cordillera of North America, which extends from above the Arctic Circle to the Sierra Madre Occidental in Mexico. Strictly speaking, the Rocky Mountains are the high peaks of the cordillera's eastern ranges, which also include the Canadian Rockies, and the Northern, Central, and Southern Rockies in the USA. Most of the mountains peak above 1,000m (3,000ft), with more than 100 summits

AMERICA'S ICON
The bald eagle is the only species of eagle endemic to North America.

above 3,000m (10,000ft). Within the belt is North America's continental divide, to the west of which rivers flow into the Pacific, while in the east they flow into the Arctic and Atlantic oceans. Geologically, the history of the cordillera is extremely complex, with large amounts of uplift taking place in the last 15 million years. The range includes intensely deformed zones with extensive folds and faults, such as the Canadian Rockies; belts of volcanic activity and lava plateaus, which are evident in Yellowstone, Wyoming; and highly metamorphosed areas with granite intrusions, including Grand Teton. Features such as Wyoming's Great Divide Basin are also part of the chain. The Alaskan ranges are snow-covered and heavily glaciated. An abundance of wildlife inhabits the cordillera, including mountain goats and sheep, bears, wolves, cougars, and moose.

FEATURES OF THE WESTERN CORDILLERA

MOUNT MCKINLEY
Permanent snow and ice cover Mount McKinley's summit in Alaska's Denali National Park.

Mackenzie Mountains

Mount Logan

Cascade Range

Sierra Nevada

Coast Ranges

MOUNT ASSINIBOINE
Straddling the British Columbia–Alberta border, Mount Assiniboine rises to 3,618m (11,870ft).

Yellowstone

Rocky Mountains

Colorado Plateau

MOUNT WHITNEY
The jagged peaks of California's Mount Whitney reach 4,418m (14,495ft).

LAND

ALASKAN OIL PIPELINES

The discovery of oil and gas in Alaska has led to the construction of huge pipelines that overcome the barrier presented by the high mountains of Alaska. However, the pipelines cross environmentally sensitive wilderness areas, creating a physical obstacle for migrating animals such as Caribou. Although burying pipelines might appear to solve such difficulties, it can actually cause further problems, as they may fracture. This is also a region of permafrost, which is unstable. In places, pipelines are elevated to allow wildlife to pass safely beneath.

ROCKY MOUNTAIN LANDSCAPE
The head waters of the Snake River, with its flat alluvial plain and terraces, lie in the Teton Range, northwest Wyoming. They are overlooked by Grand Teton peak, which reaches a height of 4,197m (13,770ft).

LAND

NORTH AMERICA *east*
Appalachians

LOCATION Running along the eastern side of North America, from Quebec, Canada, to Alabama, USA

HIGHEST PEAK
Mount Mitchell, USA
2,037m (6,684ft)

LENGTH
2,400km (1,500 miles)

AGE Paleozoic–Mesozoic

FORMATION TYPE
Continent–continent

A much-eroded, ancient, and complex mountain belt, the Appalachians were formed during a series of plate separations and collisions. Today, the

APPALACHIAN AMPHIBIAN

There are 34 native varieties of salamander resident in the Appalachian forests, including this Marbled Salamander.

chain consists of a series of ranges that increase in geological complexity from west to east. The slightly folded and uplifted plateaus in the west give way to parallel ridges and valleys, followed by the highly deformed Blue Ridge. The belt becomes less elevated closer to the Atlantic coast, where metamorphosed sediments and volcanic rocks are overlain by the younger accumulations of the coastal plain. The Appalachians are the North American continuation of Europe's Caledonian range (see p.102).

TENNESSEE MOUNTAINS
The forest-clad slopes of much of the Appalachian range disguise a geologically complex area of ancient metamorphosed rocks.

NORTH AMERICA *south*
Sierra Madre Oriental

LOCATION In eastern Mexico – extending from north to south, and bending west at the northern end

HIGHEST PEAK Cerro Peña Nevada, Mexico
3,644m (11,955ft)

LENGTH
1,100km (700 miles)

AGE Mesozoic–Cenozoic

FORMATION TYPE
Ocean–continent

Much of Mexico is elevated above 1,000m (3,000ft), with the three Sierra Madre ranges and the Mexican Volcanic Belt forming the country's mountain backbone. A continuation of the Western Cordillera, the Sierra Madre Oriental was formed by compressional tectonic forces and folding about 50–70 million years ago, which produced a long, dramatic series of alternating anticlines and synclines in limestone.

VIEW FROM ORBIT
This view from the space shuttle shows the Sierra Madre Oriental, close to the city of Monterrey.

LIMESTONE CRESTS
The sharp peaks of the Sierra Madre Oriental are formed of limestone, which was elevated by tectonic forces.

SOUTH AMERICA *west*
Andes

LOCATION Running down the western side of South America from the Caribbean Sea to Cape Horn

HIGHEST PEAK
Aconcagua, Argentina
(6,959m) 22,834ft

LENGTH
7,200km (4,500 miles)

AGE Mesozoic–Cenozoic

FORMATION TYPE
Ocean–continent

The longest mountain chain in the world (apart from the Mid-Atlantic Ridge beneath the Atlantic Ocean), the Andes is also one of the Earth's most spectacular and active mountain belts. Within it lies one of the most arid places on Earth, Chile's Atacama Desert (see p.242); the world's highest navigable body of water, Lake Titicaca (see p.189); the source of the world's greatest river, the Amazon (see pp.170–71); and the highest city in the world, La Paz, in Bolivia, which is situated at an altitude of 3,630m (11,910ft). The whole range is frequently affected by earthquakes and

FEATURES OF THE ANDES

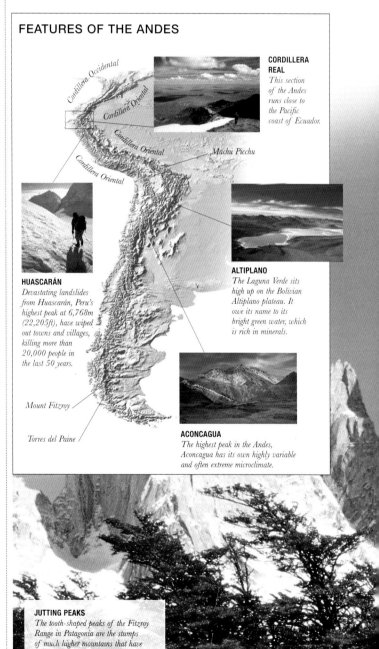

CORDILLERA REAL
This section of the Andes runs close to the Pacific coast of Ecuador.

HUASCARÁN
Devastating landslides from Huascarán, Peru's highest peak at 6,768m (22,205ft), have wiped out towns and villages, killing more than 20,000 people in the last 50 years.

ALTIPLANO
The Laguna Verde sits high up on the Bolivian Altiplano plateau. It owes its name to its bright green water, which is rich in minerals.

ACONCAGUA
The highest peak in the Andes, Aconcagua has its own highly variable and often extreme microclimate.

JUTTING PEAKS
The tooth-shaped peaks of the Fitzroy Range in Patagonia are the stumps of much higher mountains that have been steadily eroded by glaciers.

HIGH FLIER

With the largest wing area of any bird, the Andean Condor can fly at altitudes of 5,500m (18,000ft).

eruptions from 183 active volcanoes, including the highest on Earth. The mountains ascend abruptly from sea-level on the western, Pacific coast of South America to altitudes of over 6,500m (21,300ft). The belt forms a formidable physical, meteorological, and biological barrier, ranging from 100km (60 miles) wide at the southern tip of the continent, to 700km (435 miles) wide in the central region. In Peru, Bolivia, and Ecuador, between the Cordillera Occidental range in the west and the Cordillera Oriental in the east, lies the Altiplano (also known as the Puña), which is the world's most densely populated high plateau. The farmers who inhabit the Altiplano exist in one of the most hostile environments for human life on

Earth: the high altitude means that the air is thin, and the weather is extreme. The southern sector of the range, which runs through Patagonia and Tierra del Fuego, has been glaciated as far as sea-level and is characterized by numerous fiords. Geologically, the mountains are the result of the continuing eastward subduction of the Nazca Plate beneath the South American Plate. The subduction zone is marked by the Peru–Chile Trench off South America's Pacific coast, which plunges to over 8,000m (26,250ft) below sea-level. The present topography of the Andes is largely the result of deformation that has taken place during the past 50 million years, with significant elevation of the mountains occurring over the past 10 million years. As such, the belt is young in geological terms, and mountain building continues in the present. Minerals such as gold, silver, platinum, and copper are all mined in the Andes.

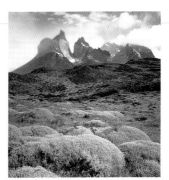

GRANITE HORNS

The granite peaks of the Torres del Paine soar to 3,050m (10,006ft) above the glacial lakes of Patagonia in southern Chile.

ALEXANDER VON HUMBOLDT

A German aristocrat, Alexander von Humboldt (1769–1859) began to explore South America in 1799 with the French botanist Aimé Bonplan (1773–1858). The pair spent five years studying the continent's geology and botany. Humboldt was the first to climb Chimborazo, Ecuador's highest peak, and describe its environment.

CITY OF THE INCAS

Situated high in the Peruvian Andes, Machu Picchu is a remarkably preserved Inca city. The exact function of the settlement is unknown, but it may have been a royal estate built by the Inca emperor Pachacuti in the 15th century. Located on a prominent ridge, partly surrounded by steep cliffs, the site includes houses, religious architecture, tombs, and agricultural terraces. When the Spanish conquistadors arrived in South America in the 16th century, Machu Picchu was abandoned. The city remained hidden for centuries until 1911, when it was found by American archaeologist Hiram Bingham.

EUROPE *east*

Urals

LOCATION Running from the Arctic Ocean to the border between Russia and Kazakhstan

HIGHEST PEAK
Narodnaya, Russia
1,894m (6,214ft)

LENGTH
2,400km (1,500 miles)

AGE Paleozoic

FORMATION TYPE
Continent–continent

The ancient, extensively eroded Urals form a wall-like, linear mountain chain traditionally regarded as the boundary between Europe and Asia. Only 200km (125 miles) wide at its broadest point, it is a narrow range. The Urals represent the seam along which the Baltic and Russian continents collided about 300 million years ago, after the vast Uralian Ocean had been completely subducted under the Russian continent. The movement that formed the mountains was part of the assembly of the supercontinent Pangea, which once covered two-fifths of the world's surface. Following subduction of the ocean crust, the compressive forces of convergence crumpled sediments on the leading edges of the two colliding continents, thickening the crust and elevating the mountains. In 1841 British geologist Roderick Murchison mapped the stratification of deposits in the western Urals. In doing so he defined the Permian Period (named after the Russian region of Perm), which extended from approximately 290 million to 252 million years ago and saw the extinction of much of the marine life of the period. Sulphide mineral deposits, including copper, iron, and zinc, were formed by hydrothermal vents on the ancient ocean floor. These are now preserved in the southern Urals and form an ore belt that is 2,000km (1,200 miles) long. The area has been one of the most important industrial regions of modern times. The central and southern Urals are heavily forested, while further north the mountains feature alpine meadows and tundra.

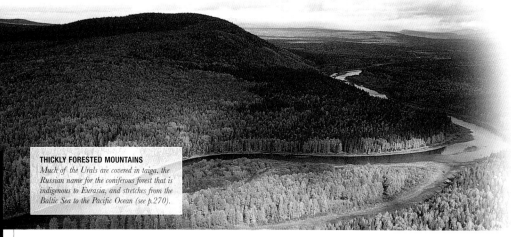

THICKLY FORESTED MOUNTAINS
Much of the Urals are covered in taiga, the Russian name for the coniferous forest that is indigenous to Eurasia, and stretches from the Baltic Sea to the Pacific Ocean (see p.270).

PLATINUM MINING

Pure platinum is an extremely rare and valuable natural mineral. It was once confused with silver, but it actually has a much higher melting point of 1,772°C (3,222°F). With a specific gravity of 21.5, platinum is the densest naturally occurring mineral. Nuggets of platinum have been found in placer deposits (see p.45), especially at Nizhniy Tagil in the Urals, where one of the largest accumulations of the mineral in the world is found.

EUROPE *northwest*

Caledonian Mountains

LOCATION Running from the Arctic Circle through Scandinavia and Scotland to northwest Ireland

HIGHEST PEAK
Galdhøpiggen, Norway
2,469m (8,100ft)

LENGTH
2,600km (1,625 miles)

AGE Paleozoic

FORMATION TYPE
Continent–continent

The Caledonian Mountains are the European section of a much longer mountain chain that continues as the Appalachians (see p.100) on the opposite side of the Atlantic Ocean. This ancient mountain belt is one of the most intensely studied in the world. This is especially true of its British ranges, studies of which generated many formative ideas about mountain building in the late 19th century. However, none of the pioneers of geology could have guessed at the extraordinary history of the Caledonian Mountains. Five hundred million years ago, North America, Scotland, and northwest Ireland were part of the ancient continent of Laurentia, and were separated from Avalonia (England, Wales, and southwest Ireland) by the Iapetus Ocean, all of which were located in the southern hemisphere. About 490 million years ago, Avalonia began to move north, subducting the Iapetus Ocean in the process. Eventually, Avalonia impacted upon Laurentia, a convergence that resulted in a period of mountain building. Much later, as the North Atlantic Ocean began to open 80 million years ago, North America split from northwest Ireland and Scotland, which converged with the rest of what is now the British Isles. The Caledonian Mountains are continuing to rise by a tiny amount each year. The range includes the North West Highlands and Grampian mountains of Scotland (which are the most elevated peaks in the British Isles) and the Jotunheimen of Norway. The rugged landscape of the range today features craggy, snow-capped peaks, glens, lochs, and fiords.

BUACHAILLE ETIVE MOR
This striking triangular peak descends to Glen Coe, in the Scottish Grampian Mountains.

NORWEGIAN FIORDLAND
With their precipitous mountainsides, the deep fiords of Norway's Atlantic coast are evidence of the incredible erosive power of glaciers.

Pyrenees

LOCATION Between France and Spain, extending from the Atlantic Ocean to the Mediterranean Sea

HIGHEST PEAK
Aneto, Spain
3,404m (11,168ft)

LENGTH
435km (270 miles)

AGE Late Paleozoic–Cenozoic

FORMATION TYPE
Continent–continent

The Pyrenees form a natural barrier between France and the Iberian Peninsula (Spain and Portugal). Two-thirds of the belt is situated in Spain, and there are relatively few natural passes between the mountains. Nevertheless, human predecessors (*Homo antecessor*) managed to cross the mountains into northern Spain approximately 800,000 years ago. The limestone caves of the Pyrenees are particularly famous for preserving some of the most recent Neanderthal remains in Europe, which are approximately 29,000 years old. The walls of the caves also contain paintings by the earliest modern humans, dating back about 15,000 years. The geological history of the Pyrenees is long, complex, and intimately associated with that of the Iberian Peninsula. During the Cretaceous Period, approximately 142 million years ago, Iberia became a micro-continent, rupturing from the major landmasses during the break-up of the supercontinent of Pangea. As the Atlantic Ocean opened, the Iberian plate was wedged between Europe and North Africa, leading to the initial development of the Pyrenees. Then, about 60 million years ago, rotation of the African and Eurasian plates meant that the Iberian Plate again converged with southern France. The resulting thickening and folding of the crust further uplifted the Pyrenees. The peninsula's motion ended about 10 million years ago. During the last ice age, the Pyrenees experienced extensive glaciation. The mountains are characterized by jagged peaks that are steepest on the French side of the range. In the west, the slopes are heavily wooded, but the granite peaks of the east are much starker with less vegetation. Dramatic, semicircular glaciated hollows known as cirques (see p.212) are a prominent feature of the Pyrenees, and the mountains also contain some of Europe's most spectacular waterfalls, the highest of which, at the Cirque de Gavarnie, plunges 422m (1,385ft). The wildlife of the Pyrenees includes abundant bird species, among them vultures (including the rare Lammergeier), eagles, capercaillie, and Ptarmigan. Mammals include Chamois, wild boar, lynx, and a tiny population of brown bears.

PYRENEAN IBEX
Once common throughout Europe, wild goats were depicted by early humans. The Pyrenean ibex is a surviving species though it is declining dramatically.

FRINGED PINKS
Thousands of varieties of wild flower grow in the Pyrenees, including these delicate Fringed Pinks, which are found in the Spanish mountains.

FEATURES OF THE PYRENEES

Pyrénées-Atlantiques

Mount Aneto

CIRQUE DE GAVARNIE
This sheer rock wall is the site of the highest waterfall in Europe.

HAUTES-PYRÉNÉES
Straddling the French–Spanish border, the Hautes-Pyrénées include the highest peaks in the belt.

Pyrénées-Orientales

LAND

WATCHING SPACE

The Earth's increasingly polluted atmosphere mars our view of the Universe. Building astronomical observatories as high as possible, and away from heavily populated areas, minimizes the effects of atmospheric pollution and light interference. The Pic du Midi Observatory is situated above the clouds in the Pyrenees.

ORDESA NATIONAL PARK, SPAIN
Rising high above the tree-line, horizontal rock strata form precipitous cliffs above valleys that were once filled with glacial ice. Only the high peaks stood out above the glaciers at the height of the last ice age.

EUROPE *south*

Alps

LOCATION Extending in an arc across southern Europe from Mediterranean France to Austria

HIGHEST PEAK Mont Blanc, France 4,807m (15,771ft)

LENGTH 1,050km (650 miles)

AGE Mesozoic–Cenozoic

FORMATION TYPE Continent–continent

The largest mountain chain in Europe, the Alps contains some of the most intensely studied mountains in the world. Studies of the Alps in the 18th and 19th centuries led to early theories about mountain formation and the nature of large-scale folding and thrusting. Between 100 and 200km (60 and 120 miles) wide, the Alps form a curved fold belt, with several peaks rising to over 4,000m (13,000ft). The west of the chain includes the Maritime and Pennine Alps; the central ranges include the Bernese (or Central) Alps; and the eastern ranges

include the Dolomites and the Austrian Alps. In the past, the mountains have formed a physical obstacle to human migrations, although roads were first built through the belt's natural passes in Roman times. The Alps were generated by the convergence of the African and Eurasian plates. This process began approximately 90 million years ago, when the African plate began to move north, subducting the ancient Tethys Ocean and uplifting the sediment on the sea floor to form faulted recumbent fold structures called nappes. Folding and thrusting

continued, with a major period of mountain building taking place 33–15 million years ago. The current landscape of the Alps is the result of glaciation during the last 2 million years. Primary features include U-shaped and hanging valleys (see p.215), and lakes such as Como (see p.193) and Garda, which have been naturally dammed by glacial moraines. The longest remaining glacier in the Alps is the Aletsch (see p.225), which extends for 25km (16 miles).

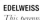

EDELWEISS

This perennial alpine flower has tufted leaves and flowers protected by thick, woolly bracts. These protect the Edelweiss from the freezing temperatures that are common close to the snow-line where it grows.

ALPINE MEADOW

Retreating glaciers allow specialized alpine plants, especially grasses and saxifrages, to colonize newly exposed rocky soils within a few years.

ALBRECHT PENCK

German geomorphologist Albrecht Penck (1859–1945) was director of the Berlin Institute of Oceanography and Geography. Penck studied the development of landforms and surface deposits in the Alps and the boulder clay of the North German Plain to determine the extent to which glaciation had affected them. This led him to propose that four main episodes of glaciation had taken place in the area. He also argued that the elevation of mountains is limited by the balance between uplift and erosion, a theory that is well illustrated by the Alps. The mountains continue to be uplifted by approximately 0.5mm (1/50in) every year, a rise that is compensated for by similar levels of erosion. His most famous work is *The Morphology of the Earth's Surface* (1894).

ICE MUMMY

In 1991, on the Alpine border between Italy and Austria, the body of Otzi, as he was later named, was discovered. He was so well preserved in ice that he was thought to have died recently. However, the discovery of his bow, arrows, and copper axe suggested that he was a Neolithic hunter. A radiocarbon age of 5,200 years confirmed this. An arrow embedded in Otzi's back suggests that he was attacked while climbing over the mountains.

FEATURES OF THE ALPS

Bernese Alps

Bavarian Alps

Austrian Alps

Pennine Alps

Dolomites

Finsteraarhorn

Matterhorn

Muritime Alps

MONT BLANC
The highest mountain in the Alps, Mont Blanc was first climbed in 1786.

NORTH FACE OF THE EIGER
At 3,970m (13,025ft) high, with exposed, rocky, cliff-like walls, the Eiger was not climbed until 1858, and its north face defied all attempts until 1938.

GROSSGLOCKNER
A classic glacial horn in the Hohe Tauern range, Grossglockner is the highest mountain in the Austrian Alps, at 3,798m (12,461ft).

FORMIDABLE MATTERHORN
*With its pyramid-shaped peak and
precipitous rock walls sculpted by glacial
ice, the Matterhorn, 4,478m (14,692ft)
high, is seen as the epitome of the alpine
mountain form.*

EUROPE *southwest*
Sierra Nevada

LOCATION In southern Spain, running west–east between Granada and the Mediterranean Costa del Sol

HIGHEST PEAK Mulhacén, Spain 3,481m (11,421ft)

LENGTH 100km (63 miles)

AGE Mesozoic–Cenozoic

FORMATION TYPE Continent–continent

Southern Spain's snow-capped Sierra Nevada mountain range forms a dramatic backdrop to the Mediterranean holiday beaches of the Costa del Sol. The range is the most southerly part of the more extensive Betic Cordillera, which run southwest to northeast from Cadiz to Alicante, and continue offshore to the Balearic Islands of Majorca, Minorca, and Ibiza. The formation of the Sierra Nevada was contemporary with that of the Atlas Mountains (see opposite) and the European Alps (see pp.104–05). It resulted from the northwards movement of the African Plate during the Cenozoic Era. The Sierra Nevada continues to rise by about 3mm (¹/₈in) every 100 years. The southern folds of the range, known as Las Alpujarras, are deep valleys that provide fertile farming land.

ARID BADLANDS
Deforestation and overgrazing of fragile, semi-arid lands have resulted in erosion and the formation of semi-desert badlands in the Sierra Nevada.

EUROPE *central*
Carpathians

LOCATION Forming an arc from southern Poland through Slovakia, Ukraine, and into central Romania

HIGHEST PEAK Gerlachovka, Slovakia 2,655m (8,711ft)

LENGTH 1,450km (900 miles)

AGE Mesozoic–Cenozoic

FORMATION TYPE Continent–continent

APOLLO BUTTERFLY
A huge conservation programme was undertaken to preserve this species from extinction in the Pieniny range of the Polish Carpathians.

The Carpathians are an extension of the European Alps, and they contain a complex mixture of ancient rocks covered by younger sediments that are often highly folded and faulted.

Many of the rocks that form the range were once deposits in the Mesozoic Tethys Ocean. The highest Carpathian peaks are the granitic Tatra Mountains in Slovakia, where steep, rocky walls rise above U-shaped valleys. In Romania, where more than half of the mountains are situated, the chain breaks up into several ranges, the loftiest being the Transylvanian Alps. Broad, fertile valleys, lakes, and limestone plateaus are all features of the range.

STEEP-SIDED VALLEY
Pasture land is grazed by sheep at the base of sharp, towering Carpathian peaks in Slovakia.

EUROPE *south*
Dinaric Alps

LOCATION Running along the coast of the Adriatic Sea from Slovenia into northern Albania

HIGHEST PEAK Durmitor, Yugoslavia 2,522m (8,274ft)

LENGTH 750km (470 miles)

AGE Mesozoic–Cenozoic

FORMATION TYPE Continent–continent

The northwest–southeast trend of the Dinaric Alps parallels Italy's Apennines, from which they are

DURMITOR, YUGOSLAVIA

separated by the Adriatic Sea. Deep gorges have been cut into the mountains by rivers such as the Neretva. The soluble nature of the limestone that forms the mountains has led to the development of the region's famous karst landscape (see p.201). Below ground, extensive cave systems have developed, and in places cavern collapse has formed large hollows called poljes.

EUROPE *east*
Caucasus Mountains

LOCATION Running between the Black Sea and Caspian Sea along the border of Russia and Georgia

HIGHEST PEAK El'brus, Russia 5,642m (18,510ft)

LENGTH 1,200km (750 miles)

AGE Late Paleozoic–Cenozoic

FORMATION TYPE Continent–continent

PONTIC MOUNTAINS, TURKEY
On the southern shore of the Black Sea, the Lesser Caucasus fold structure continues westwards as the Pontic Mountains.

One of Europe's natural boundaries in the east, the Caucasus Mountains consist of two parallel ranges separated by a central trough. The southeastern peaks are mainly limestone, which has formed karst landscapes. A higher range, formed of igneous rocks, dominates in the northwest. The mountains contain one of the world's deepest caves, Snezhnaya, Georgia, which is 1,470m (4,823 ft) deep.

BELOLAKAYA
This peak attracts alpinists, trekkers, and tourists. It is one of several high mountains in the western Caucasus, the tallest of which is Dombay Ul'gen, at 4,042m (13,262ft).

AFRICA *northwest*

Atlas Mountains

LOCATION Extending from the Atlantic coast of Morocco to the Mediterranean east coast of Tunisia

HIGHEST PEAK Toubkal, Morocco 4,165m (13,665ft)

LENGTH 2,400km (1,500 miles)

AGE Mesozoic–Cenozoic

FORMATION TYPE Continent–continent

The Atlas Mountains form a barrier between the Mediterranean Sea and the Sahara. Many of the tallest peaks preserve evidence of glaciation during the last ice age, with cirques (see p.212) and periglacial features (see p.296) evident. The mountains do not form a continuous chain, but are a series of ranges that are interspersed with plateaus, basins, and gorges. The most prominent range is the High Atlas, which runs inland from Agadir on Morocco's west coast for 650km (400 miles) and contains several snow-capped peaks, including the highest, Toubkal. The eastern ranges of the

ATLAS MONKEY
The Barbary Ape is actually a monkey that has become adapted to living in the rocky cliffs and high-altitude oak and cedar forests of the Atlas range.

Atlas form less elevated plateaus. In the north, the mountain slopes receive ample rainfall and are forested with cedar, pine, and oak. The more southerly ranges are more arid, with salt flats occurring in those areas of the Atlas close to the Sahara. An earthquake in 1960 destroyed Agadir and confirmed the presence of major active faults separating the Atlas from the North Saharan Basin. Like the European Alps (see pp.104–05) and Spain's Sierra Nevada (see opposite), the Atlas Mountains were built by plate convergence between Africa and Europe, beginning about 60 million years ago. However, as is also true for Central Europe, there are folds and faults in the Moroccan ranges that were created during an era known as the Variscan orogeny, a period of mountain building that occurred about 300 million years ago. Younger sedimentary rocks, including many limestones that were originally deposited on the floor of the Tethys Ocean, eventually covered these folds. The northernmost ranges were formed

WATER SOURCES

In the arid regions of the Atlas Mountains, water is a scarce commodity, and many communities depend upon meltwater streams formed by the winter snows. In places, the water is collected in deep cisterns cut into the rock centuries ago. With the advent of global warming there is a risk that diminishing snowfalls will result in water shortages for the inhabitants.

by folding that began 60 million years ago. Further movement of the African Plate, approximately 20 million years ago, deformed rocks in central Tunisia and Algeria, and elevated the central plateaus. The mountains are rich in minerals, including coal, iron, gold, silver, and phosphate minerals.

FEATURES OF THE ATLAS MOUNTAINS

TOUBKAL
Toubkal is permanently snow-covered and preserves evidence of glaciation.

MIDDLE ATLAS
The forested Middle Atlas is a northeast-trending range, situated in Morocco.

ANTI-ATLAS RANGE
Between the High Atlas and the Saharan Basin, the Anti-Atlas contain some of the chain's oldest rocks.

LAND

BARREN SLOPES
The inhabitants of ancient settlements continue a precarious existence in the arid parts of the Atlas. Survival depends on local microclimates and the availability of water for plant growth and domestic uses.

AFRICA south
Drakensberg Plateau

LOCATION Extending from north-eastern to southern South Africa, through Swaziland and Lesotho

HIGHEST PEAK Ntlenyana, Lesotho 3,482m (11,424ft)

LENGTH 1,290km (800 miles)

AGE Mesozoic–Cenozoic

FORMATION TYPE Rift

A vast, westward-dipping escarpment, the Drakensberg range is one of the world's largest elevated plateaus. It separates a narrow coastal plain from southern Africa's vast interior of savanna and desert. The east of the plateau is dominated by the Great Escarpment, which soars to over 3,300m (10,000ft), high enough for frost action to fracture the rocks. In places, the sheer scarp face rises for over 2,100m (7,000ft) from its base to the crest. The Drakensberg Plateau consists of sedimentary rocks capped with volcanic deposits. The base of the plateau was built up by the non-marine Karoo sediments that were laid down about 250–300 million years ago. They begin with glacial deposits (the Dwyka tillite) and pass up into terrestrial coals. The summit of the plateau contains remnants of the ancient continent called

FEATURES OF THE DRAKENSBERG PLATEAU

NTLENYANA
The highest point of the plateau is Mount Ntlenyana.

Mont-aux-Sources

Giant's Castle

Great Karoo

GRASS PEAKS
Lesotho is located in the highest part of the Drakensberg Plateau.

ROCKY MAMMAL
Related to early hoofed mammals, the rock hyrax inhabits rocky slopes in colonies of up to 40 for protection against predators.

ABOVE THE CLOUDS
The Great Escarpment of the Drakensberg rises high above the low clouds of the coastal plains. The clouds bring moisture to the lower slopes, while the top of the plateau is much drier.

Gondwanaland, which were originally close to sea-level before being elevated prior to the break-up of the landmass 200 million years ago. A rising hotspot domed the region, stretching and rifting the crust as Africa and South America separated. Subsequently, basalts erupted through volcanic fissures in the underlying sediment, a process that continued for about 50 million years. These layers of basalt originally covered an area of approximately 2 million square km (800,000 square miles), a region that includes much of southern Africa and parts of what is now Antarctica. The basaltic deposits were originally 1,500m (4,900ft) thick, but erosion has heavily dissected them. The resulting landscape of the Drakensberg Plateau is incredibly varied, including steep sandstone cliffs, free-standing pinnacles, torrential waterfalls, and extensive caves. Major peaks include Mont-aux-Sources (which is the origin of three rivers, including the Tugela) and Giant's Castle, so named because its steep, rocky cliffs resemble battlements. Rivers rising in the mountains, such as the Tugela and Orange, have carved impressive gorges through the rock. The diverse and inaccessible landscape, which also includes extensive high grasslands, provides habitats for an astonishing array of flora and fauna, with about 300 species of indigenous plant life. Drakensberg's name is taken from the Afrikaans for "dragon's mountain", but it is also known by its Zulu name of Ukhahlamba.

BLYDE RIVER CANYON
The Three Rondavels (also known as the Three Sisters) form part of the Blyde River Canyon in the Transvaal, South Africa. The cliffs of the canyon rise up to 800m (2,600ft).

ASIA west
Zagros Mountains

LOCATION Running from eastern Turkey through northern Iraq to southern Iran and the Persian Gulf

HIGHEST PEAK Damavand, Iran 5,671m (18,603ft)

LENGTH 1,530km (950 miles)

AGE Mesozoic–Cenozoic

FORMATION TYPE Continent–continent

The Zagros Mountains run parallel to the valley of the Euphrates River and the Persian Gulf. Part of an unstable fold belt, the range is vulnerable to earthquakes, as it includes a complex zone of thrust faulting and volcanism. In the centre of the region lies an area of salt domes up to 1,500m (5,000ft) high. Many of the Zagros Mountains are perennially snow-capped.

OIL-RICH HILLS

The sediments of the western foothills of the Zagros Mountains are a substantial source of hydrocarbons. Folding has produced anticlines, which trap petroleum in reservoirs beneath impermeable rock. However, some oil seeps to the surface where volatile gases burn off.

PARS SNOW FIELDS
Although on the same latitude as southern Turkey in the Mediterranean, the Pars region of the Zagros Mountains rises to over 5,000m (16,400ft), and is covered with snow in winter.

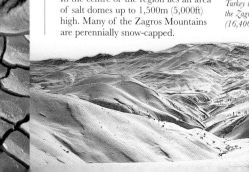

ASIA central
Altai Mountains

LOCATION Running from eastern Kazakhstan through Russia and Mongolia to western China

HIGHEST PEAK Belukha, Russia 4,506m (14,783ft)

LENGTH 2,000km (1,250 miles)

AGE Late Paleozoic

FORMATION TYPE Continent–continent

The Altai mountain system forms the northern rim of the Dzungarian Basin depression in western China. Much of

SNOW LEOPARD
This endangered species of big cat is ideally suited to the cold mountains of the Altai, where it hunts small mammals and birds.

the range exceeds 3,000m (10,000ft), and there are numerous glaciated peaks over 4,000m (13,000ft) in the Mongolian sections. The highest peak, Mount Belukha, lies in the north at the headwaters of the rivers Ob' (see p.101) and Irtysh in Russian Siberia.

MONGOLIAN HIGHLANDS
The Altai Mountains rise above the cold steppe grasslands of Mongolia, home to nomads and their herds of horses, camels, goats, and sheep.

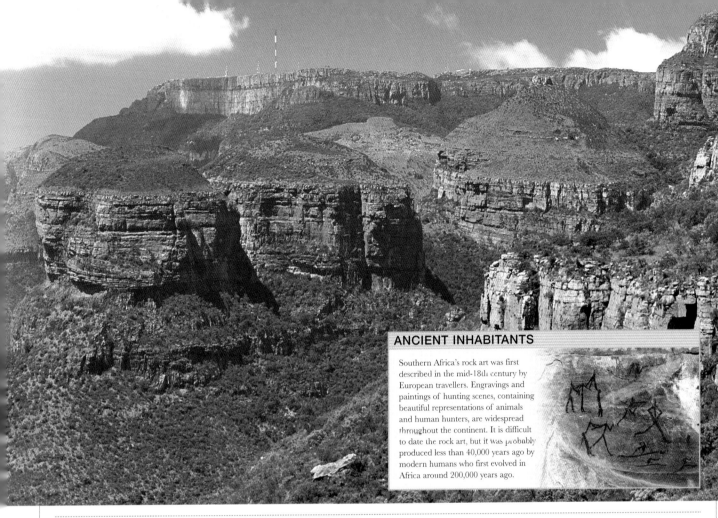

ANCIENT INHABITANTS

Southern Africa's rock art was first described in the mid-18th century by European travellers. Engravings and paintings of hunting scenes, containing beautiful representations of animals and human hunters, are widespread throughout the continent. It is difficult to date the rock art, but it was probably produced less than 40,000 years ago by modern humans who first evolved in Africa around 200,000 years ago.

ASIA central

Tien Shan Mountains

LOCATION To the north of the Tarim Basin between western China, Kyrgyzstan, and Kazakhstan

HIGHEST PEAK Pik Pobedy, Kazakhstan 7,439m (24,407ft)

LENGTH 2,250km (1,400 miles)

AGE Late Paleozoic–Cenozoic

FORMATION TYPE Continent–continent

With more than 30 peaks of 6,000m (20,000ft) or more in height, the Tien Shan mountain belt is an imposing physical barrier. In 1856 Russian

KHAN TENGRI
Inylchek, the largest glacier in the Tien Shan, flows for 62km (39 miles) down the western slopes of the Khan Tengri massif.

explorer Peter Semonyov became the first European to survey the Tien Shan, whose Chinese name translates as "celestial mountains". The belt consists of a series of parallel ranges that extend for about 2,800km (1,740 miles), with Ozero Issyk-Kul' – one of the largest mountain lakes in the world – located in the northeastern end of the range. The western Alai range includes many lakes,

GLACIER COVER
Peaks that rise above 4,000m (13,000ft) in the Tien Shan are capped by glaciers, covering an area of about 9,500 square km (3,670 square miles).

and the surrounding peaks average about 4,600m (15,000ft) in height. In the east, the mountains of the Tien Shan become lower and narrower, but then rise again to over 5,000m (16,400ft) in the Bogda Shan range, with Bogda Feng in China ascending to 5,445m (17,864ft). The east–west trending folds of the range expose lower Paleozoic rocks that have been folded, faulted, and uplifted in a series of tectonic events that included early subduction and subsequent continent–continent collision. These disturbances continue in the present, with massive earthquakes associated with major faults in the region. The Tien Shan range separates two major topographical depressions, the southerly Turpan Depression and

MOUNTAIN FARMS
Fertile pastures flank the Tien Shan Mountains of Kyrgyzstan and Kazakhstan. Herds of goats, sheep and horses are farmed in the region.

the northern Dzungarian Basin. The floor of Turpan Pendi is 154m (505ft) below sea-level. When the English explorer Charles Howard-Bury visited the area in June 1913, he marvelled at the diversity and profusion of wild flowers, commenting that he had never "seen such a luxuriant flora" as he discovered in the alpine meadows of the Tien Shan. The mountains are the natural habitat of many domesticated ornamental and edible plants, including fruit trees, roses, tulips, and onions. The Tien Shan's animal life includes the native White-clawed Bear.

ASIA central
Himalayas

LOCATION Running southeast from northern Pakistan and India across Nepal to Bhutan

New Delhi
Ganges

HIGHEST PEAK Mount Everest, Nepal 8,850m (29,035ft)

LENGTH 2,300km (1,400 miles)

AGE Cenozoic

FORMATION TYPE Continent–continent

FEATURES OF THE HIMALAYAS

Nanga Parbat
Karakoram Range
Plateau of Tibet
Lhotse
Makalu
Kanchenjunga

K2
At 8,611m (28,253ft) above sea-level, K2, the second highest mountain in the world, was first conquered in 1954 by a team of Italian climbers.

ANNAPURNA
At 8,091m (26,545ft) high, the north face of Annapurna was first climbed by a French team led by Maurice Herzog in 1950.

EVEREST'S PEAK
Only when first surveyed in 1852 was Everest confirmed to be the world's highest peak.

In addition to being the highest mountains on Earth, the Himalayas are also one of the youngest mountain belts. Formed within the last 50 million years, the belt is largely composed of deformed and metamorphosed rocks from the Indian crustal plate. Mountain building began with the collision of the Indian continental plate and Southeast Asia. This convergence caused India's northern edge to shorten by about 2,000km (1,200 miles), thickening the Indian crust to 55km (34 miles) beneath the Himalayas and 70km (43 miles) below Tibet. The elevation of the Himalayas transformed the region's climate, establishing the annual Southeast Asian monsoon, with its regular torrential rains. Between 250 and 350km (155 and 218 miles) wide, the mountains form a virtually impassable barrier, although one species, the Bar-headed Goose, regularly flies across the peaks from Central Asia to the Indian subcontinent. A series of ranges run parallel along the length of the Himalayan chain. In the south, the mountains rise from the flat, fertile Ganges Plain to the low, gently folded Siwalik Range. This range contains numerous fossils of early land-living mammals, including the first apes, which have been found to be 5–25 million years old. A major thrust

NORGAY AND HILLARY

New Zealander Edmund Hillary (1919–2008) and Nepali Tenzing Norgay (1914–86) were the first people to reach the summit of Everest, on 29 May 1953. Hillary went on to lead the first overland crossing of Antarctica, and Tenzing to train guides at the Mountaineering Institute in Darjeeling, India.

fault separates the Siwaliks from the central Himalayas, which rise up to 5,000m (16,400ft) high. Geologically complex, this range includes slices of Precambrian and Paleozoic rocks covered with younger sediments. Brought to the surface by great thrust faults, these rocks have been deeply eroded, and frequent landslides still occur in the region. To the north are the Great Himalayas, which soar to more than 7,000m (23,000ft) above sea-level. These mountains are formed of Upper Paleozoic rocks, slices of the Tethys Ocean floor, and granite intrusions that have been thrust over early Cenozoic sediments. Many peaks in this range reach over 8,000m (26,000ft) and are covered with permanent snow and glaciers. Two major rivers, the Indus (see p.183) and the Brahmaputra, have their sources in these mountains.

HIMALAYAN POPPIES
Many varieties of poppy collected in the Himalayas in the 19th century are today familiar garden plants all over the world.

Beyond and to the north of the Great Himalayas lies the vast Plateau of Tibet. The Himalayas are still rising, at rates of up to 4mm (¹/₁₆in) a year, growth that is offset by the processes of weathering and erosion. Because the belt is so vast, plant species are varied, with tea cultivated on the lower slopes and oak, rhododendrons, and pine forests growing on the higher slopes. The highest peaks are inhospitable, with little or no vegetation.

MOUNTAIN OF RUBBISH

Since the summit of Mount Everest was first reached in 1953, more than 3,000 people have ascended the mountain, and over 200 have perished in the attempt. For many, climbing Everest is now merely another extreme sport, but the business provides a valuable income for the local population. However, the disposal of rubbish from climbing parties is now a major concern. Debris, including empty gas bottles, does not rot away at altitude and is difficult to bury.

PLATEAU OF TIBET
With an average altitude of 5,000m (16,400ft), the Tibetan Plateau, seen in this picture taken from the Space Shuttle, is the highest and largest plateau in the world.

FROM OCEAN TO SKY
Many Himalayan rocks were originally sediments on the Tethys Ocean floor. Now they lie within the highest mountains in the world, many of which rise over 8,000m (26,000ft) above sea-level.

LAND

AUSTRALASIA *Australia*
Great Dividing Range

LOCATION Running from the Cape York Peninsula, Queensland, along Australia's eastern coast to Tasmania

HIGHEST PEAK Mount Kosciuszko, Australia 2,228m (7,310ft)

LENGTH 3,600km (2,250 miles)

AGE Paleozoic

FORMATION TYPE Ocean–continent

To the first Europeans who arrived there, the elevated eastern margin of the Australian continent, now known as the Great Dividing Range, seemed to be a single mountain chain rising abruptly from the narrow coastal plain. However, approached from Cairns in the north, the chain forms an uplifted plateau with a great scarp face set back inland. The Great Dividing Range actually consists of a complex of tablelands and lowlands, rising to higher, alpine-like peaks in the south. The landscape ranges from green hills covered with lush tropical rainforest in Queensland, to snow-covered mountains in New South Wales. The mountains are the source of several major rivers, including the Murray (see p.183) and the Darling. The wildlife inhabiting the range is as diverse as the landscape, and includes kangaroos and platypuses. The highest peak, Mount Kosciuszko, was first noted by Polish-born explorer Paul Strzelecki in 1829, and is named after a Polish national hero.

BLUE MOUNTAINS
Trees cling to the rugged slopes of the Three Sisters, an outcrop in the Blue Mountains, New South Wales.

BREAD KNIFE, WARRUMBUNGLE
The peaks of the Warrumbungle Range, including the Bread Knife (shown here), are the remnants of ancient volcanoes.

AUSTRALASIA *New Zealand*
Southern Alps

LOCATION Running the length of New Zealand's South Island, from northeast to southwest

HIGHEST PEAK Mount Cook, New Zealand 3,744m (12,284ft)

LENGTH 500km (310 miles)

AGE Cenozoic

FORMATION TYPE Ocean–continent

A spectacular range of glaciated mountains, valleys, and fiords, the Southern Alps dominate New Zealand's South Island. The range is at its highest near the centre, where the snow fields around Mount Cook feed glaciers such as the Tasman Glacier (see p.232), which flows for 27km (17 miles). The Southern Alps were formed by the convergence of the Australian and Pacific plates. The relatively young range – it was formed in the last 60 million years – is still tectonically active and continues to experience uplift. Year-round rain from westerly winds is among the heaviest in the world, with up to 8m (26ft) falling in a year. Thus the western slopes of the range are clad in forest, while in the more arid rain-shadow to the east, tussocky grasses grow, providing pasture for summer grazing by highland sheep.

SOUTHERN PEAK
Mount Cook is just one of many peaks above 3,000m (10,000ft) in the Southern Alps.

ALPINE PARROT
The Kea, a large, opportunistic parrot, has prospered better than its relative, the endangered and flightless Kakapo.

MITRE PEAK, FIORDLAND
South Island's southwest coast is deeply indented with glacial fiords and valleys flanked by steep, triangular peaks.

Transantarctic Mountains

LOCATION Extending across Antarctica from Oates Land to the Antarctic Peninsula

HIGHEST PEAK Mount Kirkpatrick, Antarctica 4,528m (14,856ft)

LENGTH 3,500km (2,200 miles)

AGE Late Paleozoic–Cenozoic

FORMATION TYPE Continent-continent

The curved belt of the Transantarctic Mountains separates the highly elevated, ancient region of Greater Antarctica in the east from the much younger and lower Lesser Antarctica in the west. More than three-quarters of the continent is covered with a deep ice-sheet (see pp.230–31) but several mountain peaks over 4,000m (13,000ft) high emerge from it. The belt extends northwest through the continent and includes many volcanoes, some still active, including Deception Island. It is thought to mark a region along the western edge of Greater Antarctica that has been subjected to repeated compression and extension events over very long periods. The mountains continue offshore to form the South Sandwich volcanic island arc and the southwestern end of the Pacific Ring of Fire.

DRY VALLEY
With temperatures permanently below freezing and lying in a rain-shadow, some parts of Antarctica's Dry Valley have seen no rainfall for more than 2 million years.

FEATURES OF THE TRANSANTARCTIC MOUNTAINS

Elephant Island

MT WILLIAM RANGE
The Mount William Range is situated on the Antarctic Peninsula.

Antarctic Peninsula

Transantarctic Mountains

LESSER ANTARCTICA

South Geomagnetic Pole

GREATER ANTARCTICA

Vinson Massif

Mount Erebus

ROYAL SOCIETY RANGE
The Royal Society Range rises from the Scott Coast, in Victoria Land.

Oates Land

PAST CLIMATES

On Antarctica's Alexander Island, a fossilized conifer tree has been preserved that was alive in the mid-Cretaceous Period, approximately 100 million years ago. The tree is surrounded by fossils of its foliage and those of liverworts and ferns. It was entombed as it grew by sediments from floods. At the time, Antarctica was in a polar position, and the presence of such coniferous woodlands is convincing evidence of a much warmer climate during the period.

DEEP IN SNOW
Forming the northeast coast of the Ross Ice Shelf, the mountains of Queen Maud Land hold back the East Antarctic Ice-sheet except where glaciers spill through.

Volcanoes

VOLCANIC ERUPTIONS OF MOLTEN ROCK from within the Earth are awesome demonstrations of the pent-up heat energy stored within our planet. The world is dotted with volcanoes and their rock products, both ancient and modern – reminders of the Earth's long history of volcanism. The variety of materials volcanoes produce, their styles of eruption, and the edifices they create all reflect the geological environments within which they develop. Active volcanoes are found on land and, above all, in the deep sea, and their distribution – which is far from random – reflects the continuing dynamism of the planet.

Erupting Magma

Volcanism is the process by which magma – molten rock from inside the Earth – rises through the Earth's crust onto the surface. Magma chambers within the crust are created by localized melting and upward migration of partially molten crust and mantle rock. This melting requires special conditions, such as the ascent through convection of solid mantle rock beneath oceanic spreading ridges, the addition of seawater at subduction zones, or the presence of rising mantle plumes beneath hotspot volcanoes. Magma travels from the chamber up to the Earth's surface either through fractures in the crust or by literally melting a path through the surrounding rock. A volcano is both the vent at the Earth's surface through which volcanic materials erupt and the edifice created by their accumulation around the vent. As well as magma that erupts as lava, volcanic products include gas, ash, and fragmented rocks (see p.117). These can pour gently out onto the Earth's surface or be blasted through the atmosphere, to be spread globally by high-level winds (see p.116).

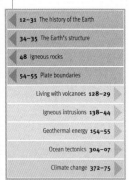

VISIBLE FROM SPACE
The scale and power of volcanic eruptions, such as this one at Rabaul, blast gas and debris high into the stratosphere. They can be seen even from space.

volcanic bombs

pyroclastic flow

surrounding country rock

magma-filled cracks and fissures

spreading eruptive cloud

erupting volcanic vent

layers of lava and pyroclastic materials

magma chamber

VOLCANISM
A typical volcanic system is based around a central "plumbing" network that transfers magma from its crustal chamber to the surface.

VOLCANIC COMPLEX
The Tengger volcanic complex in Java (foreground) consists of five overlapping volcanoes. In such cases, the vents can have intricate underground connections.

LAND

Lavas and Volcanoes

Volcanic material erupted at the Earth's surface varies according to the properties of the magma from which it is derived. Differences in chemical composition, gas content, and temperature all affect the way in which magmas erupt, and therefore the type of landforms and volcanoes they produce. Magmas that have high silica content and low temperature are very viscous and slow-moving. If they reach the surface with high gas content, their eruptions are highly explosive. If they lose their gas during ascent, they instead erupt as lava. Silica-rich lavas are thick, slow-moving block lavas that do not travel far from their source. They are associated with subduction at destructive plate margins and the assimilation of rock materials from continental crust. Basaltic lavas, including pahoehoe and 'a'a, have low silica content and high temperatures. They are extremely fluid and can travel at high speeds – up to 100kph (60mph) – over great distances. They are associated with hotspot activity, such as that under Hawaii, as well as ocean-floor spreading, where they produce pillow lavas (see pp.304–05).

PAHOEHOE (KILAUEA)
Known by its Hawaiian name, this fluid basaltic lava cools to form a glassy skin. It can have a flat, hummocky, or ropy surface produced by further flow after the skin has formed.

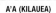

A'A (KILAUEA)
Pronounced "ah-ah", this fast-flowing basaltic lava has a rough texture, formed as the surface cools and fractures.

BLOCK LAVA (VOLCAN DE COLIMA)
Silica-rich, viscous lavas, such as andesites and rhyolites, typically flow as piles of large, fractured blocks.

SHIELD VOLCANO (MAUNA KEA)
Fluid basaltic lavas that can flow easily across the ground tend to build massive volcanoes with low, angled slopes and a shield-shaped profile.

STRATOVOLCANO (MOUNT FUJI)
The flanks of these large, often steep-sloped volcanoes are built up of alternating layers of more viscous lava and pyroclastic deposits (see p.117).

DOME VOLCANO (MOUNT ST. HELENS)
Lava domes are rounded, steep-sided mounds of silica-rich lava that is too viscous to flow very far from the vent before it cools and crystallizes.

CINDER CONE (CERRO NEGRO)
Steep, straight-sided cinder cones are made of loose, angular, volcanic rock fragments that fall from the eruption cloud and accumulate above a vent.

fissures in rock

layers of volcanic rock from earlier eruptions

minor eruptive activity continues

volcanic cone may form

crater lake

continuing eruption

emptying magma chamber

depleted chamber

collapsed volcano edifice

cooling residual magma

CALDERA FORMATION
A caldera is a broadly circular depression formed when a volcano's magma chamber is emptied As the chamber becomes depleted, and support of the overlying rock is removed, the volcano's summit collapses, forming a caldera.

Eruption Styles

Volcanologists traditionally have recognized different styles of volcanic eruption, although these styles can often mark different phases in a single event. Strombolian eruptions are spasmodic and discrete explosive bursts, a few seconds long, which eject pyroclastic materials (see opposite page) a relatively short distance into the air. High gas pressures fragment magma within the vent, but with frequent release no sustained eruption cloud develops. Vulcanian eruptions are more violent, producing highly fragmented ash and rock. Eruptive columns can rise 10–20km (6–12 miles), with ash spread over huge areas. Plinian eruptions expel large columns of pyroclasts and gas at high velocities (hundreds of metres per second) up to 45km (30 miles), well into the stratosphere. Collapse of such columns can produce deadly pyroclastic flows, containing gas and pyroclasts of all sizes, travelling at high speeds and covering large distances. In contrast, Hawaiian eruptions produce copious low-viscosity lavas, associated with shield volcanoes. Where similar eruptions occur in shallow water, they are known as Surtseyan. These eruptions can be highly explosive as a result of water invading the vent, expanding as it turns to steam, and fragmenting the magma to blast out glassy fragments.

PLINIAN ERUPTION (MAYON)
These eruptions produce massive clouds of expanding gas that carry volcanic materials high into the atmosphere. They are named after Pliny the Younger, who described the eruption of Vesuvius in 79 CE.

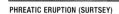

PHREATIC ERUPTION (SURTSEY)
Phreatic eruptions are steam-driven explosions produced when water, either underground or on the surface, is heated by magma or hot rocks, and expands rapidly.

FISSURE ERUPTION (KILAUEA)
In 1971, lava erupted from this fissure, which extends southwest from Halemaumau crater at Kīlauea volcano, Hawaii, and covered the surrounding landscape in basalt.

LAHAR (MT. PINATUBO)
The saturation of volcanic ash by water, from heavy rain, glacial meltwater, or drainage of crater lakes, can generate catastrophic mud or debris flows, called lahars, that devastate surrounding landscapes.

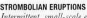

STROMBOLIAN ERUPTIONS
Intermittent, small-scale explosive eruptions like this one in Hawaii are produced as gas bubbles through a magma column in a vent.

MONITORING VOLCANOES

Many millions of people live near dangerously active volcanoes, often because their agriculture relies on rich volcanic soils (see pp.128–29). Advance notice of when eruptions might occur is highly desirable but it also has to be consistently accurate for local populations to heed the warnings. Unlike major earthquakes, which can happen with little or no warning, large-scale volcanic eruptions are often preceded by warning signs. Volcanologists have developed a number of techniques for monitoring the evolution of magmas beneath volcanoes and anticipating when volcanic activity is likely to develop into a potentially dangerous phase. These include measuring and interpreting the seismic activity that accompanies eruptions, analysis of changes in gases expelled from volcanic vents, and remote sensing by satellite to measure any changes in the elevation or shape of the volcanic edifice.

SEISMIC READINGS
Volcanologists use seismometers to detect vibrations caused by fracturing rock, magma movement, or bursting gas bubbles prior to eruptions.

Volcanic Deposits

Many different types of volcanic material can be preserved in the Earth's rock record, and their analysis reveals a great deal about the nature of past volcanism. Although lavas are the best known volcanic products and can vary considerably in composition, texture, and volume (see p.115), fragmented volcanic rock materials, or pyroclasts, are in many ways the most interesting and have the greatest impact on life. They are produced by explosive eruptions of parent magmas that evolve into gaseous columns containing fragmented rock, minerals, and glassy shards. Deposits are classified by particle size. The smallest, usually called ash, is fine enough to stay aloft for days to weeks and can be distributed globally by high-altitude winds. Fragments can also combine with hot gases to produce glowing pyroclastic flows rolling across landscapes at up to 200kph (125mph). At the other end of the scale, some volcanoes have been known to eject rock fragments bigger than a house up to several kilometres. Tephra is a collective term for fragments of volcanic rock and lava of all sizes that are blasted into the air.

LAYERED DEPOSITS
Pyroclastic eruptive material is deposited in a similar way to sediments and accumulates as stratified layers.

ASH BURIAL
Volcanic deposits of all sizes can smother and bury landscapes and buildings, as here on Montserrat, and totally extinguish life.

LAVA BOMBS
Large fragments of ejected molten rock take on aerodynamic shapes as they travel through the air.

LAND

Volcano Distribution

The global distribution of volcanoes clearly relates to the Earth's tectonic plates. About 80 per cent of volcanoes above sea-level occur at convergent plate boundaries, 5 per cent occur at divergent boundaries, and mantle hotspots account for the rest, found away from plate boundaries. The volcanic chains around the Pacific (called the Ring of Fire) include volcanic island arcs, formed by ocean–ocean plate convergence, and Andean-style continental arcs, produced by ocean–continent convergence. Continental plate divergence generates rift volcanoes, such as those of eastern Africa, while oceanic plate divergence forms ridges, such as that of the mid-Atlantic, and isolated volcanic islands.

volcanic island
ocean–ocean convergence
active hotspot volcano
mid-ocean ridge
ocean–continent convergence
volcanic island arc
young mountains, including volcanoes
continental plate
subduction zone
oceanic plate
mantle hotspot
mantle upwelling
subduction zone

VOLCANOES AND PLATES
Volcanic activity is closely associated with the movement of tectonic plates. Most active volcanism is found at undersea mid-ocean ridges where crust is being pulled apart. It is also produced by convergent plate boundaries, where subduction occurs, and rising mantle hotspots.

VOLCANO PROFILES

The pages that follow contain profiles of many of the the world's most significant and best-known volcanoes. Each profile begins with the following summary information:

HEIGHT Elevation above sea-level of each volcano's highest point. Due to volcanic activity this figure is likely to change over time

TYPE Stratovolcano, shield volcano, cinder cone, caldera, fissure vent, maar (vent formed by steam explosions), tuff cone, lava dome, flood basalt, complex

LAST ERUPTION Date of the last confirmed eruption, or, in the case of ancient volcanoes, an estimate based on rock records

NORTH AMERICA northwest
Novarupta

LOCATION In the Katmai region of the Alaskan Peninsula, in the northwest USA

HEIGHT 841m (2,760ft)

TYPE Caldera, lava dome

LAST ERUPTION 1912

Although Novarupta is the lowest volcano in the Katmai area of Alaska, it was formed, in 1912, by the biggest volcanic eruption of the 20th century. Within 60 hours, some 30 cubic km (7 cubic miles) of silica-rich rhyolitic magma blasted out of Novarupta. Most of it fell back to Earth as ash, while the remainder formed a pyroclastic flow – the renowned Valley of Ten Thousand Smokes (VTTS) ash flow (see p.148). At the end of the eruption, two calderas formed. An indistinct shallow depression about 2km (1.2 miles) wide formed at Novarupta and was followed by the extrusion of a lava dome, 65m (215ft) high and 380m (1250ft) wide, at the vent of the VTTS ash flow. A much larger collapse caldera, about 5km (3 miles) wide, was formed at Katmai volcano 16km (10 miles) to the east, as its underground magma reservoir drained towards Novarupta. Traces of ash that settled after the 1912 eruption have been found in Greenland ice cores.

PLUG DOME
Novarupta's lava dome was formed as masses of viscous lava piled over and around the vent. As it expanded from within, its surface hardened and cracked.

NORTH AMERICA west
Mount Rainier

LOCATION In the northern Cascade Range, Washington State, west USA

HEIGHT 4,392m (14,410ft)

TYPE Stratovolcano

LAST ERUPTION 1894

Heavily glaciated, with an ice-filled summit crater complex, Mount Rainier is the highest peak in the Cascade range. The collapse of a much larger structure about 5,600 years ago produced great lahars that flowed more than 100km (60 miles) to Puget Sound. The present-day cone, capped by overlapping craters, formed during a major explosive eruption about 2,200 years ago.

MOUNT RAINIER CAPPED WITH SNOW

NORTH AMERICA west
Columbia River Plateau

LOCATION Ranging across southern Washington, northern Oregon, and Idaho

HEIGHT Up to 2,000m (6,600ft)

TYPE Flood basalt

LAST ERUPTION About 15 million years ago

Between 17 and 15 million years ago, about 170,000 cubic km (40,000 cubic miles) of basaltic lava poured out of deep crustal fissures to create the Columbia River Plateau. Many of the flows are over 100km (160 miles) long and up to 30m (100ft) thick, and some cooled to form distinctive shrinkage columns. More than 95 per cent of the basalts may have been erupted in less than 2 million years. The origin of the eruption is thought to have been a rising mantle plume or hotspot beneath the continental crust, which produced partial melting in the upper mantle. The increased heat flow caused the crustal rocks above to dome and stretched, creating deep cracks that tapped the magma below and allowed it to flow out at the surface.

TWIN SISTERS
These basalt pillars were isolated about 15,000 years ago when catastrophic floods carved great channels in the Plateau.

NORTH AMERICA west
Crater Lake

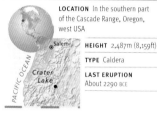

LOCATION In the southern part of the Cascade Range, Oregon, west USA

HEIGHT 2,487m (8,159ft)

TYPE Caldera

LAST ERUPTION About 2290 BCE

Crater Lake, the second deepest lake in North America at 589m (1,934ft) deep, fills a caldera 14km (9 miles) wide and is surrounded by a spectacular rock wall. The caldera marks the site of a complex of overlapping volcanoes, known as Mount Mazama. This complex was built up 420,000–40,000 years ago and erupted 6,850 years ago in one of the biggest eruptions of the Holocene (the last 10,000 years). A huge Plinian blast showered ash as far away as Alberta, Canada, and pyroclastic flows travelled up to 40km (25 miles) from the volcano. A series of now-lake-covered lava domes formed on the caldera floor a few hundred years after its formation.

VOLCANIC DEPOSITS
Crater Lake's "Pinnacles" are pyroclastic flow deposits that have eroded into dramatic spires.

FLOODED CALDERA
Crater Lake fills an almost perfectly circular caldera. The lake's surface is broken by Wizard Island, a cinder cone that erupted out of the caldera floor.

LAND

Mount St. Helens

LOCATION In the northern region of the Cascade Range, Washington State, west USA

HEIGHT 2,549m (8,363ft)

TYPE Stratovolcano

LAST ERUPTION 2008

The strikingly symmetrical cone of Mount St. Helens had long been admired as America's Mount Fuji. However, on 18 May 1980, in one of the world's best-documented eruptions, the top 1,400m (4,600ft) of the volcano was destroyed, leaving a horseshoe-shaped caldera. Magma intrusion caused the north flank to bulge outward and then collapse in a debris avalanche, uncorking an explosive eruption. The avalanche travelled about 25km (16 miles) at speeds of up to 75m (250ft) per second, filling a valley with debris up to 195m (640ft) deep. An explosive blast of hot gases and magma travelled ahead of the debris avalanche, flattening more than 10 million trees over about 600 square kilometres (230 square miles). Later, collapse at the base of the eruptive column produced numerous pyroclastic flows, at temperatures of about 700°C (1,300°F). Formed in nine eruptive phases beginning 50,000–40,000 years ago, Mount St. Helens has been the most active volcano in the Cascade Range during the Holocene Epoch (the last 10,000 years). The modern volcano has been constructed within the last 2,500 years as basaltic, andesitic, and dacitic magma erupted from both summit and flank vents.

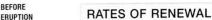

BEFORE ERUPTION
The volcano's conical peak was flanked by evergreen forests and grassy meadows.

AFTER ERUPTION
Seared by a lethal combination of red-hot gases, rocks, and ash, the landscape to the north of the volcano resembled a desolate moonscape.

RATES OF RENEWAL

Catastrophic volcanic eruptions can destroy the plant and animal life of a region. Mount St. Helens provided an invaluable opportunity to monitor the regeneration of wildlife after an eruption. Studies revealed that recolonization occurs at a much faster rate than scientists had estimated. Mats of river algae (see below) and sprouting shrubs were harbingers of regrowth, followed by birds, small mammals, and, eventually, elk.

WILDLIFE RETURNS
Although about 2,000 elk died in the eruption, large numbers have since returned to the area to graze.

PLINIAN ERUPTION
In 1980, Mount St. Helens produced a Plinian-style eruption, blasting an eruptive column of gas, ash, and pumice fragments 24km (15 miles) into the atmosphere.

08:32:47
1

08:32:53
2

08:33:00
3

08:33:19
4

THE MOUNTAIN EXPLODES
As the north side of the volcano collapsed, a rock avalanche was set in motion (1). Pressure inside the volcano was released, and clouds of ash blasted out (2–3). These eventually caught up with and overtook the avalanche (4).

Kilauea

LOCATION On the southeast coast of Hawaii, the most southeasterly of the Hawaiian Islands

HEIGHT 1,222m (4,009ft)

TYPE Shield volcano

LAST ERUPTION 2010

LAVA FIELD
Low-viscocity, basaltic lava streams down the flanks of Kilauea. Lava flows can eventually reach the coast, where they cascade into the sea.

Kilauea is the most active of the overlapping volcanoes that have built up the island of Hawaii over the past million years. With its massive low-angle slope profile and wide caldera, it is a typical shield volcano built up by frequent summit and flank basaltic lava flows interspersed with lava-lake activity within the crater. About 90 per cent of Kilauea's surface is formed by lava that is less than 1,100 years old. Since 1983, during a period of constant eruption, flows have covered over 100 square kilometres (40 square miles) and destroyed up to 200 houses. Most of Kilauea is hidden beneath the sea. Hawaii is part of a chain of volcanic islands built up over the past 75 million years as the Pacific Plate passed over a mantle hotspot at a rate of about 9cm (3½in) per year.

SAMPLING LAVA

Sampling a volcano's lava is one way to monitor changes in its behaviour. Volcanologists studying Kilauea throw hammer-headed cables into lava tubes or, as shown here, take hand samples directly from lava flows or vent spatter. It is important to take hot lava samples, to obtain rapidly quenched glass for analysis.

Mauna Loa

LOCATION In the centre of Hawaii, the most southeasterly of the Hawaiian Islands

HEIGHT 4,170m (13,681ft)

TYPE Shield volcano

LAST ERUPTION 1984

SUMMIT CRATERS

Rising nearly 9km (5½ miles) from the ocean floor, and covering about half the island of Hawaii, Mauna Loa is the largest active volcano in the world. Almost 90 per cent of its surface is basaltic lava less than 4,000 years old, erupted from flank fissures and overflowed from a summit lava lake. There have also been large-scale submarine avalanches, one of which travelled nearly 100km (60 miles).

NORTH AMERICA *south*

Parícutin

LOCATION In the Mexican Volcanic Belt, of southwestern Mexico, inland from the Pacific coast

HEIGHT 2,809m (9,216ft)

TYPE Cinder cone

LAST ERUPTION 1952

VOLCANO ABLAZE

Parícutin is the best-known volcano of about 1,000 volcanic centres in the Michoacán–Guanajuato volcanic field. It is a cinder cone that started to erupt from a cornfield in 1943 and grew to 336m (1,102ft) within a year. The eruption continued until 1952, adding an extra 88m (288ft) to its height. Parícutin provided volcanologists with the rare chance to witness and document the birth, growth, and death of a volcano.

NORTH AMERICA *south*

Colima

LOCATION In the Mexican Volcanic Belt, of southwestern Mexico inland from the Pacific coast

HEIGHT 3,860m (12,664ft)

TYPE Stratovolcano

LAST ERUPTION 2011

Colima is the most prominent complex in the western Mexican Volcanic Belt. It is made up of the 4,320m (14,173ft) Nevado de Colima and the younger 3,860m (12,664ft) Volcán de Colima, an active stratovolcano that grew on the south flank of Nevado in a southward-moving pattern typical of the belt. Volcán de Colima is Mexico's most active volcano – its active cone lies within a 5km- (3-mile-) wide caldera formed by the collapse of an ancestral cone. Major slope failures at both Nevado and Volcán de Colima have formed a thick apron of debris-avalanche deposits. One of the biggest known occurred about 18,000 years ago, travelling for 120km (70 miles) to the Pacific coast. The volcanic complex began to grow in late Pleistocene times, and recorded eruptions date back to the 16th century with occasional major explosive eruptions. The most recent, in 1913, destroyed the summit and left a steep-walled crater that was refilled and then overtopped by the growth of a lava dome that has fed five block lava flows since 1961.

SHEER FLANKS
The steep profile of the Volcán de Colima has been shaped by viscous block-lava flows.

GAS SAMPLING
Volcanologists collect samples from a fumarole field at the rim of Colima's crater. Monitoring composition and temperature of the gases can help scientists understand and predict the volcano's behaviour.

NORTH AMERICA *south*
Popocatépetl

LOCATION In the Mexican Volcanic Belt, within the Puebla region of south-central Mexico

HEIGHT 5,452m (17,887ft)

TYPE Stratovolcano

LAST ERUPTION 2011

Popocatépetl is North America's second highest volcano, towering over Mexico city to its northwest. With its symmetrical shape, summit glaciers, and frequent eruptions during recorded history, it has an imposing

STEEP-WALLED CRATER
Popocatépetl's deep, oval-shaped crater has near-vertical walls. On the crater floor, a succession of sporadically erupting lava domes has evolved.

presence. From the Pleistocene Epoch onwards, the volcano has grown to 28km (17½ miles) across. The summit crater is 670m (2,200ft) in diameter and up to 450m (1,480ft) deep. Since Popocatépetl's formation, at least three previous cones have been destroyed by gravitational collapse. These have produced massive debris-avalanche deposits to the south. Three major Plinian eruptions have occurred over the last few thousand years, most recently in 800 CE, producing pyroclastic flows and large-volume lahars. The Aztecs recorded frequent historical eruptions before the arrival of Western explorers in the 15th century, and gave the volcano its name, meaning "smoking mountain".

FERTILE SOILS

Volcanic products are rich in minerals and glass that can produce very fertile and well-drained soils. In highly populated areas, such as here in the shadow of Popocatépetl, the fertile soil is of great benefit to local farmers, despite the potential risks.

NORTH AMERICA *south*
El Chichón

LOCATION In an isolated part of the Chiapas region of southeastern Mexico

HEIGHT 1,060m (3,478ft)

TYPE Lava dome

LAST ERUPTION 1982

This lava-dome and tuff-cone complex was relatively unknown until 1982, when it produced a series of highly explosive eruptions. Pyroclastic flows swept outward for more than 8km (5 miles), destroying 9 villages and killing more than 2,000 people. The magma was extremely sulphur-rich, and sulphuric acid droplets forming in the stratosphere produced brilliant sunsets around the globe.

ACIDIC POST-ERUPTION CRATER LAKE

CENTRAL AMERICA
Masaya

LOCATION Between the west coast of Lake Nicaragua and the Pacific coast, southwestern Nicaragua

HEIGHT 635m (2,083ft)

TYPE Caldera

LAST ERUPTION 2008

ESCAPING GASES

One of Nicaragua's most active volcanoes, Masaya is an 11km- (7-mile-) wide caldera, with more than a dozen vents, surrounded by walls 300m (985ft) high. The twin cones of Masaya and Nindiri have been the source of frequent recorded eruptions. A major Plinian eruption of basaltic tephra occurred about 6,500 years ago. Since then, frequent lava flows have covered much of the caldera floor, and in 1670 CE one overtopped the northern rim.

CENTRAL AMERICA
Arenal

LOCATION On the southeastern shore of Lake Arenal in central Costa Rica

HEIGHT 1,657m (5,436ft)

TYPE Stratovolcano

LAST ERUPTION 2010

Arenal is the youngest and one of the most active volcanoes in Costa Rica. The 1968 Vulcanian eruption signalled the start of the current long-term eruptive period. It threw large bombs up to 5km (3 miles) from the crater and generated pyroclastic flows (one of which killed 70 people) before releasing viscous lava flows from vents at the summit and the upper part of its western slope.

INCANDESCENT ROCK AVALANCHES

CENTRAL AMERICA
Soufrière Hills

LOCATION Occupies the southern half of the island of Montserrat in the eastern Caribbean Sea

HEIGHT 915m (3,002ft)

TYPE Stratovolcano

LAST ERUPTION 2011

Soufrière Hills is a complex volcano, with a series of lava domes forming its summit area. Although swarms of seismic shocks had been felt at 30-year intervals throughout the 20th century, the volcano was thought

NEW DELTA
Some pyroclastic flows have travelled all the way to the coast and discharged over and into the sea, creating new deltas.

to be inactive. Then, in an eruption beginning in 1995, pyroclastic flows and mudflows overran and destroyed Plymouth, Montserrat's capital, burying it under several metres of pyroclastic deposits. The southern end of the island was evacuated and, inevitably, the population suffered major disruption. As the activity has continued, Soufrière Hills has become one of the world's most closely monitored volcanoes.

ERUPTION CLOUD
Soufrière Hills produces Plinian eruptions, sending huge clouds of ash high into the air and smothering the surrounding area.

Nevado del Ruiz

LOCATION In the northern region of the Cordillera Central range, central Colombia

HEIGHT 5,321m (17,457ft)

TYPE Stratovolcano

LAST ERUPTION 1991

The modern volcano of Nevado del Ruiz sits within the caldera of the older Ruiz volcano. Its cone consists of a series of lava domes, with the summit occupied by the Arenas crater, 1km (3,300ft) wide and 240m (790ft) deep. The volcano's flanks are shaped by large landslides. Although Nevado del Ruiz is only about 500km (300 miles) north of the equator, its position high in the Andes means that it is capped throughout the year by large volumes of snow and ice. Because of this, heat released by eruptions has, during recorded history, caused summit glaciers to melt, creating devastating lahars. In 1985, Nevado del Ruiz was the scene of South America's deadliest volcanic eruption and one of the worst volcanic disasters of modern times (see panel, right). A relatively small volume of hot ejecta, spewed across the snow- and ice-covered summit, proved to be a lethal combination.

BROAD MASS
Nevado del Ruiz is a wide, sprawling volcano that covers over 200 square km (77 square miles).

LAHAR DISASTER

On 13 November 1985, pyroclastic flows, released by a small eruption, melted the summit ice-cap, triggering a series of devastating lahars. Channelled down narrow valleys for up to 100km (60 miles), they wiped out the town of Armero and killed more than 23,500 people. When the flows stopped, they set like concrete, offering victims little chance to escape.

Galeras

LOCATION At the southern end of the Cordillera Central range, southwest Colombia

HEIGHT 4,276m (14,029ft)

TYPE Complex volcano

LAST ERUPTION 2010

Now a modern cone positioned within an older caldera, Galeras has been active for more than a million years. Major eruptions and weakening of the edifice on many occasions have led to debris avalanches, pyroclastic flows, and widespread air-fall deposits. Situated next to the city of Pasto, the volcano is closely monitored.

PASTO'S VOLCANIC BACKDROP

Cotopaxi

LOCATION At the southern end of the Cordillera Central range, northern Ecuador

HEIGHT 5,911m (19,393ft)

TYPE Stratovolcano

LAST ERUPTION 1940

The glacier-clad Cotopaxi is the highest active volcano on Earth. One of Ecuador's most active volcanoes, it has a steep-sided, almost perfectly symmetrical cone capped with deep craters nested within the summit.

ICY CRATER
Situated in the northern Andes, Cotopaxi is the highest active volcano in the world. Its peak is clad with glaciers and a constant snow covering.

VOLCANIC DEBRIS
A huge block of volcanic rock lies on a flank of Cotopaxi where it was probably deposited by a large debris avalanche or powerful lahar.

The present cone, scarred by lava flows and lahars, has been constructed over the last 5,000 years. Cotopaxi has a long history of explosive eruptions, including that of 1534, which put an end to a battle between the Incas and Spaniards. In one of its most violent recorded eruptions, in 1877, an eruptive column collapsed, generating pyroclastic flows and lahars that devastated nearby valleys and flowed over 100km (60 miles) into the Pacific Ocean.

Cerro Azul–Quizapu

LOCATION In the southern Andes, central Chile, close to the border with Argentina

HEIGHT 3,788m (12,428ft)

TYPE Stratovolcano

LAST ERUPTION 1967

The steep-sided Cerro Azul volcano is located at the southern end of a volcano chain called the Descabezado Grande–Cerro Azul eruptive system. It has a 500m- (1,640ft-) wide summit crater and several flank cinder cones, including the three La Resoloma craters to the west and Los Hornitos to the southwest. Quizapu is a vent on the northern flank that formed in 1846 with the emission of a large volume of lava. In 1932, Quizapu was the site of one of the largest explosive eruptions of the 20th century, ejecting a large volume of tephra and creating a crater up to 700m (2,300ft) wide and 150m (490ft) deep.

QUIZAPU CRATER

Paraná Plateau

LOCATION Across southern Brazil, eastern Paraguay, northern Argentina, and northwest Uruguay

HEIGHT Up to 1,000m (3,300ft)

TYPE Fissure vent

LAST ERUPTION About 120 million years ago

The eruption about 120 million years ago of more than 750,000 square km (290,000 square miles) of basaltic lava in the Paraná region of eastern South America coincided with the splitting of that continent from Africa and the opening of the south Atlantic Ocean. Heat from within the mantle formed the Walvis hotspot under the Paraná region of eastern South America and Namibia in southwest Africa, which at the time were joined together. Doming of the crust over a 1,000km- (625-mile-) wide zone developed deep and extensive fractures, through which lava poured onto the Earth's surface. Continuing volcanic activity led to further rifting between the continents and the formation of a new ocean basin. The hotspot is today marked by the volcanic island of Tristan da Cunha, which last erupted in 1961.

ATLANTIC OCEAN *north*

Grímsvötn

LOCATION Lying largely beneath the Vatnajökull ice-cap of central Iceland

HEIGHT 1,725m (5,659ft)

TYPE Caldera

LAST ERUPTION 2011

Iceland's most active volcano in recorded history, Grímsvötn is largely covered by the Vatnajökull ice-cap. Only the southern rim of its 8km- (5-mile-) wide caldera is exposed above the ice, and heat from the

LAKI FISSURE
The Laki fissure system is 27km (17 miles) long and contains over 140 craters.

volcano frequently causes floods of melted glacier ice (jökulhlaups). Long fissures extending from the volcano include the well-known Laki fissure, which produced the largest lava flow in recorded history. In 1783 about 15 cubic km (3½ cubic miles) of lava were erupted over a period of seven months. More than 9,000 people died from starvation and disease in what became Iceland's worst natural disaster.

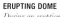

ERUPTING DOME
During an eruption in 1998, a plume 10km (6 miles) high erupted from the caldera.

EUROPE *west*

Antrim Plateau

LOCATION On the coast of County Antrim in northeastern Northern Ireland

HEIGHT Up to 550m (1,800ft)

TYPE Fissure vent

LAST ERUPTION About 55 million years ago

About 55 million years ago, a rising mantle plume caused the northwest of the British Isles and southeast Greenland to dome upwards. Rifting and sea-floor spreading erupted a pile of basaltic lavas up to 2km (1¼ miles)

thick, with flows up to 8m (26ft) thick. The lava flows are interbedded with pyroclastic material, and plant fossils in the beds show a humid temperate climate. The Giant's Causeway, a group of thousands of mostly hexagonal basalt columns, is world-famous for its spectacular appearance.

THE GIANT'S CAUSEWAY

EUROPE *central*

West Eifel Field

LOCATION In the Rhine Valley, south of the city of Cologne, western Germany

HEIGHT 600m (1,968ft)

TYPE Maars, cinder cones

LAST ERUPTION 7,000–11,000 years ago

The West Eifel Field is associated with the Rhine Rift (see p.87). Over the last 730,000 years, it has seen alternating episodes of Strombolian and phreatic activity, producing some 240 cinder cones, maars, and small

MAAR MINING

stratovolcanoes. They cover an area of about 600 square km (230 square miles), with the last eruption occurring 7,000–11,000 years ago. More than 70 maars, up to 1km (3,300ft) in diameter and up to 200m (650ft) deep, were formed between 12,500 and 10,000 years ago, when the end of the last ice age produced abundant meltwater.

EUROPE *west*

Chaîne des Puys

LOCATION In the Auvergne region of central France, in the northern Massif Central

HEIGHT 1,464m (4,803ft)

TYPE Cinder cones, lava domes, maars

LAST ERUPTION About 4040 BCE

The Chaîne des Puys was keenly studied by 19th-century scientists and played an important role in the history of geology. It is a series of cinder

cones, lava domes, and maars aligned north to south. The maars are craters formed by explosive eruptions, rimmed by ejected debris, and often filled by lakes. Their formation began about 70,000 years ago, with pyroclastic flows and long lava flows, and finally ended about 6,000 years ago. The most recent volcanic activity occurred near Besse-en-Chandesse. It has been radiocarbon-dated at around 4040 BCE and included powerful explosions that created Lac Pavin Maar.

VOLCANO CHAIN
A series of about 90 cinder cones, maars, and lava domes extends across nearly 50km (35 miles) of France's northern Massif Central.

EUROPE *south*

Stromboli

LOCATION One of the volcanic Aeolian Islands off the north coast of Sicily in the Mediterranean

HEIGHT 926m (3,038ft)

TYPE Stratovolcano

LAST ERUPTION 2011

The small island of Stromboli is an active volcano rising about 3,000m (9,850ft) from the ocean floor. It is one of the few almost continuously erupting volcanoes on Earth, having been active since records began more than 2,500 years ago. Stromboli's active summit vents are located in the Sciara del Fuoco, a curved scarp that was formed by a slope failure about 5,000 years ago. The volcano gave its name to one of the main types of volcanic eruption (see p.116). Most of its activity is moderate in scale,

consisting of brief, but explosive, ejections of glowing lava fragments to heights seldom more than 150m (490ft) and, less frequently, lava flows. Periods of more intense activity can produce prolonged eruptions from fountains and ejection of large bombs.

INCANDESCENT DISPLAY
This long-exposure photograph shows a typical small-scale explosive eruption ejecting glowing rock particles into the air.

LAND

UNPREDICTABLE ERUPTIONS
Predicting volcanic eruptions is difficult. Puyehue in Chile lay dormant for decades and then erupted June 2011. Ash clouds from the eruption, seen here illuminated by lightning, darkened skies as far away as Argentina.

EUROPE *south*

Mount Etna

LOCATION On the eastern side of the Mediterranean island of Sicily, southwest of the Italian mainland

MEDITERRANEAN SEA
Messina
Mount Etna
Sicily
Catania

HEIGHT 3,350m (10,991ft)

TYPE Stratovolcano

LAST ERUPTION 2013

Etna is Europe's highest volcano, and has been almost continuously active since observations were first recorded, about 2,500 years ago. About 2.5 million years old, Etna probably originates from a mantle hotspot. The volcano has a tall cone with a base circumference of about 150km (95 miles) and a surface area of about 1,600 square km (620 square miles). Etna's most prominent feature is the Valle del Bove, a 10km- (6-mile-) wide horseshoe-shaped caldera open to the southeast. The summit is a complex structure of old and new craters, and currently there are four active craters. The sides of the volcano are scored by deep fissures that radiate from the summit. Up to 200 small ash cones are present on its flanks, with three larger cones near the summit. Etna produces basaltic lava that has low viscosity, and lava flows extend to the foot of the volcano on all sides, reaching the sea over a broad area on the southeast flank. The summit craters are in a permanent state of low-level activity, with lava fountains erupting and phreatic explosions (see pp.116–17). Although Etna has not been considered an especially explosive volcano, at times it can be spectacular. Etna's largest and most famous eruption, in 1669, lasted 122 days. Earthquakes opened a 12km (8-mile-) long fissure and outpourings of basaltic lavas rapidly overwhelmed nearby villages (see panel, right). The 1986 summit eruption produced lava fountains that jetted up to 1.6km (1 mile) above the crater, and a column of ash and gas that rose 10km (6 miles) into the atmosphere. More recently, eruptions in both 2001 and 2002 again brought Etna to the world's attention.

DIVERTING LAVA FLOWS

Efforts to divert destructive lava flows on Etna date as far back as 1669, when lava overwhelmed a number of villages and threatened the town of Catania. A party was sent to try and breach a levee and allow the lava to spread in a different direction, away from the town. However, this action met with opposition from neighbouring villagers, and the lava flow was eventually left to enter the town. In recent years, methods have involved the use of industrial equipment to build earth dams and concrete barriers, and even the use of explosives. However, most lava-diversion attempts meet with only temporary success.

RIVER OF FIRE
Broad rivers of alkali basaltic lava flow down the lava field of the Valle del Bove on Etna's southeast flank in January 1992.

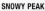

SNOWY PEAK
Close to Etna's summit, the desolate wasteland of solid lava and ash is covered with snow for much of the year. Its fertile lower slopes are widely cultivated.

1 **2** **3** **4**

ERUPTIVE DISPLAY
On 28 July 2001, explosions from Etna's newly formed Lago cone hurled clouds of ash high into the air (1 and 2). Later, molten materials were discharged from two separate vents simultaneously (3 and 4).

STROMBOLIAN ACTIVITY ON ETNA
Fountains of fluid lava and violent ejection of partially molten volcanic bombs, seen in this long-exposure photograph, are typical of Strombolian eruptions (see p.116).

OUT OF THE ASHES
Planted in pits designed to trap water, vines flourish in arid but fertile volcanic soil on Lanzarote, the easternmost of the Canary Islands.

LIVING WITH VOLCANOES

Volcanoes and the materials that they produce are essential for life on Earth. Without them, surface water would not have formed, and living things could not have evolved. Volcanoes also raise minerals and melts from deep in the Earth's crust, helping to create fertile soil. But this beneficial role comes at a price, because eruptions are among the most deadly hazards in the world. That danger cannot be removed, but with modern technology the risk it carries can be reduced.

Volcanoes as Neighbours

Although volcanoes have always been feared, people recognized their beneficial effects long before anything was known about the chemistry of soils. In Sicily, for example, the lower slopes of Mount Etna have been farmed for several thousand years, and were an important source of agricultural produce in classical times. On the Indonesian island of Java, weathered volcanic soil currently supports one of the densest populations on the Earth, with an average of nearly 800 people per square kilometre (2,100 per square mile). By way of contrast, the Amazon Basin, which is situated on almost exactly the same latitude as Java and enjoys a similar climate, is non-volcanic, and suffers from extremely poor soils, which are difficult to cultivate successfully.

Mount Etna has erupted more than 200 times in recorded history, but, despite this turbulent past, it has inflicted relatively little loss of human life. Etna's immense size means that most farms are distant from the summit, and the mountain's lava streams often follow predictable paths that people can avoid. Many volcanoes in populated regions, however, are prone to violently explosive eruptions (see p.116). Java's volcanoes fall into this category, as do those of Mount Pinatubo, in the Philippines. When the latter erupted in 1991, the death toll was high, and thousands of farms were buried by ash.

STANDING SENTINEL
A volcano rises high above rice-fields and buildings in Japan. More than 60 volcanoes are recorded as active in the Japanese archipelago.

Warning Signs

Modern volcanology began in the early 1900s, when an observatory was built on Kilauea – the world's largest active volcano – in Hawaii. Before this, people relied on a mixture of observation and superstition to judge when a volcano might erupt. Seismic tremors provided some clues, as did the sudden escape of gas, but just as much attention was paid to unusual behaviour in wild animals. Unfortunately, these portents often turned out to be unreliable – a fact vividly demonstrated in 79 CE, when Mount Vesuvius in Italy erupted, burying Pompeii and its inhabitants under several metres of ash (see p.130).

Volcanologists now gather several kinds of data to predict volcanic activity. One of the most useful is the physical deformation that occurs when magma rises up through a volcano's interior. Sudden expansion – such as that witnessed in Mount St. Helens, USA, in 1980 – is one of the surest signs that an eruption is imminent. Until recently, deformation measurements had to be taken manually, using instruments fixed to a crater's rim, but measurements can now be done remotely by satellite-based radar without any human presence at the crater.

CLOSE ESCAPE
These houses in Shimabara, Japan, were damaged after Mount Unzen erupted in 1993 – about 200 years after the last devastation.

Monitoring Volcanoes

Seismic activity is the most widely monitored parameter at active volcanoes – a warning sign is an increase or, just as ominously, a sudden stop in movement. Such information is gathered by automated seismic sensors, and is then transmitted to research stations for analysis. Seismic sensing provided advance warning of the Mount Pinatubo eruption, although, because of its immense scale, not everyone was able to escape.

Moving magma causes changes in a volcano's magnetic field, and vent-gas analysis provides a further line of evidence, because the concentration of gases changes as hot magma approaches the surface. Originally developed in Japan, vent-gas analysis can signal increased volcanic activity months before a volcano explodes, and, after an eruption, it also provides confirmation that volcanic activity is in decline. As yet, a fail-safe method of predicting eruptions does not exist, but with these monitoring techniques that goal may not be far off.

GAS ANALYSIS
A volcanologist collects gas samples on the island of Vulcano, off the north coast of Sicily. The last major eruption here was in 1890.

GAS EMISSIONS
The toxic acidic gas sulphur dioxide is emitted by active volcanoes. At Mount St. Helens, sulphur dioxide emissions reached peak levels during the 1980 eruption, and then gradually subsided. The measurements were made by a sampling aeroplane.

[bar chart: Annual emission rate (tonnes per day) vs Year, with values decreasing from about 2,300 in 1980 to near 0 by 1988; x-axis years 1980, 1981, 1982, 1983, 1984, 1985, 1986, 1987, 1988; y-axis 0, 500, 1,000, 1,500, 2,000, 2,500]

LAND

EUROPE *south*

Vesuvius

LOCATION On the eastern coast of the Bay of Naples, 12km (7 miles) east of Naples in southwest Italy

HEIGHT 1,281m (4,203ft)

TYPE Complex volcano

LAST ERUPTION 1944

Vesuvius is a frequently active volcano overlooking the Bay of Naples. Its cone, with a base circumference of about 70km (45 miles), sits within the caldera of an older volcano, Monte Somma, that formed about 17,000 years ago. Vesuvius is best known for its Plinian eruptions, such as the one in 79 CE that destroyed Pompeii and Herculaneum (see panel, below). Since the modern cone formed, there have been eight major eruptions, accompanied by large pyroclastic flows and surges, and high eruptive columns capable of carrying pumice, ash, and bombs tens of kilometres into the air. In 1631, during the largest eruption since 79 CE, pyroclastic flows reached as far as the sea. More recently, Vesuvius erupted in 1906 and 1944, causing fatalities on both occasions. Today, about 3 million people live within the eruptive range of Vesuvius, and evacuation plans are in place.

GIANT PROFILE
The city of Naples sits in the shadow of Vesuvius, whose fertile slopes are dotted with villages and vineyards.

DESTRUCTION OF POMPEII

Most of the victims of the eruption that destroyed Pompeii in 79 CE died very suddenly, smothered by fast-moving, high-temperature pyroclastic surges. A town of about 20,000 people, Pompeii was buried under 3m (10ft) of materials that effectively "fossilized" the inhabitants and building remains.

LAST MAJOR ERUPTION
The 1944 eruption of Vesuvius claimed the lives of 27 people. As the average repose time between eruptions is 50 years, the next eruption is overdue.

EUROPE *southeast*

Santorini

LOCATION One of the volcanic Greek Cyclades Islands in the eastern Mediterranean Sea

HEIGHT 367m (1,204ft)

TYPE Caldera

LAST ERUPTION 1950

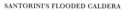

SANTORINI'S FLOODED CALDERA

Santorini is a complex of overlapping volcanoes and calderas forming a circular group of islands with steep, inward-facing walls. The most recent caldera-forming eruption occurred in about 1640 BCE, when about 58–68 cubic km (14–16 cubic miles) of material was ejected, and the current sea-filled caldera was formed. It is thought that this eruption might have caused the collapse of the Minoan civilization. New islands in the centre of the caldera were formed by a series of eruptions beginning in 197 BCE.

EUROPE *south*

Vulcano

LOCATION One of the volcanic Aeolian Islands off the north coast of Sicily in the Mediterranean Sea

HEIGHT 500m (1,640ft)

TYPE Stratovolcano

LAST ERUPTION 1890

The island of Vulcano is the source of the word "volcano" – according to Roman legend, Vulcano was home to Vulcan, the god of fire, and his forges. It also gives its name to the Vulcanian style of eruption, which is characterized by moderate-to-violent eruptive columns dominated by viscous and solid ejecta. Although it is only a small island (with an area of 22 square km/8.5 square miles), Vulcano is constructed of four volcanic complexes that have developed over the last 120,000 years. The Piano caldera, in the southern half of the island, is overlapped to the north by the Fossa cone, a modern volcano that last erupted in 1888–90. Vulcanello, on the northern tip of the island, is a partly submerged volcano with a lava platform, which now forms a low peninsula. The Vulcano complex also includes a combination of hot springs, mud pots, and active fumaroles.

NEARBY VILLAGE
A busy seaside town on the neighbouring island of Lipari sits in the shadow of the summit of the active Vulcano.

FUMAROLE GASES
Vulcano has become a popular site with volcanologist who monitor the gases emitted by the many steaming fumaroles on the volcano's flanks.

ATLANTIC OCEAN *east*

Pico de Teide

LOCATION On Tenerife, one of the Canary Islands in the Atlantic Ocean, off the northwest coast of Africa

HEIGHT 3,715m (12,188ft)

TYPE Stratovolcano

LAST ERUPTION 1909

The island of Tenerife was formed by a complex of overlapping volcanoes that remain active today. Pico de Teide lies within the 17km- (10-mile-) wide Las Cañadas caldera. An eruption in 1492 was witnessed by Christopher Columbus on his way to the New World.

FLANK CONE

AFRICA *east*

Erta Ale

LOCATION The prominent feature of the Erta Ale range in the Danakil Desert, northeastern Ethiopia

HEIGHT 613m (2,011ft)

TYPE Shield volcano

LAST ERUPTION 2011

The remote Erta Ale is a shield volcano 50km (30 miles) wide that rises to over 600m (2,000ft) from below sea-level. Its 1.6km- (1-mile-) wide elliptical summit crater contains circular, steep-sided pit craters. Another, larger, elongated depression parallel to the Erta Ale range is located to the southeast of the summit and is bounded by curvilinear fault ridges. Recent basaltic lava flows have erupted from these

VOLCANO CAULDRON
Within the summit crater, fountains of molten lava break through the churning lava lake's solidified, black surface crust.

fault fissures into the caldera and have overflowed its rim. Erta Ale is Ethiopia's most active volcano, and its summit pit craters are renowned for their perpetually churning lava lakes. These have been active since at least 1967, but possibly since 1906, which would make it one of the longest known eruptions in recorded history. Recently, fissure eruptions have occurred on the volcano's northern flank.

PIT CRATER
The smaller of the two summit craters, Erta Ale's active south pit crater is about 150m (500ft) across its almost perfectly proportioned diameter.

AFRICA *east*

Mount Kilimanjaro

LOCATION At the southern end of the Great Rift Valley's eastern fork, in northeastern Tanzania

HEIGHT 5,895m (19,340ft)

TYPE Stratovolcano

LAST ERUPTION Unknown

Africa's highest mountain, Kilimanjaro is one of several volcanoes whose formation is associated with the eastern part of the Great Rift Valley (see pp.88–89). An elongated complex cone, more than 50km (30 miles) long, it consists of three volcanoes. The mountain was mainly constructed during the Pleistocene Epoch (1.8 million–10,000 years ago) but includes a group of nested summit craters that are apparently younger. Kibo is the highest and central cone and erupted between the other two – Shira and Mawenzi. It is topped by a glacier-covered subsidence caldera with an inner crater called the Ash Pit. The 3.5km- (2¼-mile-) wide caldera gives the summit its broad, elongated profile. Most of the 250 flanking lava and

UNIQUE VEGETATION
This water-holding cabbage in tussock grassland is typical of the specially adapted alpine vegetation.

cinder cones are less than 100m (330ft) high. Recent volcanic activity has been mostly confined to fumaroles around Kibo's crater. Lying just 320km (200 miles) north of the equator and yet high enough to be snow-capped, Kilimanjaro supports a unique ecosystem adapted to a wide range in temperature.

GLOBAL WARMING

Global warming is transforming one of Africa's most iconic landmarks. Recent studies have suggested that since 1912 more than 80 per cent of the ice and snow at its summit has melted, and that by 2020 what remains may have vanished. As well as reshaping a dramatic skyline, the consequences for communities that rely on the meltwater could be huge.

MASSIVE MOUNTAIN
Rising from the savanna plains of eastern Africa, the massive Kilimanjaro is one of the most famous and most imposing volcanoes in the world.

AFRICA *central*

Lake Nyos

LOCATION One of the craters on the Oku Volcanic Field in northwestern Cameroon

HEIGHT
3,011m (9,878ft)

TYPE Maar

LAST ERUPTION
Unknown

Lake Nyos, which lends its name to this volcano, lies within the crater of one of 29 maars in what is known as the Oku Volcanic Field. This, in turn, is part of a zone of crustal weakness, called the Cameroon Volcanic Line, which encompasses the Cameroon Mountain stratovolcano and extends for about 1,600km (1,000 miles), with half its length submerged in the Atlantic Ocean. The Lake Nyos crater might have been created by an explosive phreatic eruption about 500 years ago. Its rim, which is up to 1.8km (1 mile) wide, is made up of fragments of basaltic ejecta containing large shattered blocks of granite. Lake Nyos was brought to the world's attention by a catastrophe in 1986 that killed about 1,800 people (see panel, above). This release of a great cloud of noxious gas was caused by the lake's water being saturated with carbon dioxide seeping from underground springs. It is thought that the gas could have been released from the water at the bottom of the lake by a landslide or earthquake. Since 1990, a team of French scientists has been working to degas the lake, and a series of pipes has been installed to try to prevent future build-ups of carbon dioxide.

DEADLY GASES

In 1986 the release of a suffocating carbon-dioxide cloud from Lake Nyos killed around 1,800 people along with over 6,000 cattle. Up to 1 cubic km (¼ cubic mile) of the gas, travelling at nearly 50kph (30mph), was channelled down surrounding valleys for about 23km (14 miles). As it moved the heavy gas hugged the ground, displacing the air and asphyxiating all humans and animals in its path.

CRATER LAKE
The crater lake is more than 200m (650ft) deep, and during the rainy season excess water often floods over the rim and down the nearby valleys.

AFRICA *central*

Nyiragongo

LOCATION At the southern end of the Great Rift Valley's western fork, Democratic Republic of Congo

HEIGHT
3,470m (11,384ft)

TYPE Stratovolcano

LAST ERUPTION 2011

One of the most active volcanoes in the world, Nyiragongo is famous for the lava lake in its summit crater, first discovered by the German explorer Adolf von Gotzen, in 1894. On 10 January 1977, lava broke through the crater walls and travelled at up to 100kph (60mph) towards the city of Goma, killing 50 to 100 people. The lake started to build up again in 1982, and Goma was partially overrun by lava flows in January 2002.

CHURNING LAVA

AFRICA *east*

Ol Doinyo Lengai

LOCATION At the southern end of the Great Rift Valley's eastern fork, northeastern Tanzania

HEIGHT 2,890m (9,482ft)

TYPE Stratovolcano

LAST ERUPTION 2010

The cone-building stage of this 370,000-year-old symmetrical volcano ended about 15,000 years ago. Its summit consists of two craters. The inactive older southern crater is covered with vegetation and volcanic ash. Activity in the northern crater is centred around many hornitos (stacks pushed up from an underlying lava flow) and small cones. Ol Doinyo Lengai is most renowned for being the only volcano in recorded history known to have erupted compositionally unique carbonatite lavas and tephra. With a viscosity close to that of water (due to low silica content), its lava is the most fluid in the world, and also the coolest, with temperatures up to only 590°C (1,100°F). This lava flows black during the day, glows a deep red at night, and when it comes in contact with water a chemical reaction turns it white. Long-term lava effusion has been punctuated with some ash eruptions, and strong explosive eruptions were recorded in 1917, 1940, 1960, and 1966.

ACTIVE CRATER
The volcano's crater has gradually filled up with ash and rock. During a 1998 eruption, lava began to flow over the rim.

STEEP PROFILE
The imposing, steep-sided form of Ol Doinyo Lengai rises from the flat, wide plain, south of Tanzania's Lake Natron.

MOUNTAIN OF GOD
Ol Doinyo Lengai is known to the Masai as the "Mountain of God". Local villages rely on tourists who visit the volcano.

AFRICA east
Piton de la Fournaise

LOCATION On the French island of Réunion in the Indian Ocean, off the east coast of Madagascar

HEIGHT 2,631m (8,632ft)

TYPE Shield volcano

LAST ERUPTION 2010

Mauritius
St-Denis
Réunion — Piton de la Fournaise
INDIAN OCEAN

One of the biggest and most active volcanoes in the world, Piton de la Fournaise originated from a mantle hotspot under the Indian Ocean. Much of its 530,000-year eruption record has overlapped with that of the nearby Piton des Neiges shield volcano. Eastward slumping of the volcano produced three successive calderas, formed 250,000, 65,000, and less than 5,000 years ago. A 400m- (1,300ft-) high cone lies in the centre of the youngest of the three, Caldera de l'Enclos Fouque. The summit of the cone comprises two craters – Bory and the larger Dolomieu, from which most of the recent eruptions have originated. More than 150 eruptions have been recorded since the 17th century, producing fluid basaltic lava flows. The volcano's activity is closely monitored by an observatory on its slopes.

VOLCANO TOURISM

Every year over 300,000 tourists are drawn to the isolated island of Réunion especially to visit Piton de la Fournaise. As one of the world's most active volcanoes, it offers the chance to witness at first hand the awe-inspiring scene of an eruption. Hiking paths wind through the dramatic landscape and lookout points offer safe viewing platforms.

FURNACE PEAK
An active cone in the summit crater of the volcano belches fumes as molten lava wells up inside. In English, Piton de la Fournaise translates as "Furnace Peak".

ASIA north
Siberian Traps

LOCATION Centred on the town of Tura on the central Siberian Plateau, northern Russia

HEIGHT Up to 500m (1,650ft)

TYPE Fissure vent

LAST ERUPTION About 250 million years ago

Noril'sk
Siberian Traps

One of the largest and most enigmatic of flood basalt effusions, the Siberian Traps cover more than 300,000 square km (115,000 square miles) of Arctic wilderness. About 1.5 million cubic km (360,000 cubic miles) of lava erupted through the Earth's crust within about a million years. This outpouring does not appear to be connected to rifting, although it may have been the result of a mantle plume. The timing of the formation of the Siberian Traps coincides with the Permo-Triassic extinction event – the largest extinction in the Earth's history (see pp.22–23). It has been argued that gases associated with such a massive eruption could have had enough effect on global climates to disrupt the food chain severely by damaging plant growth on a global scale.

ASIA northeast
Kliuchevskoi

LOCATION Near the eastern coast of the Kamchatka Peninsula, eastern Siberia, Russia

HEIGHT 4,835m (15,863ft)

TYPE Stratovolcano

LAST ERUPTION 2011

Kliuchevskoi
Kamchatka Peninsula
PACIFIC OCEAN
Petropavlovsk-Kamchatskiy

Symmetrical, snow-capped Kliuchevskoi is the highest and most active of a chain of volcanoes along the eastern side of the Kamchatka Peninsula. Since its formation about 6,000 years ago, it has frequently produced explosive and effusive eruptions without any extended periods of inactivity. Numerous cones and craters have been formed during the past 3,000 years by more than 100 flank eruptions. However, most recorded eruptions have originated from the 700m- (2,300ft-) wide summit crater, which is frequently reshaped. Many of Kliuchevskoi's eruptions have been viewed from space (see far right).

ERUPTION FROM SPACE
Photographed by astronauts on the space shuttle Endeavour, the eruption on 30 September 1994 sent a massive ash plume to a height of 18km (11 miles).

SYMMETRICAL PEAK
Kliuchevskoi is a perfectly symmetrical stratovolcano formed by layers of pyroclastic materials and lava flows.

ASIA *east*
Mount Fuji

LOCATION About 90km (55 miles) southwest of Tokyo, on the Japanese island of Honshu

HEIGHT 3,776m (12,388ft)

TYPE Stratovolcano

LAST ERUPTION 1707

Japan's highest mountain, Mount Fuji is a symbol of its homeland around the world, and one of a chain of volcanoes along the western margin of the Pacific Ocean. It is a typical stratovolcano, with a steep-sided, symmetrical cone built up of layers of lava flows alternating with ash and other debris. Growth of the present volcano began 11,000 years ago on top of older volcanic remnants. Within 3,000 years, about 80 per cent of the current bulk of the volcano had built up in outpourings of basaltic lava. During the long eruptive history that followed, lava flows and violent eruptions were emitted from the 700m- (2,300ft-) wide summit crater and numerous flank vents, building up more than 100 cones. Some of these lava flows blocked river drainage to the north, forming the Fuji Five Lakes area, which has become a popular tourist area. The last eruption, in 1707, was the largest in historical times. It formed a large new crater on the east flank and deposited ash on Tokyo, over 90km (55 miles) to the northeast.

ANNUAL FESTIVAL

The Fujiyoshida Fire Festival, held at the end of August each year, is the highlight of Mount Fuji's tourist season. Shrines are dedicated to the goddess of Mount Fuji to give thanks for a safe climbing season. The mountain is the sacred epicentre of the country and climbing it is treated by many as a religious experience.

ICONIC BEAUTY
The picturesque symmetrical cone of Mount Fuji has been celebrated by hundreds of artists. On a clear day, the mountain can be seen from over 150km (90 miles) away.

ASIA *east*
Baitoushan

LOCATION Straddling the mid-section of the border between China and North Korea

HEIGHT 2,744m (9,003ft)

TYPE Stratovolcano

LAST ERUPTION 1903

The Baitoushan (or Changbaishan) stratovolcano, 60km (38 miles) wide, was built up over an older shield volcano. In around 1000 CE, one of the largest eruptions in recorded history formed its summit caldera, 5km (3 miles) wide and 850m (2,790ft) deep. This is now filled by the scenic Lake Tianchi, or Sky Lake. Tephra were deposited more than 1,600km (1,000 miles) away in northern Japan. Only five eruptions have been recorded since the 15th century.

SKY LAKE IN THE BAITOUSHAN CALDERA

ASIA *east*
Mount Unzen

LOCATION On the Shimabara Peninsula, to the east of Nagasaki on the Japanese Island of Kyushu

HEIGHT 1,500m (4,921ft)

TYPE Complex volcano

LAST ERUPTION 1996

The huge Unzen volcanic complex includes three large stratovolcanoes within a 40km- (25-mile-) long rift valley. The Mayu-yama lava dome complex formed about 4,000 years ago and was the source of a massive debris avalanche on 21 May 1792. The avalanche generated a tsunami up to 55m (180ft) high that devastated the coastline and killed more than 14,500 people. Subsequent eruptive activity has been restricted to the summit and flanks of the Fugen-dake volcano. The most recent period of sustained volcanic activity, during 1990–95, was centred around the growth of a new summit lava dome. It has been estimated that during this time more than 10,000 pyroclastic flows were generated by the dome collapsing. Many of these flows swept up to 5km (3 miles) down the local river valleys, destroying hundreds of homes and causing many fatalities.

SCENE OF DEVASTATION
In May 1993, a massive pyroclastic flow, travelling at great speed, destroyed everything in its path, including houses along the coast a few kilometres away.

MAURICE AND KATIA KRAFFT

French volcanologists Maurice and Katia Krafft became famous for filming the hazardous nature of pyroclastic flows. Tragically, in 1991, while filming on Mount Unzen, they were killed by an incandescent ash flow that swept suddenly down the mountain.

ASIA southeast
Mount Pinatubo

LOCATION On the west coast of the island of Luzon in the Philippines

HEIGHT 1,486m (4,875ft)

TYPE Stratovolcano

LAST ERUPTION 1993

In June 1991, Mount Pinatubo, a relatively unknown complex of lava domes, erupted in the second most violent volcanic explosion of the 20th century. A series of Plinian eruptions sent about 10 cubic km (2 cubic miles) of rock and ash 40km (25 miles) into the atmosphere. Huge pyroclastic flows incinerated land up to 17km (11 miles) from the volcano, and lahars destroyed villages up to 60km (38 miles) away. The top 250m (820ft) of the mountain collapsed, leaving a summit caldera. Although monitoring had given enough warning for a timely evacuation of the local population, 300 people were killed directly by the eruption, partly due to the simultaneous arrival of Typhoon Yuna. As well as causing widespread disruption (see panel, right) the ash darkened the sky for a number of days. A month after the eruption, fine aerosol particles had circled the Earth, and had even reduced global temperatures. Lahars redistributing the deposits of the eruption continue to pose a threat to local populations.

ESCAPING THE ASH

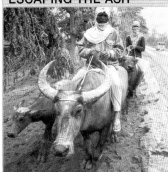

Volcanic ash causes severe disruption both on the ground and in the air. At least 14 airliners flew into emissions from the 1991 eruption and several had to make emergency landings with badly damaged engines. Fine ash can also cause health problems for local populations. The eruption filled the air and covered the ground with huge amounts of ash. A major increase in respiratory illnesses such as bronchitis was reported at the time, and some believe that ash contamination could still be killing people today.

CALDERA LAKE
The 2.5km- (1½-mile-) wide summit caldera created by the 1991 eruption is partially filled by a lake.

RACING THE FLOW
A lucky individual makes a dramatic escape from a pyroclastic flow, travelling at speeds of more than 80kph (50mph), released by the 1991 eruption.

LAND

ASIA southeast
Tambora

LOCATION On the island of Sumbawa, one of the Lesser Sunda Islands, Indonesia

HEIGHT 2,850m (9,350ft)

TYPE Stratovolcano

LAST ERUPTION About 1967

MASSIVE CALDERA

The 1815 eruption of Tambora was the largest in recorded history. It ejected more than 150 cubic km (30 cubic miles) of volcanic materials, producing a caldera 6km (4 miles) wide and 1,250m (4,100ft) deep. More than 10,000 people were killed by pyroclastic flows, and many thousands more were victims of subsequent famine and disease. Worldwide circulation of the dust and gas produced global climate change and a series of highly coloured sunsets famously painted by William Turner. The year 1816 was to be known as the "year without a summer".

ASIA southeast
Taal

LOCATION South of Pinatubo on the west coast of the island of Luzon in the Philippines

HEIGHT 400m (1,312ft)

TYPE Caldera

LAST ERUPTION 1977

One of the most active and powerful volcanoes in the Philippines, Taal has erupted more than 30 times since records began in 1572. Its caldera, 20km (12½ miles) wide, is filled by Lake Taal. The 5km- (3-mile-) wide Volcano Island in the north of the lake has been the focus of all of the volcano's recorded eruptions. This complex of stratovolcanoes, tuff rings, and cones has produced massive pyroclastic flows and surges. A 1911 eruption killed 1,300 people, and 200 died in 1965. Since 1991, Taal has showed signs of increased activity.

LAKE TAAL, THE FLOODED CALDERA

ASIA *southeast*

Merapi

LOCATION On the Indonesian Island of Java, just north of the city of Yogyakarta

HEIGHT	2,968m (9,737ft)
TYPE	Stratovolcano
LAST ERUPTION	2003

Lying in one of the world's most densely populated areas, Merapi is one of Indonesia's most active volcanoes. The upper part of the volcano is unvegetated due to frequent eruptions of pyroclastic flows and lahars, which have accompanied the growth and collapse of the steep-sided summit lava dome. The dome occupies an unsupported position, at the western edge of the summit, making it prone to collapse, especially during periods of active dome growth. The collapses release pyroclastic flows that have devastated cultivated lands and caused many fatalities throughout recorded history. Eruptions of Merapi frequently produce hot, pyroclastic flows, formed by gravitational collapse from lava flows and domes, and sometimes known as Merapi-type pyroclastic flows. Merapi was one of a dozen "decade" volcanoes chosen in 1991 for scientific monitoring as part of the United Nations International Decade for Natural Disaster Reduction.

EVACUATION

Merapi's proximity to one of the world's most densely populated areas poses a constant threat. In such situations, advance warning of eruptions and effective crisis management are important. In February 2001, volcanologists monitoring the volcano issued a maximum alert, and thousands of villagers, already affected by ash falls, had time to flee to safety.

2010 ERUPTION
This satellite image shows one of a series of eruptions of Merapi in late 2010 that killed more than 250 people.

ASIA *southeast*

Krakatau

LOCATION A volcanic island in the Sunda Strait between Sumatra and Java, Indonesia

HEIGHT	813m (2,667ft)
TYPE	Caldera
LAST ERUPTION	2011

An eruption in around 416 CE caused the ancestral Krakatau volcano to collapse, and formed a 7km- (4-mile-) wide caldera. The regrown volcano was dramatically transformed in 1883 by one of the most notorious volcanic eruptions in recorded history. Earthquakes during the late 1870s preceded a series of eruptions, culminating in a massive explosion on 27 August 1883 that was heard on Rodrigues Island, 4,653km An eruptive column rose more than 25km (16 miles) above sea level, showering ash and pumice over the region and blotting out sunlight for two days. Pyroclastic flows travelled up to 40km (25 miles) across the sea and destroyed coastal communities in Sumatra. Situated in one of the busiest shipping lanes in the world, Krakatau's eruption was seen and logged by several vessels. The caldera collapse displaced enormous volumes of seawater and generated a series of tidal waves, or tsunamis, that devastated coastal settlements and killed more than 36,000 people. Two-thirds of the island was consumed in the collapse. Four decades later, a post-collapse cone, known as Anak Krakatau, appeared within the caldera.

EARLY COLONIZER
As Krakatau's vegetation has been repeatedly eliminated, species like this Morning Glory provide excellent models of tropical vegetation succession.

CHILD OF KRAKATAU
Anak Krakatau ("Child of Krakatau") has frequently erupted since 1928. Since its formation, it has been rising out of the sea and continues to grow with increased activity.

STROMBOLIAN DISPLAY
Krakatau typically exhibits fairly mild Strombolian or Vulcanian eruptions. These produce basaltic lava flows and fountains or ash and lava bombs.

ASIA *southeast*
Rabaul

LOCATION On the east end of New Britain Island, Papua New Guinea

HEIGHT 688m (2,257ft)

TYPE Caldera

LAST ERUPTION 2011

Two major caldera-forming eruptions, about 7,100 and 1,400 years ago, formed the 14km- (9-mile-) wide Rabaul caldera and Blanche Bay, a broad, sheltered harbour for the city of Rabaul. The outer flanks of the volcano are made up of pyroclastic-flow deposits. Three small volcanoes lie outside the caldera to the north and east. Several pyroclastic cones on the caldera floor have explosively erupted in recorded history, including the Vulcan cone, formed during a large eruption in 1878. The most recent period of unrest began in 1971 with frequent seismic activity. During 1984, up to several hundred tremors a day were recorded, and part of the harbour was elevated by over 1m (3ft). In 1994, the powerful and simultaneous

BILLOWING ASH CLOUD
During activity in 2000, Rabaul's Tavurvur cone erupted a cloud of ash and debris that travelled more than 1.5km (1 mile) into the atmosphere.

eruption of the Vulcan and Tavurvur cones forced the temporary abandonment of Rabaul, the largest city in New Britain. Between 1995 and 2003, the volcano remained active with intermittent ash emissions.

AUSTRALASIA *New Zealand*
Ruapehu

LOCATION About 40km (25 miles) southwest of Lake Taupo on the North Island of New Zealand

HEIGHT 2,797m (9,176ft)

TYPE Stratovolcano

LAST ERUPTION 2007

Ruapehu is the tallest mountain on New Zealand's North Island, and one of its most active volcanoes. A 100-cubic-km (24-cubic-mile) volcanic complex, it is surrounded by a ring of volcanic debris produced by a series of eruptions between about 22,600 and 10,000 years ago. The active vent near its summit contains a crater lake that formed about 3,000 years ago. There have been about 50 eruptions since the mid-19th century. Explosive phreatic eruptions from this crater lake have frequently produced lahars, one of which destroyed a railway bridge and train in 1953, killing 151 people.

EXPLOSIVE OUTPUT
During an eruption in 1996, the snow-covered Ruapehu released huge clouds of ash that covered surrounding ski fields and disrupted air traffic.

ANTARCTICA *central*
Mount Erebus

LOCATION On Ross Island in the Ross Sea, just off the Scott Coast, Victoria Land

HEIGHT 3,794m (12,447ft)

TYPE Stratovolcano

LAST ERUPTION 2003

Mount Erebus is the most southerly volcano on Earth to have been active in recorded history. Overlooking McMurdo Sound, it is one of three major volcanoes on Antarctica's Ross Island. Its summit has been modified by successive generations of caldera formation. A summit plateau at about

3,200m (2,000ft) marks the rim of the youngest caldera, within which the modern cone was constructed. The elliptical crater at the summit, which is 600m (2,000ft) wide and 110m (360ft) deep, is unusual in having a small but persistent lava lake on its floor. The lava is also of unusual alkaline composition. High temperature anomalies associated with the lava lake can even be detected from space by satellites. The glacier-clad volcano was erupting when first sighted by Captain James Ross in

INSIDE EREBUS ICE
An abseiler descends into an ice cave near the crater of Mount Erebus. These caves were formed by volcanic heat rising to the surface from below.

1841 (see panel, right), and Strombolian activity was also seen in December 1912, when the volcano was visited by members of Scott's Antarctic expedition. More recently, fluxes in the emission of sulphur dioxide from the volcano have been measured as part of a global programme to try to correlate such gas emissions to the eruptive process. Continuous lava-lake activity with minor explosions, punctuated by occasional larger Strombolian explosions that eject bombs onto the crater rim, have been documented since 1972.

JAMES CLARK ROSS

In 1831 the British naval explorer Sir James Clark Ross (1800–62) discovered the magnetic north pole while on expedition in the Arctic. From 1839 to 1843, he headed an expedition to the Antarctic, in the course of which he discovered the sea and island that now bear his name. Ross named the volcano after his ship.

MASSIVE PROFILE
With a bulk of 1,700 cubic km (400 cubic miles), Mount Erebus is one of the world's most impressive volcanoes.

LAND

Igneous Intrusions

AN IGNEOUS INTRUSION FORMS when magma – molten or partially molten rock – invades cracks in existing rock or stagnates within the Earth's crust and solidifies to form new rock. Magma is generated in the crust and upper mantle, and because it is hot and contains water and gases it migrates upwards. A small proportion erupts from volcanoes at the surface (see p.115). However, most magma cools and crystallizes beneath the surface to create igneous intrusions. Because they are formed underground, these rock formations, which include batholiths, dykes, and sills, are seen as features of the landscape only after erosion has stripped away the rocks that cover them.

Intruding Magma

Igneous intrusions form when cooling, crystallization, and loss of gases cause a once fluid and buoyant magma to solidify. Most rocks that form intrusions originate as either granitic or basaltic magma. Granitic magmas have a low density, and small volumes (a few kilometres across) rise slowly through the Earth's upper crust, pushing existing rock (termed country rock) aside. However, very large granite masses, which are perhaps 1,000 times larger, are formed when magma digests and incorporates heated country rock. This surrounding rock begins to melt, and elements of it are assimilated into the magma, which then sets. Such processes generally take place deep within the Earth's crust, and granite intrusions are typically found in areas of active mountain building. Basaltic magmas are less dense and more fluid. They inject into cracks and zones of weakness in country rock, and they are most commonly seen as dykes or sills (see opposite page). These intrusions have the same composition as extruded basaltic lava, but contain larger crystals. The crystals within basaltic magma can settle at different rates to form distinctive layers of rock that have different abundances of minerals.

INTRUSIVE CONTACT
Here, dark, sedimentary country rock has been assimilated into an intruding magma, which has crystallized to form this pink granite.

PEGMATITE
The very large crystals in this pegmatite in Utah, USA, were formed by an intruding granite magma that was rich in water and gases.

LAYERED INTRUSION
These igneous rocks with differing compositions were created in layers as dark, heavy crystals settled and cooled in still molten magma.

DYKE WALL
This dyke wall in Colorado, USA, has been formed by the erosion of the surrounding country rock, leaving strong igneous rock protruding from the ground.

LAND

CRYSTAL STRUCTURE

As all igneous rocks are formed by cooling of magma, their primary characteristic is a mosaic of interlocking crystals. The tight jigsaw pattern of crystal boundaries gives igneous rocks their high strength. Crystal size depends largely on the rate of cooling. Intrusive magmas lose heat slowly into the surrounding rocks, so they have larger crystals than extrusive rocks, which cool rapidly in air or water. The minerals of igneous rocks are mostly silicates; in this microscopic view of granite, the feldspars and quartz are grey, while the biotite appears as several different strong colours.

TYPES OF IGNEOUS INTRUSION
Most igneous intrusions are classified by their size and shape. The intrusions shown here range from relatively small horizontal sills and vertical dykes, to conical ring dykes, volcanic plugs, lens-shaped laccoliths, and huge batholiths, which can be more than 100km (60 miles) in length.

Intrusive Rock Bodies

Different types of igneous intrusions can be named according to their shape, which is related to the type of rock that forms them. Granitic magmas are usually viscous, so they tend to form huge batholiths that have an area of at least 100 square kilometres (40 square miles). Basaltic magmas are more fluid, so they flow into thin gaps and cool vertically as dykes, which run through the rock strata, or they set horizontally as sills along bedding planes (the boundaries between layers of sedimentary rock). Because rock cools more slowly underground than it does on the surface, the rocks that form igneous intrusions have larger crystals than those formed when lava solidifies at the surface. Those that form dykes are medium-grained, and are usually dolerite, whereas those that form larger intrusive bodies, such as batholiths and stocks, are coarse-grained gabbro or granite. Ring dykes, which are shaped like vertical tubes, are formed as magma fills cracks created by its upward pressure. Cylindrical plugs are formed from magma that has cooled inside volcanic vents. Laccoliths are large, lens-shaped intrusions that are usually formed of gabbro. Lopoliths are lenses and sheets that are also primarily gabbro, and are found in basins that have sagged under the weight of the intrusion.

ring dykes erode to form circular outcrop patterns

volcanic plug with radiating dykes

parallel dyke swarm

batholith exposed at surface

lens-shaped laccolith

sill forms between bedding planes

dyke forms vertically through rock strata

country rock

massive batholith

stock forms a mass that bulges upward

SIERRA NEVADA, USA
Almost the entire Sierra Nevada range is a massive batholith, which was formed by multiple phases of granitic magma intrusion. This cooled beneath the surface of the Earth before being exposed by subsequent erosion.

ECONOMIC IMPORTANCE

Intrusive igneous rocks are so strong that they are widely quarried to make hard rock aggregate, which is required in huge quantities for use in the manufacture of concrete and to build roads. Some types of granite are also highly valued as large blocks of cut rock – known as dimension stone. Strong, unfractured, and light in colour, granite is sawn and polished to make thin slabs of glossy stone for use as cladding on buildings. The granite in this Sardinian quarry is cut out by powerful water jets and traditional wire saws, without using explosives.

SILL AND DYKE
The pale, banded, metamorphosed sedimentary rocks in this hillside exposure in Oregon, USA, are cut by two small intrusions of darker dolerite. One is a dyke that has filled a tension fissure cutting across the beds (bottom); the other is a sill that has injected along a single bedding plane (top).

EXPOSED DYKE
The typically hard rock of an igneous intrusion forms the core of this rocky crag in Colorado, USA. Debris eroded from the margins forms the more gentle slopes, which contrast with the sharp profile of the intrusion.

IGNEOUS INTRUSION PROFILES

The pages that follow contain profiles of some of the world's igneous intrusions. Each profile begins with the following summary information:

AGE When the igneous intrusion was formed

TYPE Batholith, dyke, dyke swarm, ring dyke, sill, plug, stock, layered intrusion

ROCK The main rock type that makes up the intrusion

ARCTIC
Skaergaard

LOCATION In the coastal mountains of eastern Greenland, just to the north of the Arctic Circle

AGE 60 million years

TYPE Layered intrusion

COMPOSITION Gabbro

Dissected by deep, glaciated valleys and fiords, and exposed in the soil-free mountains of Greenland, the Skaergaard intrusion is the world's most intensively studied large igneous body. Where it is exposed at the surface, the intrusion is about 10km (6 miles) across. It is notable for its vast sequence of layered rocks, which were formed by differentiation of a mass of basaltic magma. Crystals of dense, silicate minerals sank through the liquid remnants of the original magma, but were interrupted by convection currents as they did so. When this happened, the magma composition changed, with bands of rock forming from different minerals as the layers accumulated and cooled progressively. The dominant gabbro layers near the base of the intrusion contrast with the small layer of granophyre, which was the last rock to crystallize at the end of the batholith's molten life.

CLEAN ROCK
The Arctic conditions lead to frost shattering (see p.56), which leaves bare outcrops of igneous rock. This makes Skaergaard the perfect place to study magmas and rocks.

COLOUR-CODED
Colour changes identify the mineral layers within the Skaergaard gabbro, and lumps of coarse, pegmatitic material are remnants of olivine-rich layers that fragmented before they solidified.

NORTH AMERICA *northwest*
Mackenzie Dykes

LOCATION Stretching between Great Slave Lake and the Arctic coastline of northern Canada

AGE 1,260 million years

TYPE Dyke swarm

COMPOSITION Dolerite

Hundreds of parallel intrusions form the largest dyke swarm in the world, which is exposed in the ice-scoured lowlands of the Canadian Shield. The dykes formed when magma intruded into fissures that opened along a zone of tension above an active mantle plume. Flood basalts formed where huge volumes of magma spilled onto the surface, and layered-gabbro intrusions have been detected at depth. The result is a trinity of forms that record the formation of new crust in the Earth's distant past.

MACKENZIE DYKE SWARM

NORTH AMERICA *northeast*
Palisades Sill

LOCATION Formed along the New Jersey side of the Hudson River, northward from New York City, USA

AGE 190 million years

TYPE Sill

COMPOSITION Dolerite

GEORGE WASHINGTON BRIDGE
Anchored within the diabase that forms the Palisades Sill, this suspension bridge spans the Hudson River from New Jersey to Manhattan in New York City.

For 80km (50 miles), the Hudson River flows beneath the dark wall of the Palisades Sill. Nearly horizontal, this dramatic outcrop is a sheet of intrusive dolerite. The sill is about 330m (1,100ft) thick, and intruded into now-eroded Triassic sandstones at shallow depth. Where the base of the sill is exposed, there is about 15m (50ft) of fine-grained dolerite that chilled rapidly against the contact rock. Above this is a 5m- (18ft-) thick layer that is predominantly olivine. This was the first mineral to crystallize, and its dense crystals sank through magma that was still 95 percent liquid. The Palisades Sill is a clear example of the differentiation of magma, with rocks of varying compositions created from the same source.

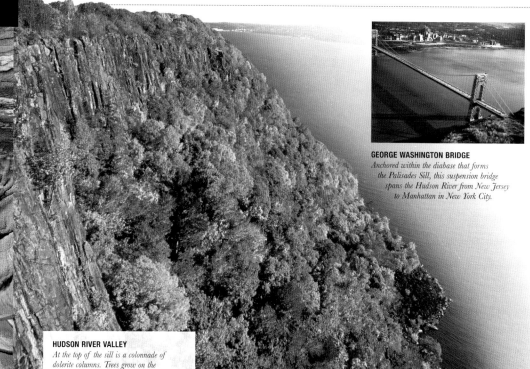

HUDSON RIVER VALLEY
At the top of the sill is a colonnade of dolerite columns. Trees grow on the weathered fragments of these structures, which have fallen to the base of the cliff.

Devil's Tower

LOCATION In the Great Plains of Wyoming, USA, just northwest of the Black Hills of Dakota

AGE 40 million years

TYPE Plug

COMPOSITION Phonolite

The Devil's Tower originated as a volcanic vent, but it owes its spectacular appearance to erosion, which has removed the surrounding sedimentary rock to expose igneous rocks that cooled and solidified underground. The original volcano lost its gas pressure by exploding to the surface through a cover of sediment, but much of the magma remained in an underground plug that was nearly 300m (1,000ft) in diameter. As it cooled, the magma contracted and fractured, forming polygonal joints. When the cooling fronts moved inward, these fractures evolved into remarkably uniform columns. (A similar phenomenon occurs when mud dries to form polygonal cracks.) The tower reaches a height of 264m (867ft). Horizontal columns also intruded from the edge of the plug, but never extended far. Most of this fringe of horizontal columns has been eroded, though where it is not masked by debris, some can be seen in the flared base of the tower. The phonolite that forms the Devil's Tower is derived from continental crust; it contains less silica than the other rhyolitic magmas, and is distinguished by its small crystals of dark green aegirine, a pyroxene mineral that is rich in sodium.

SUMMIT OF THE TOWER
The domed peak of the intrusion exposes the tops of the columns that form the mass of the Devil's Tower.

ABOVE THE CLOUDS
On a cool morning, the Devil's Tower rises through a layer of cloud to mimic the situation about 15 million years ago, when much less of the intrusion was projecting above the surrounding land.

LAND

ROCK CLIMBING

The splendid columnar joints of the Devil's Tower intrusion provide perfect routes for the more serious breed of climber who enjoys long crack lines in very strong rock. However, natural cooling is never perfect, and some columns do merge or split, so climbers have to choose which joints they pursue with care.

WYOMING'S WONDER
The striking structure of the Devil's Tower has distinguished it as a sacred place for some American Indians. It appeared in the film Close Encounters of the Third Kind.

THE WINGED ROCK
Though the Navajo name suggests that Ship Rock flew to its present site, the geological wings are the remarkable dykes that now stand high as walls across the desert of New Mexico.

Ship Rock

LOCATION In the desert of New Mexico, USA, west of the San Juan Mountains

AGE 30 million years

TYPE Plug

COMPOSITION Lamprophyre

Though it now stands 500m (1,700ft) above the surrounding plains, Ship Rock formed underground when magma cooled within the feeder pipes of a volcano. The lavas and pyroclastic deposits of the volcano have since disappeared, and subsequent erosion of the underlying soft shales has steadily lowered the surface of the surrounding plains. The resistant rock of the plug is far less worn, and stands high above the desert. The upper part of Ship Rock is a lava breccia which was created when rock was shattered by explosive eruptions within the volcano's vent. When this happened, the rocks that constitute today's summit were probably less than

VOLCANIC REMNANTS
The rock exposures in the desert around Ship Rock are the volcanic remnants of intrusions that were once buried deep beneath the surface of the Earth.

1,000m (3,300ft) below the Earth's surface. The lamprophyre that forms the intrusion is similar to dolerite, except that it contains more mica and less feldspar. It also contains small masses (xenoliths) of peridotite and eclogite. This suggests that the magma had a source deep within the upper mantle. In addition to feeding the main conduit, magma also ascended into radiating fissures, where it cooled to form the dykes that distinguish Ship Rock. These were exposed as the adjacent surface eroded, resulting in spectacular dyke walls. The rock ribs are about 3m (10ft) thick and they stand 20m (65ft) high, and the longest dyke stretches for nearly 3km (2 miles).

El Capitan and Half Dome

LOCATION Within Yosemite National Park, Sierra Nevada, California, USA

AGE 82 million years

TYPE Batholith

COMPOSITION Granite and granodiorite

Known as the Incomparable Valley, Yosemite cuts deep into the largest and strongest of the Sierra Nevada granitic intrusions, and is bounded by the huge, steep vertical cliffs that make it so famous. Like all batholiths, the Sierra Nevada is not formed from a single type of granite. It consists of a series of intrusions that were emplaced over 50 million years during the Cretaceous Period, when the region

EL CAPITAN
Towering above Lower Yosemite Valley, this rock wall is a result of erosion, which has shaped this part of the huge Sierra Nevada batholith.

sat above an active convergent plate boundary. Two of the batholith's most distinctive outcrops are El Capitan and Half Dome. The composition of the intrusions varies, as different magmas invaded different areas of country rock. El Capitan – Yosemite's highest rock wall – is formed of a true granite, but Half Dome – the area's steepest wall – is formed of granodiorite, which contains less alkali feldspar. Both are massive rocks with few weaknesses, as is typical of the largest batholiths.

HALF DOME
Yosemite's most famous landmark is the rounded end of a granite ridge between two deep valleys. One side of Half Dome was broken off at a major joint during glacial sculpting of the region.

Chuquicamata

LOCATION In the Atacama Desert of northern Chile, between the Andes and the Pacific Ocean

AGE 33 million years

TYPE Stock

COMPOSITION Granodiorite

DESERT COPPER MINE

The porphyritic granodiorite intrusion at Chuquicamata is associated with the largest of several porphyry copper ore bodies that are found throughout the western mountains of North and South America. Metal sulphides are dispersed throughout the stock, and half a million tonnes of copper are mined every year from over 4 billion tonnes of ore. Mining has created an open pit that is over 4km (2½ miles) long and 810m (2,650ft) deep.

SOUTH AMERICA *east*
Sugar Loaf

LOCATION Overlooking the entrance to Guanabara Bay, Rio de Janeiro, Brazil

AGE 800 million years

TYPE Batholith

COMPOSITION Granite

TOURISM

Rock that is almost white, bold curves, and towering cliffs are the characteristic features of mountains cut into the granites that form large batholiths. The resulting landscapes are often tourist attractions. Few are finer than Rio de Janeiro's two dramatic granite peaks, the Sugar Loaf and Corcovado, which can be ascended by cable car or tram.

The Sugar Loaf is solid granite, and is actually a tiny part of a huge batholith that stretches along the Brazilian coast on either side of Guanabara Bay. It was formed by partial melting within a belt of metamorphic gneisses at the centre of a plate convergence zone that was active about 800 million years ago in late Precambrian times. Since then, erosion has left stumps of granite that form the magnificent peaks enclosing Rio de Janeiro.

Sugar Loaf is not the highest promontory in the area as it rises to only 395m (1,295ft), but its rounded profile makes it so distinctive. The rounded outline is typical of exposed masses of strong, homogenous, joint-free granite that were once at the core of a massive batholith. When intrusive granite crystallizes, it is confined by horizontal and vertical stress, due to weight of the rock above it. Once exposed, these stresses are lost, and the rock relaxes, opening curved joints as it does so. Erosion strips away these shells of rock, each time exposing a smoothly curved surface.

BRAZIL'S GRANITE ICON
The smooth, rounded structures of the Sugar Loaf and the peninsula that extends to it are both formed from the huge mass of granite at the core of a batholith.

EUROPE *north*
Ardnamurchan

LOCATION A peninsula to the north of the Isle of Mull on the west coast of Scotland

AGE 60 million years

TYPE Ring dyke complex

COMPOSITION Gabbro

A complex of gabbroic ring dykes forms the Point of Ardnamurchan, which is about 8km (5 miles) across and is the most westerly point of the British mainland. A decline in pressure over a large magma chamber caused conical fractures to form. Magma intruded into these fissures to form dykes. Subsequent cone-shaped sheet intrusions then formed when magma pressure increased. Above these deep intrusions, huge volcanic craters erupted lavas and pyroclastic deposits.

POINT OF ARDNAMURCHAN

EUROPE *north*
Castle Rock

LOCATION Beneath the castle in the centre of the city of Edinburgh, Scotland

AGE 325 million years

TYPE Plug

COMPOSITION Dolerite

Edinburgh's great crag of black dolerite, which is now crowned by a castle and walled courtyard, is the exposed feeder pipe of an ancient volcano. The entire volcanic edifice has long been lost to erosion, and its only remnant is the basaltic magma that solidified deep beneath the eruption crater. The magma cooled more slowly than the extruded, air-cooled basaltic lavas and so formed large crystals, which are typical of dolerite. About one million years ago, during the last ice age, ice sheets swept over Castle Rock; however, the tough dolerite plug remained in place. Ice flowed around the crag, and deposited till debris (see p.61) in its unscoured lee. This resulted in the formation of the long, eastern rampart that now supports the High Street of Edinburgh's Old Town. The modern landform is a classic example of a feature known as a crag-and-tail.

EDINBURGH'S ROYAL ROCK
The hard black dolerite of Castle Rock's intrusive plug forms a crag far steeper than the ancient volcano that once existed here.

EUROPE *north*
Fair Head Sill

LOCATION Forming a coastal headland near Ballycastle, County Antrim, Northern Ireland

AGE 58 million years

TYPE Sill

COMPOSITION Dolerite

FAIR HEAD SILL

The great prow of Fair Head is the exposed edge of an 80m- (260ft-) thick dolerite sill, which intruded into Carboniferous sandstones as lavas poured across the rest of the region. The sill is scored by columnar cooling fractures, and is notable for its huge sandstone xenoliths.

LAND

Whin Sill

LOCATION Underlying England's northern Pennine hills, with outcrops at the edges

AGE 295 million years

TYPE Sill

COMPOSITION Dolerite

Whin is an Old English quarryman's word for hard black stone. This aptly describes the dolerite that forms Whin Sill. In the late Carboniferous Period, basaltic magma rose from beneath the Earth's crust and spread to intrude along shallow bedding planes in sedimentary rocks. The intrusion is complex, as it cuts across the bedding to form sheets at multiple levels and

COLONNADED ESCARPMENT
Rough columnar jointing in the dolerite adds texture to the long escarpment cliffs wherever Whin Sill emerges above the surface.

HADRIAN'S WALL

An escarpment that extends right across the Pennines marks the northern edge of Whin Sill. It was used as a natural line of defence in 122 CE, when the Roman emperor Hadrian built a wall to keep the Scots out of the Roman province of Britannia.

appears to have been fed by more than one magma chamber. Whin Sill is therefore not a single sill, but is actually a collection of cross-cutting sills and flat, lens-shaped intrusions. Nevertheless, at many outcrops it is a uniform and unbroken sheet of dolerite that is approximately 30m (100ft) thick.

Great Dyke

LOCATION Stretching from north to south across almost the whole of Zimbabwe

AGE 2,600 million years

TYPE Layered intrusion

COMPOSITION Serpentinite

Called a dyke because it is long and thin at the surface, most of this intrusion is about 5km (3 miles) wide, and so is too large to be a true dyke. It consists mainly of peridotite and dunite, which have altered to become serpentinite, though its upper layers consist of gabbro. Within the intrusion, crystal settling has created chromite bands that are the world's largest source of chromium ore. The mineral bands show a synclinal structure (see p.96), suggesting that the igneous body is actually a lopolith. However, its base is hidden, and its margins are both major faults, so Great Dyke may be best classified as a layered intrusion.

LINEAR INTRUSION
This satellite image shows the long, thin range of wooded hills that marks the line of the Great Dyke across the plains of Zimbabwe.

Aïr Mountains

LOCATION In the northern part of Niger, Africa, within the southern Sahara Desert

AGE 410 million years

TYPE Ring dyke complexes

COMPOSITION Granite

The major ring dyke complexes of the Aïr Mountains were formed where three continental plates collided. Each complex is about 60km (37 miles) in diameter and contains one or more ring dykes that are 20–200m (65–650ft) thick. Before the plates welded together to form the huge basement block of northern Africa, their boundaries were subduction zones (see p.54–55), melting rock and generating magma. Around the junction, granitic magmas reached the surface, creating huge explosive volcanoes, whose lavas and pyroclastic deposits have since eroded. Further eruptive phases caused declines in the underground magma pressure, resulting in large caldera collapses. Beneath the surface, gigantic blocks of rock subsided inside huge conical ring fractures. Then more magma rose through these new fractures. Some of the new magma fed younger volcanoes, but the magma that solidified within the fissures created ring dykes. Erosion has brought the modern surface down to a level that cuts through the ancient intrusive rings.

MINING URANIUM

Granitic magmas contain traces of uranium. When erosion exposed the Aïr dykes, mountain streams carried the uranium as soluble oxides into sedimentary basins. There, low-oxygen conditions in nearly stagnant lakes caused precipitation of the uranium. Today it is mined from the exposed basins in Niger's desert, but its original source was the Aïr intrusions.

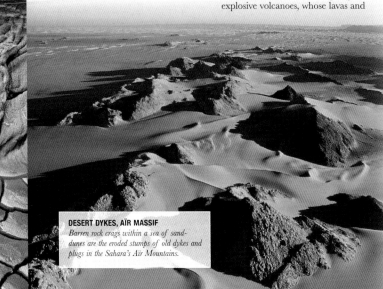

DESERT DYKES, AÏR MASSIF
Barren rock crags within a sea of sand-dunes are the eroded stumps of old dykes and plugs in the Sahara's Aïr Mountains.

Salvesen Mountains

LOCATION At the southern tip of the island of South Georgia, in the South Atlantic

AGE 127 million years

TYPE Stock

COMPOSITION Granite

The roots of the island of South Georgia are intrusive igneous rocks, though they form only a small part of the modern outcrops. Stocks of white Cretaceous granite are intruded into Jurassic basaltic lavas and dolerite dykes – both of which are black, so they create striking colour contrasts in exposures across the Salvesen Mountains, the most jagged of the island's ice-bound mountain ranges. Both the granite and the basalt are remnants of rising magma formed on a divergent plate boundary where the southern Atlantic opened. The main ranges of South Georgia, famously crossed by Ernest Shackleton in 1916, are less rugged and precipitous than the Salvesen Mountains, as they are made of folded sandstones. These were formed from sand deposition, the sediment for which was derived from erosion of the igneous rocks and rifting continental blocks.

Hot Springs and Geysers

HOT SPRINGS, SPOUTING GEYSERS, fumaroles, boiling mud pots, and many mineral deposits are all evidence of the Earth's internal heat. They all depend upon the underground heating of water by hot rocks. Once hot water and steam have been generated, they are forced to the surface, often charged with dissolved minerals and gas. Hot springs produce warm water steadily, while geysers release intermittent bursts, often with copious amounts of steam. Fumaroles are vents where only steam and other gases escape.

Geothermal Systems

The flow of internally generated heat up to the Earth's surface is almost constant over the globe, but in some places the heat flow is much higher and produces hot springs and associated geothermal phenomena. These zones of high heat-flow tend to occur at the margins of the Earth's tectonic plates and are normally associated with volcanism. Many active volcanoes are underlain by reservoirs of partially molten rock, centres of heat at abnormally shallow depths. Any groundwater coming into contact with these hot rocks is heated, but because it is under pressure at depth the boiling point is raised above normal and the water becomes superheated. Heated water tends to rise towards the surface, losing pressure as it does so. Flashing over into steam may then propel the water upwards with such force that it gushes forth above ground as a geyser.

WHITE DOME GEYSER
Hot underground rock turns groundwater to steam and boiling water, which spurts into the air from this geyser in Yellowstone, USA.

some rainfall adds to groundwater

hot spring

groundwater percolating downwards

water temperature raised by contact with hot rocks

heated water starts to move upwards

geyser

superheated water rising to the surface

water further heated under pressure

heat from earth's interior

GEOTHERMAL SYSTEMS
Geysers and hot springs are generated by the cycle of cold, descending surface water being heated by hot rock or magma, expanding, and being driven back towards the surface.

USING GEOTHERMAL ENERGY
Many hot springs, such as these in Kusatsu, Japan, are harnessed for heat, power, and domestic uses.

Water Deposits

Much of the water that feeds hot springs and geysers originates as rainwater, infiltrating below ground through joints or cracks to the local water-table. Where groundwater is heated by a geothermal source, it rises, drawing in additional cold groundwater towards the heat source as it does so. While underground, the heated water dissolves soluble minerals from the rocks, but, on reaching the surface, evaporation and cooling cause some of these dissolved minerals to be re-precipitated. The resulting deposits are dominated by silica, calcium, sodium, and potassium carbonates and chlorides, but include other minerals and metals, such as copper and lead, depending upon the local rocks.

BUBBLING CAULDRON
The constantly boiling waters of Punchbowl Spring, Yellowstone, USA, are contained within a raised rim of carbonate deposits (travertine), about 75cm (2½ ft) high, which is shaped like a punch-bowl.

SULPHUR CRYSTALS
Hot gases expelled from volcanic fumaroles often leave deposits, such as these sulphur crystals on Vulcano, in the Aeolian Islands.

HOT SPRING AND GEYSER PROFILES
The pages that follow contain profiles of a selection of the world's hot springs and geysers. Each profile begins with the following summary information:

TYPE Hot spring, mud pool, geyser, or fumarole

FREQUENCY Interval between periods of activity

LAND

Yellowstone

LOCATION In Yellowstone National Park, Wyoming, USA, between the Bighorn Basin and Snake River Plain

TYPE Geysers, hot springs

FREQUENCY Old Faithful 45–110 mins, Steamboat Geyser irregular

Yellowstone displays some of the most spectacular hydrothermal activity in the world, especially from its dramatic geysers (about 200 in number), of which Old Faithful is the most famous. There are also thousands of fumaroles, hot springs, and boiling mud pools. This thermal activity is a reminder that Yellowstone is the site of one of the largest explosive volcanic eruptions in recent history, which led to the collapse of an ancient volcano, about 600,000 years ago, to form a giant caldera. The magma chamber that fed the original volcano is still present, about

SURVIVING THE WINTER
For many generations, American bison have trekked to Yellowstone's hot springs and pools in winter, to benefit from the warmer temperatures and to feed on the plants that grow there.

6km (3¾ miles) below Yellowstone, and is the heat source for the present geothermal activity. Plentiful rainfall keeps its hydrothermal system well charged with water. The geysers form where the underground circulation of hot water is restricted. Under pressure at depth, water is superheated without boiling. As it rises, pressure decreases, allowing steam to form, which further accelerates upward movement. Water

TERRACED WATERFALLS AND POOLS
Each day, evaporation deposits two tonnes of carbonate mineral at Mammoth Hot Springs, which enlarges the ever-changing Minerva Terrace.

and steam then gush out at the surface as geysers. Gushing ceases when the hotwater reservoir is exhausted. The period between gushes depends on the time it takes for the underground system to recharge. Famously, Old Faithful produces columns of steam and water 30–55m (100–180ft) high every 67 minutes on average. At Yellowstone, the water temperature at 200m (660ft) depth is 200°C (392°F). This hot underground water not only supplies geysers but also springs. The rising hot water dissolves soluble minerals from the surrounding rocks, but, on surfacing, evaporation and cooling reverse the process, and mineral deposits form, such as those at Minerva Terrace. At Mammoth Hot Springs, terraces of limy flowstone (see p.201) contain beautiful, variably coloured pools at different temperatures – their colours produced by species of temperature-sensitive algae. Boiling mud pools are normally grey, but in Yellowstone's Fountain Paint Pot these too are multicoloured, and up to 20m (66ft) in diameter.

THE LODGEPOLE PINE
The dominant tree of Yellowstone is the Lodgepole Pine, so called because its straight trunk is ideal for use as tepee poles. Its needle-shaped leaves point downwards so the snow slips off them in winter.

ERUPTING GEYSER
Castle Geyser is one of Yellowstone's 200 or so active geysers, which are a constant reminder that the region is still geologically active.

LIFE AT HIGH TEMPERATURES

Prismatic Pool hot spring (shown below) is host to aquatic algae and other micro-organisms that can survive high temperatures. Investigation of their tolerance of extreme conditions is providing insights into how life may have originated in the extremely harsh environments of the early Earth, and whether life can exist in the even more difficult conditions found on other planets. Thermophiles (heat-loving organisms) are among the most primitive forms of life. Over 4 billion years ago, the Earth's surface was hot, and the atmosphere charged with carbon dioxide, nitrogen, and methane. Similar conditions are found in hot springs today, making them natural laboratories for studying life's origins.

OLD FAITHFUL
After the famous geyser jets a spout of hot water around 50m (165ft) into the air every 45–110 minutes, water and steam droplets hang in the air for about four minutes.

LAND

NORTH AMERICA *northwest*
Valley of Ten Thousand Smokes

LOCATION Near Katmai, in the Aleutian Range at the northeast end of the Alaskan peninsula, USA

TYPE Fumaroles

FREQUENCY Extinct

In 1912, about 22km (13 miles) of the Ukak valley was filled by the largest pyroclastic flow of modern times as it poured from vents near Mount Katmai (see p.118). The area is called the Valley of Ten Thousand Smokes because, for 15 years afterwards, vaporized water from the stream and wet sediments continued to escape the surface through small holes and cracks.

THE SMOKING VALLEY

NORTH AMERICA *west*
Fly Geyser

LOCATION On the flat, high plains adjacent to the Black Rock Desert, northwest Nevada, USA

TYPE Geyser

FREQUENCY Continuous

This geyser has three outlets and is surrounded by hot-water pools contained by terraces of travertine (calcium carbonate). Over the years, the geyser has built up three rocky pinnacles of mineral deposits that continuously spout water. Some of the pools have been enlarged, allowing them to cool enough for bathing. Lying at an altitude of 1,300m (4,270ft), the Fly Geyser region receives an annual rainfall of less than 300mm (11¾ in).

Nevertheless this, combined with run-off from the surrounding mountains, is sufficient to feed the local aquifer. The adjacent Black Rock Desert is the dry bed of a lake that covered about 22,420 square km (8,660 square miles) during the last ice age. Its sediments are floored by Pleistocene basaltic lavas, and the presence of the geyser shows that there must still be an associated magma chamber or intrusion at shallow depth, acting as a heat source.

THREE-VENTED GEYSER
Travertine terraces surround Fly Geyser's continuously spouting trio of cones, which jet from the ancient dry lake floor of the Black Rock Desert.

NORTH AMERICA *west*
Soda Springs

LOCATION At the head of the Bear River valley, southeastern Idaho, USA

TYPE Geyser

FREQUENCY Hourly

It is claimed that Soda Springs is the only geyser in the world to be made by human activity. On 30 November 1937, a well was drilled for hot water to supply a swimming pool. At about 100m (330ft) down, the drill hit a reservoir containing a pressurized mixture of carbon dioxide and hot water. The drill-hole provided an escape route, sending a geyser 50m (165ft) into the air. The borehole was capped and fitted with a valve, which restricts activity to once an hour. This part of the Bear River valley contains numerous other hot springs, such as Steamboat Springs, so called because of the steampipe-like noise that the hot water makes as it gushes forth. In the 19th century, migrants travelling the Oregon Trail stopped here to bathe and to wash their clothes.

MANMADE GEYSER
Idaho's Soda Springs geyser is perhaps the only man-made geyser in the world, capped in such a way that it erupts every hour, on the hour.

SOUTH AMERICA *west*
El Tatio geysers

LOCATION Northeast of San Pedro de Atacama in the Chilean Andes, South America

TYPE Geysers, hot springs, and fumaroles

FREQUENCY Variable

At an altitude of 4,321m (14,176ft), the El Tatio geysers, hot springs, and fumaroles are the highest in the world. The area of thermal activity covers 10 square km (4 square miles) of a rift-valley floor. Water surfaces at temperatures of about 86°C (187°F) – the boiling point for water at this altitude. The water reservoir is within volcanic rocks capped by impermeable layers; faults conduct the hot water to the surface. The exact heat source is unknown, but is likely to be magma or an igneous intrusion beneath the valley.

FUMAROLES AT EL TATIO

ATLANTIC OCEAN *north*
Geysir

LOCATION In the Haukadular rift valley, 80km (50 miles) east of Reykjavik, southwest Iceland

TYPE Geyser

FREQUENCY 8–10 hours

The term geyser is derived from this feature, first described in 1294. Although there has been no volcanic activity here for about 10,000 years, temperatures below ground may reach 240°C (464°F). In 1915, Geysir became dormant, but earthquake activity in 1935 reactivated it for a time. After earthquakes in June 2000, Geysir currently erupts every 8–10 hours.

WATER BUBBLING IN GREAT GEYSIR

LAND

Strokkur Geyser

LOCATION In the Haukadalur rift valley, 80km (50 miles) east of Reykjavik, southwest Iceland

TYPE	Geyser
FREQUENCY	8 mins

Strokkur, whose name means "churn" in Icelandic, is one of the most famous geysers in Iceland. It became active following an earthquake in 1789, and erupted regularly until 1896, when another earthquake blocked its flow. In 1963 the conduit was cleaned out by local people, and it has been active ever since. The eruption of the geysers in this area is driven by rising hot and pressurized water flashing into steam. Water at a depth of 23m (75ft) is at a temperature of about 120°C (248°F), but the weight of the water in the conduit above prevents it from boiling. At 16m (52ft), the temperature of the water may rise above boiling point and raise the water in the conduit slightly, setting off a chain reaction. The pressure decrease allows more water to boil and flash into steam, which in turn drives the water upwards with increasing velocity to erupt at the surface. When the water in the upper part of the conduit has erupted, an action lasting just a few minutes, the steam phase is exhausted and the cycle begins again. With nearby Geysir (see opposite), Strokkur is one of Iceland's leading tourist attractions. There are a number of hot springs in the vicinity, as well as steam vents and colourful algal deposits.

REGULAR CYCLE
Strokkur's eight-minute repeat cycle owes its regularity to human intervention. In 1963, the conduit was cleaned to ensure regular eruptions.

WELLING UP
The interval between Strokkur's eruptions depends on the time its reservoir channels take to refill and raise their temperature back to the critical point.

Chaudes-Aigues

LOCATION In the town of Chaudes-Aigues, in the Auvergne region of the Massif Central, France

TYPE	Hot springs
FREQUENCY	Continuous

The name Chaudes-Aigues literally means "hot waters". The inhabitants of this small medieval town still enjoy central heating developed from the world's first geothermal system, established in the 14th century. First used by the Romans in the time of Nero, over 30 hot springs provide the hottest spring waters in Europe, at 82°C (180°F). Today Chaudes-Aigues is a spa town, famed for the curative powers of its hot, mineral-enriched spring waters. The hot springs are probably related to volcanic heat below the Chaîne des Puys (see p.123) and the famous spring waters of Volvic, even though Chaudes-Aigues lies 100km (60 miles) to the south. The Chaîne des Puys includes about 90 cinder cones and maars (explosion craters formed without basaltic lava flows), many aligned along northeast–southwest fissures. The last volcanic activity occurred about 6,000 years ago.

Lardarello

LOCATION In the central region of the Colline Metallifere (Metalliferous Hills), Tuscany, central Italy

TYPE	Hot springs
FREQUENCY	Continuous

One of the world's largest geothermal fields and one of the oldest centres of geothermal power production, Lardarello has been generating electrical power since 1904. The heat source is located some distance below the surface in metamorphic rocks. Above, permeable limestones covered by impermeable shales and clays are folded into a dome, forming a trap for hot water and steam. Faults through the arch of the dome channel water to the surface, where they form hot springs.

USING STEAM TO PRODUCE ELECTRICITY

Solfatara

LOCATION West of Vesuvius, on the northern shore of the Bay of Naples, southern Italy

TYPE	Hot springs, fumaroles
FREQUENCY	Continuous

Solfatara is a crater lying within an ancient volcanic caldera called the Phlegrean Fields. About 40 hot springs and numerous fumaroles venting volcanic gases litter the caldera. Those of Solfatara's crater were believed by the Romans to cure a host of medical conditions, but are now the site of intense scientific research into the frequency and intensity of earthquakes, and changes in gas composition. The Bay of Naples, including the port of Pozzuoli, has risen and subsided by several metres over the last few millennia, accompanied by countless earth tremors (15,000 were detected between 1982 and 1984 alone). These movements affect the aquifer below Solfatara and water levels in the various wells of the region. The present Solfatara well was built in the early 19th century to extract alum (potassium aluminium sulphate) from the spring water. Deep magma chambers heat the overlying hydrothermal system, whose temperature varies from 200° to 250°C (390° to 480°F) if there is a rapid inflow of seasonal rain.

STEAMING FUMAROLES
Bocca Grande ("Large Mouth"), shown here, is the largest fumarole at Solfatara. It was described by Virgil as the entrance to Hell.

EXTREME ENVIRONMENT
*These hot springs are produced by Ethiopia's
Dallol volcano, which lies 45m (175ft) below
sea-level. Biologists are interested in finding
out how microbial life can survive in such
extreme environments.*

EUROPE *south*

Lipari

LOCATION One of the Aeolian Islands, in the Mediterranean Sea, 35km (22 miles) off northern Sicily

TYPE Fumaroles

FREQUENCY Continuous

Lipari is one of the Aeolian Islands, an active volcanic arc to the north of Sicily. The volcanoes are the result of subduction of the African plate beneath the southern edge of the Eurasian plate. This stimulates partial melting that feeds the volcanoes at the surface. In the past, volcanic activity on Lipari has produced highly viscous lavas, often with a glassy crust. Today, deep pockets of magma at depth produce vigorous fumarolic activity at the surface, and monitoring shows a wide range of temperatures over time, from about 200°C (392°F) to as much as 650°C (1,202°F). This is associated with increasing gas flow from depth and thermal expansion, which opens new conduit cracks. There is concern that volcanic activity is moving north from the nearby island of Vulcano and could cause an eruption near Lipari.

AFRICA *east*

Bogoria

LOCATION On Lake Bogoria, at the foot of the Laikipia Escarpment, Kenya, East Africa

TYPE Hot springs and geysers

FREQUENCY Continuous

Hydrothermal features are rare in Africa but are present on the western and southern sides of Lake Bogoria. Here, groundwater is heated at depth by igneous intrusions buried below the valley's sediments and volcanic infill. As it rises, the hot water dissolves soluble salts (especially sodium carbonate) from the highly alkaline volcanic rocks. The hot springs feed soda lakes, which are home to alkali-tolerant algae and brine shrimps, upon which flamingos feed.

LAKE BOGORIA GEYSER AND HOT SPRINGS

ASIA *northeast*

Nagano

LOCATION In the central Japan Alps, northwest of Tokyo, Honshu island, Japan

TYPE Hot springs and fumaroles

FREQUENCY Continuous

The hot springs and fumaroles of the resort of Yamanouchi near Nagano are famous for their unusual inhabitants – Japanese macaque monkeys. The fumaroles expel sulphur-dioxide-enriched steam, and the hot springs, with their mineral-enriched waters, feed a series of pools. In the 1960s the macaques discovered the benefits of immersing themselves in the hot water, and soon it became part of their behavioural culture, passed on from generation to generation. Today, they bathe in two specially excavated pools; people bathe elsewhere.

JAPANESE MACAQUES AT NAGANO
About 250 Japanese macaques use the hot springs at Nagano, where snow may persist for four months of the year.

ASIA *northeast*

Beppu

LOCATION In Beppu city, on the northeastern shore of Kyushu island, Japan

TYPE Geyser, hot springs, mud pools, and fumaroles

FREQUENCY 20–25 mins

The active volcanism of the Japanese islands means that the country is also rich in hot springs, which are now used for a variety of domestic, social, and industrial purposes. Beppu city is Japan's largest spa resort, with many fumaroles and mudpools, 2,849 springs, and the Tatsumaki Jigoku

BEPPU'S STEAM POWER
These chimneys are not releasing pollutants, but excess steam from the geothermal energy plant, which powers local industry and heats homes.

COMMUNITY BATHING

The curative and restorative properties of Japan's hot springs have been appreciated for hundreds of years, and bathing in the hot springs is something of a national recreation. Beppu's hot baths range from domestic tubs in private houses, to free municipal facilities for poorer citizens, to luxurious private baths where the rich can relax, meet friends, and gossip.

HOT SPRING AT BEPPU
Blood Pond Jigoku is so called because the water is charged with red mud. The red colour is caused by iron oxide.

geyser. The volume of hot water that gushes from this hydrothermal system exceeds 136,000 kilolitres (36 million gallons) each day, giving it the second highest output in the world. Beppu has a number of hot springs, or jigokus (a Buddhist word meaning "burning hell"), including: Blood Pond Jigoku, where red mud emerges with the boiling water; Ocean Jigoku, with its blue water; and Tatsumaki Jigoku geyser, which spouts water 20m (66ft) every 25 minutes. The springs are situated around two faults, Kannawa to the north and Asamigawa to the south. Their heat source is associated with 100,000-year-old buried lava domes which previously generated volcanism in the area. The abundant hot water, which surfaces at temperatures of 40–100°C (104–212°F), has been harnessed for domestic and industrial use, processing food, breeding fish, and producing geothermal power.

Waimangu

LOCATION In Waimangu Valley, near Rotorua, on the North Island of New Zealand

TYPE Fumaroles

FREQUENCY Continuous

The volcanic belt of North Island, New Zealand, was the site of several very large explosive eruptions in the past 10,000 years. Its volcanoes, near the southwest end of the Pacific's Ring of Fire (see p.117), are associated with subduction of the Pacific plate. Waimangu Valley is a bleak area of raw volcanic craters, boiling pools, and occasional geysers. It lies 10km (6 miles) southwest of Lake Tarawera and close to Lake Rotomahana. One geyser, which appeared in 1902 and lasted until 1905, spouted water 450m (1,475ft) into the air at intervals of between 5 and 30 hours and was the highest geyser plume ever recorded. Above the Waimangu Valley, there used to be scattered geysers and a series of tiered pink and white terraces, known as the White Terraces, which contained water-filled silica deposits. Maoris had traditionally used the site for bathing and cooking, and Waimangu was later

INFERNO CRATER
One of the attractions of Waimangu Reserve is this water-filled crater, which is a reminder of the 1886 eruption of Mount Tarawera.

WARBRICK TERRACE
The mineral deposits and hot-water pools of Warbrick Terrace are a reminder of the world-famous White Terrace, destroyed in 1886.

regarded as the Yellowstone of its day, but early on the morning of 10 June 1886 all of these features were obliterated by a violent eruption of nearby Mount Tarawera. Within a couple of hours, a massive volume of basaltic scoria was blasted from a fissure 17km (11 miles) long. Fragments of the scoria fell over a huge area, some landing 30 km (18 miles) away. The eruption also

buried three Maori villages, killing 155 people. One of these villages has now been re-excavated, in a similar way to Pompeii (see p.130), while the cliffs above Lake Rotomahana still steam perpetually. The cratered fissure is still visible as a chasm on Mount Tarawera.

Rotorua

LOCATION In the town of Rotorua, near Lake Rotorua, on the North Island of New Zealand

TYPE Geysers, hot springs, and fumaroles

FREQUENCY Virtually continuous

Rotorua is a modern lakeshore resort which lies in an extremely fertile region of volcanic hills and lakes around Lake Rotorua. Settled since the 14th century by the Arawa group of Maori tribes,

the area lies in the north of the Taupo Volcanic Zone, which encompasses active geysers, fumaroles, hot springs, and boiling mud pools. This hydrothermal activity is all that remains of one of the most violent volcanic eruptions of the last 2,000 years. Around 180 CE, extensive pyroclastic flows from the Taupo Volcanic Zone covered the area, devastating all life. The event passed without human record as the Maoris had not yet colonized the island. Today, Geyser Flat has seven active geysers; the most spectacular is Prince of Wales Feathers, a triple geyser that spouts to a height of 12m (40ft) and is always followed by an eruption of the Pohutu geyser, which rises to 30m (100 ft).

INDICATOR GEYSER
The Prince of Wales Feathers geyser resembles an emblem on the prince's coat of arms. It was named following a royal visit in the early 1900s.

GEOTHERMAL POWER

Wairakei near Rotorua was the second geothermal field to be developed after Lardarello (see p.149). Water heated to boiling point by an igneous intrusion rises through a permeable volcanic ash aquifer. Wairakei is liquid-dominated and benefits from high pressure. Since the geothermal aquifer has been punctured by boreholes, the rising water crosses its flash-point and turns to steam on its way to the surface.

The regular sequential timing of the geysers suggests that they are linked. They also have associated boiling mud pools, formed by steam leaking from underground geothermal reservoirs. Lady Knox geyser lies 24km (15 miles) to the southeast. It is artificially encouraged to spout to a considerable height by a daily dose of soap suds.

WAI-U-TAPU MUD POOLS
A mixture of black sulphide with white silica and kaolin clay gives these mud pools their distinctive colour, while rising gas generates the bubbles.

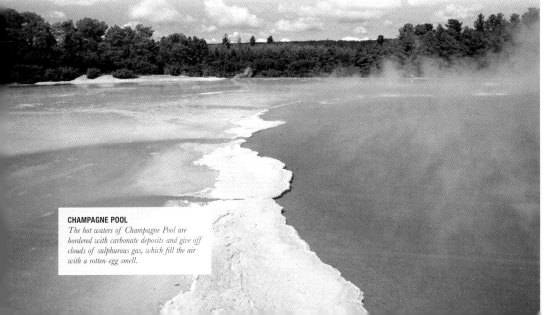

CHAMPAGNE POOL
The hot waters of Champagne Pool are bordered with carbonate deposits and give off clouds of sulphurous gas, which fill the air with a rotten-egg smell.

WINTER WARMTH
Bathers enjoy a refreshing dip at the Svartsengi geothermal power plant in Iceland, which is one of the world's leading producers of such energy.

GEOTHERMAL ENERGY

The Earth's internal heat represents a vast and practically inexhaustible source of energy, yet such geothermal energy is exploited only to a limited extent. This may change if economically viable methods are found of harnessing it. Geothermal energy is mainly produced by natural radioactive decay of uranium, thorium, and potassium. Unlike energy from fossil fuels, it also generates little carbon dioxide, so does not contribute significantly to global warming (see pp.376–77).

Reservoirs in Rocks

The Earth's core is at a temperature of about 4,000°C (7,200°F). Heat constantly flows through the mantle and crust (see p.35) and escapes through the atmosphere to cold outer space. Over most of the planet's surface, such heat flow cannot be felt, let alone put to work. However, in areas where the heat energy of the Earth has been concentrated, such as active volcanic zones, geothermal energy can be exploited. Here, intense heat can boil groundwater that is close to the surface, creating underground reservoirs of superheated water or steam. If the water escapes upwards, it can emerge in hot springs, geysers, or fumaroles.

Hot springs were used to heat houses in Roman times, about two millennia ago, and the practice still continues in Iceland and Japan. This simple method of tapping geothermal energy does have some disadvantages. The water from hot springs often gives off sulphurous gases, and it can only be used locally, because its temperature soon falls if it is piped far from its source.

A much more flexible way of exploiting geothermal energy is to harness it for the generation of electricity. The world's first such geothermal power plant opened at Larderello, Italy, in 1904, and installations now operate in more than 20 countries worldwide. Most of these power plants tap into existing reservoirs of steam or water, which drive the turbines. The largest plant – at the Geysers in northern California, USA – generates more than 1,500 megawatts (MW) of electrical power, which is sufficient to supply about half a million homes.

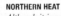

NORTHERN HEAT
Although it is not far from the Arctic Circle, tomato plants can be grown in this geothermally heated greenhouse in Hveragerdhi, Iceland

Low-Level Heat

Even in regions in which the Earth's heat flow is not concentrated, geothermal heat can be used as a way of saving energy. Through a closed system of underground pipes, a heat pump can transfer geothermal heat between a house and the ground beneath it, but it does not create the heat. During the winter, the ground temperature is often higher than the air in unheated rooms. As a result, water in the pipes collects heat from the ground and releases it indoors. In the summer, the situation is reversed. The pump acts as an air-conditioner, because the water absorbs heat as it flows indoors, and releases it back into the ground.

This way of exploiting geothermal energy works best in areas with continental climates, in which there is a large difference between winter and summer temperatures. In such conditions, a geothermal heat pump can cut electricity or fuel use by up to 50 per cent – saving money as well as reducing carbon dioxide emissions.

Untapped Resources

At present, geothermal sources meet only a tiny fraction of the world's total energy requirements, and most of this energy comes from regions in which there is geothermally heated water underground. However, much more widespread than these hydrothermal reservoirs are hot, dry rocks. If ways can be found to extract their heat, geothermal energy production could soar.

Several major engineering problems have to be overcome before this goal is realized. One is that zones of hot, dry rock are typically 2km (1¼ miles) or more underground. Once a borehole has been drilled to this depth, the heat energy has to be collected and brought to the surface. In experimental wells, water has been used to fracture the rock, creating fissures that fill with steam. The steam then travels to the surface, where its energy can be utilized. Enhanced Geothermal Systems (EGS) are currently being tested in a range of countries, and one station in the Netherlands is already operational.

LEADING GEOTHERMAL PRODUCERS

Geothermal energy currently provides for less than 0.02 per cent of the world's annual energy needs. With the exception of Iceland, most producers are located in the volcanically active Pacific Rim.

Country	Production (MW)	Global proportion (%)
USA	3,086	28.8
Philippines	1,904	17.8
Indonesia	1,197	11.2
Mexico	958	8.9
Italy	843	7.9
New Zealand	628	5.9
Iceland	575	5.4
Japan	536	5.0
El Salvador	204	1.9
Kenya	167	1.6

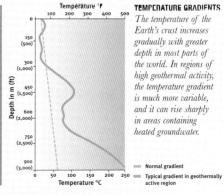

TEMPERATURE GRADIENTS
The temperature of the Earth's crust increases gradually with greater depth in most parts of the world. In regions of high geothermal activity, the temperature gradient is much more variable, and it can rise sharply in areas containing heated groundwater.

Normal gradient
Typical gradient in geothermally active region

SHAPING THE SURFACE
Meandering across the Kenyan countryside, the present channel of the River Mara bypasses land scarred by old meanders and ox-bow lakes.

RIVERS AND LAKES

RIVERS FLOW AND LAKES FORM in all but the world's hottest, coldest, and driest places. They hold a small, but vital, proportion of the Earth's surface fresh water: lakes hold about half of one per cent, and river channels contain much less – about one-fortieth of one per cent. This tiny fraction is, however, disproportionally significant, because rivers shape the land. Rivers are the most powerful erosive force on Earth – across the continents, the dominant landscape is one of hill slopes and river valleys.

Given time, rivers can wear down mountains and carry them to the sea. Powered by the force of gravity, the world's rivers deliver about 20 billion tonnes of land surface to the oceans every year. Many rivers are old in geological terms, and have increased in size with age, forming systems that drain continents. Some have hollowed out vast caves and run largely underground. By comparison, most lakes are very young, temporary accumulations of water that will inevitably shrink and disappear.

Rivers

RAIN OR MELTED SNOW that does not evaporate flows downhill across the land surface. This surface flow is channelled by small irregularities into tiny rivulets that merge and flow down gullies into streams. These accumulate water and increase in size along their courses, cutting valleys and receiving the inflow of smaller tributaries and seepage from ground water. The nature and form of a river depends on its rate of descent, the amount of water and the steadiness of its flow, and the underlying geology. These factors dictate the rates of erosion and deposition and, consequently, the degree to which the river modifies the landscape.

Drainage Basins

A river and its tributary streams form a system that collects all the run-off (surface flow) within its drainage basin. The mountains, or other high ground, that separate the drainage basins of different river systems are called the watershed. A notable example is the Continental Divide along the Rocky Mountains in North America, which separates eastward- and westward- flowing rivers. River systems form different patterns of drainage on the landscape, depending on the rock type, slope of the land, and movements of the Earth's crust. The most common pattern is dendritic, where tributary streams join a main river like the branches of a tree. The points where rivers join together are called confluences. In addition to its tributaries, groundwater seeping into the river channel may account for up to 30 per cent of a river's total volume. Most of the water carried in a river eventually flows into the sea.

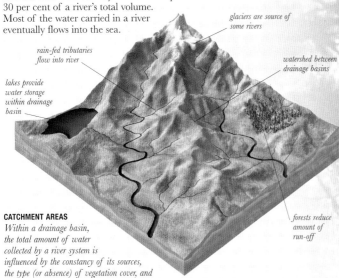

glaciers are source of some rivers

rain-fed tributaries flow into river

watershed between drainage basins

lakes provide water storage within drainage basin

CATCHMENT AREAS
Within a drainage basin, the total amount of water collected by a river system is influenced by the constancy of its sources, the type (or absence) of vegetation cover, and how much water is diverted for use by humans.

forests reduce amount of run-off

HEAD-WATERS TUMBLE
High in the mountains of Jotunheimen National Park in Norway, meltwater flows over bare rock on its way to becoming a river. Head-waters such as these need not necessarily flow through permanent channels.

LAND

YELLOWSTONE FALLS

The upper courses of many rivers – such as the Yellowstone River in Wyoming, USA (shown here) – include dramatic waterfalls, rapids, and gorges.

Erosion and Transport

The size and amount of material carried by rivers varies enormously. Even the slowest, smoothest flow of water will wash away small particles of rock. The turbulent flow of a river, with churning currents and sudden changes in velocity, has much greater power. The flow of water erodes the banks and bed by friction, suction, and solution. This flow also carries with it large quantities of solid material – the products of weathering or the river's own processes. It is this material, known as a river's sediment load, that usually accounts for most of its erosive force, through the abrasion of sand, gravel, pebbles, and boulders rolling and bouncing along the river-bed. Most solid material is, however, transported in suspension as fine particles of clay and silt.

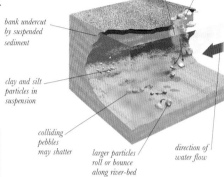

sediment cloud

undercut bank collapses

RIVER EROSION

Small particles are washed away, suspended in the water flow. Larger particles become concentrated on the river-bed where the current is strongest, and multiple impacts gradually reduce their size.

bank undercut by suspended sediment

clay and silt particles in suspension

colliding pebbles may shatter

larger particles roll or bounce along river-bed

direction of water flow

POTHOLES

Potholes, such as these in South Africa, form if hard boulders are "trapped" in depressions of softer rock and then swirled around by turbulent currents.

EROSION BY UNDERCUTTING

This section of canyon wall in Zion National Park, USA, has been undercut by the river – not by the gentle flow pictured, but by winter floodwaters crashing through the gorge.

Deposition

When the sediment-carrying capacity of a river decreases, deposition occurs. This can happen for a number of reasons – for example, where the current lessens as the river bends, widens, flattens, or floods it banks. Erosion and deposition are closely interlinked processes and may take place simultaneously on opposite banks of the same river bend. The most prominent features produced by deposition are point bars along riverbanks, and riffles, sand bars, and islands in midstream. The floodplains and deltas seen in the lower courses of rivers are depositional features on a much grander scale.

SANDBANKS

Point bars are deposited along a river's banks below the surface, where the water flow is slowest.

deposition of coarse sediment

deposition of fine sediment

sand bar

beach

alluvial fan below surface

cloud of fine sediment

DEPOSITION

When a river widens, the flow of water spreads and slows. Coarse particles fall out of suspension first, with the finer particles deposited downstream in a steep-faced fan. As the flow spreads out, a sand bar is deposited in the middle where the current is weakest.

DRIED-UP RIVER

In summer, when water levels fall and evaporation increases, rivers such as the Yellow River shrink, revealing beds of dried mud.

EROSION AND DEPOSITION

Where the current is strongest, a river's bank is undercut; where the water moves more slowly on the other side, deposition occurs.

Upper Courses

In most rivers, the upper course is characterized by steep descent and the inflow of many small tributaries. The river is usually narrow and fast-flowing, and it erodes a distinctive V-shaped valley that zigzags between interlocking spurs. The rate of flow along the upper course may be highly variable, depending on seasonal factors such as snow-melt or heavy rainfall, and most mountain rivers are subject to regular flooding. Most of the valley-cutting takes place when the river is in flood. Flooding also maintains small floodplains where the river crosses flatter ground. When crossing a high, sloping plateau, a river may cut a deep gorge and become incised, particularly if the plateau is being uplifted.

PREDICTING FLOODS

In the UK, the Environmental Protection Agency uses radar sensors carried by aircraft to determine precisely the height of land along the margins of rivers that are liable to flood. Using this information, scientists run computer simulations that predict the effects on the land of a river rising to a particular height. Areas that are more vulnerable to flooding can be identified and the flood defences planned accordingly.

FLOOD RISK
This computer-generated image shows the effects of a 1.5m- (5ft-) high rise in the level of a river in the north of England.

RAPID DESCENT
Rates of erosion are very high in steep mountain valleys where rivers race downhill.

WATERFALL
At the base of most waterfalls, such as this one in California, USA, the waters erode a plunge pool, which is enlarged by the scouring action of rock fragments from the cliff-face.

WATERFALLS AND RAPIDS
Rapids form where a river rapidly cuts downwards through the rock along its bed. Uneven rates of erosion leave large rocks standing above the water surface. Waterfalls often occur when the geology of the river-bed changes from a hard rock to a relatively soft one.

FERTILE RIVER VALLEY
This combination of cone-shaped hills and a flat valley floor is typical of rivers flowing through limestone valleys in the tropics and subtropics.

Lower Courses

Rivers generally flow down gentler gradients in their lower courses compared to their upper reaches. Few such rivers follow one straight channel: some braid into numerous channels separated by temporary islands; others meander in great looping curves. A meandering river may cut rapidly downwards, forming an incised meander, or it may wander from side to side, creating a wide, flat valley with steep sides. Meanders that are cut off as the river shifts its course form distinctive ox-bow lakes. Deposition rates are high along lower courses and are often linked to seasonal flooding. Sediments deposited by floodwaters may build up into deep beds. Flooding also produces natural levees (raised banks) along stretches of riverbank.

ox-bow lake, formed by abandonment of meander

levee made of sediments deposited by earlier floods

wide river valley bordered by low bluffs

point bar on inside bank of meander

floodplain

shallow, transient river channel

old river channel

FLOODPLAINS
A floodplain landscape (left) is subject to constant change as the river shifts its meandering course, leaving behind levees, ox-bow lakes, and abandoned channels. Because floodplains are flat and regularly covered with rich alluvial deposits, they are attractive both for agriculture and human settlement. Floodplains are some of the most densely populated areas in the world.

BRAIDING ON LOWER COURSE
This pattern of braided channels on a river in Denali National Park, Alaska, USA, will remain stable until the flow of the river changes.

CLEARING WATERWAYS

Rivers that are used for navigation often need to be dredged to clear them of sediment and vegetation. Some large river highways have to be dredged constantly in order to keep important navigation channels open. Here, a dredger is clearing a deepwater channel in the bed of the Mississippi – a river particularly prone to such problems, as it carries half a billion tonnes of sediment to the sea each year.

Deltas

Many rivers flow into the sea through a delta – a wide, flat region where the river branches into numerous distributary channels, and where new land is being created as the river deposits any material it is still carrying in suspension. The smallest particles may be carried a considerable distance out to sea, as fresh water slowly mixes with seawater. A typical delta takes the form of a broad fan that slopes gently seawards. Its shape depends on the balance between the river's flow, the tide, currents, and wave action. In some cases, the river's flow or coastal currents may be too strong for a delta to form. Some rivers form deltas when they enter lakes, but these lacustrine deltas, as they are known, have a steeper slope because water mixing takes place more rapidly.

BIRD'S-FOOT DELTA
Well-defined, elongate distributaries are characteristic of bird's-foot deltas, such as the Mississippi delta shown above.

FAN DELTA
In this satellite image, the fertile Nile delta contrasts with the surrounding desert sands. Constant wave action keeps the delta's coastline smooth and distinct.

RIVER PROFILES
The pages that follow contain profiles of the world's main rivers. Each profile begins with the following summary information:

LENGTH Distance from source to mouth

VERTICAL FALL Height descended by river from source to mouth

BASIN AREA Area drained by the main river and all of its tributaries

MAIN TRIBUTARIES Subsidiary rivers that flow into the main river

LAND

NORTH AMERICA *northwest*

Mackenzie

LOCATION	In northeast Canada, flowing from Great Slave Lake into the Beaufort Sea in the Arctic Ocean
LENGTH	1,705km (1,060 miles)
VERTICAL FALL	156m (512ft)
BASIN AREA	1.8 million square km (700,000 square miles)
MAIN TRIBUTARIES	Liard, Great Bear, Peel

PINGO ON MACKENZIE RIVER DELTA
Isolated in Canada's Northwest Territories, the Mackenzie delta surrounds a pingo of sediment pushed up by the growth of a buried block of ice during the seven-month-long winter.

The basin of the Mackenzie River is the largest in Canada and the second largest in North America. From the western end of Great Slave Lake, the river flows northwest, mainly over ground subject to permafrost,

CARIBOU
The Mackenzie lowlands, which are covered with a mosaic of forests, swamps, shrubland, and grassy tundra, are home to herds of Caribou.

and into the sea through a seasonally marshy delta. In winter the river freezes along its entire length. For the most part it is a broad river, 1.5–6.5km (1–4 miles) wide, which has steep gravel banks and frequently braids into channels. Mackenzie waters leaving Great Slave Lake are clear, any sediment having been deposited in the lake. The waters of the main tributary, the Liard, are very muddy, and the two flows do not completely mix for some 320km (200 miles) downstream of their confluence. Midway along its course, the Mackenzie meets Great Bear River, which drains Great Bear Lake.

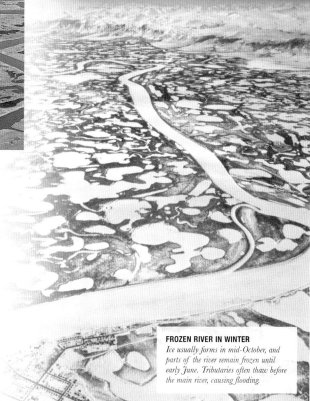

FROZEN RIVER IN WINTER
Ice usually forms in mid-October, and parts of the river remain frozen until early June. Tributaries often thaw before the main river, causing flooding.

NORTH AMERICA *northeast*

Hudson

LOCATION	In New York State, USA, and flowing into the Atlantic Ocean at New York City
LENGTH	507km (315 miles)
VERTICAL FALL	1,371m (4,323ft)
BASIN AREA	34,628 square km (13,370 square miles)
MAIN TRIBUTARIES	Mohawk

From its source in Lake Tear of the Clouds, a post-glacial lake in the Adirondack Mountains, the Hudson flows southeast to its confluence with the Mohawk near Albany, then turns southwards for the last 240km (150 miles)

of its course. The lower Hudson Valley (and that whole section of eastern coastline) was drowned by the sea at the end of the last ice age, leaving a submarine canyon about 180km (110 miles) long. Tidal influence extends as far as Albany, which has a 1.4m- (4½ft-) high tide. A prominent feature of the lower valley is the Palisades (see p.180), a series of steep cliffs where the river cuts into hard rock. Since its exploration by Henry Hudson in 1609, the river has been commercially important. Nineteenth-century improvements, notably the Erie Canal, connected the Hudson with the Great Lakes, and the rapidly extending western "frontier". It remains a major river highway.

HUDSON PASSING MANHATTAN ISLAND
The shipping piers seen here along Manhattan's Lower West Side underlines the Hudson's importance as a transport route.

NORTH AMERICA *northeast*

St. Lawrence

LOCATION	Flows from Lake Ontario to the Atlantic Ocean; forms part of the Canada–USA border
LENGTH	1,244km (760 miles)
VERTICAL FALL	75m (246ft)
BASIN AREA	1.3 million square km (500,000 square miles)
MAIN TRIBUTARIES	Ottawa, St. Maurice

The St. Lawrence River is the outflow for the whole of the Great Lakes system. It is a very young watercourse that began flowing only about 7,000 years ago, as a result of post-glacial uplift in the Great Lakes basin. The wide plains of the St. Lawrence valley formed before the river began to flow, when the area was inundated by a shallow sea. The upper part of its course is wide and for the first 184km (114 miles) forms the border between Canada and the USA. The river then narrows through a series of rapids towards Montreal, where it widens again. Lake St. Pierre, midway between Montreal and Quebec City, marks the start of the St. Lawrence estuary. Downstream of Quebec City, the lower estuary extends from Île d'Orléans to the island of

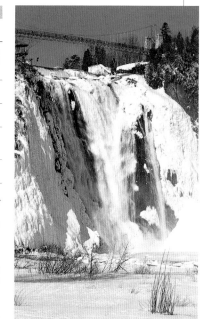

FROZEN FALLS IN WINTER
Water plunging over the Montmorency Falls on the Montmorency River in Quebec freezes as it falls, creating curtains of frozen spray.

Anticosti, where the river enters the Atlantic at the Gulf of St. Lawrence. Extensive engineering during the 20th century has transformed the river into the St. Lawrence Seaway.

Mississippi

LOCATION In the USA, flowing from near the Canadian border in Minnesota to the Gulf of Mexico

LENGTH 3,780km (2,350 miles)

VERTICAL FALL 450m (1,475ft)

BASIN AREA 3.2 million square km (1.2 million square miles)

MAIN TRIBUTARIES Missouri, Ohio, Arkansas, Tennessee

Together with its many tributaries, the Mississippi River forms a vast and ancient river system. Its drainage basin extends over almost the whole of the

United States from the Rocky Mountains to the Appalachians. The western tributaries drain the Great Plains, while the eastern ones drain the Appalachian Plateau. The source of the Mississippi is Lake Itasca in northern Minnesota, which the river leaves as a clear 3m- (10ft-) wide stream that winds eastwards through extensive marshes, fed by other lakes and streams. It then turns southwards, skirting the higher ground around the western end of Lake Superior. Downstream of Minneapolis, the Mississippi begins to collect the upper-course tributaries that give rise to its name, which means "Father of Waters"

MINNESOTA MARSHES

The low-lying and fast-eroding shoreline of Lake Minnetonka reveals the delicate balance between land and water in the wetlands of Minnesota.

MILK RIVER MEETING THE MISSOURI

The Milk River gathers some of its distinctively pale sediment as it loops through southern Canada. It meets the Missouri in Montana.

in the native Algonkian language. The influx of the Missouri River near St. Louis brings huge quantities of sediment that change the character of the river. Downstream, at Cairo, Illinois, the inflow of the Ohio River marks the original beginning of the Mississippi delta, which has been inching southwards for the last 100 million years. Flowing through a gap between the Cumberland and Ozark plateaus, the Mississippi follows a broad valley cut through the alluvial deposits by meltwater at the end of the last ice age. Although the Missouri ("Big Muddy"), 4,120km (2,560 miles) long, is considered the Mississippi's main tributary, the Ohio – length 1,570km (975 miles) – contributes the greater volume of water. Only along its lower course, south of Cairo, does the Mississippi achieve the full majesty of "Ol' Man River", more than 1,600m (1 mile) wide and carrying about half a billion tonnes of sediment to the sea each year. The delta has shifted over an area of about 320 square km (200 square miles) during the last 6,000 years, and forms a branching extension into the Gulf of Mexico, southeast of New Orleans. It is currently shrinking, due to a combination of natural and human-induced factors.

FLOOD CONTROL

Levees for protection against floods were first built on the Mississippi in the early 18th century. Long stretches are now ramparted in this way. The variable waters of the Ohio cause most floods, but in 1993, heavy rains over the northern Great Plains caused devastating floods upstream of Cairo. With little warning, East Dubuque and other towns on the upper Mississippi and lower Missouri were inundated by a so-called "100-year" event.

SLOUGHS ON MISSISSIPPI RIVER

This upstream view of the river in northern Iowa shows narrow, dead-end sloughs (backwaters) between a network of sand bars which have been stabilized by vegetation.

NORTH AMERICA *west*

Colorado

LOCATION Mainly within the USA, flowing from the Rocky Mountains to the Gulf of California

LENGTH
2,333km (1,450 miles)

VERTICAL FALL
4,320m (14,200ft)

BASIN AREA
632,000 square km
(244,000 square miles)

MAIN TRIBUTARIES
Green, Little Colorado, Gila

The Colorado, which drains the arid southwestern quarter of the USA, is the world's most formidable canyon-cutter. In response to the tilting uplift of the Colorado Plateau, the river has cut more than 1,600km (1,000 miles) of deep canyons, the most spectacular stretch of which is the 350km- (220-mile-) long Grand Canyon in northern Arizona. The Colorado River rises from snowmelt high in the Rocky Mountains in northern Colorado, on the westward slopes of the Continental Divide. It flows southwest across the Colorado Plateau into Utah, where the confluence with the Green River in the Canyonlands region brings waters from the northernmost reaches of its drainage basin in Wyoming. Downstream in northern Arizona, the main trunk of the Colorado's branching canyon system – the Grand Canyon – reaches 29km (18 miles) in width and cuts down through layers of sedimentary rock that record 2 billion years of geological history. Below the canyon, after exiting the plateau, the course turns southwards, forming the California–Arizona state line. Along its lower course the Colorado is a slow, meandering river, laden with fine silt and subject to flooding. The last 128km (80 miles) run through Mexico to a shrinking delta. The Colorado River is the most managed river in the world. Large-scale engineering began in the northern part of the drainage basin in the 1920s, with great tunnels cut beneath the Continental Divide to divert some of the river's water eastwards to the Great Plains.

THE GRAND CANYON
Created by the river, the magnificent rock cliffs of the Grand Canyon are preserved by the aridity of the desert climate. At the base of the canyon, the river has cut down to 1.7 billion-year-old rocks.

Subsequent attention has focused on the lower course. The 221m- (726ft-) high Hoover Dam created Lake Mead in 1935, and provides both electricity and irrigation water. Downstream, considerable amounts of water are diverted to the cities of Las Vegas, Phoenix, Tucson, San Diego, and Los Angeles. The Imperial Dam diverts most of the water that remains along the All-American Canal to California's Imperial Valley. Although the flow at the mouth of the Colorado is now much reduced, it has in the past effected great changes upon the coastline. The Gulf of California once extended much farther north until the Colorado changed its course in prehistoric times. Sediment deposited on the river's banks

COLORADO RIVER DELTA
This aerial view of the delta in Mexico shows some of the many distributary channels created when the river had a much greater flow.

dammed the Gulf, creating the current shoreline and the great Salton Sink, a stretch of former sea bed that extends inland some 480km (300 miles). In 1905 a breached irrigation channel allowed the Colorado's waters to flood into the sink, creating the 112km- (70-mile-) long Salton Sea.

CACTI BY THE COLORADO
The climate of the Colorado Plateau is hot and arid. Only cacti and low desert shrubs can grow – there are no trees, even at the river's edge.

REGULATING THE COLORADO

The 216m- (710ft-) high Glen Canyon Dam is located in Arizona about 175km (110 miles) upstream of the Grand Canyon. It was constructed in the 1960s to store water from winter rains to generate electricity later in the year, when the river's natural flow diminishes. By restricting the flow of the Colorado, the dam has had an alarming effect on the environment along riverbanks in the Grand Canyon. Instead of being scoured clean by regular winter floods, parts of the canyon are now starting to fill with sediment. In the 1990s, attempts were made to redress the balance by releasing artificial floods from the dam.

CUTTING POWER OF THE COLORADO
The erosive power of the Colorado River is clearly evident in this picture, which shows a deep channel cut through the colourful sedimentary rocks of the Grand Canyon.

NORTH AMERICA *southwest*

Rio Grande

LOCATION Flows from the Rocky Mountains to the Gulf of Mexico; is part of the USA–Mexico border

LENGTH
3,034km (1,885 miles)

VERTICAL FALL
3,650m (12,000ft)

BASIN AREA
445,000 square km (172,000 square miles)

MAIN TRIBUTARIES
Chama, Conchos, Pecos, Salado

Rising high in the San Juan Mountains of southern Colorado, the fifth longest river in North America flows through New Mexico into Texas. From El Paso on the high plains to Brownsville on the delta, the Rio Grande defines the border – 2,000km (1,250 miles) long – between Texas and Mexico. Fed by springs below the San Juan snowfield, its upper course flows eastwards along pine-forested canyons, then turns south into New Mexico, where the river has cut the Rio Grande gorge and White Rock Canyon. The middle course flows through basin-and-range terrain, skirting the San Andres Mountains, before descending through three great canyons, over 450m (1,500ft) deep, onto the Gulf Coastal Plain. In the USA, these canyons form Big Bend National Park. With much of its water being diverted for irrigation, the Rio Grande winds sluggishly across the coastal plain to the Gulf of Mexico. So much of the river's water is diverted that during long, dry periods surface flow at the delta disappears.

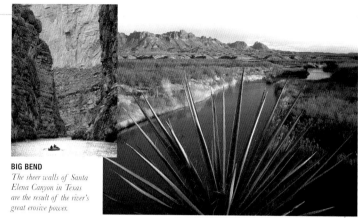

BIG BEND
The sheer walls of Santa Elena Canyon in Texas are the result of the river's great erosive power.

RIO GRANDE, TEXAS
Upstream of the Big Bend canyons, with the Chisos Mountains rising in the distance, the Rio Grande provides water to the arid landscape of the high plains.

SOUTH AMERICA *southeast*

River Plate

LOCATION On the eastern coast of South America, with Uruguay to the north and Argentina to the south

LENGTH
290km (180 miles)

VERTICAL FALL Nil

BASIN AREA
4.2 million square km (1.6 million square miles)

MAIN TRIBUTARIES
Paraná, Uruguay

Not strictly a river, nor a marine gulf, the River Plate is a huge, funnel-shaped estuary formed by the mouth of the River Uruguay coinciding with the delta of the River Paraná.

Extending over 35,000 square km (13,500 square miles), and 219km (136 miles) wide where it meets the Atlantic, the Plate receives the sediment load of three great rivers – the Uruguay, the Paraná, and the Paraguay (the major tributary of the Paraná) – that have a combined length of nearly 8,000km (5,000 miles). As a result the Plate is choked by sediment that accumulates into great shoals, where the water depth can be reduced to as little as 1.5m (5ft). Constant dredging is necessary to maintain deep-water channels to the ports of Montevideo and Buenos Aires. The catchment area of the Plate extends over parts of Argentina, Bolivia, Brazil, Paraguay, and Uruguay. The River Parana flows some 4,000km (2,485 miles) from the highlands of central Brazil to the Plate. Along its upper course, the most notable feature is the Guaira Falls, which carries several times the volume of Niagara Falls. Downstream, the River Iguaçu brings water still churning from a drop of 82m (270ft) over the spectacular Iguaçu Falls. The River Paraguay runs 2,550km (1,585 miles) from its source in the Mato Grosso region of Brazil, through the Pantanal wetlands, to its confluence with the Paraná. The river has a shallow gradient – most of its catchment area lies below 200m (650ft) – and it is subject to seasonal flooding. The River Uruguay rises on the western slopes of southern Brazil's coastal range and loops inland along a course of about 1,000km (1,600miles) to the Plate estuary.

PARANÁ RIVER DELTA
This false-colour satellite image shows an area of marshland to the north of Buenos Aires, Argentina, where the Paraná and Uruguay rivers meet.

DEVIL'S THROAT AT IGUAÇU FALLS
Upstream from its confluence with the Paraná, the Iguaçu River plunges over a great, horseshoe-shaped waterfall into a steep-sided canyon called Devil's Gorge.

Orinoco

LOCATION Flows through Venezuela from the Guiana Highlands to the Atlantic Ocean

LENGTH
2,151km (1,337 miles)

VERTICAL FALL
1,074m (3,523ft)

BASIN AREA
948,000 square km
(366,000 square miles)

MAIN TRIBUTARIES
Guaviare, Meta, Arauca, Apure, Caroni

The second longest river in South America, the Orinoco flows in a great arc through Venezuela. Its drainage basin covers about 80 per cent of that country and about 25 per cent of Colombia. The upper reaches contain two remarkable features: Angel Falls, the world's highest uninterrupted waterfall, cascades down Auyan Tebui (Devil's Mountain); and Casiquiare Channel, 355km (221 miles) long, diverts some of the Orinoco's waters southwards into the Rio Negro, a tributary of the Amazon. On the east edge of the Guiana Highlands, the Orinoco flows through a series of boulder-strewn rapids (Region de los Raudales) before turning northeastwards. The lower course is marked by numerous swamps (notably the Llanos wetlands, see p.282) before branching into a delta some 436km (270 miles) from the Atlantic coast. The main channel discharges at Boca Grande ("Big Mouth"). The rainfall that feeds the Orinoco is very seasonal, and flooding along the lower course is frequent and extensive. At the end of the dry season in April, the river at Ciudad Bolivar may be 30m (100ft) lower than at the height of the rains, in July.

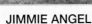

WATTLED JAÇANA
Also known as the Lily Trotter, this bird has large, spidery feet that work like snowshoes, spreading its weight and enabling it to walk on floating vegetation.

elongated toe

ORINOCO DELTA
The delta covers about 36,500 square km (14,000 square miles) and is home to the now rare Orinoco Crocodile. Many of the islands are used for cattle ranching and growing cacao.

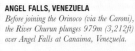

ANGEL FALLS, VENEZUELA
Before joining the Orinoco (via the Caroni), the River Churun plunges 979m (3,212ft) over Angel Falls at Canaima, Venezuela.

LAND

JIMMIE ANGEL

Angel Falls are named after American aviator Jimmie Angel (1899–1956), who first sighted the falls from the air in 1933. Four years later, he landed on top of Devil's Mountain, but damaged his plane in the process and had to trek back through rainforest to the nearest settlement. Angel, who achieved near-legendary status in Venezuela, died in Panama from injuries received in a flying accident.

SOUTH AMERICA *north*

Amazon

LOCATION Flows from the Peruvian Andes, across Brazil to the Atlantic Ocean

LENGTH 6,430km (3,990 miles)

VERTICAL FALL 5,500m (18,000ft)

BASIN AREA 7.1 million square km (2.7 million square miles)

MAIN TRIBUTARIES Juruá, Madeira, Negro

The Amazon is the world's greatest river, measured both by the size of its basin and by the volume of water it discharges. On a world scale, the

AMAZON HEADWATERS
Many of the Amazon's Andean tributaries freeze in winter, as seen here in the Bolivia Cordillera Real.

Amazon delivers about 20 per cent of all the water reaching the sea from rivers. Its nearest rivals, the Congo and Yellow rivers, each deliver only about 4 per cent of the total. Some 16km (10 miles) wide at Manaus, while still 1,600km (1,000 miles) from the sea, it is truly a giant river. The Amazon flows from mountainsides and glacier-fed lakes high in the Andes of southern Peru, within about 160km (100 miles) of the Pacific Ocean. The upper course, known as the River Marañón, flows north, and then turns east, descending into the Amazon Basin – a vast depression sinking under the

BRAIDED CHANNELS NEAR MANAUS
Along its middle course, the river frequently braids between strings of low islands that constantly shift as the river channel alters following seasonal rains.

weight of material eroded from surrounding highlands. Here, it meanders for more than 3,200km (2,000 miles) from Iquitos to Belém. Marshy areas along the banks are liable to seasonal floods, but most of the basin is covered by dry-footed equatorial rainforest that experiences daily convectional thunderstorms. Along its middle and lower course, the Amazon receives many tributaries from the Guiana Highlands to the north, and the Brazilian Central Plateau in the south. These sources – Andean glaciers, daily rains, and the numerous tributaries – contribute to the 770 billion litres (170 billion gallons) of water that the Amazon pours into the Atlantic every hour. The flow of the river is so strong that there is no delta; instead it discharges through a wide, mangrove-fringed estuary that straddles the equator. Despite its size, the Amazon delivers less sediment to the ocean than the Mississippi, which has only one-tenth of the Amazon's flow.

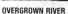

GIANT RIVER OTTER
This highly endangered mammal lives in small family groups along quiet stretches of the river throughout the Amazon Basin.

OVERGROWN RIVER
The river's placid backwaters are covered in mats of vegetation, such as these Giant Water Lilies, which provide a valuable habitat for many animals.

DEFORESTATION

The Amazon Basin cradles the greatest expanse of rainforest on Earth – an irreplaceable resource that is being destroyed at an alarming rate. The Amazonian forests (see p.265) face a number of threats – logging, large-scale agriculture, and the slash-and-burn subsistence farming of internal migrants drawn to the Amazonian frontier. Stripped of cover, and deprived of the long-term release of the nutrients locked within the trees, Amazonian soils deteriorate rapidly into barren wastes, and add to the river's sediment load. Despite widespread concern and publicity, the deforestation continues, and some experts predict a catastrophic collapse of the entire forest ecosystem within the next 30–50 years.

AMAZON TRIBUTARY
This view of the River Cuieiras (a tributary
of the Rio Negro) is typical of the Amazon
Basin – wide, unruffled rivers branching
through a seemingly endless lush rainforest.

LAND

EUROPE *west*

Thames

LOCATION In Britain, flowing across southern England from the Cotswold Hills to the North Sea

LENGTH
336km (210 miles)

VERTICAL FALL
108m (356ft)

BASIN AREA
13,600 square km
(5,200 square miles)

MAIN TRIBUTARIES
Colne, Kennet, Wey

The longest river in Britain, the Thames arises from springs in the Cotswolds, a ridge of limestone hills in south-central England. The upper course winds eastwards along the northern edge of the Chiltern Hills until it breaks through at the Goring gap near Oxford. Here, where it is known locally as the Isis, the river is about

30m (100ft) wide. The lower course flows southeast along the wide, shallow Thames valley, which is characterized by gravel terraces and clays deposited by successive pulses of post-glacial meltwater. The river is tidal for the lower 145km (90 miles) of its length, and the tidal range at London, the lowest bridging point, is about 7m (23ft). Although London's inhabitants have a comfortable relationship with the Thames, the river in fact poses a considerable threat. Heavy rains combined with exceptionally high tides have flooded the city on many occasions. Below London, the Thames widens into an estuary that is about 8km (5 miles) wide, where it discharges into the North Sea.

THE THAMES BARRIER, LONDON
The Thames Barrier is a series of huge steel gates that can be raised to protect the city against flooding at high tide.

EUROPE *southwest*

Tagus

LOCATION Flowing across the Iberian Peninsula from eastern Spain to the Atlantic coast of Portugal

LENGTH
1,007km (626 miles)

VERTICAL FALL
1,590m (5,216ft)

BASIN AREA
81,600 square km
(31,505 square miles)

MAIN TRIBUTARIES
Gallo, Zezere

Rising in the Sierra de Albarracin about 140km (90 miles) east of Madrid, the Tagus is one of several rivers that drain the Meseta Plateau. Initially fast-flowing, through limestone gorges, the

river slows and widens as it flows westwards, past the city of Toledo, through increasingly arid landscapes. For a short distance the Tagus forms part of the border between Spain and Portugal, and the final 275km (170 miles) of its course flows through Portugal. The estuary at Lisbon is one of the world's finest natural harbours. The Tagus has been widely harnessed both for power and irrigation by both countries. Upstream of the border section, a dam at Alcántara in Spain has created an artificial lake, large by European standards, that extends back nearly 160km (100 miles) along the river's middle course.

TAGUS RIVER PASSING TOLEDO, SPAIN
The oldest parts of this city, founded before the time of the Romans, are perched high on a rocky outcrop that overlooks a bend in the river's gorge.

EUROPE *west*

Severn

LOCATION In Britain, flowing from Wales through England to the Bristol Channel and the Irish Sea

LENGTH
290km (180 miles)

VERTICAL FALL
600m (2,000ft)

BASIN AREA
11,266 square km
(4,350 square miles)

MAIN TRIBUTARIES
Avon, Stour, Teme, Usk

Rising on Plynlimon mountain in western Wales, the upper course of the Severn descends 455m (1,500ft) in its first 24km (15 miles) into the Vale of Powys. After cutting the Ironbridge Gorge through hills on the English–Welsh border, the river follows a semicircular course through central England. One of its middle-course tributaries, the Warwickshire Avon, flows through William Shakespeare's home town of Stratford-upon-Avon. South of Gloucester the river widens and meanders to an estuary that discharges into the Bristol Channel below Newport. Locally, the lower course of the Severn is noted for its tidal bore, a wave that moves at speeds of about 25kph (15mph), reaching a height of nearly 3m (10ft).

EUROPE *west*

Loire

LOCATION Flows from the Massif Central to the Atlantic coast south of the Brittany peninsula in France

LENGTH
1,020km (634 miles)

VERTICAL FALL
14,850m (4,500ft)

BASIN AREA
117,000 square km
(45,000 square miles)

MAIN TRIBUTARIES
Allier, Maine, Vienne

The longest river in France, the Loire rises among volcanic peaks in the Cevennes mountains at the south-east edge of the Massif Central. Its source is

EUROPE *west*

Seine

LOCATION In northern France, flowing from the Burgundy region to the English Channel at Le Havre

LENGTH
780km (480 miles)

VERTICAL FALL
471m (1,545ft)

BASIN AREA
83,000 square km
(32,000 square miles)

MAIN TRIBUTARIES
Aube, Marne, Oise

The Seine defines what is often called the Paris Basin. Upstream of the city, the river and its tributaries have cut down through limestone to create a series of fertile plateaus that form the region known as the Île de France. Downstream of Paris, the Seine flows through chalk hills, and below Rouen follows a series of wide meanders, before widening into its estuary.

ALEXANDRE III BRIDGE, PARIS

only about 160km (100 miles) from the Mediterranean Sea and the mouth of the Rhône. Initially flowing north along a series of faulted depressions in the massif, the Loire then meanders through central France along a shallow, steep-sided valley. The river pivots west near the city of Orléans, passing Tours and Angers. Below Nantes, the Loire widens to an estuary that discharges into the Bay of Biscay at St. Nazaire. The river's flow is very irregular, and parts of the middle course, which is studded by strings of sandy islands, run almost dry in summer. In autumn and spring, heavy rains can cause flooding, especially in the lower reaches.

CHATEAU OF SULLY-SUR-LOIRE
Tree-lined banks and chateaux make the Loire valley one of the most picturesque places in France.

EUROPE *northwest*

Rhine

LOCATION Flowing from the Swiss Alps to the North Sea coast of the Netherlands

LENGTH
1,320km (820 miles)

VERTICAL FALL
2,339m (7,690ft)

BASIN AREA
220,000 square km
(85,000 square miles)

MAIN TRIBUTARIES
Main, Moselle, Neckar

The most commercially important river of western Europe, the Rhine rises high in central Switzerland. Its headwaters, the Vorderrhein and the Hinterrhein, are fed by snowmelt that reaches a maximum in June and July. The upper Rhine flows north into Lake Constance (see p.193) through a small delta. From the western end of the lake, the river continues westwards, plunging over the 30m- (100ft-) high Rhine Falls in northern Switzerland, and along the southern edge of the Black Forest mountains, before swinging north near Basel into the two-stage Rhine Valley. The upper part of the valley is a broad and ancient rift valley (see p.87) about 32km (20 miles) wide – with the

THE RHINE NEAR KAUB
The snaking course of the narrow lower valley is overlooked by hundreds of castles, some of which date back many centuries.

Vosges mountains to the west and the Black Forest to the east – the sides of which contain the river's floodplain. Just below Basel, for about 160km (100 miles), the Rhine forms part of the border between Germany and France. Downstream, the German section of river has been straightened during the last two centuries by cutting through its many meanders. After passing Mainz, the Rhine enters the lower valley, a narrow, twisting gorge, 145km (90 miles) long, cut

between the Hunsrück and Eifel hills on the western side, and the Taunus and Westerwald on the eastern side. South of Bonn, the valley widens onto a plain and the river's lower course passes the cities of Cologne, Düsseldorf, and Duisburg. The Rhine estuary begins below Emmerlich near the German–Dutch border, and the main stream enters the North Sea at Rotterdam. The River Meuse follows a parallel course to the sea and adds its waters to their combined estuary.

LAND

EUROPE *west*

Rhône

LOCATION Flowing from the Swiss Alps through France to the Mediterranean Sea

LENGTH
813km (505 miles)

VERTICAL FALL
1,800m (6,000ft)

BASIN AREA
96,000 square km
(37,000 square miles)

MAIN TRIBUTARIES
Ardèche, Arve, Isère, Saône

The Rhône is the only major European river to flow into the Mediterranean Sea. Descending from the Rhône glacier in southern Switzerland, its upper course flows westwards across the

HEADWATERS OF THE RHÔNE
The ice-cold waters of the river cross the Vallée de la Clarée near Briançon in the French Alps.

Valais region, through gorges that follow structural faults and along glaciated valleys. The river then turns north across the Alps and forms a delta as it enters Lake Geneva (see p.193). The Rhône exits the southwestern end of the lake and follows a zigzag westward course through the Jura mountains of eastern France. Near Lyons it receives the waters of its main tributary, the Saône, and turns southwards. Its lower course follows a trough between the Alps and the Massif Central. Receiving tributaries on both banks, the Rhône proceeds through a series of gorges cut through rocky outcrops, separated by sediment-filled basins with terraced sides that are often inundated by seasonal flooding. As it approaches the sea, the river

CHAMOIS
This agile antelope grazes along the upper reaches of the Rhône in the French and Swiss Alps. In winter it descends to lower levels to find food.

braids over an increasingly marshy landscape. The Rhône delta starts near Arles, where the river diverts into two main channels that flow across the Camargue wetland (see p.283) and into the sea west of Marseilles.

RHÔNE AT AVIGNON
Along its lower reaches, the Rhône can present a placid, tranquil image that is quite at odds with its wild and racing Alpine origins.

EUROPE *central*

Oder

LOCATION Flowing from the Czech Republic to the Baltic Sea in Poland

LENGTH
886km (550 miles)

VERTICAL FALL
633m (2,080ft)

BASIN AREA
119,000 square km
(46,000 square miles)

MAIN TRIBUTARIES
Neisse, Warta

The Oder rises in the mountainous northeast of the Czech Republic, but nine-tenths of its drainage basin lies within Poland, and a stretch of its lower course forms part of the Polish–German border. The river exits the mountains through a depression known as the Moravian Gate. It is a very wide river, up to 9.5km (6 miles) across in places. It is also very shallow, with an average depth of about 90cm (3ft). The river freezes for about one month in winter. As it approaches the sea, the main channel braids into several parallel streams. Below the city of Szczecin, it enters a lagoon and then flows into the Bay of Pomerania.

DAMS

Dams are some of the largest engineered structures on Earth. They supply about a sixth of the world's electricity, and they significantly reduce the risk of floods and droughts. However, in the industrialized world the construction of very large dams is almost at a standstill, largely because suitable sites have already been exploited. In developing countries, such as India and China, it continues apace.

Dams and Drainage

Earth-filled dams date back to the time of ancient Egypt, but concrete ones are a much more recent innovation. Dam-building became a matter of national prestige in the 20th century. The USA, for example, built a series of massive dams in the Colorado River basin (see p.166), and the former Soviet Union dammed its major rivers and supervised the building of the Aswan High Dam, a rock-filled barrage straddling the River Nile in Egypt (see p.177). These huge projects were followed by others in Africa and South America. One of them – the Itaipú Dam, on the border between Brazil and Paraguay – houses currently the second largest hydroelectric plant in the world.

Electricity production is the chief reason for building mega-dams but they also smooth out seasonal variations in water flow, preventing potentially dangerous floods. In China, this is one of the reasons behind the immense Three Gorges project, which regulates the River Yangtze (see p.180). It is hoped that the dam will stop disastrous floods, which over the centuries have claimed many lives.

DIVIDED BY DAMS
The erection of dams shown on the map above has limited the movements of the rare Indus River Dolphin. The dolphins are now confined to isolated pockets between dams, in which they interbreed and so jeopardize their survival.

SHAPED FOR STRENGTH
The Hoover Dam spans the lower reaches of the Colorado River. At 221m (726ft) high, it is the tallest dam in the USA.

LARGEST HYDROELECTRIC DAMS

The world's hydroelectric dams have a combined capacity of about 700,000 megawatts (MW), but they exploit only about a quarter of this energy, owing to practical and environmental considerations.

Name	Location	Max power (MW)
Three Gorges Dam	China	22,500
Itaipú	Brazil–Paraguay	14,000
Guri	Venezuela	10,000
Tucuruí	Brazil	8,370
Grand Coulee	USA	6,494
Sayano-Shushensk	Russia	6,400
Krasnoyarsk	Russia	6,000
Robert-Bourassa	Canada	5,618
Churchill Falls	Canada	5,428
Longtan Dam	China	4,900

Ecological Effects

The Three Gorges project epitomizes the environmental conundrum that dams can pose. The power they generate is renewable and theoretically pollution-free. These are major advantages for a country such as China, which still relies heavily on coal. But with extremely large dams, these benefits are offset by some serious drawbacks. By blocking sediment flow, dams deprive floodplains of fertile silt, which wetland plants need to become established on exposed soils. Instead, the silt accumulates in reservoirs, which reduces their working life.

For freshwater wildlife, large dams have mixed effects. Reservoirs create new habitats for animals, but dams form barriers that can be difficult to pass. This is a problem for migratory fish, and also for other species that normally keep on the move. Riverside plants decline when sediment levels drop, although reservoirs often make ideal homes for floating water plants. Unfortunately, these floating plants include invasive species such as water hyacinth, a problematic weed in warm parts of the world.

Gains and Losses

Dams make existing water supplies easier to exploit. In the American southwest, many farms depend on water from the Colorado Basin reservoirs, as do rapidly growing cities such as Phoenix and Las Vegas. In this region, dams attract plenty of environmental criticism, but current lifestyles there would be unsustainable without the water that dams provide.

In other parts of the world, small-scale dams are vital for rural life. In southern India, for example, thousands of hand-built reservoirs – which are known locally as tanks – capture rainwater from the annual monsoon. Without them, agriculture would be impossible during the dry season. But dams can also displace people, and threaten their livelihoods. By the time the Three Gorges project was completed in 2012, an estimated 1.3 million people had lost their homes and their farmland was submerged below a lake 600km (373 miles) long.

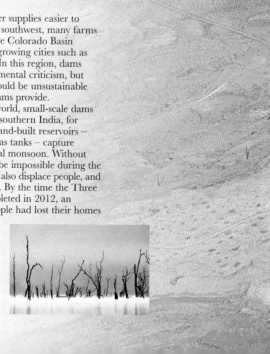

FLOODED FOREST
Rotting vegetation in newly flooded reservoirs releases methane – a gas that adds to the greenhouse effect.

LIQUID RESERVES
The Glen Canyon Dam on the Colorado River, USA, generates hydroelectric power. The water it traps is also used for drinking and irrigation.

EUROPE central

Danube

LOCATION Flowing from southern Germany to the Black Sea coast in eastern Romania

LENGTH
2,860km (1,770 miles)

VERTICAL FALL
662m (2,174ft)

BASIN AREA
816,000 square km
(315,000 square miles)

MAIN TRIBUTARIES
Drava, Sava, Tisza

Europe's second longest river, the Danube, rises in Germany from the confluence of the Brege and Brigach rivers. It flows eastwards into Austria, descending through the Hungarian

FLOODING

During the summer of 2002, unusually heavy summer rains across central Europe caused the Danube to overtop its banks in many places. Millions of people living along its course were affected, and thousands of homes were inundated, as here in the Slovak capital, Bratislava. Downstream, the Hungarian capital, Budapest, was also affected. Upstream of Bratislava, in Austria, the Danube reached an all-time high as the region experienced the heaviest rainfall ever recorded. The town of Linz and part of Vienna were flooded, despite an excellent system of flood prevention.

THE DANUBE PASSING BUDAPEST
The Chain Bridge, seen here in front of the Hungarian Parliament Building, joins what were once two separate cities – Buda and Pest.

Gate to the Little Alföld plain. After passing Budapest, the river flows southwards across the Great Hungarian Plain and between the Carpathian and Balkan mountains. Here the river has cut the deepest gorge in Europe, the Iron Gate, with sheer walls 800m (2,600ft) high. The Danube's lower course passes across the Wallachian Plain. As it nears the Black Sea, the river is deflected northwards by the ancient and eroded Dobruja Hills, before turning east once more. It discharges into the sea through three main distributaries, in a delta that has an area of about 5,000 square km (1,900 square miles).

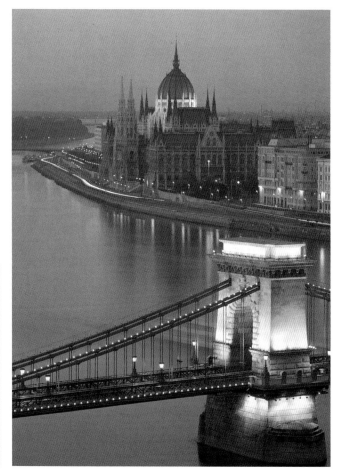

EUROPE southeast

Volga

LOCATION In Russia, flowing eastwards then southwards to the Caspian Sea

LENGTH
3,690km (2,293 miles)

VERTICAL FALL
258m (848ft)

BASIN AREA
1.4 million square km
(525,000 square miles)

MAIN TRIBUTARIES
Oka, Kama

The Volga is Europe's longest river and one of Russia's most important transport routes. The river rises 228m (748ft) above sea level in the Valdai Hills about 400km (250 miles) northwest of Moscow, and its drainage basin extends eastwards to the Urals. Its upper course runs northeast through swamp forest, lakes, and reservoirs, then turns southeast along a narrow valley between the Danilov and Uglich highlands. Near

VOLGA PASSING NIZHNIY NOVGOROD
Ice-free for about 200 days each year, the Volga has for centuries formed a river highway through the heart of European Russia.

the city of Nizhniy Novgorod, the Volga receives the waters of the Oka and increases considerably in size. The river continues its southeast course through damp forest until it passes Kazan, where it turns southwards and flows through a progressively more arid landscape. Downstream of Kazan the river, swollen by the inflow of the Kama, flows between the Volga Hills and the Turgay Plateau. The most notable feature of its middle course is the Samara Bend – a remarkable loop 160km (100 miles)

long, around a piece of high ground. Near Volgagrad the river splits in two. The Volga and its main distributary, the Akhtuba, follow a parallel course into the Caspian Depression where, downstream of Astrakhan, they discharge through a wide delta into the Caspian Sea (see p.198) about 30m (100ft) below sea level. The Volga freezes for about 100 days each year. Its importance for transport has been enhanced by the construction of canals, notably the Volga–Baltic Waterway completed during the 1960s. Numerous hydroelectric dams have also been built across its course.

VOLGA DELTA
The delta (shown here in a satellite image) is lush and well-watered compared with the barren desert landscape that surrounds it.

Nile

LOCATION Flows north from Lake Victoria and the Ethiopian highlands to the Mediterranean coast in Egypt

LENGTH
6,648km (4,132 miles)

VERTICAL FALL
1,135m (3,725ft)

BASIN AREA
3.4 million square km
(1.3 million square miles)

MAIN TRIBUTARIES
White Nile, Blue Nile

The longest river in the world, the Nile is one of the few that are recognized to have more than one main source. The longest stream of the Nile – the White Nile – flows from the northern end of Lake Victoria (see p.195) as the Victoria Nile and over the Murchison Falls into the northern part of the Great Rift Valley (see pp.88–89). The river crosses the northern end of Lake Albert (exiting as the Albert Nile) and then descends through a series of gorges to the flat, marshy plain of the Sudd (see p.285). At Khartoum, the White Nile is joined by the waters of the Blue Nile, with its source at Lake Tana in the Ethiopian Highlands. From Khartoum to southern Egypt, the Nile passes through a series of six great cataracts and then enters a long, narrow valley between desert escarpments before it widens to a broad triangular delta north of Cairo. This delta region, and a long, narrow green ribbon along the Nile, make up the 3 per cent of Egypt's land area that supports cultivation. Thanks to its two sources, the Nile provides both a constant source of water and an annual source of fertile silt. The White Nile, flowing from equatorial rain-fed lakes, ensures the Nile's constancy, but contributes only 16 per cent of its volume downstream of Khartoum. The Blue Nile contributes 84 per cent of the lower river's volume, and accounts for all of its

eyes on top of head

nostrils on top of snout

muscular, vertically flattened tail

NILE CROCODILE
This dangerous, powerful reptile is found along the entire length of the Nile and White Nile, and also on rivers in central and western Africa.

variability. The regular annual flooding of the Nile, which delivers fine, black, fertile silt across the floodplain, is caused by winter rains and snowmelt in the Ethiopian Highlands. The flood season begins in April at Khartoum and gets progressively later in the river's more northerly reaches – the high water of the floods at Cairo occurs in October. The completion of the Aswan High Dam in 1970 created a huge reservoir, Lake Nasser, which extends across the Egyptian–Sudanese border. The dam has significantly moderated the downstream flow of the Nile.

THE UPPER NILE VALLEY
As it flows through verdant forest-lined rapids in Uganda, the Victoria Nile is a foaming, turbulent, and fast-flowing river fed by heavy year-round rainfall across Lake Victoria's drainage area.

FERTILE NILE VALLEY
The banks of the Nile near Luxor are lined with fields. The farmed area extends only as far as the escarpment in the background.

ABU SIMBEL

The damming of the Nile to create Lake Nasser in the 1960s threatened to submerge several important relics of Egypt's ancient civilization, including the temple of Pharaoh Ramses II at Abu Simbel, built in the 13th century BCE. Engineers and archaeologists co-operated to carefully dismantle the temple, and reassemble it at a new site some 60m (200ft) above the waters of the lake. A smaller temple dedicated to Nefatari, Ramses' favourite wife, was moved to the same site.

LAND

THE NILE DELTA
This satellite image shows the Nile's enormous influence on Egypt. Most of the population live in the delta region, or scattered along the valley.

Congo

LOCATION Flows from the highlands of east Africa across the continent to the Atlantic Ocean

LENGTH
4,670km (2,900 miles)

VERTICAL FALL
1,760m (5,780ft)

BASIN AREA
3.5 million square km
(1.4 million square miles)

MAIN TRIBUTARIES Kwa, Lualaba, Sangha, Ubangi

LIVING BETWEEN RIVER AND RAINFOREST
The Congo's banks are lined with villages like this. The villagers benefit from plentiful food and easy transport, but have to live with the risk of flooding.

UPPER CONGO
The upper reaches of the Congo are a hot, wet, sparsely populated and little-explored region of the African continent.

The Congo is second only to the River Amazon in the volume of water it carries to the oceans. It is the second longest river in Africa, and sweeps in a great anticlockwise loop that drains most of central Africa. The Congo's headwaters are fed by rains on the western slopes of the East African Plateau near the southern end of Lake Tanganyika (see p.196) in Zambia. The upper course collects several smaller rivers and flows though rapids and small lakes before descending over the seven-stage Boyoma Falls upstream of Kisangani, and entering the Congo

BOYOMA FALLS
Fish are a great natural bounty for the people of the Congo Basin. In swirling rapids like this one upstream of Kisangani, fish are harvested in conical traps hung from stout, wooden scaffolding.

Basin – the vast, near-circular depression that extends over most of the river's catchment area. The river widens considerably over the lowlands, reaching widths of up to 13km (8 miles) in places, with strings of islands dividing the flow into several channels. Most of the basin is covered by tropical rainforest, and there are extensive marshes along the river margins and between the many tributary streams. This rain marsh, as it is known, is subject to flooding at all times of the year, especially in the western half of the basin. When tributaries that usually reach their highest level at different times happen to reach peak flow simultaneously, flooding can be extensive. The Congo leaves its basin flowing southwest through a narrow gorge, known as the Chenal or Corridor, that it has cut through the Bateke Plateau. It then widens and flows into the Malebo

Pool, a lake 27km (17 miles) wide. The city of Brazzaville is located on the northern shore, while Kinshasa stands on the southern shore. Upstream of the pool, the Congo is navigable for more than 1,600km (1,000 miles) of its length. Downstream of Malebo, a series of rapids and waterfalls, which long hindered European exploration of the river, block direct access to the sea. Over about 320km (200 miles), the river descends nearly 300m (1,000ft) and then continues along a gorge and through mangrove forests to the Atlantic. The flow of the Congo is so strong and constant that no delta

has formed; instead the flow continues along a submarine canyon, depositing its sediment in a great fan on the ocean floor. Many of the features on the River Congo (including the Malebo Pool, Boyoma Falls, and the town of Kisangani) were formerly named after British explorer Henry Stanley who, together with his French rival Pierre Brazza, was among the first Europeans to explore this region of Africa.

AFRICA *west*

Niger

LOCATION Flows from Guinea through the southern Sahara to the Atlantic Ocean in Nigeria

LENGTH
84,180km (2,600 miles)

VERTICAL FALL
850m (2,800ft)

BASIN AREA
1.9 million square km (730,000 square miles)

MAIN TRIBUTARIES
Bani, Benue, Kaduna

The major river of West Africa, the Niger rises in the Fonta Djallon highlands of northern Guinea. It flows northeast over the lowlands of the Sahel, then curves through the Sahara Desert before turning southeast to pass through Niger and Nigeria. The river flows through dense rainforest before reaching the sea, forming a delta in the Gulf of Guinea.

NIGER DELTA
The delta where the Niger meets the sea is dwarfed by its inland delta, but is still the largest in Africa and is mainly covered in dense mangrove forest.

AFRICA *southeast*

Zambezi

LOCATION Flowing from the highlands of central Africa to the Indian Ocean in Mozambique

LENGTH
3,540km (2,200 miles)

VERTICAL FALL
1,460m (4,800ft)

BASIN AREA
1.3 million square km (500,000 square miles)

MAIN TRIBUTARIES
Kafue, Shire

Africa's fourth largest river rises as a small spring in the Kalene Hills of southwestern Zambia, and then flows eastwards, gaining water from many small tributaries. The Zambezi attains a width of about 1,700m (5,500ft) before plunging over the spectacular Victoria Falls, 108m (355ft) high. Downstream of the falls, where the river forms the border between Zambia and Zimbabwe, its deep, wide valley has been flooded by a lake 280km (175 miles) long, which formed following the construction of the Kariba Dam in 1959 to generate electricity for the region.

HIPPOPOTAMUS
Plant-eating hippopotamuses live in the shallows along the Zambezi's edge and can easily capsize canoes and other small craft.

VICTORIA FALLS IN ZAMBIA
More than double the height and width of Niagara Falls (see p.186), the local name for this magnificent waterfall, Mosi-oa-Tuya, translates as "the smoke that thunders".

ASIA *west*

Euphrates

LOCATION Flows from the mountains of eastern Turkey to the Persian Gulf

LENGTH
2,800km (1,740 miles)

VERTICAL FALL
2,080m (8,800ft)

BASIN AREA
1.1 million square km (430,000 square miles)

MAIN TRIBUTARIES
Tigris

Together with its main tributary and near twin, the Tigris (which is 1,890km/1,180 miles long), the Euphrates forms the largest river system in western Asia. Its headwaters originate in the highlands of eastern Turkey. The Tigris rises about 80km (50 miles) to the east, and collects much of its downstream waters from the Great and Little Zab rivers, which flow from the Zagros Mountains in Iran. For most of their length, the rivers follow nearly parallel courses to the sea, giving rise to the old name for Iraq – Mesopotamia ("land between two rivers"). As they descend from the highlands, the two rivers follow deep, converging valleys that define a triangle of desert known as Al Jazirah ("the Island"). Near Baghdad they come within 80km (50 miles) of each other, only to diverge again. In their lower courses, the rivers' channels are branching and highly unstable. Their combined floodplain is dissected by numerous abandoned channels and irrigation canals. The two rivers meet at Basra and then follow a single course, known as the Shatt al 'Arab, through extensive reed-filled marshes to their outflow at the head of the Persian Gulf.

WARS OVER WATER

In the rain-starved Middle East, water is the most precious of all natural resources. The Ataturk Dam across the Euphrates is one of several that have been constructed in Turkey. These have greatly restricted the downstream flow of the river, and the governments of both Syria and Iraq have protested strongly about Turkey's "theft" of the water.

THE EUPHRATES VALLEY
Upstream of its confluence with the Tigris, the Euphrates flows along a high-sided valley, the floor of which has been levelled by successive floods and course changes.

ASIA east

Yangtze

LOCATION In China, flowing from the Himalayas to the East China Sea in the Pacific Ocean

LENGTH
6,300km (3,900 miles)

VERTICAL FALL
5,480m (18,000ft)

BASIN AREA
2 million square km
(760,000 square miles)

MAIN TRIBUTARIES
Han Shui, Ya-lung Chiang

The Yangtze is the longest river in Asia and the third longest in the world. It rises in the Kunlun Mountains, south of the Takla Makan desert, and flows southeastwards across the Tibetan Plateau along narrow, steep valleys. Over the first 1,600km (1,000 miles), the Yangtze descends at an average rate of about 2m per kilometre (10ft per mile). The river then turns eastwards across Sichuan Province before flowing through the famous Yangtze Gorges. The three gorges have a combined length of about 90km (56 miles) and are no more than 180m (600ft) wide, with rock walls towering 350–600m (1,200–2000ft) above the river. It is here that the Three Gorges Dam, the largest in the world, was opened in 2012. Once across the dam, the Yangtze reaches depths of more than 150m (500ft), making it the deepest river in the world. The river exits the gorges onto a lake-strewn plain and loops south along a wide valley, exiting onto the southern edge of the North China Plain. Along parts of the lower course, the normal river level can be several metres above that of the plain, kept safely in check by natural and artificial levees. The waters of the Yangtze are essential to this densely populated rice-growing area, where the summer drought can last for eight weeks. Conversely, when the rains finally arrive, the Yangtze frequently overtops its banks, flooding huge areas. After meandering northeastwards, the river divides into several distributaries and forms a delta. Shanghai is located between the outflow of the main southern distributaries. The Yangtze has always been China's most commercially important river, and is linked by the Grand Canal, 1,600km (1,000 miles) long, to the Yellow River and Beijing to the north.

YANGTZE HEADWATERS
In the Tibet Autonomous Region of China, the upper course of the Yangtze River flows through icy mountain scenery that is almost barren of vegetation.

YANGTZE RIVER DOLPHIN
This endangered mammal is found in the lower Yangtze. Overhunting and pollution have greatly reduced its numbers.

THE YANGTZE GORGES
At the top left of this image, the river can be seen snaking through the Yangtze Gorges before widening and looping across the downstream plain.

FLOOD LEVEES

Constant maintenance is essential to keep the levees along the Yangtze in good condition and safely above the level of the river. Records reveal that there have been catastrophic floods at least 100 times in the last 2,000 years. The floods of 1932 and 1954, though not as high as some in the river's history, inundated the cities of Nanjing and Wuhan, killed about 300,000 people, and made 40 million homeless.

YANGTZE FISHERMEN
The crew of a traditional fishing boat cast their nets on the Yangtze as it flows along one of the many valleys it has cut through the undulating hills of Sichuan Province.

ASIA east

Yellow River

LOCATION In China, flowing across the north of the country from the Tibetan Plateau to the Yellow Sea

LENGTH
5,460km (3,390 miles)

VERTICAL FALL
4,500m (15,000ft)

BASIN AREA
1.9 million square km
(740,000 square miles)

MAIN TRIBUTARIES
Wei He, Fen He

Also called the Huang-He or Huang-Ho, the Yellow River is China's second longest river and the muddiest river in the world. It carries 30 times more silt per cubic metre of water than the River Nile, and it delivers as much sediment to the sea as the Ganges but transported in a much smaller overall flow. Rising on the Tibetan Plateau, the Yellow River follows an erratic course across northern China. Initially fast-flowing over barren upland, the river descends onto a high plateau

JAPANESE CRANE
This endangered water bird is famous for its elegant and intricate courtship dance, and is considered to be a symbol of happiness and good luck.

covered by loess deposits that date from the last ice age and are several hundred metres thick in places. It is here that the river collects its heavy load of sediment. The river continues southwards onto the North China Plain, then east to its current delta to the north of the Shandong peninsula. Between 206 BCE and 1949, some 1,092 major levee breaches resulted in catastrophic floods and the loss of millions of lives. The river's course has shifted some 26 times and by as much as 320km (200 miles). A flood control system has been put in place with embankments, reservoirs, and controlled flooding. The lower reaches are ramparted by levees, which in places lift the river bed several metres above the surrounding countryside.

YELLOW RIVER AT LAJIA
In Qinhai Province, western China, the Yellow River flows through narrow valleys and across small floodplains with fields of rape and barley.

HOKOU FALLS
The yellow colour of the river, caused by suspended particles of loess, shows as it falls between Shanxi and Shaanxi provinces in central China.

ASIA northwest

Ob'

LOCATION In Russia, flowing across Siberia to the Kara Sea in the Arctic Ocean

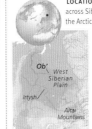

LENGTH
3,700km (2,300 miles)

VERTICAL FALL
Exact source unknown

BASIN AREA
3 million square km
(1.2 million square miles)

MAIN TRIBUTARIES
Chulym, Irtysh, Tom

ASIA south

Irrawaddy

LOCATION In Burma, flows from the Mishmi Hills to the Andaman Sea in the Indian Ocean

LENGTH
2,100km (1,300 miles)

VERTICAL FALL
Exact source unknown

BASIN AREA
411,000 square km
(158,000 square miles)

MAIN TRIBUTARIES
Chindwin

ASIA south

Mekong

LOCATION Flows from western China through Laos and Cambodia to the South China Sea

LENGTH
4,000km (2,500 miles)

VERTICAL FALL
4,950m (16,250ft)

BASIN AREA
795,000 square km
(305,000 square miles)

MAIN TRIBUTARIES
Kang, Mun, Srepok

The longest river in Southeast Asia, the Mekong rises on the Tibetan Plateau, where it flows along deep valleys and is part of the Burmese–Laotian border. Downstream it forms part of the Thai–Laos border, flowing through Cambodia before forming a delta near Hô Chi Minh City in Vietnam.

The Ob' drains the sixth largest catchment area in the world, and some authorities combine it with the Irtysh to form a single river 5,400km (3,360 miles) long. The Ob' rises in the foothills of the Altai Mountains and flows northwards through progressively colder and drier forest landscapes, and then across open tundra, where it separates into two channels, the Greater Ob' and Lesser Ob'. The streams recombine before flowing into an elongated delta that has been partly submerged beneath the sea in the Gulf of Ob'. The river is frozen for up to 200 days per year.

Rising from the meltwaters of east Himalayan glaciers, the Irrawaddy flows southwards to Mandalay and its confluence with the Chindwin. It then meanders through the dry central region of Burma, where it provides much-needed irrigation water. It follows a narrow valley east of the Arakan Yoma highlands, forming a triangular delta west of the Gulf of Thailand. Rangoon is located on one of the numerous distributaries.

PANNING FOR GOLD AT PAGAN, BURMA
In northern Burma, the Irrawaddy and many of its tributaries contain placer deposits, carried down from the mountains when the rivers are in flood.

RAPIDS ON THE MEKONG RIVER
The border of Thailand and Laos sees the Mekong pass through spectacular rapids. Local people fish in swirling pools by the riverside.

LAND

Ganges

LOCATION Flows along the southern edge of the Himalayas to the Bay of Bengal in India

LENGTH
2,506km (1,557 miles)

VERTICAL FALL
3,030m (10,000ft)

BASIN AREA
1.6 million square km
(625,000 square miles)

MAIN TRIBUTARIES
Brahmaputra, Ghaghar, Yamuna

UPPER COURSE OF THE GANGES
In the mountainous north of India, every small area of riverside lowland, overlooked by Himalayan foothills, is intensely cultivated.

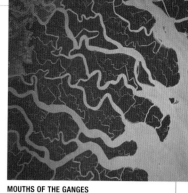

MOUTHS OF THE GANGES
This satellite view shows some of the river's thousands of silt-laden distributaries winding between forested areas of consolidated ground.

The River Ganges, sacred to the Hindu religion, drains about a quarter of India, and delivers more sand and silt to the sea than any other river in the world. Boosted at the head of its delta by the inflow of its largest tributary, the Brahmaputra, the Ganges discharges about 2 billion tonnes of sediment each year. Rising in the southern Himalayas, on the Indian side of the border with China, the Ganges is formed by the confluence of the Alaknanda and Bhagirathi rivers. The upper course flows westwards, then southwards, and descends onto the north Indian plain about 110km (70 miles) east of Delhi. The river's middle course meanders sluggishly eastwards along a wide floodplain covered with sandy alluvial deposits. Over a distance of more than 1,600km (1,000 miles), the river falls only about 180m (600ft). After passing Varanasi and Patna, the Ganges skirts the northern slopes of the Rajmahal Hills and turns southeast onto the Bengal lowlands. Here, the river divides into many distributaries, creating a network of interlacing channels that stretches 400km (250 miles) across the northern coast of the Bay of Bengal. The main western distributary is the Hooghly, which flows through Calcutta. Most of the Ganges delta, is in Bangladesh, and Dhaka is situated at the northeastern corner. In total the Ganges delta covers an area of about 56,980 square km (22,000 square miles). The seaward fringes, known as the Sundarbans, are densely forested in places, and are one of the last refuges of the Bengal Tiger.

HEADWATERS OF GANGES
The Bhagirathi Valley in Uttar Pradesh, India, is overlooked by the mountain glaciers that are the source of the Ganges.

FLOODING IN BANGLADESH

The Bengal Basin, within which the Ganges delta lies, covers 252,000 square kilometres (97,000 square miles) is prone to seasonal flooding caused by monsoon rains. However, an even greater flood threat is posed by the tropical cyclones that sometimes sweep up the Bay of Bengal from the Indian Ocean. Storm surges inundate much greater areas than ordinary riverine floods and can extend over 75 per cent of Bangladesh's land area, most of which is less than 10m (33ft) above sea level. Despite the danger of flooding, the area has a population of about 90 million, and the rich, alluvial soils are intensively farmed. The floods of August 2007 affected almost the entire country. Homes were lost, crops and cattle were destroyed, and roads and bridges were washed away.

GANGES AT VARANASI
The River Ganges is considered sacred by Hindus, and millions of pilgrims visit the city of Varanasi each year to immerse themselves in the holy waters.

LAND

Indus

LOCATION Flows from the Tibetan Plateau across the Himalayas to the Arabian Sea

LENGTH
2,900km (1,800 miles)

VERTICAL FALL
4,848m (16,000ft)

BASIN AREA
1.2 million square km
(450,000 square miles)

MAIN TRIBUTARIES
Chenab, Kabul, Jhelum, Sutlej

The greatest of the trans-Himalayan rivers, the Indus flows from headwaters fed by snowmelt high in southwest China. The upper course flows northwest through the disputed territory of Jammu and Kashmir, along a wide, faulted valley, between the foothills of the Karakoram and Zaskar mountains. The Indus then turns southwest into Pakistan, where it crosses the Himalayas south of the

INDUS RIVER IN KASHMIR
The river flows sedately past sandy terraces that correspond to higher levels in the past, when the river was swollen by snowmelt, and more turbulent.

INDUS RIVER AT SHARDU
In northern Kashmir the upper course of the river flows through a bleak landscape with the Karakoram Mountains in the background.

EARLY CIVILIZATION

The Indus – like the Nile, Euphrates, and Yellow rivers – gave rise to the first civilizations. Over 4,000 years ago, people of this region lived in cities of baked-brick houses, paved streets, and sewers. Some of them used animal-decorated seals like this one, written in an as yet undeciphered script.

Hindu Kush, flowing through gorges, the floors of which are more than 3,650m (12,000ft) below the surrounding peaks. After its confluence with the River Kabul between Peshawar and Islamabad, the Indus crosses the Potwar Plateau and descends onto the Punjab Plain, where it receives many tributaries flowing from the southern foothills of the Himalayas. Skirting the northern fringes of the Thar Desert, the last 480km (300 miles) of the river's course meander across a wide floodplain, and downstream of Hyderabad it splits into several distributaries, forming a delta known as the "Mouths of the Indus". The city of Karachi is located at the northern end of the delta.

Murray

LOCATION In Australia, flows from the southern end of the Great Dividing Range to the Indian Ocean

LENGTH
2,590km (1,610 miles)

VERTICAL FALL
2,050m (6,750ft)

BASIN AREA
1.1 million square km
(412,000 miles)

MAIN TRIBUTARIES
Darling, Murrumbidgee

The Murray, with its major tributary, the Darling, forms Australia's only major river system – one that drains the temperate southeastern corner of an otherwise mainly arid continent. Their combined catchment area contains

GALAH
The Galah is the most widespread cockatoo in Australia and is common around the River Murray.

more than 80 per cent of the country's irrigated farmland. From a source high in the Australian Alps, about midway between Canberra and Melbourne, the Murray flows northeast and then turns westwards, descending into the Murray Valley near the town of Wagga Wagga. The valley is flanked by the Riverina Plains of New South Wales to the north and the plains of northern Victoria to the south. Along its middle course the river receives its main tributaries, which bring waters from the northern part of the catchment area. For the last 650km (400 miles) of its course, the Murray flows through South Australia along a series of deep gorges separated by shallow lakes. The river exits into the ocean through the Coorong Lagoon

(see p.285), into Encounter Bay south of Adelaide. The level of the Murray is erratic, especially during droughts, and the river dried up completely three times between 1800 and 1950. Recently, its flow has been increased by diverting water from the south-flowing Snowy River into its headwaters, as part of the Snowy Mountains hydroelectric scheme.

BIG BEND
High yellow cliffs border the River Murray at Big Bend, which is a 10km- (6-mile-) long, 180-degree S-bend in the river's course.

Lakes

A LAKE FORMS when surface water collects in a depression that has no immediate outlet. The water level rises until an outlet is formed, by which time a substantial amount of water may have accumulated. Lakes vary enormously in size and depth: some are no deeper than the average pond, while others are more than a kilometre deep and some have beds below sea-level. Some lakes are millions of years old, but most are much younger, and date back to the end of the last ice age. Not all lakes consist of fresh water. Some, mainly in arid regions, are saline, with levels of salinity varying from slight to six times that of seawater.

Lake Formation

Some lakes, such as Baikal and Tanganyika (see p.196), formed in depressions along fault lines or in areas of rifting (see p.98). Others, such as the huge Caspian Sea (see p.198), were once part of an ocean, but have become cut off from the larger body of seawater. A few lakes have been formed by volcanic action, when lava dams a river or a caldera is formed. Most, however, are the result of glaciation, and this is reflected in their distribution. Most North American lakes, for example, are located in areas that 25,000 years ago were under a thick ice-sheet. Glaciers create lakes in two main ways: valley floors are hollowed and deepened by glacial erosion and later filled in by water; and the ridges of moraine deposited by glaciers (see p.215) form dams across valleys that trap water behind them.

FAULT LAKE
Loch Ness in Scotland fills a basin formed by an elongate, ancient structural fault, whose movement weakened the rocks that were further eroded by glaciations.

KETTLE LAKES
Kettle lakes, seen here in central Chile, form when large blocks of melting ice become surrounded by glacial debris. Such lakes have no outlet.

CALDERA LAKE
A near-circular caldera lake on the Kamchatka Peninsula in eastern Siberia is enclosed by the rim of an extinct volcano. The rounded outline is characteristic of this type of lake.

Inflow and Outflow

Lakes receive much of their inflow from surface water that may carry a considerable amount of sediment. Most lakes have a single outflow into a river system – those without a defined outflow are described as unchannelled. Some lakes in arid regions have no outflow at all – the inflow is balanced by evaporation. Geologically speaking, most lakes are short-lived, due to infilling by sediment and lowering of the water level through the down-cutting action of the outflow river.

lake terrace marks position of past high-water level

one of several lake inflows

sediment deposited by inflow forms alluvial fan

former outflow at higher level

present outflow of lake

layered sediment on lake bed

LAKE FEATURES
Even the deepest lakes will eventually become shallow as they fill with sediment. Deposition is greatest where rivers flow into the lake. Infilling may sometimes give rise to wetlands.

MORAINE LAKE
Peyto Lake, in Alberta, Canada, formed in a glaciated valley when meltwater became trapped by moraines deposited across the valley during successive stages of glaciation.

LAKE PROFILES

The pages that follow contain profiles of the world's main lakes. Each profile begins with the following summary information:

AREA Area covered by the lake

MAXIMUM DEPTH Deepest part of the lake

ELEVATION Height of lake above sea-level

OUTLET Main river flowing out of the lake

NORTH AMERICA *northwest*
Great Bear Lake

LOCATION In the Northwest Territories, in the far northwest of Canada, on the Arctic Circle

AREA 31,150 square km (12,024 square miles)

MAXIMUM DEPTH 446m (1,464ft)

ELEVATION 186m (610ft)

OUTLET Great Bear River

Great Bear Lake is the largest lake entirely within Canadian territory and the fourth largest in North America. Its northern shores lie within the Arctic Circle, and it is the largest inland body of water to exist at such a high latitude. The lake is irregular in shape and branches into three arms at the western end. The water is deepest near the eastern shoreline. The lake was formed by the scouring action of glaciers as they flowed from the North American ice-sheet down river valleys. Lakes formed in this way are often called piedmont lakes. When the glaciers melted at the end of the last ice age, their waters became trapped behind moraines, forming a huge lake that has since partially drained, leaving as remnants Great Bear Lake, Great Slave Lake (see below), and the numerous small lakes that lie between

them. The lake is situated in gently rolling wilderness, with evergreen forest along its southern shores and tundra extending to the north. Its waters are often cited as an example of a pristine lake environment, although it has far fewer fish species than lakes of comparable size in more temperate regions, because its waters are much colder. The only settlement on its shores is the former mining centre of Port Radium, named after the radioactive element, which was

shipped from the mines here during World War II to make the first atomic bombs. Great Bear Lake receives inflow from the Whitefish River on its northwestern arm, and from other smaller rivers. The Great Bear River exits from the western end of the lake, flows westwards, and delivers its waters into the Mackenzie River about 480km (300 miles) upstream from the delta. Great Bear Lake and River both freeze over for about seven months each year.

BROWN BEAR
The Grizzly or Brown Bear is a top predator of forests around the lake's southern shores.

ECHO BAY ON THE NORTH SHORE
In summer, even the remotest northern bays are free of ice. In winter, the frozen lake and the shore are covered in snow.

NORTH AMERICA *northwest*
Great Slave Lake

LOCATION In the Northwest Territories of Canada, east of the Mackenzie Mountains

AREA 28,568 square km (11,027 square miles)

MAXIMUM DEPTH 614m (2,016ft)

ELEVATION 156m (512ft)

OUTLET Mackenzie River

Great Slave Lake is the second largest lake in Canada and the main reservoir for the Mackenzie River system. The lake is irregular in shape and has a rocky, mainly forested shore with wide bays and numerous islands. It is located along the boundary between the ancient rocks of the Canadian Shield and the newer strata underlying the Great Plains. At Great Slave Lake this division is marked by a large inlet that extends northwards from the northern shore. The lake's waters support a small commercial fishery. Other developments around its shores include the gold-mining town of

Yellowknife, on the northern arm of the lake, and several small tourist resorts. The main inflow is the Slave River, which enters the southern shore bringing water from Lake Athabasca and the Peace River. The Mackenzie River exits from the southwestern end of the lake and is the sole outflow. The lake freezes in winter and is ice-free for only four months of the year.

LAKE COASTLINE
The shores of Great Slave Lake are covered with dense coniferous forest, the tops of which stand out above a layer of morning fog that has formed on the lake's surface, enshrouding an offshore island.

NORTH AMERICA *north*
Lake Winnipeg

LOCATION In south-central Canada, in the province of Manitoba southwest of Hudson Bay

AREA 23,750 square km (9,167 square miles)

MAXIMUM DEPTH 36m (118ft)

ELEVATION 217m (712ft)

OUTLET Nelson River

Lake Winnipeg is a shallow lake at the eastern edge of the Great Plains. It is the remnant of a much larger glacial lake that also included lakes Manitoba and Winnipegosis. Much of its water comes from the Saskatchewan River, which flows from the Canadian Rockies to the west. Another inflow, the Red River, drains the high plains. The Nelson River flows from the northeast end of the lake into Hudson Bay.

ROCKY SHORELINE

NORTH AMERICA *northeast*
Great Lakes

LOCATION On the border of the USA and Canada – Lake Michigan is entirely within the USA

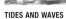

AREA Superior 82,367 square km (51,159 square miles), **Michigan** 58,000 square km (36,024 square miles), **Huron** 59,570 square km (37,000 square miles), **Erie** 25,820 square km (16,037 square miles), **Ontario** 19,010 square km (11,807 square miles)

MAXIMUM DEPTH Superior 406m (1,333ft), **Michigan** 281m (923ft), **Huron** 228m (749ft), **Erie** 64m (210ft), **Ontario** 224m (735ft)

ELEVATION Superior 183m (601ft), **Michigan** 177m (580ft), **Huron** 176m (578ft), **Erie** 174m (571ft), **Ontario** 75m (246ft)

OUTLET St. Lawrence River

The Great Lakes form the largest system of freshwater lakes in the world, with a combined surface area of 244,000 square km (95,500 square miles). The system drains from west to east, discharging into the sea from Lake Ontario through the St. Lawrence River (see p.164). The gradient between the lakes is generally very shallow. Superior drains into Michigan through the St. Mary's River. Michigan has almost the same level as Huron, and the two are connected by the Straits of Mackinac, 6km (4 miles) wide. Huron drains

through the St. Clair River, Lake St. Clair, and the Detroit River into Erie, which is drained in turn by the Niagara River into Lake Ontario. The descent between Erie and Ontario is greater than between any of the others, and includes the spectacular Niagara Falls, 51m (167ft) high. The Great Lakes were formed during the last ice age, when successive episodes of glaciation eroded a landscape of mountains and river valleys. When the ice melted, Superior, Michigan and Huron were all part of one huge lake (known as Lake Algonquin), which drained into the Ottawa River. Post-glacial uplift altered the drainage patterns, and the lakes began to take on their present shape about 10,000 years ago. The present shorelines became stable about 3,000 years ago, but the western end of Lake Erie is still sinking at about 2mm ($\frac{1}{10}$in) per year. Only the western and northern shores of Superior are rocky; the other shores are covered by thick glacial deposits, with concentric ridges of terminal moraine at the southern ends of Michigan and Huron. Numerous cities, including Buffalo, Chicago, Cleveland, Detroit, Milwaukee, and Toronto, are situated around the lakes.

TIDES AND WAVES
Although the Great Lakes are unaffected by tides, the wind can produce waves that buffet the shores of Lake Superior like breakers against the seashore.

CLIFFS CAUSED BY UPLIFT
These cliffs along the northern shore of Lake Superior were created when the land rebounded from the crushing weight of the glaciers that covered it during the last ice age.

NIAGARA FALLS
The Horseshoe Falls, 800m (2,625ft) wide, on the Canadian side of the Niagara River, are named after their distinctive shape.

URBAN SHORELINE

The cities around the Great Lakes withdraw huge amounts of water each day for municipal and industrial use. Most is returned to the lakes after appropriate treatment. Chicago, however, sends 10.9 billion litres (2.4 billion gallons) of water a day to the Mississippi. Combined with lower than average rainfall in recent years, this loss of water is beginning to affect the level of the lakes. The long-term effects of this fall remain unclear.

CLEARING A PATH
During the winter months, the Coast Guard uses powerful icebreakers to keep the Great Lakes shipping routes open – in this case Thunder Bay on Lake Superior.

NORTH AMERICA *east*
Lake Seneca

LOCATION In the USA, in west central New York state south of Lake Ontario

AREA 174 square km (67 square miles)

MAXIMUM DEPTH 198m (650ft)

ELEVATION 135m (443ft)

OUTLET Seneca River

Lake Seneca is one of the famed Finger Lakes, a series of long, narrow lakes that lie roughly parallel with each other on the undulating uplands to the south of Lake Ontario. The lakes were formed more than a million years ago, during the last stages of the most recent ice age, when a series of shallow glaciated valleys running on a north–south axis became blocked at both ends by glacial moraines. Seneca is the second largest of the Finger Lakes and is by far the deepest, with parts of its bed lying 54.5m (180ft) below sea-level. The lake receives water from streams draining the surrounding hills, including Catherine Creek and the Keuka Lake outlet. Its outflow, the Seneca River, exits at the northeastern corner and, having received the waters of Lake Cayuga, flows into the Oswego River, which event ually discharges into Lake Ontario.

NORTH AMERICA *west*
Lake Tahoe

LOCATION In the USA, in the Sierra Nevada mountains between Nevada and California

AREA 499 square km (193 square miles)

MAXIMUM DEPTH 500m (1,640ft)

ELEVATION 1,900m (6,200ft)

OUTLET Truckee River

The fifth deepest lake in the world, Lake Tahoe originated in a deep depression between two faults that subsequently became dammed by lava flow. Although fed by small streams all around its shores, the main inflow is at the southern end, through the Upper Truckee Marshes. The Truckee River flows out of the northwestern end of the lake into Nevada. Lake Tahoe is a popular tourist destination.

DEEP BLUE WATERS OF LAKE TAHOE

NORTH AMERICA *southeast*
Lake Okeechobee

LOCATION In the USA, at the northern edge of the Everglades in central Florida

AREA 1,895 square km (732 square miles)

MAXIMUM DEPTH 4.5m (15ft)

ELEVATION 4m (13ft)

OUTLET Unchannelled

Lake Okeechobee is the main reservoir of fresh water feeding the Everglades' "river of grass" – although it no longer flows with enough force to keep the tide at bay in southern Florida. The lake lies in a shallow, sloping depression that was once part of the sea bed, and is dammed along its southern shore by an accumulation of peat. The lake receives water from the Kissimmee River and from Lake Istokpoga. There is no channelled outflow – the lake's waters flow south through the Everglades on a broad front. Since the 1950s, numerous canals have been constructed to divert the lake's water for agriculture, and to meet the increasing demand of resort towns along Florida's eastern coastline.

OKEECHOBEE PLANT LIFE
The marshy areas around the lake are colonized by a variety of aquatic plants, such as these waterlilies. Some are native; others are introduced.

NORTH AMERICA *west*
Great Salt Lake

LOCATION In the USA, to the west of the Rocky Mountains, in northern Utah

AREA 5,000 square km (1,930 square miles)

MAXIMUM DEPTH 12m (39ft)

ELEVATION 1,280m (4,200ft)

OUTLET None

The Great Salt Lake is the largest inland body of salt water in the western hemisphere, and at 25 per cent salinity is about five times saltier than the sea. It is a remnant of the prehistoric Lake Bonneville, which covered most of the floor of the Great Basin (see p.240) during the last ice age. The present lake is surrounded by great tracts of sand, salt flats, and salt marsh and receives most of its inflow from the Bear Creek and Weber rivers, which bring waters from the Wasatch Range along the eastern shore. The area of the lake is extremely variable – between 1964 and 1987, it more than doubled in size, reaching a maximum area of nearly 6,000 square km (2,300 square miles). A causeway constructed in the 1950s divides the lake into two parts. The smaller northern section is both shallower and saltier than the rest of the lake.

SALT LAKE SHALLOWS
Because the lake lies in a shallow basin, small changes in its level have large effects on its surface area, exposing or submerging large areas of its bed.

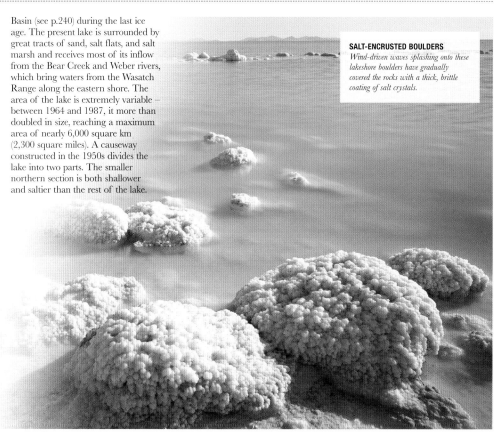

SALT-ENCRUSTED BOULDERS
Wind-driven waves splashing onto these lakeshore boulders have gradually covered the rocks with a thick, brittle coating of salt crystals.

(see p.240)

Lake Titicaca

LOCATION In the central Andes, on the Altiplano plateau, bordered by Peru and Bolivia

AREA 8,772 square km (3,386 square miles)

MAXIMUM DEPTH 281m (923ft)

ELEVATION 3,812m (12,516ft)

OUTLET Desaguadero River

Lake Titicaca is the largest freshwater lake in South America, and the highest lake of any significant size in the world. The lake is situated in a structural depression at the northern end of the high Altiplano plateau that separates the Eastern and Western cordilleras of the Andes. Roughly oval in shape, the lake is 195km (120 miles) long and about 80km (50 miles) wide. It is divided into two unequal parts by

a narrow strait known as the Tiquina. The lake bottom slopes down from west to east. The lake is widest at the northwest, and the deepest parts are near the northern end, where the shoreline is defined by the Bolivian Cordillera Real mountains. The southeastern part of the lake, below the Tiquina, is much shallower, with an average depth of about 9m (30ft). Titicaca receives inflow from across the northern part of the Altiplano and is fed by more than 20 rivers, the largest of which is the Ramis. Each year the level of the lake fluctuates by up to 4m (13ft), with the highest levels occurring after the summer rains between December and March. Evaporation in the arid mountain climate removes about 95 per cent of the lake's inflow. The sole outflow, the Desaguadero, exits from the shallow southern end of the lake and flows some 300km (185 miles) south to Lake Poopó, which has no outlet to the sea. The evidence of terraces made by former shorelines shows that Titicaca was much larger during the period immediately after the last ice age. Stretches of the present shoreline are covered by marshes and beds of totora reeds. These reeds are

STRAITS OF TIQUINA
This view looking eastwards across the straits into the deeper section of the lake shows the bleak, rocky landscape that makes up much of its northern shoreline.

still used by some of the people living around the lakeshores, to make boats, houses, and floating islands in the traditional manner. Three fish species have evolved in the waters of the lake, which because of the high altitude contain about one-third less oxygen than fresh water at sea-level. These endemic species supported a small local fishery, but their population was devastated by the introduction of trout for commercial fisheries during the 1930s. The shipping route across Lake Titicaca is a vital link in the railway network that connects land-locked Bolivia with the sea.

VICUÑA
Adapted to high altitude living, the Vicuña grazes on the grasslands of the Altiplano. Its domesticated cousin, the Alpaca, is raised for the fibres of its coat.

INCA SETTLEMENTS

The Inca, who flourished until about 500 years ago, considered Lake Titicaca to be the sacred and ancestral home of their agriculture and their civilization. According to legend, their sun god,

Manco Capac, sprang from the waters of the lake and founded the Inca dynasty at Cusco. The ruins of Inca buildings are still to be found around the lakeshores and on some of the islands, providing ample evidence of great skill at building with large blocks of unmortared stone.

LAND

REED BOATS ON UROS ISLAND
Boats made from slim bundles of totora reeds are moored to an island made of larger bundles of reeds, forming a thick floating platform on which houses are built.

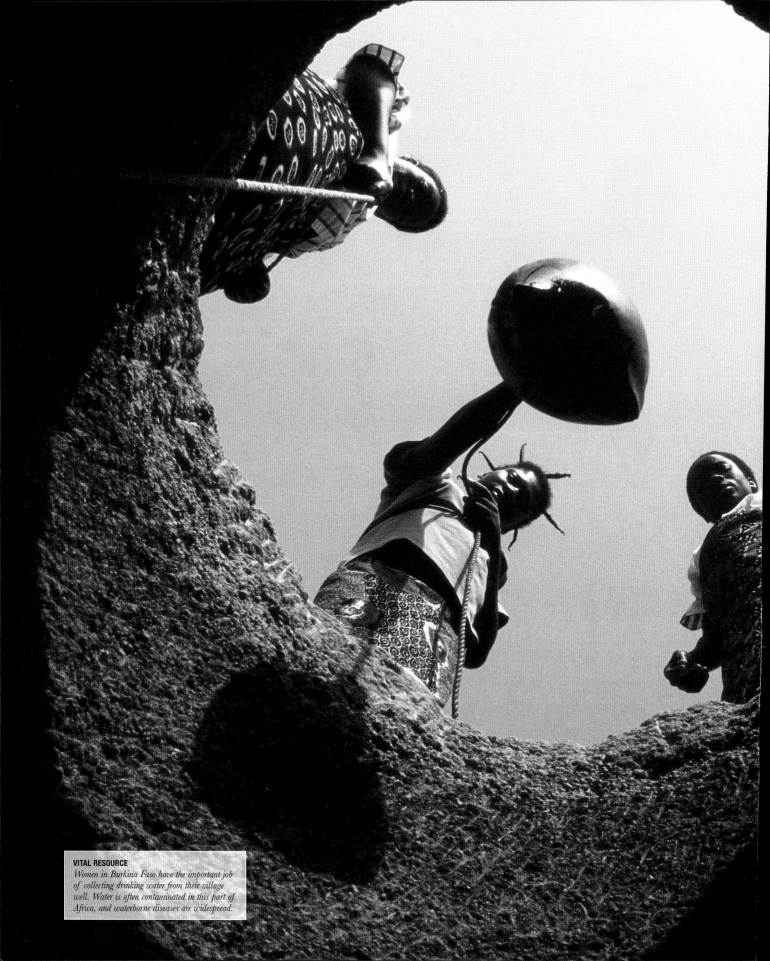

VITAL RESOURCE
Women in Burkina Faso have the important job of collecting drinking water from their village well. Water is often contaminated in this part of Africa, and waterborne diseases are widespread.

FRESHWATER QUALITY

Throughout human history, water has played a dual role: as a life-giving liquid and as a resource for waste disposal. Without careful management, these two uses can conflict, potentially dangerously. In the developed world, water pollution reached crisis proportions around the mid-twentieth century, but is now increasingly controlled. In developing countries, poor water quality remains a major health threat.

Natural Purification

In nature, pure fresh water is rare. Ground-water is normally purer than surface water, because it is filtered by porous rock. It contains dissolved minerals, but very little organic matter. Surface water also contains minerals, but, even when it looks clean, it often teems with living things and their dead remains. The vast majority of its living inhabitants are micro-organisms, such as bacteria. Most of the bacteria need oxygen to break down and purify organic matter in the water, and this process is most effective when the water contains high levels of dissolved air. Natural purification is also helped by water movement, becaues this stirs up sediment and dissolves more air. However, if water becomes overloaded with organic matter – for example, from human sources – the normal waste-disposal system may break down.

Eutrophication

In fresh water, two mineral nutrients – nitrogen and phosphorus – are essential for the growth of micro-organisms. These nutrients are often scarce, and the growth of micro-organisms stops once they have been used up. When untreated sewage and agricultural run-off enter the water, nitrogen and phosphorus levels can suddenly climb, and the micro-organism population booms. This creates more living matter, which uses up oxygen. As oxygen levels plunge, fish and other animals die, and the waterway fills with organic sludge. This process, which is known as eutrophication, is prevented by treating sewage before it is discharged, and by controlling fertilizer use.

ALGAL BLOOM
Lush growths of algae are a sign of eutrophication, which causes oxygen levels in water to fall.

Pollution

Untreated waste is also hazardous because it may contain disease-carrying micro-organisms. Normally, clean and waste water are kept apart during water treatment and waste management, but if this separation is breached – for example, through lack of sanitation – waterborne diseases can spread. To prevent this, water is periodically tested for indicator organisms, such as the bacterium *Escherichia coli*, a common resident of the human intestine. If large numbers of *E. coli* are detected in drinking water, immediate action is needed to trace their source.

Water pollution is caused not only by micro-organisms but also by industrial waste, which affects water quality in different ways. Synthetic

WARNING SIGN
In this river, industrial pollution is very evident. Other kinds of water pollution can be much harder to detect.

organic chemicals can enter freshwater food chains, and from there they can reach drinking water supplies. These chemicals include pesticides, herbicides, and pharmaceutical drugs, as well as substances that are utilized in manufacturing. Industrial waste can also contain inorganic pollutants, such as acids, zinc, and lead, many of which are known to be toxic. Safety limits for synthetic organics, which are relatively recent "inventions", are much more difficult to gauge, especially as thousands of new organics are synthesized every year.

Heat is another form of pollution that affects many urban rivers. One of the chief sources is industrial effluent, particularly water that is used to cool power stations. Heat affects the growth of plants and animals. It also reduces the amount of oxygen that water can carry – something that affects much aquatic life.

WASTE DISPOSAL
Water offers a cheap and easy way for industry to dispose of waste.

Future Trends

The increasing global population and the spread of industrialization mean that water pollution will remain an acute problem in many parts of the world. According to UN figures released in 2003, two million tonnes of human waste alone are dumped each day into rivers, lakes, and streams – a figure that is likely to increase. In developed countries, economic growth has helped to bring about improvements in water quality, but many developing countries are finding it difficult to follow this trend.

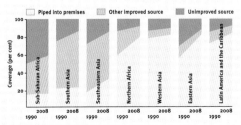

ACCESS TO CLEAN WATER
Within the developing world, campaigns have increased the number of people with access to clean, piped drinking water. But Sub-Saharan Africa, Southern Asia, and Southeastern Asia still have major problems with water supply.

LAND

CENTRAL AMERICA
Lake Nicaragua

LOCATION In the southwest of Nicaragua, only 15km (9 miles) from the Pacific coastline

AREA 8,150 square km (3,146 square miles)

MAXIMUM DEPTH 70m (230ft)

ELEVATION 32m (105ft)

OUTLET River San Juan

The largest body of fresh water in Central America, Lake Nicaragua is oval in shape and was once a wide bay on the ocean coastline. The present lake was formed when volcanic activity on the Pacific Rim (see p.117) produced

TOUCAN
The Chestnut Mandibled Toucan nests high in the forest canopy on hillsides around the lake.

a narrow ridge that extended from the Cordillera de Guanacaste mountain range northwards, cutting off the bay from the sea. This 19km- (12-mile-) wide ridge now forms the lake's western shoreline. The bay's salt water has been gradually freshened by rain-fed streams flowing down the surrounding hills, combined with a steady outflow to the sea. This process has produced a unique combination of animal life, and Lake Nicaragua is the only lake in the world to have freshwater species of marine animals such as sharks and swordfish. The lake is dotted with hundreds of islands, some of which contain active volcanoes. Among the many rivers flowing into the lake is the River Tipitat, which drains Lake Managua, located to the northwest. Lake Managua was formed and freshened by the same processes that created Lake Nicaragua. The River San Juan flows from the southeastern corner of the lake through dense rainforest to the Caribbean Sea. Locally, the lake is famed for its apparent tides, which are in fact standing waves that oscillate across the lake surface – caused by winds blowing up the San Juan valley.

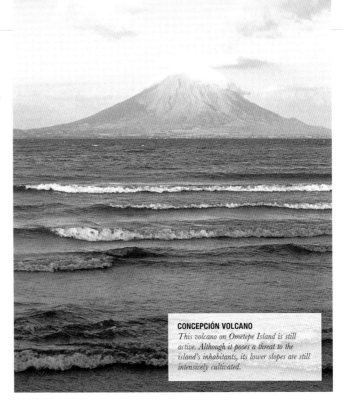

CONCEPCIÓN VOLCANO
This volcano on Ometepe Island is still active. Although it poses a threat to the island's inhabitants, its lower slopes are still intensively cultivated.

EUROPE *north*
Lake Ladoga

LOCATION In the Karelia region of northwestern Russia, to the east of the Baltic Sea

AREA 17,675 square km (6,823 square miles)

MAXIMUM DEPTH 230m (755ft)

ELEVATION 5m (16ft)

OUTFLOW River Neva

The largest lake in Europe, Ladoga lies in a glacially modified depression. The water is deepest near the high, rocky cliffs of the northern shores. In the south, the lake is much shallower, with a low shoreline. Ice starts to form in December, and the entire lake freezes between January and May. Ladoga is fed by several rivers and two smaller lakes nearby. The River Neva flows from the southwestern corner of the lake and then through St. Petersburg about 40km (25 miles) to the west.

BATTERED SHORELINE
The bleak, rocky shores of Lake Ladoga are sometimes pounded by wind-driven waves up to 4.5m (15ft) high.

EUROPE *northwest*
Loch Ness

LOCATION In Inverness, Scotland, in the northwestern part of the Scottish Highlands

AREA 56 square km (22 square miles)

MAXIMUM DEPTH 230m (755ft)

ELEVATION 16m (52ft)

OUTFLOW River Ness

Famous for the monster "Nessy" that is said to inhabit its depths, Loch Ness is a long, narrow lake at the northern end of the Great Glen, a valley excavated along an ancient fault, which bisects Scotland diagonally between the Grampian Mountains and the North West Highlands. Over time, movement on the ancient strike slip fault has displaced the rocks on either side by over 100km (60 miles). Erosion has excavated a valley 39km (22 miles) long and 1.5km (1 mile) wide in the weakened fault rocks. Subsequent glaciation has further deepened the lake to depths of over 100m (330ft) and filled it with glacial meltwater.

URQUHART CASTLE ON LOCH NESS

EUROPE *northwest*
Lake Windermere

LOCATION In the Lake District of northwestern England, east of the Irish Sea

AREA 15 square km (6 square miles)

MAXIMUM DEPTH 64m (210ft)

ELEVATION 39m (128ft)

OUTFLOW River Leven

Windermere, the largest lake in England, formed at the end of the last ice age in a deep, glaciated valley that runs north–south through the Cumbrian Mountains. It is a long, narrow lake, deepest at the northern end. Fed by rain and snow from the surrounding highland, Windermere also receives waters from other nearby lakes, including Grasmere. Water flows out through the River Leven.

LAKE DISTRICT
Windermere is the largest of 17 major lakes that comprise England's Lake District.

EUROPE *northwest*
Lough Derg

LOCATION In the southwest of the Republic of Ireland at the boundary of counties Tipperary, Galway, and Clare

AREA 118 square km (46 square miles)

MAXIMUM DEPTH 36m (118ft)

ELEVATION 34m (112ft)

OUTFLOW River Shannon

Lough Derg is located at the southern extremity of Ireland's central plain, about 30km (18 miles) upriver from the mouth of the River Shannon. The irregularly shaped lake lies in a glaciated section of the Shannon valley. The narrow southern arm, the deepest part of the lake, was formed during the last ice age, when ice was forced into the neck of the gorge through which the river now exits the lake. The northern area of the lake is shallow – with an average depth of 4m (13ft) – and surrounded by flat land and, in places, by large reed-beds.

EUROPE *central*
Lake Constance

LOCATION In the northern Alps, bordered by Austria, Germany, and Switzerland

AREA 541 square km (209 square miles)

MAXIMUM DEPTH 252m (827ft)

ELEVATION 395m (1,295ft)

OUTFLOW River Rhine

Lake Constance occupies the lower part of the valley created by the Rhine Glacier during the last ice age. Measuring 64km (40 miles) long and 13.5km (8½ miles) wide, it is central Europe's second largest freshwater

BATH-HOUSE ON LAKE CONSTANCE

lake, and supplies drinking water to about 4.5 million people. The marshes along the lake margins support large numbers of waterfowl and shorebirds. The River Rhine enters the lake at the southeastern end, on the Swiss–Austrian border. At the western end of the lake, where the glacier spread out over low foothills, the lake splits into two arms. The Rhine exits through the southern arm at the German–Swiss border.

EUROPE *central*
Lake Geneva

LOCATION In the northwestern Alps, bordered by France and Switzerland

AREA 581 square km (224 square miles)

MAXIMUM DEPTH 310m (1,018 ft)

ELEVATION 372m (1,221ft)

OUTFLOW River Rhône

Lake Geneva is the largest of the Alpine lakes, forming a broad crescent, with the River Rhône entering from the southeastern tip and exiting from the southwestern tip. Although the lake is only 14 km (8½ miles) across at its

widest point, strong winds can cause violent storms, which are more characteristic of an inland sea. The northern shoreline is densely populated, the main cities being Geneva and Lausanne. The south-facing slopes along the lakeshore near Lausanne form the largest wine-producing area in Switzerland.

VITICULTURE ON THE NORTHERN SHORE

EUROPE *central*
Lake Como

LOCATION In Lombardy, northern Italy, near the southern edge of the Alps

AREA 146 square km (56 square miles)

MAXIMUM DEPTH 410m (1,346ft)

ELEVATION 198m (650ft)

OUTFLOW River Adda

Lake Como is the deepest of the Alpine lakes. It has three branches, each about 25km (15 miles) long and about 4km (2½ miles) wide. Its inverted Y-shape is defined by deep, faulted valleys that were produced during the formation of the Alps. The valley floors have been depressed and eroded by subsequent glaciations, which accounts for the lake's great depth – although it is an Alpine lake, parts of its

bed are more than 200m (660ft) below the level of the Mediterranean Sea. Despite being surrounded by mountains – up to 2,400m (8,000ft) high at the northern end, descending to about 600m (2,000ft) in the south – the lake enjoys a mild Mediterranean climate and is a popular tourist destination. Lake Como receives most of its water from the snow-fed River Adda, which flows from the eastern Alps and enters the lake's northern arm. The lake also receives the inflow of numerous other rivers and streams. The Adda is the lake's sole outflow – it exits from the southeastern arm and is a tributary of the River Po.

LAKE COMO AND BELLAGIO
This view up the northern arm of the lake shows a high wedge of rock known as Bellagio (right centre). During the last ice age, this outcrop caused the lake-forming glacier to split into two arms.

ANCIENT RESORT
Como's spectacular mountain setting and mild climate have made it a popular resort for at least 2,000 years. Some towns around the lake date back to the Roman period.

AFRICA *north*

Lake Chad

LOCATION	On the southern fringes of the Sahara Desert, bordered by Cameroon, Chad, Niger, and Nigeria
AREA	Highly variable
MAXIMUM DEPTH	10m (33ft)
ELEVATION	280m (920ft)
OUTFLOW	Bahr el Ghazal

Lake Chad is a large, shallow, oval lake, with a highly variable surface area. The level of the lake fluctuates annually, according to patterns of rainfall in the western Sahel. Generally it covers between 10,000 and 25,000 square km (3,800 and 10,000 square miles). Changes in level have a major impact because the lake is shallow, averaging only about 4m (13ft). In 1970, when

DRY LAKE BASIN
The Chad Basin has been drying out for centuries. During the drought of the 1970s and 1980s, the northern part of the lake almost dried out completely.

Lake Chad was at its maximum, it was the fourth largest lake in Africa, and since then it has shrunk dramatically. This is due to short-term drought and increased use of the lake's waters for irrigation, but there is also a long-term downward trend. Lake Chad is all that remains of a much larger lake, which 10,000 years ago was about 50m (165ft)

deeper. The present lake is divided into two by a sandy ridge known as the Great Barrier, that runs east–west and is breached by a single channel. The northern part of the lake is the deepest, and has a shoreline of inlets, islets, and peninsulas, formed by dunes up to 30m (100ft) high. The southern part is shallower, and around the inflow of the

SHRINKING LAKE
The shallow southern part of the lake is becoming colonized with beds of papyrus reeds that allow wind-blown sand to accumulate more quickly.

River Chari the shoreline supports marshes. The Chari flows from the Ubangi Plateau to the south and provides 95 per cent of the lake's inflow. The rain-fed water of the Chari also accounts for the lake's continuing freshness in a desert climate. If the level falls, it is the deeper, northern portion that is most likely to dry out completely, because the Great Barrier cuts it off from the Chari's inflow. When levels are at their highest, excess water flows westwards along the Bahr el Ghazal.

AFRICA *east*

Lake Turkana

LOCATION	In the Great Rift Valley, bordered by Ethiopia and Kenya
AREA	6,750 square km (2,606 square miles)
MAXIMUM DEPTH	110m (360ft)
ELEVATION	360m (1,180ft)
OUTFLOW	None

Also known as Lake Rudolf, Turkana is a narrow lake, 265km (165 miles) long, running through the middle of the eastern arm of Africa's Great Rift Valley. It is the remnant of a larger lake that 5,000 years ago was three times as long, about 80m (260ft) deeper, and drained northeastwards into the White Nile. The present lake is deepest in the centre and at the southern end, where it is dammed by a lava flow. The lake has three islands, all of which are extinct volcanoes. The southern shores, once part of the lake bed, consist of

mud flats and dunes. The River Omo, flowing in at the northern end, brings water from the southern Ethiopian Highlands, and accounts for almost all the lake's inflow. With no outflow, Lake Turkana loses water mainly through evaporation in the hot, arid climate. The rate of evaporation is increased by strong winds, which often blow across the lake. Lake Turkana is subject to seasonal and periodic changes in level, but the overall trend is downwards. Since 1900, the level of the lake has dropped by about 15m (50ft).

VOLCANIC PEAK
The steep slopes of South Island, a large volcano (visible in the distance in this picture), descend to the deepest part of Lake Turkana.

FISHING AT TURKANA

The waters of Lake Turkana are rich in fish species, and fishing the lake has been the mainstay of some lakeside populations for thousands of years. The lake continues to produce about 1,000 tonnes of fish each year, but stocks of the main food fishes – Nile Perch, tilapia, and tiger fish – are dwindling. To maintain the size of the catch, an increasing number of species are being harvested for food. Sport fishermen also use the lake.

NABUYATOM VOLCANIC CONE
The southern end of Lake Turkana is enclosed by a rugged volcanic landscape of old lava flows, and overlooked by extinct cinder cones.

Lake Victoria

LOCATION	Bordered by Kenya, Tanzania, and Uganda between the arms of the Great Rift Valley
AREA	68,000 square km (26,250 square miles)
MAXIMUM DEPTH	84m (270ft)
ELEVATION	1,134m (3,725ft)
OUTFLOW	River Nile

Lake Victoria is the largest lake in Africa, the second largest freshwater lake in the world, and the main reservoir on the River Nile. The lake is roughly square in shape and is situated in the middle of the plateau that separates the western and eastern arms of the Great Rift Valley. It formed about 2 million years ago, when tilting of the crust between the arms diverted surface water into a shallow depression on the plateau's surface. Lake Victoria has no major inflows – its level is maintained by year-round heavy rainfall across the lake's surface and run-off from the surrounding upland. Its shores are one of the most densely populated parts of Africa, and the cities of Kampala, Kisumu, and Mwanza are situated around the lake. Many of the lake's numerous islands are also inhabited. The northern shore has numerous long, thin peninsulas, between which there are areas of swamp that extend far inland and provide a refuge for the rare Sitatunga antelope. Lake Victoria is about 2 million years old – which is ancient by lake standards – and several hundred endemic species have evolved, mainly cichlid fishes. The introduction of the Nile Perch (a food fish endemic to the River Nile and Lake Turkana) into the northern part of lake has proved an ecological disaster for local species. The perch is a voracious predator that has now spread to all parts of the lake, and the native fish population has been catastrophically reduced.

TRANSPORT ROUTES
Steamships criss-cross the lake between cities, but life around the lakeshore mainly relies on even older forms of agriculture and transport.

COLLECTING FRESH WATER
Lake Victoria's extensive shoreline provides ready access to water for millions of people.

Lake Nakuru

LOCATION	In western Kenya, in the eastern arm of the Great Rift Valley
AREA	40 square km (15 square miles)
MAXIMUM DEPTH	3m (10ft)
ELEVATION	1,760m (5,780ft)
OUTFLOW	None

Lake Nakuru is a small, shallow, salty and alkaline lake – a remnant of a much larger lake that has shrunk to almost nothing over the last 10,000 years. At least once during the 20th century, Lake Nakuru has dried out completely. It is popular with tourists because of the hundreds of bird species that congregate there – particularly the spectacular flamingos.

FLAMINGOS FLOCKING ON THE LAKE

Lake Manyara

LOCATION	In Tanzania, southeast of the Serengeti Plain and northwest of the Masai Steppe
AREA	230 square km (85 square miles)
MAXIMUM DEPTH	Not known
ELEVATION	945m (3,100ft)
OUTFLOW	None

Lake Manyara lies at the southern end of the eastern arm of the Great Rift Valley, beneath the sheer rock walls of the valley's western escarpment. The lake has no perennial surface water sources, just a few occasional streams. Most of its inflow comes from beneath its shallow bed, having percolated down from the volcano-strewn Ngorongoro Highlands. This groundwater is saturated with minerals derived from volcanic rock. Despite there being extensive salt and soda deposits along areas of the lakeshore, its water is tolerated by catfish and bream, and by hippopotamuses. The Lake Manyara National Park, on the western shore, was established in the 1960s specifically for the protection of elephants, but is more famous for its tree-climbing lions. Visitors can also see more than 300 bird species.

Lake Nyasa

LOCATION	At the southern end of the Great Rift Valley, bordered by Malawi, Mozambique, and Tanzania
AREA	6,400 square km (2,470 square miles)
MAXIMUM DEPTH	706m (2,318ft)
ELEVATION	500m (1,640ft)
OUTFLOW	River Shire

Lake Nyasa is the most southerly of the Great Rift Valley lakes and was formed by the same rifting process that produced Lake Tanganyika (see p.196), which lies about 350km (220 miles) to the northwest. The long, narrow lake basin is delimited mainly by faults. Lake Nyasa is deepest in the north, where the bottom drops away sharply from the western shore. It becomes increasingly shallow towards the southern end, where its only outlet, the River Shire, flows sluggishly out of Monkey Bay to join the River Zambezi. In contrast, it receives water from no fewer than 14 rivers. Lake Nyasa has more fish species than any other lake in world, with perhaps as many as 1,000 different cichlid fishes living in its surface waters. However, as with other deep tropical lakes, there is no vertical circulation of water. The deep waters lack oxygen and are saturated with noxious gases such as hydrogen sulphide, methane, and carbon dioxide, produced by decomposition of vegetation that has sunk to the bottom.

STILL WATERS
A placid, sand-fringed lagoon on the northern shore gives no clue that Lake Nyasa is the second deepest lake in Africa.

AFRICA east

Lake Tanganyika

LOCATION At the southern end of the Great Rift Valley, between Burundi, Dem. Rep. of Congo, and Tanzania

AREA 32,000 square km (12,350 square miles)

MAXIMUM DEPTH 1,471m (4,800ft)

ELEVATION 773m (2,538ft)

OUTFLOW River Lukuga

The second deepest lake in the world, Tanganyika is a long, narrow lake extending 660km (410 miles) along a block-fault depression (graben) formed by the rifting process in East Africa about 15 million years ago (see pp.88–89). It has steep-sided, forested shorelines, with the Mitumba Mountains along the western shore towering about 2,000m (6,600ft) above the lake. The eastern shore is dominated by the highlands of the East African Plateau. There is lakeside lowland only where rivers enter or leave the lake. A subsurface ridge extends across the middle of the lake, dividing it into two extremely deep basins. The year-round heavy rain washes in large quantities of sediment that have accumulated in layers up to 5km (3 miles) deep. The main inflows are the River Ruzizi, which enters at the northern end, descending 600m (2,000ft) from Lake Kivu; the River Malagarasi on the eastern shore; and the River Kalambo, which enters on the southern tip, its waters having plunged over a 215m- (705ft-) high waterfall before reaching the lake. The single outflow, the Lukuga, exits midway along the western shore and adds its flow to the headwaters of the River Congo. Sometimes the outflow becomes blocked by floating vegetation, causing local flooding.

LEMON CICHLID
This species of cichlid, found only in the southern part of the lake, is one of dozens of species of cichlid that are unique to Lake Tanganyika.

HENRY MORTON STANLEY

The British-born American journalist and explorer Henry Morton Stanley (1841–1904) famously "found" the "missing" British missionary-explorer David Livingstone in 1871 at Ujiji on the eastern shore of Lake Tanganyika. They then explored the northern end of the lake, looking for the source of the Nile. In 1874 Stanley organized and led a further expedition that crossed Africa coast to coast, from west to east.

EASTERN SHORE
The densely forested slopes of the Mohale Mountains in Tanzania descend smoothly to the water's edge – there are no beaches or lakeshore lowlands.

ASIA northeast

Lake Baikal

LOCATION In Russia, south of the Central Siberian Plateau, near Mongolia

AREA 31,500 square km (12,160 square miles)

MAXIMUM DEPTH 1,741m (5,716ft)

ELEVATION 456m (1,497ft)

OUTFLOW River Angara

Baikal is the deepest lake in the world, containing about 20 per cent of the world's surface fresh water. The lake is 636km (395 miles) long and about 50km (30 miles) wide. It formed in a deep and ancient block fault some 25 million years ago, which also makes it the oldest lake in the world. The fault appears to be still active, as the lake is widening by about 2.5cm (1in) per year. On its western side, Baikal is lined by mountains; the eastern shoreline has gentler slopes. The deepest parts are in the centre and near the southern end. Layers of sediment on the lake bed are up to 7km (4 miles) thick in places. The continual descent of cold water keeps the bottom levels well oxygenated, and animal life is found at all depths. The lake receives inflow from many rivers, mainly along its eastern shore, and these include the Barguzin and the Selenga, which forms a delta as it enters the lake. Baikal also receives water below its surface from hot, freshwater vents in the lake bed. Irkutsk is situated near the southern end of the lake on its single outflow, the River Angara. The lake is ice-free for about six months each year. It was declared a UNESCO World Heritage Site in 1996.

STORM CLOUDS OVER LAKE
During the winter months, the surrounding mountains channel fierce storms along Lake Baikal.

FISHING

Lake Baikal provides an important source of food to the people living on its shores, despite remaining frozen much of the time. Local fishermen employ traditional methods to fish through a hole cut in the winter ice. The major food fish is the Omul, but 56 species of fish occupy the lake, and more than half of them are only found here.

BAIKAL SEAL
The world's only freshwater seal is just one of the 1,500 or so plant and animal species that are unique to the lake.

ARAL SEA SHORELINE
The volume of water entering the Aral Sea from the Syr Darya River has shrunk considerably because of the demand for water for crop irrigation.

Aral Sea

LOCATION North of the Kara Kum Desert, bordered by Kazakhstan and Uzbekistan

AREA around 7,000 square km (2,700 square miles)

MAXIMUM DEPTH 58m (190ft)

ELEVATION 40m (121ft)

OUTFLOW None

Once the world's fourth largest inland body of water with an area of about 68,000 square km (26,300 square miles), the Aral Sea is now drying up and has been reduced to a tenth of its former size – making it one of the most conspicuous examples of man-made desertification. Fifty years ago it was a

wide, shallow, saline sea – healthy and full of life. In the mid-20th century, its fisheries accounted for 3 per cent of the total catch of the former Soviet Union, but now the fish stocks have declined because the water salinity has increased. The Aral Sea was cut off from the oceans during the last ice age but maintained its size in the arid Central Asian climate because of the inflow of two mighty rivers – the Syr Darya, flowing down from the Tien Shan Mountains into the northern end, and the Amu Darya, bringing water from the Pamirs and entering along the southern shore, where it formed a large delta. In the 1930s, increasingly large amounts of water were diverted from these rivers to provide irrigation water for vast fields of cotton. While cotton production soared, the lake began to shrink, slowly at first and then alarmingly quickly. By 2007 it was reduced to four smaller lakes, and by 2009 the southeastern lake had

disappeared. In 2005 a dam was built in an effort to replenish the North Aral Sea, and by 2008 its water level rose sby 24m (79ft), and the salinity fell, allowing fish stocks to revive. The shrinking of the Aral Sea has reduced the humidity of the local climate, so that summers are now hotter and winters are colder. Millions of tonnes of dust and mineral salts have been blown away by the wind, adversely affecting the health of 5 million people who have to breathe the dust-laden air.

WATER PIPELINES

Toxic dust blowing from the desert created by the evaporation of the Aral Sea has contaminated water supplies over a wide area. Muynoq is located near the Amu Darya delta, once the region's greatest source of fresh water. It was a thriving port, but is now 56km (35 miles) from the coast of the Aral Sea. Today, its inhabitants must rely on water brought from distant reservoirs along pipelines such as the one shown below.

RECEDING SEA
The Aral Sea was once busy with ships, the fishing industry alone employing more than 60,000 people. Now rusting hulks lay stranded as monuments to the vanishing sea.

ASIA *west*
Caspian Sea

LOCATION On the borders of Azerbaijan, Iran, Kazakhstan, Russia, and Turkmenistan

AREA 371,000 square km (143,000 square miles)

MAXIMUM DEPTH 950m (3,120ft)

ELEVATION 30m (100ft) below sea-level

OUTFLOW None

The world's largest inland body of water, the saline Caspian Sea occupies an ancient, tilted depression in the Earth's surface. The water is deepest at the southern end, where the Elburz Mountains line its shores. Cut off from the Mediterranean Sea by falling water levels during the last ice age, the Caspian has no outflow, and owes its continuing existence to the Ural and Volga rivers, which supply much of its inflow. The eastern shore is defined by the cliffs of the arid Ustyurt Plateau, and the Kara Kum Desert lies to the southeast. The water's salinity varies from 1 per cent in the north, near the Volga inflow, to about 20 per cent in the shallow Kara Bogay Bay on the eastern shore, which is almost totally cut off from mixing with the rest of the Caspian's waters. (Ocean salinity averages about 3.5 per cent.) For

OIL EXTRACTION

The Caspian Sea's oil reserves equal those of the USA, and the region is being transformed by the oil industry, whose activities pose a threat to water quality. Oil extraction has expanded from Baku in Azerbaijan on the Caspian's southwest shoreline to include newly developed oil and gas fields in Kazakhstan at the northern end of the Caspian.

thousands of years, the water level of the Caspian Sea has experienced dramatic and unpredictable fluctuations. For example, the water rose 2.5m (8ft) between 1978 and 1995.

STERLET
This smaller relative of the caviar-producing sturgeon is one of the Caspian's most valuable food fish.

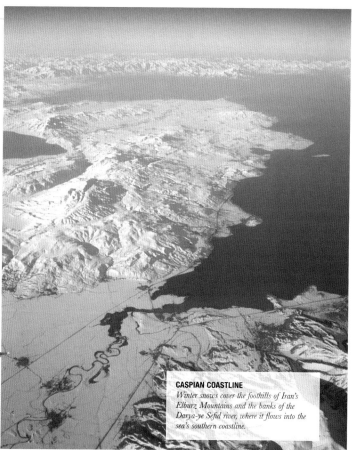

CASPIAN COASTLINE
Winter snows cover the foothills of Iran's Elburz Mountains and the banks of the Darya-ye Sefid river, where it flows into the sea's southern coastline.

ASIA *central*
Lake Balkhash

LOCATION In southeastern Kazakhstan, south of the Central Kazakh Uplands

AREA 18,200 square km (7,025 square miles)

MAXIMUM DEPTH 25m (82ft)

ELEVATION 340m (1,115ft)

OUTFLOW None

Balkhash is a long, narrow, curved lake, situated in an east–west depression. The lake is divided into two parts by the Sarymsck Peninsula, which juts out from the southern shore. Water freshness in the wide and

shallow western part of the lake has been maintained by inflow from the river Ili but increased water extraction from the river threatens this supply of freshwater. The lake narrows and deepens to the east, and there is little mixing between the two parts of the lake. The water in the eastern part has much higher levels of dissolved minerals because it receives only the inflow of minor rivers. The level of the lake fluctuates seasonally by about 3m (10ft), and during the last 100 years Balkhash's area has varied by up to 50 per cent – from 15,600 square km (6,000 square miles) to 23,400 square km (9,000 square miles). There are valuable copper deposits on the northern shore that are processed in the nearby town of Balkhash.

ASIA *west*
Sea of Galilee

LOCATION In northern Israel, close to the borders with Syria and Lebanon

AREA 166 square km (64 square miles)

MAXIMUM DEPTH 48m (157ft)

ELEVATION 212m (696ft) below sea-level

OUTFLOW River Jordan

Known also as Lake Tiberias, and renowned from the Bible, the Sea of Galilee is a small, shallow, pear-shaped lake situated in a deep, rifted depression that is an extension of Africa's Great

Rift Valley. The River Jordan flows southwards along the rift and through the lake. To its north, around the inflow of the Jordan, is the narrow, fertile Gennesaret Plain, with the Golan Heights to the northeast in Syria. The lake's western shores lie beneath the sheer wall of the rift, and the southern shores are confined by a volcanic ridge. Inflow from the Jordan diminished until 2009 as water was diverted for irrigation upstream of the lake, leading to an increase in the lake's salinity. However, rising fresh water input since then has lowered the salinity.

SOUTHEASTERN SHORELINE
The Sea of Galilee is seen here from the southeastern shore. The wall of the rift is visible across the water to the west.

DIVIDED LAKE
The Sarymsck Peninsula, across the middle of Lake Balkhash, is visible near the centre of this space shuttle image.

ASIA west
Dead Sea

LOCATION North of the Red Sea, bordered to the west by Israel and to the east by Jordan
AREA 810 square km (313 square miles)
MAXIMUM DEPTH 330m (1,084ft)
ELEVATION 427m (1,401ft) below sea-level
OUTFLOW None

The Dead Sea lies in a depressed piece of continental crust (graben) that separates two tectonic plates, the Sinai Subplate and the Arabian Plate. To the north and south the basin is bordered by igneous intrusions called sills. Fed by the River Jordan, and having no outflow, the Dead Sea is the lowest lake in the world – its surface is the lowest point on the Earth's land surface, at 427m (1,401ft) below sea-level. It is also one of the saltiest lakes, with an average salinity of about 32 per cent. The Dead Sea achieved its greatest extent about 10,000 years ago, and it has been shrinking slowly ever since. It is currently about 80km (50 miles) long and up to 18km (11 miles) wide. Inflow from the River Jordan and the occasional rain shower are insufficient to balance the very high rates of evaporation. Recently the rate of shrinkage has increased because of the diminished flow of the Jordan. During the last quarter of the 20th century the area of the lake declined by about 20 per cent, and the level of the lake is currently dropping at a rate of about 1m (39in) per year. The Lisan Peninsula, which once divided the lake into northern and southern parts, now forms the southern shoreline. What was the southern part of the lake now consists only of evaporation pans for salt and mineral production. In the deepest part of the lake, where the bottom waters are very dense and saline, there is little vertical mixing. The deepest water in the Dead Sea is many thousands of years older than the surface waters.

DEAD SEA COASTLINE
The paler sediments seen here on the barren shoreline of the Dead Sea indicate that the water level was once much higher.

LAKESIDE SALT DEPOSITS
As the waters of the Dead Sea evaporate, they leave behind an unearthly landscape dotted with mounds of salt crystals and pools of extremely saline liquid.

ASIA southeast
Qinghai Hu

LOCATION In the Nan Mountains of north central China, east of the Qaidam Pendi basin
AREA 4,460 square km (1,772 square miles)
MAXIMUM DEPTH 38m (125ft)
ELEVATION 3,200m (10,500ft)
OUTFLOW None

Qinghai Hu is a shallow, slightly saline lake situated in a broad depression on a high plateau and ringed by mountains. It is the largest lake in China and is also known as Koko Nor, and alternatively as the Blue Lake because of its intense colour. The area of the lake varies seasonally, and approaches 6,000 square km (2,300 square miles) when water levels are at their highest. Terraces around the shores indicate much higher levels during the last ice age, when Qinghai Hu probably drained westwards into the Tarim Basin.

QINGHAI HU SHORELINE

ASIA southeast
Lake Toba

LOCATION In North Sumatra Province on the Indonesian island of Sumatra
AREA 1,100 square km (425 square miles)
MAXIMUM DEPTH 529m (1,737 ft)
ELEVATION 905m (2,970ft)
OUTFLOW River Asahan

Lake Toba is the largest caldera lake in the world and is situated high in the Barisan Mountains of northern Sumatra. The lake is oval in shape – 90km (56 miles) long by 30km (19 miles) wide and the cliffs of the enclosing caldera rim rise up to 1,200m (3,940ft) above the surface.

It is over 460m (1,518ft) deep. Lake Toba is situated on an active fault line that runs the length of Sumatra, and was formed as a result of four catastrophic explosive eruptions, the last of which took place about 74,000 years ago, which emptied and collapsed a subterranean chamber, producing a caldera that soon filled with water. Subsequent uplift produced the large island of Samosir, with an area of 640 square km (250 square miles), in the middle of the lake. At the northern end of the lake, water enters via the Sipiso-Piso waterfall. The River Asahan exits from the southern end of the lake and flows into the Indian Ocean.

SAMOSIR ISLAND
Samosir, in the centre of Lake Toba, occupies about one-third of the lake. The rich volcanic soils on the island are intensively cultivated.

AUSTRALASIA Australia
Lake Eyre

LOCATION In the state of South Australia, south of the Simpson Desert
AREA 9,700 square km (3,745 square miles)
MAXIMUM DEPTH 5.5m (18ft)
ELEVATION 16m (53ft) below sea-level
OUTFLOW None

A salt lake of variable size, Lake Eyre is the lowest point on the Australian continent. It receives water from ephemeral streams, fed by erratic rainfall over much of central Australia. Thought to have once dried out completely, the lake reached its present size following exceptionally heavy rains at the end of the 20th century.

DRY LAKE BED
This dried-out area of lake bed is covered by thick deposits of gypsum overlain by a thin crust of salt.

Underground Rivers and Caves

BENEATH THE SURFACE in many of the Earth's limestone regions are large passages and caves. These are formed as limestone dissolves in slightly acidic water. As groundwater seeps downwards, tiny fractures gradually enlarge into open passages. When streams and rivers are swallowed by caves, erosion continues more rapidly. Underground rivers scour out huge waterfall shafts, and dissolve great tunnels. Subsequently, chambers are modified by rock-fall from unsupported ceilings, and seepage water creates calcite deposits. Young, actively forming caves have noisy streams while older, inactive caves are silent and often decorated with strange formations and, in rare cases, prehistoric art.

Limestone in Solution

Limestone is rock mostly composed of calcium carbonate that dissolves in naturally acidic water. Rainwater absorbs carbon dioxide from the air and from microscopic soil organisms to become weak carbonic acid. As it seeps downwards, it can dissolve large amounts of limestone. If that water then drips out into a cave, it loses carbon dioxide into the air and deposits excess calcite (calcium carbonate) as stalactites and stalagmites (see opposite) in order to maintain its chemical equilibrium.

STRAW STALACTITE
Tiny crystals of calcite can be seen here growing inside a water drop at the end of a cave straw (miniature stalactite) just 5mm (⅓ in) in diameter.

TRACING STREAMS

Underground streams can be tracked through large caves, but not where they are lost in narrow fissures. Then their courses are traced using fluorescent dyes, such as fluorescein. Even when diluted by many converging cave streams, this dye can be detected in minute quantities at a spring to prove the underground flow path from a distant sinkhole.

Underground Erosion

When streams pass underground, two main types of cave passage are formed – canyons and tubes. Underground streams and waterfalls above the water-table cut deep, twisting canyon passages, by removal of limestone in solution and sediment abrasion of their floors. Below the water-table, caves are full of slowly moving water, which dissolves limestone walls, floors, and ceilings equally, creating tubular tunnels. Many caves descend steeply to the water-table and then continue sideways, as flooded passages, until they intersect the surface, where the emerging water forms a spring (also known as a resurgence).

LIMESTONE LANDSCAPE
Sinking streams, bare rock pavements, and scattered sinkholes (or dolines) form the visible half of a limestone landscape. The unseen half is the network of cave passages, some with rivers, and others that are now dry and contain calcite deposits.

scree slope
river disappears down doline
sinkhole formed by dissolution or collapse of limestone
limestone pavement formed by solution at surface
underground river
surface eroded most severely along lines of weakness in rock
horizontal gallery formed when water-table was at higher level

LAND

Cave Deposits

Sand, mud, calcite, gypsum, and guano are all common cave deposits, but the most widespread and beautiful are those made of calcite. Groundwater saturated with calcium carbonate deposits calcite in the form of stalactites where water drips from a cave roof. Stalagmites form where the water hits the cave floor. Banks of solid calcite on the walls and floors of caves are called flowstones. A rimstone pool forms on the surface of a flowstone deposit where water collects behind a wall of calcite. More calcite may be deposited as water flows over and down the wall. Most cave calcite contains traces of uranium; the radioactive decay of its atoms can be used to determine the age of deposition, and thus to date the cave.

ARAGONITE CRYSTALS
In Australia's Jenolan Caves, tiny crystals of aragonite (a form of calcium carbonate) grow under thin films of water derived from condensation or seepage.

CAVE PEARLS
These calcite spheres in Golconda Cavern, UK, are cave pearls, which grew by rolling around in a shallow pool disturbed by dripping water.

Karst Landscapes

Karst is defined as a limestone landscape with underground drainage. It is distinguished by extensive patches of bare rock, because the weathering of limestone produces little or no soil. Rock outcrops exposed to rainfall are fretted by grooves called karren, formed as weakly acidic rainwater runs across them. They start as narrow fissures on joints or meandering grooves, and evolve into deep gullies between pinnacles of remnant limestone. Sinkholes or dolines formed by collapses in the surface can merge to form large sunken regions, equivalent to valleys in other landscapes. As the sinkholes expand, the residual hills between them become cones, or can be undercut to form towers. The weathering of karst landforms relies on abundant rainfall and lush vegetation (to provide carbon dioxide through its decay), so the most mature karst and the largest caves form in wet, tropical areas.

LIMESTONE PAVEMENT
This pavement in England's Pennines was scraped clean by glaciers during the last ice age and then etched with deep fissures by post-glacial rainwater.

TOWER KARST SCENERY
Isolated limestone towers with vertical cliffs overlook the wide plain around Yangshuo, in Guangxi, southern China. They represent the ultimate mature karst landscape; tower karst is also known by its Chinese name, fenglin.

PINNACLE KARST
With razor edges honed by tropical rainfall, spectacular pinnacles and blades of limestone rise clear of the rainforest canopy on the karst hills of Gunung Mulu National Park, Sarawak, Malaysia.

LEVIATHAN CAVE
This cave, in Nevada, USA, was formed by a river that has now disappeared. The impressive arch shape is due to later collapse of the roof.

UNDERGROUND RIVERS AND CAVES PROFILES

The pages that follow contain profiles of some major underground rivers and caves. Each profile begins with the following summary information:

LENGTH Total length of all the passages within the cave system

DEPTH Vertical distance from the cave entrance to its deepest known point

LAND

NORTH AMERICA *west*

Carlsbad Cavern

LOCATION In the Guadalupe Mountains of southeastern New Mexico, USA

LENGTH 50km (31 miles)

DEPTH 316m (1,037ft)

Left high and dry in the mountains of the Chihuahua Desert, Carlsbad Cavern has no underground river and almost no dripping water, but is a gigantic relic of long-finished karst solutional processes. It is formed in Permian limestones that were invaded by fluids rising from the hydrocarbon reservoirs in the Delaware Basin, just to the east. These fluids were rich in corrosive sulphuric acid that dissolved the limestone, removing it in solution on an unusually large scale. The Big Room, which was formed about 4 million years ago, displays evidence

BATS AT THE CAVE ENTRANCE
Every evening, hundreds of thousands of Mexican Free-tailed Bats leave their daytime roost in Bat Cave to feed in the surrounding countryside.

STALAGMITE MIMICRY
This small stalagmite has grown a bulbous top with stalactite ribs hanging below, so that it is now always known as the "bashful elephant".

of this very unusual origin. Although rarely noticed by visitors, there are thick banks of chalky white gypsum left by the chemical reaction between the sulphuric acid and the limestone. Only later was Carlsbad Cavern invaded by percolating rainwater, which both continued the excavation by solution, and also deposited the massive calcite stalactites and stalagmites. Just inside its gaping entrance, the spacious Bat Cave once held thick deposits of bat guano, most of which was mined out in the 1800s to use as fertilizer. It was the miners who first explored the extensive lower passages, which contain many classic cave features. The descending Main Corridor is floored by huge limestone blocks, called breakdown, that have fallen from the faulted roof, totally changing its shape from the original

solutional cave. Lower down in Carlsbad Cavern, the Boneyard is a complex of small, unmodified chambers and tunnels that show how the limestone was dissolved in random shapes when the cave was full of water. Beyond this, the famous Big Room is not so much a great chamber as a giant, twisting passage that is over 120m (400ft) wide in places. Most of Carlsbad Cavern is decorated with a profusion of calcite deposits, and the Big Room contains some very large stalagmites within its high, open space. The Big Room is the end of the cave section open to the public, but large tunnels descend beneath it, ending at the Lake of the Clouds, named after the huge bulbous stalactites that hang over a deep pool where the cave meets the present-day water-table.

DRIPSTONE DECORATIONS
Minor irregularities in the cave wall cause drips of water to deposit calcite, creating little flowstone terraces. Water dripping off the terraces deposits more calcite as curtains and fringes of stalactites.

PAINTED GROTTO
In this corner of Carlsbad Cavern's Big Room, calcite is coloured by natural pigments of iron oxides and hydroxides. The Big Room has an area of 33,210 square metres (357,480 square ft).

PAPOOSE ROOM
This chamber gets its name from a Native American word for a small child. The cavity was originally created by sulphuric acid; the stalactites were later formed by carbonic acid.

NORTH AMERICA east
Mammoth Cave

LOCATION In southwest Kentucky, USA, beneath the Chester Upland

LENGTH 563km (352 miles)

DEPTH 115m (377ft)

By far the longest cave system known in the world, Mammoth Cave has a huge network of passages on many levels. The nearly horizontal Carboniferous limestone in which it occurs carries water from sinkholes on the Pennyroyal Plateau to springs, along the Green River. There are many cave passages, each with a long, meandering canyon that passes into an elliptical tube beneath the water-table. Downcutting of the Green River has caused the water-table to fall in successive stages, leaving many large, dry,

GYPSUM FLOWER
The curved crystals of gypsum flowers form where water carries calcium sulphate from the overlying sandstone down into the limestone and out into the caves.

abandoned tubes. The highest level of caves contains sediments that are 2.3–3.5 million years old; these survive beneath the protective sandstone ridges of the Chester Upland. Most of the youngest caves drain through the ridges, where they connect with some of the older caves, while a few pass beneath the intervening Houchins and Doyel valleys. Except where shafts drop down through the limestone beds, most caves follow the same bedding planes within the rock sequence. Consequently, there are numerous chance passage intersections, which have linked the caves into the one extraordinarily long system.

vestigial eye

white coloration is common in cave-dwelling species

EYELESS CAVE-DWELLER
Due to the lack of light, this Indiana Eyeless Crayfish has no need for eyes or colour pigment, but instead has extended sensory feelers.

ABANDONED TUBULAR CAVE
The many long, tubular tunnels of Mammoth Cave were formed below the water-table before it fell to a lower level.

CENTRAL AMERICA
Windsor Caves

LOCATION Beneath the Cockpit Country of western Jamaica, close to the north coast

LENGTH 3km (2 miles)

DEPTH 20m (65ft)

The forest-covered hills in Jamaica's Cockpit Country are often likened to an upturned egg-box. They constitute a famous example of cone karst and are drained entirely underground. Windsor Great Cave is one of the few caves known in the karst; it is a high-level remnant of an ancient drainage system, now largely choked with calcite deposits. There is a small cave stream, but the main drainage lies unseen below the water-table at greater depths within the limestone.

WINDSOR GREAT CAVE

NORTH AMERICA south
Sistema Huautla

LOCATION In the Sierra Mazateca, part of the Sierra Madre del Sur, in Oaxaca, Mexico

LENGTH 56km (39 miles)

DEPTH 1,475m (4,840ft)

The limestone highlands of the Sierra Mazateca contain one of the world's finest collections of caves. Nita Nanta is the highest entrance to one of a dozen caves that converge in Sistema Huautla; each is a narrow stream canyon broken by a staircase of waterfall shafts. To the south, the giant

dolines of San Agustin drain into shafts that feed the underground river. The combined waters then drop down into a largely unexplored flooded zone. The main passage loops far below the water-table before emerging from underwater passages in Santo Domingo Canyon. As the canyon has cut deeper, it has triggered changes throughout the cave system. Fresh stream passages have been formed under now-abandoned tunnels. The oldest passages include chambers, modified by massive roof collapse, near the foot of the San Agustin shafts.

EXPLORING THE HUAUTLA CAVES
Cascading streamways and lashing waterfalls make exploration in Huautla both challenging and exciting for cavers.

SOUTH AMERICA east
Gruta do Janelão

LOCATION In the middle São Francisco valley of Minas Gerais, eastern Brazil

LENGTH 5km (3 miles)

DEPTH 150m (500ft)

Within the dense primary forest of the Peruaçú nature reserve, there is a broad, almost horizontal limestone bench, less than 200m (650ft) thick, which is broken by a series of wide, deep collapse dolines. These are windows into Janelão, a spectacularly large cave that winds beneath the bench. It is also a singularly beautiful cave. Gruta do Janelão means "cave of the windows", and it is named after the daylight that pours in to illuminate a cave passage about 90m (300ft) high and 60m (200ft) wide. A stream winds between great sandbanks on the cave floor, and terraces of ancient sediment rise high on the

CAVE OF THE WINDOWS
Daylight from holes in the roof (and the presence of a person sitting on a sandbank at the lower right in this photograph) make it possible to appreciate the sheer size of the cave.

walls, which suggest that a far larger river flowed through the cave in the distant past. Giant stalactites hang from the cave roof – one has been measured as 28m (92ft) long, and is perhaps the longest stalactite in the world. There are also massive banks of calcite flowstone on the walls and floors of the cave. The whole site is the product of karst processes that have been active for a very long time, but the exact age of the cave is not yet known.

GIANT CRYSTALS
Discovered in 2000, Mexico's Cave of Crystals preserves spectacular crystals up to 12m (39ft) long. Formed of gypsum, a calcium-sulphate mineral, they grew in hot, mineral-rich waters that filled the cave 500,000 years ago.

EUROPE *northwest*
Ease Gill Caverns

LOCATION Beneath Leck and Casterton Falls in the northern Pennine karst, England

LENGTH 70.5km (44 miles)

DEPTH 211m (692ft)

Dozens of streams drain through this rambling series of caves, before resurfacing at Leck Beck Head. The present-day inlet passages are long, clean-washed stream canyons, interrupted by vertical waterfall shafts; some intersect with old, abandoned tunnels. The large, high-level tunnels, which date from the Pleistocene Epoch, have calcite decorations and are partly choked with in-washed sediments.

CAVE SHAFT
This deep, vertical shaft with its waterfall is created where a cave stream drops from one level to another. It forms a staircase-like descent through the limestone beneath Leck Fell in Yorkshire.

EUROPE *west*
Lascaux

LOCATION In the side of the Vézère Valley within the Dordogne karst of western France

LENGTH 150m (500ft)

DEPTH 10m (30ft)

This tiny remnant of an ancient cave passage was long ago left high and dry in a limestone hillside. The passage was later truncated as erosion wore away the hillside, leaving an open entrance in the side of the Vézère Valley. Lascaux was found by people of the Solutrean and Magdalenian cultures in the Old Stone Age (or late Paleolithic), about 17,000 years ago. They walked into the open cave and well into its dark zone, where they painted on the upper walls and arched ceilings of the first five small chambers, using natural pigments of ochre, iron oxide, and charcoal. They produced beautiful figures of horses, aurochs, bulls, and stags, and even created narrative strips of hunting scenes. The cave was rediscovered in 1940, when local boys pursued their dog down a small hole in the rocks and soil that masked the entrance. Its wealth of Paleolithic art is regarded as the finest in the world.

PALEOLITHIC CAVE ART
The perfect proportions of the animals within the ceiling frieze in Lascaux's Great Hall of the Bulls reflect the superb skills of bygone cave artists.

PRESERVATION

When the Lascaux cave was opened to visitors, the ancient paintings were damaged by new calcite deposition induced by environmental changes and were discoloured by algae from spores carried in through the enlarged entrance. Preservation and visitor access could not coexist. Visitors to Lascaux now see an exact replica of the cave and its paintings.

EUROPE *west*
Vercors

LOCATION In the limestone lower Alps of the Provence Alpes region, southeast France

LENGTH Numerous long caves

DEPTH 1,271m (4,170ft)

With an area of over 1,350 square km (521 square miles), Vercors is the largest karst area in Europe. Formed in Cretaceous limestone more than 400m (1,300ft) thick, it contains many long, deep, and spectacular caves. Their passages are a mix of large, old, dry tunnels with calcite deposits, and narrow streamways with many fine waterfalls. The most famous cave is the very deep Gouffre Berger. Narrow shafts descend to the Grand Galerie, which is decorated with very large stalagmites. The tunnel follows the slope of the limestone beds for 3km (2 miles), to a flooded zone behind the resurgence in the Cuves de Sassenage.

GOURNIER CAVE LAKE, VERCORS
Just inside the resurgence entrance to the Gournier Cave, a placid lake lies beneath a profusion of calcite stalactites and flowstone cascades.

EUROPE *west*
Grotte Casteret

LOCATION In the crest of the Spanish Pyrenees, within the Ordesa National Park, Spain

LENGTH 500m (1,600ft)

DEPTH 35m (115ft)

Grotte Casteret is a limestone cave in which water seeps in as a liquid and then freezes on entering the cave. Such ice caves, as they are known, are rare because they rely on delicately balanced microclimates. Though high in the Pyrenees, the ground is not frozen, so water can seep into the limestone. However, in winter cold air becomes trapped in the cave and remains there for most of the summer. Water freezes almost as soon as it drips into the cave, creating huge icicles and columns of glass-clear ice. The floor of the main chamber is a sheet of ice, which overflows in a frozen cascade to another ice floor in a lower chamber.

ICE CAVE
This grand ice column in Casteret's main chamber is a rare and transient feature. If the cave warms, it will melt; if it cools, groundwater will be unable to enter and replenish the ice.

CURTAINS OF ICE
Glass-clear icicles drape the walls of Grotte Casteret wherever seepage water emerges from the limestone fissures.

EUROPE *south*

Skocjanske Jame

LOCATION In the heart of the Kras region of Slovenia, between Trieste and Ljubljana

LENGTH
5.8km (3²/₃ miles)

DEPTH 250m (800ft)

With a tourist pathway built high on the walls of its huge river passage, Skocjanske Jame is one of the most spectacular show caves in the world. Beside the village of Matuvan, the River Reka sinks through two giant dolines and runs beneath cliffs over 100m (330ft) high into the yawning cave entrance. There the underground river flows in a deep canyon cut down into a wider ancient passage, which now survives as high-level ledges adorned with calcite deposits. The abandoned gallery, which was the river's outlet before the canyon developed, is now blocked by massive calcite deposits and debris from a gigantic collapsed doline. The cave is the largest river sink in the Kras – the limestone region that gives its name to karst landscapes around the world.

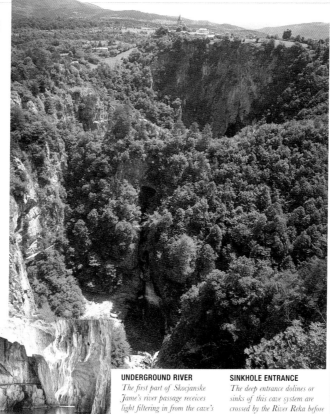

UNDERGROUND RIVER
The first part of Skocjanske Jame's river passage receives light filtering in from the cave's giant entrance.

SINKHOLE ENTRANCE
The deep entrance dolines or sinks of this cave system are crossed by the River Reka before it finally sinks underground.

EUROPE *southeast*

Optimisticheskaya

LOCATION Beneath the Dniester Valley, northwest of the Black Sea, in western Ukraine

LENGTH
212km (132 miles)

DEPTH 15m (50ft)

Limestone is not the only rock that can be dissolved to form caves. For more than a million years, groundwater has drained through a thin bed of gypsum lying beneath a limestone and clay cover in the area of the Ukraine called the Podil's'kyy flatlands. Water, flowing along joints and faults in the gypsum below the water-table, dissolved the walls to make each into a long, narrow fissure. These intersect with each other to create a seemingly endless underground maze, which has been left dry by the falling water-table. The Optimisticheskaya network is accessible only through a single entrance, dug through the floor of a doline in 1966 by local cavers. Removal of gypsum in solution continues today, creating another generation of caves to the south of Optimisticheskaya, where the gypsum still lies below the water-table.

LAND

AFRICA *south*

Cango Caves

LOCATION In the Swartberg Mountains to the east of Cape Town, South Africa

LENGTH
5.3km (3¹/₃ miles)

DEPTH 60m (200ft)

Isolated in a narrow outcrop of Precambrian limestones in the highlands near Oudtshoorn, the Cango Caves are remarkable for their wealth of calcite deposits. They are a remnant of a major channel below the water-table that was drained when nearby surface valleys were cut to lower levels. Subsequently calcite deposition has occurred on a massive scale,

LARGE DRIPSTONE DEPOSIT

leaving a spectacular array of flowstone and large stalagmites. Bushmen left paintings on the walls of the entrance chamber thousands of years ago, but the entrance was lost, and rediscovered by local farmers only in 1780.

BOTHA'S HALL
The chambers of Cango Caves are sections of a larger main passage, separated from neighbouring sections by walls and columns of calcite.

ASIA *west*

Krubera

LOCATION High on the Arabika Massif of the Western Caucasus Mountains in Georgia

LENGTH 5km (3 miles)

DEPTH 1,710m (5,610ft)

Krubera was established as the world's deepest known cave following exploration in January 2001. Thick Mesozoic limestones form spectacular karst across the summits of the Western Caucasus, and explorations in the 1980s found a number of deep cave systems, including Krubera, draining the glaciated Ortobalangan Valley. Krubera is a steeply descending cave system with a single active streamway of narrow, meandering canyons, broken by nearly 40 major shafts and numerous smaller cascades. The bottom chamber is blocked by boulders that prevent access into the main river passage, which must exist to drain all the caves of the western Arabika. The proven resurgence of the cave water is at springs on the shore of the Black Sea, another 530m (1,740ft) below the level of the bottom of the known cave. In early 2003, the depth record went to Gouffre Mirolda in France, now known to be 1,733m (5,685ft) deep.

ASIA *southeast*

Nanxu Arch

LOCATION Beside the Guanyuan Cave System, on the Li River in southern China

HEIGHT 60m (200ft)

WIDTH 40m (130ft)

The beautiful rock arch standing above Nanxu is the last surviving remnant of a large, old cave passage that once passed through the towering limestone hills in the karst of southeastern China. The arch's smooth profile is a result of surface weathering after the cave passage was exposed. The small river that formed the old cave now sinks just below the arch, into the younger Guanyuan Cave System.

LIMESTONE ARCH

ASIA *southeast*

Gunung Mulu

LOCATION In the rainforests of Sarawak, near the border with Brunei on the island of Borneo, Malaysia

LENGTH Over 320km (200 miles) in total

DEPTH 470m (1,542ft)

In 1978, British cavers discovered a series of gigantic caves with some of the largest passages in the world, all beneath the rainforests of the Gunung Mulu National Park. Deer Cave (Gua Payau) has a single passage over 100m (330ft) high and wide for its entire 1km- (3,500ft-) long route through a limestone ridge. Good Luck Cave (Lubang Nasib Bagus) has a long stream passage that leads into Sarawak Chamber – the

NESTING BIRDS

Thousands of swiftlet nests, made of moss and saliva, are glued to the walls of the Mulu caves, and swiftlets constantly fly through the darkness, navigating by echo location with distinctive clicks. Local people use swiftlet nests to make birds'-nest soup, but due to conservation measures in the cave the birds here are safe from all predators except voracious racer snakes, which are excellent climbers.

SKYLIGHT
Daylight filtering through the forest canopy beams down a hole in the roof of a gallery in the tourist section of Clearwater Cave.

world's largest underground space, 700m (2,300ft) long and over 300m (1,000ft) wide beneath an arched limestone roof over 100m (330ft) high. Clearwater Cave (Gua Air Jernih) has over 110km (69 miles) of passages that have already been mapped. The lower levels have a major river draining through massive canyon passages, while the upper levels are huge, abandoned tubes decorated with calcite deposits. All these caves have been formed by the copious flows of rainwater draining from the sandstone mountain of Gunung Mulu (Mount Mulu) into the steep limestone ridges of Api and Benarat, and out onto the shale

lowlands of the Melinau River. Wherever a river met the limestone, a cave formed and then matured into a large tunnel. As the ground surface lowered, the rivers created successive newer caves at lower levels and abandoned the older passages above. Dating of sediments in Clearwater Cave shows that the caves have evolved over a period of 2 million years. Throughout this period, surface erosion has progressively lowered the sandstone hills and shale lowlands. In contrast, erosion of the limestone has occurred largely underground, and minimal surface lowering has left the cavernous hills as ever-higher features of the changing landscape.

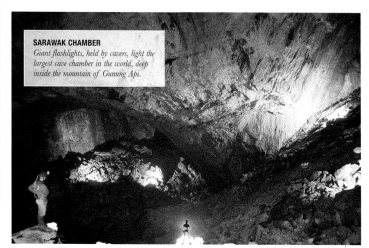

SARAWAK CHAMBER
Giant flashlights, held by cavers, light the largest cave chamber in the world, deep inside the mountain of Gunung Api.

BATS LEAVING DEER CAVE
Every evening a seemingly endless procession of bats trails out of the cave entrance en route to feed on insects living in the nearby rainforest.

DEER CAVE, SARAWAK
The world's largest passage is lit by daylight from its southern entrance. The cave floor is covered by stream sediments and guano from the 2 million bats roosting overhead.

ASIA east
Akiyoshi-do

LOCATION Beneath the Akiyoshi-dai Plateau, at the western tip of the island of Honshu, Japan

LENGTH
8.7km (5½ miles)

DEPTH 137m (450ft)

The rolling limestone plateau of Akiyoshi-dai contains a host of caves, the longest and most important being Akiyoshi-do. A stream enters the cave via two sinkholes and then passes through a short flooded section, before entering a passage with tall chambers that were created by successive collapses of the cave roof. The main passage is part of the lowest cave level, and its wide stream canyon has been carved into the floor of an original tubular cave that appears to be at least 100,000 years old. A layer of volcanic ash within the cave sediments is dated to about 34,000 years ago. The famous Hyakumai pools lie in the large stream passage that leads to the tall resurgence entrance in the foot of a cliff.

THE CASCADE OF HYAKUMAI-ZAI
Each terraced rimstone pool is retained by a calcite barrier that is deposited by the overflow of calcium-carbonate-saturated water.

ASIA southeast
Ha Long Bay

LOCATION On the coast of Vietnam facing the Gulf of Tongking, close to the Chinese border

LENGTH Numerous short caves

DEPTH All less than 70m (230ft)

With its 1,969 limestone islands, Ha Long Bay provides one of the world's most distinctive and spectacular landscapes. Most of the islands are fringed by vertical cliffs, and many are just individual towers taller than they are wide. Since invasion by the sea, marine erosion has undercut the cliffs, so that the island profiles are even steeper than those of the inland towers well-known across the border in southern China. There are hundreds of caves within the islands of Ha Long Bay, but none is long or deep because they are limited by the sizes of the islands. Some caves are remnants of ancient systems, now decorated with calcite deposits. Other younger caves have natural tunnels at sea-level, which lead through the limestone hills into drowned dolines – hidden inland lakes that have no other access to the outside world.

HANG BO NAU
A vista of limestone hills and islands is framed by the mouth of the Bo Nau Cave, the remnant of an ancient passage on Island 268 in Ha Long Bay.

ASIA southeast
Tham Hinboun

LOCATION East of the Mekong River in the limestone mountains of Khammouan, Laos

LENGTH 12.4km (7¾ miles)

DEPTH 40m (130ft)

The Hinboun River flows through this cave for a distance of over 7km (4.5 miles), and is the world's longest navigable underground river. The cave originated with a switchback route, following fractures and bedding in the limestone. Subsequently, the high passages were eroded by retreating waterfalls, while the lower ones were removed by solution of their underwater ceilings. Today the cave is an almost horizontal tunnel passing between two open karst basins.

AUSTRALASIA Australia
Koonalda Caves

LOCATION Beneath the Nullarbor Plain, close to the coast of South Australia

LENGTH 1,200m (4,000ft)

DEPTH 80m (260ft)

The flat, barren landscape of the Nullarbor Plain is broken by more than 130 large dolines, formed by surface collapse. Koonalda is one of these, where a very large cave passage is accessible below the debris. The Nullarbor Plain is made of Miocene limestone that has been drained by underground passages since it was uplifted about 14 million years ago. The caves formed as widely spaced tunnels, filled with slowly moving water at or below the water-table. During later phases of uplift, the water-table fell, leaving some of these passages dry. Further collapse of limestone ceilings has left high chambers, some of which have broken out at the surface, creating the collapse dolines that are the caves' only entrances. Koonalda has four chambers in its main passage, besides the one that forms its entrance. Between the collapse features, the stable sections of cave roof arch over long lakes of clear, brackish water. At the end of the third lake, the roof dips, and the cave continues as a submerged tunnel.

DOLINE ENTRANCE
The 40m- (130ft-) wide entrance of Koonalda Caves provided easy access for Aboriginal flint miners more than 20,000 years ago.

AUSTRALASIA Australia
Jenolan Caves

LOCATION In the western flank of the Blue Mountains, in New South Wales, Australia

LENGTH 10.6km (6⅔ miles)

DEPTH 85m (280ft)

Australia's best-known tourist caves were discovered in around 1838 by escaped convict and bushranger James McKeown. They lie in a narrow outcrop of Silurian limestone that is crossed by the Jenolan River. Grand Arch, at just 120m (400ft) long, is all that remains of an ancient cave; but to either side the limestone contains a host of smaller cave passages with streams still flowing through the lower levels. Some Jenolan caves were formed in Permo-Carboniferous times before being completely filled with Permian carbonates and gravels. Later streams have re-excavated a few of the old caves, or cut new ones through the limestone.

JUBILEE CAVE
Delicate calcite crystals that grow in pools of calcium-carbonate-saturated water are a feature of this richly decorated part of the Jenolan Caves.

GRAND COLUMN
This large stalagmite in River Cave has developed an apron of stalactites and curtains below its overgrown top.

LAND

WALL OF ICE
*As the Hubbard Glacier meets the sea in
Disenchantment Bay, ice detaches from
its 90m- (300ft-) high terminal wall.
These chunks of ice form icebergs, which
then float away into the Gulf of Alaska.*

GLACIERS

ABOUT ONE-TENTH OF the Earth's land surface is covered in ice masses known as glaciers, which hold some 67 per cent of the world's fresh water. Glaciers are among the most beautiful natural phenomena, and they also have a profound effect on terrain, carving out landscapes and transporting vast amounts of rock as they advance and retreat across remote areas of the planet. Glaciers come in many different forms and sizes. For example, some glaciers carry pinnacles of ice, streams of water, or even lakes on their surfaces. Others have volcanoes underneath them, colonies of worms living inside them, or long floodwater channels running through their interiors. In recent years, glaciers have become an important focus of study – melting of large fractions of the world's glaciers could lead to a substantial rise in sea-level. Their behaviour in response to global warming is therefore being closely monitored.

Glaciers

A GLACIER IS AN ACCUMULATION of many layers of snow, transformed over time and by their own weight into a mass of ice that persists from year to year. This ice mass slowly deforms and begins to move, mostly travelling downhill. A small glacier may be no bigger than a football field, but the largest, called ice-sheets, can be continent-sized. Glaciers are an important reserve of fresh water, and can act like time capsules, holding information – in the form of trapped air, chemicals, and dust – that tells us much about changing climatic conditions over hundreds of thousands of years.

Glacier Structure

Most glaciers except for the very largest descend from a mountain area and flow down a valley. The top of the glacier usually lies in a bowl-shaped area called a cirque. The ice below the cirque is often broken up by deep cracks called crevasses, formed in response to stress as the ice grinds over uneven bedrock. Over time, rocks fall onto the glacier or become attached to the moving ice and are plucked off the bedrock. They are deposited at the melting terminus (snout) of the glacier, leaving a debris pile called a terminal moraine, or at the sides (forming lateral moraines). Where glaciers join, rocks carried on their edges merge to form a surface stripe called a medial moraine. Broadly similar processes occur in larger glaciers, although these are less constrained by topography (see p.214).

UPSTREAM FEATURES
The Bagley Ice-field in Alaska, 8km (5 miles) wide, is typical of the upper areas of a glacier, which are composed of clean ice fractured by crevasses.

rock-fall

cirque

cirque

ice-fall, where glacier flows over steep gradient

crevasses on surface of ice-fall

rock avalanche

medial moraine

crevasse

lateral moraine

threshold lip of cirque

terminus (snout)

terminal moraine

MERGING GLACIERS
Two glaciers, originating from separate cirques, merge and continue down a valley. A wide medial moraine marks where they have joined. At the terminus, a lake of meltwater forms behind the terminal moraine.

englacial debris

rock plucked from valley floor

meltwater stream on glacier surface

stream sinks down shaft (moulin)

glacial lake

streams

outwash plain

MELTWATER STREAM
A glacier's surface may be broken up by streams of meltwater and studded with boulders.

TERMINUS
Glaciers can be hundreds (or even thousands) of metres deep. This is most apparent at a glacier's terminus, where an enormous cliff or mound of ice can be seen, as here in Harriman Fiord, Alaska.

MELTWATER CAVES
Ice caves, such as this one in Alaska's Muir Glacier, are formed by meltwater streams eroding vertical sinkholes, tunnels, and finally large chambers within the ice.

LAND

Glacier Ice

Newly fallen snow contains masses of air
between individual snowflakes. As more
settles onto a previously fall, the flakes
beneath are compressed and deformed,
by partial melting and refreezing, into
smaller, rounder ice particles. These
adhere to each other, initially forming
small ice granules and then a material
consisting of larger granules, known as
firn. As more snow falls, further
compression occurs, causing the firn to
weld into solid, dense glacial ice.

AIRBORNE SNOW

SNOW
(85–90% AIR)

GRANULAR ICE
(30–85% AIR)

FIRN
(20–30% AIR)

BLUE ICE
(LESS THAN 20%
AIR, AS BUBBLES)

STAGES OF FORMATION
*As glacial ice is formed, there is a
gradual decrease in the proportion
of air to snow or ice. Depending
on the location of the glacier, the
process can take anything from
5 to 3,000 years.*

BLUE ICE
*Dense glacial ice owes its intense colour to its
crystalline structure, which absorbs all except the
shortest (bluest) wavelengths of visible light. Blue
ice is stronger and contains less air than white ice.*

Movement

In the upper parts of a glacier, known as the
accumulation area, there is a net gain of ice each
year, as some of each winter's snowfall remains
until the next winter. From here, ice flows downhill
due to gravity. The mechanism of ice movement
varies. In some glaciers (called warm-based), a thin
layer of water forms under the glacier, allowing the
ice to slide over the bedrock. In others (cold-based),
the base of the glacier is frozen to the bedrock, so
ice can move only by slow deformation. Eventually
the ice reaches the lower parts of the glacier, where
it melts and evaporates or, in some glaciers, breaks
off as icebergs. This lower zone of the glacier,
where there is a net loss of ice over the year, is
called the ablation area. The section between the
accumulation and ablation areas, where ice gains
and losses are in balance, is called the equilibrium
zone. The difference between the glacier's overall
ice gains and losses is called its mass balance.

CALVING ICE
*Some glaciers end in
lakes or the sea, where
huge chunks of ice calve
(break off) and float
away as icebergs.*

accumulation
of ice from
snowfall

accumulation
area, above
equilibrium zone

direction of movement
of glacial ice

equilibrium zone

loss of ice by evaporation
of surface meltwater

ablation
area, below
equilibrium zone

loss of ice
in meltwater
streams

flow path of
ice in glacier

snout

SHIFTING BALANCE
*The position of the equilibrium zone
along the length of the glacier varies from year to
year depending on the climate. If ice accumulation
lessens or ablation increases, the section of the
glacier that is in balance will move up the glacier.*

Advance and Retreat

Over a period of years, if more ice forms on a glacier than
melts, the glacier must grow. It may widen, thicken, or
advance (or any combination of the three). Conversely, if
more ice is lost than forms, the glacier shrinks. The ice in its
lower parts may thin and stagnate, or the snout may retreat –
or both. Since 1900, most glaciers
around the world have retreated,
although within this time there have
also been periods of advance, both by
groups of glaciers and by individual
glaciers (especially by surge-type glaciers
with cyclical patterns of rapid advance
and slow retreat). The vast majority of
scientists believe the overall trend of
retreat is due to global warming, which
is, at least in part, due to human activity.

RETREATING GLACIER
*The Blomstrandenbreen Glacier
in Svalbard, Norway, retreated
dramatically between 1922 and
2002, as shown by two photos
taken from the same location in
1922 (above) and 2002 (left).*

ADVANCING GLACIER
*When a glacier
advances, it simply
brushes aside objects
such as trees. Here, the
Taku Glacier, which
advanced more than
7km (4⅓ miles)
between 1899 and
1989, pushes through a
hundred-year-old forest
near Juneau in Alaska.*

Types of Glacier

Glaciers vary enormously in their size and form. The largest, called continental ice-sheets, and somewhat smaller glaciers called ice-caps, almost totally submerge the landscapes on which they lie. These glaciers are slightly dome-shaped. Driven by gravity, the ice in them flows outward from their centres towards their edges, where channels of ice flow, called ice-streams and outlet glaciers, are visible. Outlet glaciers are bounded by ice-free ground, while ice-streams are surrounded by slower-moving ice. The other main types of glaciers are found in areas where the ice flow is constrained by mountains. An ice-field is a huge expanse of ice at high altitude, partly hemmed in by mountains, that gives rise to numerous outlet glaciers. A cirque glacier is a small glacier mainly confined to a depression on the flank of a mountain. Where ice flows out of a cirque and extends far down a valley, the result is a valley glacier. This can be tens or even hundreds of kilometres long. When a valley or outlet glacier flows into a flat, lowland area, it may spread out into a wide expanse of ice called a piedmont lobe.

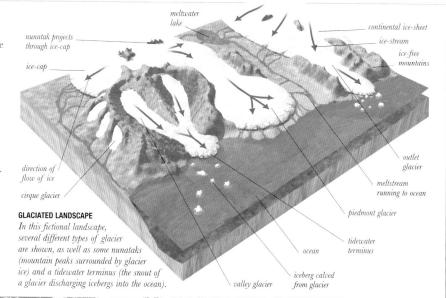

meltwater lake
nunatak projects through ice-cap
continental ice-sheet
ice-stream
ice-free mountains
ice-cap
outlet glacier
direction of flow of ice
meltstream running to ocean
cirque glacier
piedmont glacier
tidewater terminus
ocean
iceberg calved from glacier
valley glacier

GLACIATED LANDSCAPE
In this fictional landscape, several different types of glacier are shown, as well as some nunataks (mountain peaks surrounded by glacier ice) and a tidewater terminus (the snout of a glacier discharging icebergs into the ocean).

ICE-SHEET MARGIN
Thin meltwater streams can be seen here on the surface of the Greenland Ice-sheet at one of the points where it meets the sea.

OUTLET GLACIERS
Several outlet glaciers from the Spitsbergen Ice-cap on Svalbard, Norway, flow through lines of nunataks towards the sea.

PIEDMONT GLACIER
This satellite image shows Alaska's Malaspina Glacier. This consists almost entirely of an enormous piedmont lobe, the world's largest.

VALLEY GLACIER
The Aletsch, a 23km- (14-mile-) long valley glacier, flows through the Swiss Alps. The lower part of the glacier is shown here.

CALIFORNIAN GLACIATED LANDSCAPE
McGee Creek in the Sierra Nevada, USA, is a U-shaped valley sculpted by a glacier during the last ice age. An array of cirques, horns, and arêtes can be seen among the mountains in the background. In the foreground are distinct lateral moraines – ridges formed from rock debris deposited at the side of the glacier.

Glacial Erosion

Glaciers erode mountainous regions into characteristic shapes, some of which only become apparent when the glaciers eventually melt and disappear (as at McGee Creek, opposite below). Erosion occurs partly by the plucking of rocks from valleys and mountainsides as they freeze to glacial ice, and partly by the moving mass of ice and its rock load grinding or abrading the bedrock. At the head of a glacier, the ice typically carves out a cirque. Where two cirques back up against each other, ridges called arêtes are formed; three or more cirques can combine to produce a pyramidal peak called a horn. Downstream, a glacier moving through a valley will usually deepen and broaden the valley from a V-shape into a U-shaped profile. Another common feature is the hanging valley. This is seen where glacial erosion has occurred faster in the main valley than in a smaller tributary valley. When the glaciers melt, the tributary is left suspended high above the more deeply carved main valley. Landscapes like the one shown in the illustration on the right can be seen today in many mountainous regions of Europe and North America, such as parts of Norway, northern Britain, and the Rocky Mountains in Canada and the USA.

CIRQUE AND ARETE
This deeply eroded cirque, with a long ridge, or arête, at its crest on the far side, sits above Gryllefjord in Norway.

HANGING VALLEY
Like many hanging valleys, this one in Muldalen, above Tafjord in Norway, sometimes discharges a waterfall over a cliff into the main valley below.

pyramidal peak (horn) — lip of cirque — cirque — arête — hanging valley — U-shaped valley — waterfall

tarn (small lake in scooped-out base of cirque) — river — moraine-dammed lake — terminal moraine marks limit of glacier's advance

GLACIER-ERODED LANDSCAPE
This landscape illustrates some of the typical features that might be seen in the upper and middle parts of valleys that were once filled with glaciers.

ERODED VALLEY
The floor of this valley has been deeply eroded by past glaciation.

Deposition

When glaciers melt, they deposit material on the landscape. Much of this matter is a mixture of particles, ranging in size from sand grains to boulders, called till. The deposits come in many forms. For example, a terminal moraine is a broad ridge of till marking the furthest point that a glacier advanced. An esker is a twisting ridge of sand and gravel that snakes its way across the landscape. It is formed from material deposited by a stream that once flowed under the glacier. A drumlin is a long, cigar-shaped mound of till that was smoothed in the direction of the glacier's flow. An erratic is a large, rounded boulder that a glacier carried far from its source in the mountains and eventually deposited at its terminus. When an ice block detaches from a melting glacier and is partially buried by deposits from meltwater streams, it melts and creates a depression in the layer of till called a kettle hole. If the depression fills with water, it becomes a kettle lake. When a meltwater channel becomes choked with coarse material, it causes the river to divide into a series of diverging and converging segments, known as braided streams.

KETTLE LAKE
This kettle lake lies in Dolma La Pass, one of the routes to Mount Kailas, the sacred mountain of Tibet, which is known locally as Ghang Rimpoche, or "jewel of snow".

ERRATIC
This erratic boulder in Yorkshire, UK, was transported by a glacier and then deposited on top of younger rock.

DEPOSITIONAL FEATURES
A melting glacier typically leaves several of the features seen here. Over large parts of lowland North America and Europe, deposits such as these can still be discerned in the landscape, providing clues to the region's glacial history.

tunnel — terminus of melting glacier — esker revealed as ice melts — swarm of drumlins — outwash plain consisting of sand, gravel, and pebbles deposited by meltwater streams — braided streams — kettle lake — erratic — terminal moraine — meltwater stream breaking through terminal moraine

World Distribution

Glaciers can form only on areas of land where there is some snowfall and very low temperatures persist for much of the year. The only places that satisfy both these conditions are close to the poles or in high mountain areas. The world's largest glaciers are massive ice-sheets that cover Antarctica, while in high northern latitudes huge areas of glaciation exist over Greenland, parts of Iceland, Norway, and Alaska. Closer to the equator, the extensive high-altitude glaciers of the high Alps and Himalayas are diminishing, as are the smaller glaciers of the tropics, which are found in the northern Andes and on the highest mountains of Africa and Mexico.

GLACIER PROFILES

The pages that follow contain profiles of a selection of the world's glaciers. Each profile begins with the following summary information:

TYPE Cirque glacier, valley glacier, piedmont glacier, outlet glacier, ice-cap, ice-field, or ice-sheet

TERMINUS Terrestrial snout, terrestrial lobe, tidewater (sea-calving) front, or lake-calving front (Cirque, valley, piedmont, and outlet glaciers only)

AREA Surface area (All glacier types)

LENGTH Distance from source to terminus (All glacier types except ice-caps and ice-sheets)

STATUS Advancing, retreating, stable, or uncertain (since 2000)

NORTH AMERICA *northwest*
Worthington Glacier

LOCATION In the central part of the Chugach Mountains, south-central Alaska, USA

TYPE Valley glacier

TERMINUS Terrestrial snout

AREA 8 square km (3 square miles)

LENGTH 6km (4 miles)

STATUS Retreating

A small valley glacier, the Worthington descends from 2,000m (6,500ft) up, and terminates close to a major highway. The changing shape of boreholes drilled through the glacier to the bedrock has revealed that at least 20 per cent of the glacier's movement is due to its internal deformation – the rest is due to slippage over the bedrock.

DOUBLE-ARMED TERMINUS

NORTH AMERICA *northwest*
Columbia Glacier

LOCATION Descending from the Chugach Mountains to Prince William Sound, south-central Alaska, USA

TYPE Valley glacier

TERMINUS Tidewater (sea-calving) front

AREA 920 square km (360 square miles)

LENGTH 50km (31 miles)

STATUS Retreating

One of the fastest-moving glaciers in North America, the Columbia is also one of the most rapidly retreating. Between the 1970s and 2001, the velocity of the ice near its terminus reached an astonishing 30m (100ft) per day, though it has since slowed. The glacier's fast forward movement has been cancelled out by the rapid calving of icebergs at its terminus. As a result, since 1982, the terminus has retreated about 16km (10 miles) and thinned considerably. Since 2011, it has split in two. The glacier's retreat cannot solely be attributed to global warming, as other nearby glaciers are not retreating

SURFACE DEBRIS
Parts of the lower glacier are covered in a thin layer of rock debris that has concentrated at the surface as the ice has melted.

as rapidly. Instead, they point to special factors related to the bedrock channel beneath the front of the glacier. This is very deep and slants backwards, and as a result, the front of the glacier is almost afloat on meltwater, explaining why it moves forward so quickly. The high ice velocity in turn increases the rate at which icebergs are calved, and causes ice to be lost faster than it can be replenished by the glacier's upper parts.

CONCEALED TERMINUS
The bulk of the Columbia terminus is hidden beneath Columbia Bay, an offshoot of Prince William Sound. Calved icebergs are a recognized hazard to shipping in the area.

NORTH AMERICA *northwest*
Margerie Glacier

LOCATION In the St. Elias Mountains, descending to Glacier Bay, southeastern Alaska, USA

TYPE Valley glacier

TERMINUS Tidewater (sea-calving) front

AREA 112 square km (43 square miles)

LENGTH 34km (21 miles)

STATUS Stable

The Margerie Glacier is one of several tidewater glaciers that originate from the eastern end of the St. Elias Mountains. They then descend to discharge ice into a large inlet of the Gulf of Alaska called Glacier Bay, which became a National Park in 1980 and a World Heritage Site in 1992. The terminus of the glacier is in Tarr Inlet at the northern end of the Bay. At one time, about 100 years ago, the Margerie was a mere tributary of a much larger glacier, the Grand Pacific Glacier, which filled the whole of Tarr Inlet. Earlier still, when the English naval officer Captain George Vancouver discovered Glacier Bay in 1794, the entire bay was filled with ice. Since then the Grand Pacific has shrunk and Margerie has become a calving glacier in its own right. Today, it is one of the most spectacular glaciers in the Bay, towering about 80m (265ft) above the sea surface. Unlike most other Alaskan glaciers, it has not markedly retreated in recent years.

WALL OF BLUE ICE
The Margerie Glacier regularly discharges large chunks of blue ice from its 1.5km- (1-mile-) wide terminus into Glacier Bay, with thunderous cracking noises.

NORTH AMERICA *northwest*
Mendenhall Glacier

LOCATION Descending from the Juneau Ice-field, Coast Mountains, southeastern Alaska, USA

TYPE Outlet glacier

TERMINUS Lake-calving front

AREA 80 square km (31 square miles)

LENGTH 27km (15 miles)

STATUS Retreating

The Mendenhall is an outlet glacier from the Juneau Ice-field, a vast area of ice that straddles the border between Alaska and British Columbia. The glacier terminates in a lake 3km (2 miles) long, not far from the city of Juneau. In recent years, the glacier has had some periods of very rapid retreat, for example 200m (650ft) in 2004, while at the same time the lake has much increased in size. It is anticipated that the glacier will finally recede out of the lake by about 2020. Once the glacier can no longer calve icebergs, its rate of retreat should slow.

SURFACE MELTWATER
Streams, such as the one shown here, can develop where surface ice melts faster than it can be absorbed by the glacier.

Malaspina Glacier

LOCATION On the coastal side of the St. Elias Mountains, southeastern Alaska, USA

TYPE Piedmont glacier

TERMINUS Terrestrial lobes

AREA 3,200 square km (1,240 square miles)

LENGTH 45km (28 miles)

STATUS Retreating

Named after an Italian, Alessandro Malaspina, who explored this part of Alaska in 1791, the Malaspina Glacier is famous for containing the world's largest piedmont lobe. It is also the second largest glacier in North America. It consists of three lobes, each fed by different outlet glaciers that flow out of a large ice-field lying high up in the St. Elias Mountains behind the Malaspina. The largest of these feeder glaciers is the Seward Glacier (seen in the image below as the blue ribbon of ice entering from the top). This feeder is itself 4km (2½ miles) wide at its lower end – it gives rise to the largest, central lobe of the Malaspina. To the west, the Agassiz Glacier (the blue stream at the top left of the image) feeds a smaller western lobe. To the east, the Hayden and Marvine glaciers give rise to a small eastern lobe. Seismic surveys have shown that the Malaspina is up to 600m (2,000ft) thick, and that, roughly in the middle of the glacier, ice at its base is eroding the bedrock at a depth of about 300m (1,000ft)

ICE WORM

The tiny Ice Worm is one of very few species of animal known to be able to survive in glacier ice. This one is about 12mm (½ in) long.

below sea-level. From there, the ice is actually forced upwards towards the lobe-shaped terminus of the glacier, where it melts and deposits the rock debris as till. All around the 100km- (60-mile-) long terminus of the glacier is a region of stagnating ice, thickly overlain with rock debris. Surrounding this is a wide area of till studded with meltwater lakes and kettle holes. At its southern end, the glacier almost reaches sea-level at Sitkagi Bluffs on the Gulf of Alaska. There, a series of terminal moraines protects it from contact with the open ocean. If the sea-level were to rise sufficiently to connect the glacier to the ocean, the glacier would start calving icebergs and would probably retreat significantly. A remarkable feature of the Malaspina, and

ALTERNATING CURRENTS

Much of the Malaspina Glacier's surface is covered in a complex pattern of contorted medial moraines. These are an indication of surge behaviour – that is, patterns of alternating fast and slow ice flow.

some other coastal glaciers in Alaska, is the occurrence of Ice Worms. These small segmented worms are found in colonies of millions of individuals near the ice surface during the day; at night they burrow deep into the ice. The worms are thought to survive by feeding on green algae that grow near the surface of the glacier.

TERMINAL LOBE

In this false-colour satellite image of the Malaspina Glacier, taken by NASA's Landsat 7 in 2000, the ice and snow show as blue and white, the red areas are rock, and the brown patches are bands of vegetation.

CAPE YORK, NORTH GREENLAND
In this sunset view of the Greenland coast, the ice-sheet is visible in the central background, with an outlet glacier descending to the frozen sea. Calved icebergs are locked in the sea ice.

Greenland Ice-sheet

LOCATION Covering 80 per cent of the island of Greenland in the Arctic Circle

TYPE Ice-sheet

AREA 1.71 million square km (660,000 square miles)

STATUS Retreating

Greenland Ice-sheet

Jakobshavn Glacier

WEATHER STATIONS

Since 1990, several automatic weather station have been established on the ice-sheet as part of the Greenland Climate Network project. As of 2012, 13 of these were recording and transmitting weather data, such as air temperature and wind speed, via satellite links to a research centre in the USA. It is hoped that analysis of the data will help establish whether the climate around the ice-sheet is warming and the extent to which this is linked to ice thinning. So far, the results are inconclusive, although a clear increase in average winter temperature has been measured at some stations.

Despite its name, Greenland is mostly covered in a thick layer of ice. A single glacier, the Greenland Ice-sheet, makes up most of this ice, although smaller ice-caps occur at the edges. The main ice-sheet is the northern hemisphere's largest glacier, with an average thickness of about 1,670m (5,500ft) and a volume of 2.85 million cubic km (0.68 million cubic miles). Its surface is slightly domed, reaching about 3,290m (10,800ft) above sea-level, slightly to the southeast of the island's centre. A second, lower dome lies in the southeast corner. From these domes, ice moves slowly towards the edges of the ice-sheet. Around most of its periphery, the ice is constrained by coastal mountains, so there are few places where it meets the sea along a broad front. As a result, Greenland has no ice-shelves, but in many places, large outlet glaciers flow through valleys between the mountains and discharge enormous quantities of icebergs into the sea. One of the main outlets, Jakobshavn Glacier in west Greenland, is the world's fastest-flowing glacier. At its terminus, the ice flows at speeds of about 1m (3ft) per hour, producing over 90 million tonnes of icebergs per day. The ice-sheet's high albedo (see p.365) keeps its summer temperature far lower than it would be otherwise. There are concerns, however, that the ice-sheet is melting due to global warming. It is so large that it contains about 6.5 per cent of the world's fresh water reserves, and if it melted completely, the oceans would rise by about 7m (23ft). A 2012 study found that the ice-sheet lost volume at a rate of about 150 cubic kilometres (36 cubic miles) a year between 1992 and 2011. Although in percentage terms this is a small rate of loss, the melting seems to be accelerating. Analysis of ice samples formed more than 100,000 years ago indicates that Greenland has warmed significantly in the past without the ice completely disappearing.

BEACHED ICEBERGS
Most North Atlantic icebergs originate from the Greenland Ice-sheet. The icebergs enrich the sea around Greenland with fresh water and oxygen, attracting an abundance of fish.

ICEBERG MAKER
Eqi Glacier is a typical iceberg-calving glacier in West Greenland. Its terminus rises 100m (330ft) above the sea and extends another 900m (3,000ft) below water level. When the icebergs fall into the sea, they can cause tidal waves 10m (32ft) high

LAND

NORTH AMERICA *northwest*
Athabasca Glacier

LOCATION Extending from the Columbia Ice-field, in the Rocky Mountains of Alberta, Canada

TYPE Outlet glacier

TERMINUS Terrestrial snout

AREA 5 square km (2 square miles)

LENGTH 5km (3 miles)

STATUS Retreating

The Athabasca is one of more than 20 outlet glaciers from the Columbia Ice-field, the largest body of ice in the Rocky Mountains, with a surface area of 350 square km (135 square miles). Remarkably, the water run-off from this ice-field flows into three different oceans: the Pacific, Atlantic, and Arctic. The top part of the Athabasca Glacier, which descends from the ice-field at an altitude of about 2,700m (8,860ft), consists of three huge ice-falls, which appear like a series of giant steps. Further down, the glacier descends gently and spreads out to a broad snout. The depth of the ice over the whole glacier varies from about 90 to 300m (300 to 1,000ft). The Athabasca has been shrinking since about 1850 and is estimated to have lost 50 per cent of its mass since 1900. Currently, its rate of retreat is about 3m (10ft) a year. Where the glacier has paused in its retreat, distinct ridges of large terminal moraines are clearly visible.

red carotenoid pigment

thick algal cell wall

WATERMELON SNOW
The patches of "pink snow" found on some glaciers, including the Athabasca, are actually colonies of bright red algae.

NORTH AMERICA *northwest*
Kaskawulsh Glacier

LOCATION In the St. Elias Mountains, 35km (22 miles) south of Kluane Lake, Yukon, Canada

TYPE Valley glacier

TERMINUS Terrestrial snout

AREA 1,100 square km (420 square miles)

LENGTH 70km (43 miles)

STATUS Retreating

Arguably the most spectacular glacier in Canada, the Kaskawulsh is notable for its sheer size and its impressive medial moraines (see below). These formed as a result of the merging of tributary glaciers into the main glacier trunk. The snout gives rise to the Slims River, which maintains the level of the Yukon's largest lake, Kluane Lake.

AERIAL VIEW OF KASKAWULSH GLACIER

EVIDENCE OF RETREAT
Piles of moraine surround the snout and sides of this glacier. High up on the horizon is the Columbia Ice-field.

NORTH AMERICA *northwest*
Palisade Glacier

LOCATION In the southern part of the Sierra Nevada range, central California, USA

TYPE Cirque glacier

TERMINUS Lake-calving front

AREA 0.5 square km (⅕ square mile)

LENGTH 900m (3,000ft)

STATUS Retreating

The Palisade is one of about 100 small glaciers in the Sierra Nevada that have survived since the last ice age. At its top is a horizontal crack, called a bergschrund, which formed when the glacier fractured and its main mass slipped down, leaving a wall of ice frozen to the rock.

THE HEAD OF THE PALISADE GLACIER

SOUTH AMERICA *west*
Pastoruri Glacier

LOCATION In the southern part of the Cordillera Blanca, Andes, north-central Peru

TYPE Cirque glacier

TERMINUS Terrestrial snout

AREA 2 square km (1 square miles)

LENGTH 3km (2 miles)

STATUS Retreating

The tropical regions of South America still harbour a few areas of glaciation, such as the Pastoruri Glacier in Peru. Occupying the flank of a 5,240m- (17,200ft-) high Andean peak, it has steep, cliff-like edges and is usually covered in soft snow, with a few heavily crevassed areas. Over 15 per cent of its ice has melted in the last 35 years.

PASTORURI GLACIER, LOOKING DOWNHILL

SOUTH AMERICA *southwest*
Southern Patagonian Ice-field

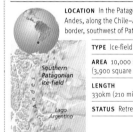

LOCATION In the Patagonian Andes, along the Chile–Argentina border, southwest of Patagonia

TYPE Ice-field

AREA 10,000 square km (3,900 square miles)

LENGTH 330km (210 miles)

STATUS Retreating

The Southern Patagonian Ice-field is the largest glaciated region in the southern hemisphere outside of Antarctica. It is the main remnant of a much larger area of glaciation (about 40 times bigger in area) that extended over much of the southern Andes about 10,000 years ago. Like all ice-fields, it is a single, extensive, mostly level-surfaced mass of ice that covers most of a mountain region, apart from the highest peaks and ridges. Monte Fitzroy at 3,359m (11,020ft) and volcano Lautaro at 3,623m (11,886ft) are two of the main peaks that the ice-field surrounds. At its widest point, the ice-field is about 50km (31 miles) across, and its average width is some 30km (19 miles). On its western side, nearly 50 significant outlet glaciers flow out of it, reaching sea-level in the rugged fiords on the coast of Chile. Many of these fiords are choked with ice. On the eastern side, which is mainly in Argentina, large outlet glaciers calve icebergs into extensive lakes at about 200–270m (650–900ft) above sea-level. Three of these lakes (Lago Martin, Lago Viedma, and Lago Argentino) can be seen in the image below. The lakes occupy valleys that were filled by large glaciers during the last ice age. Comparison of various aerial and satellite photographs of the ice-field taken since 1945 has shown that, with a few exceptions, most of its outlet glaciers have retreated over the past 50 years or so.

ICE-CAP REMNANT
This satellite photograph showing the vast extent of the Southern Patagonian Ice-field was taken looking towards the northeast.

LAKE-CALVING FRONT
*Ice-block falls from this 60m- (200ft-)
high wall can produce waves big enough
to drown people on the nearby shore.*

SOUTH AMERICA *southwest*

Perito Moreno Glacier

LOCATION Extending from the Southern Patagonian Ice-field, southern Argentina

TYPE Outlet glacier

TERMINUS Lake-calving front

AREA 200 square km (80 square miles)

LENGTH 20km (12 miles)

STATUS Stable

Perito Moreno is an impressive outlet glacier from the Southern Patagonian Ice-field (see opposite), descending to the east of the ice-field, where it calves icebergs into the largest lake in Argentina, Lago Argentino. Unlike most outlet glaciers in the region,

GLACIER TERMINUS
When the Perito Moreno Glacier advances, it forms a dam between Lago Argentino (on the right in this photograph) and Brazo Rico (on the left).

its terminus has scarcely changed its position in the last 90 years. During that period, the glacier has made temporary advances every five years or so, each time blocking off an arm of the lake, called Brazo Rico. Whenever this happens, a separate lake has been created, with a rising water level that floods a large area of grassland. After six to 12 months, but always in summer, the lake bursts through the ice dam, discharging about a billion tonnes of water in 24 hours and flooding nearby shores.

EUROPE *northwest*

Vatnajökull Ice-cap

LOCATION In the southeast of Iceland, covering about 8 per cent of the island

TYPE Ice-cap

AREA 8,160 square km (3,150 square miles)

STATUS Retreating

Vatnajökull Ice-cap

Vatnajökull, a classic ice-cap, is the biggest glacier by volume in Europe and one of several ice-caps on Iceland. Roughly ellipse-shaped, the glacier completely covers the mountainous terrain it sits on and is slightly domed. Its average thickness is about 400m (1,300ft). Numerous outlet glaciers, including surging glaciers, drain into

BREIDAMERKURJÖKULL
This is the largest outlet glacier of the Vatnajökull Ice-cap, seen here calving ice into a small lake.

the sea from the ice-cap. Iceland lies in a region of high tectonic activity, and there are several active volcanoes and volcanic fissures under the western parts of Vatnajökull. In a few areas, heat from these melts the base of the ice-cap, creating subglacial lakes. In October 1996, a volcanic fissure erupted a plume of ash and steam some 3,000m (10,000ft) into the air. Meltwater from the ice-cap filled the subglacial caldera of the Grimsvotn volcano (see p.123). When the caldera overflowed, some 3,000 billion litres (65 billion gallons) of water flooded out from beneath the glacier (see panel below).

FLOODING HAZARD

Glaciers can cause catastrophic floods, and because the problem is so common in Iceland, glaciologists have adopted an Icelandic word, jökulhlaup ("glacier flood"), to refer to the phenomenon. Icelandic jökulhlaups result from subglacial volcanic activity, but in other parts of the world, a more common cause is the bursting of lakes (which have either overfilled or were previously ice-dammed), as glaciers melt and disintegrate. The Vatnajökull flood of 1996 (see above) destroyed many roads and bridges below the glacier.

SUBGLACIAL ERUPTION
In December 1998, an eruption at the edge of Grímsvötn sent a plume of ash and steam 10,000m (33,000ft) up into the air above the ice-cap.

LAND

EUROPE *north*
Kongsvegen Glacier

LOCATION In western Spitsbergen, Svalbard, 1,250km (775 miles) north of the Norwegian mainland

TYPE Outlet glacier

TERMINUS Tidewater (sea-calving) front

AREA 80 square km (31 square miles)

LENGTH 20km (12 miles)

STATUS Stable

Svalbard is an archipelago under Norwegian jurisdiction in the Arctic Ocean. Its largest island, Spitsbergen, is about 80 per cent covered in glaciers, of which one of the best studied is the Kongsvegen. This is classified as a polythermal glacier, which means that there are large temperature variations within it – a cold surface layer of ice, 50–160m (160–520ft) thick, overlies a much warmer layer of ice at its base. Ice flow in polythermal glaciers tends to increase during the summer over the lower part of the glacier. This is thought to be caused by a build-up of meltwater beneath the glacier, lubricating its flow. In recent years, the terminus of Kongsvegen has been retreating. However, because it is a surge-type glacier (see p.213), this does not necessarily mean that the amount of ice in the glacier is falling. Indeed, detailed mass-balance studies conducted since 1987 have indicated that the glacier has actually slightly gained in ice mass overall.

DIRTY ICE CLIFF
This partially grounded cliff of ice, visible at one side of the glacier's terminus, contains medial moraines and englacial rock debris.

MERGED GLACIER TERMINUS
At its terminus, the Kongsvegen merges with another glacier, the Kronebreen. The merged glaciers calve icebergs into Kongsfjorden along a front 4km (2½ miles) wide.

EUROPE *north*
Jostedalsbreen Ice-field

LOCATION In southwestern Norway, west of the Jotunheimen Mountains and north of Sognafjord

TYPE Ice-field

AREA 400 square km (150 square miles)

LENGTH 65km (40 miles)

STATUS Retreating

Jostedalsbreen is the largest glacier on the European mainland, a remnant of a vast ice-sheet that covered the whole of Norway until about 10,000 years ago. It survives in southwest Norway primarily because of high regional snowfall rather than particularly cold temperatures, and this is reflected by a high rate of melting at the snouts of its 50-odd outlet glaciers.

EUROPE *north*
West Svartisen Ice-cap

LOCATION In the coastal area of central Norway, at the latitude of the Arctic Circle

TYPE Ice-cap

AREA 200 square km (77 square miles)

STATUS Stable

The West Svartisen Ice-cap occupies a plateau near the Norwegian coast, with most of its surface lying above 1,100m (3,600ft). Like Jostedalsbreen, it owes its existence more to high snowfall than to low temperature. The ice-cap's surface is featureless and slightly domed, but at its edges are a number of outlet glaciers. One of these, Engabreen, is notable on several counts. First, it is

ENGABREEN GLACIER
This arm of the West Svartisen Ice-cap descends to a lake that is just a few metres above sea-level.

the lowest-lying glacial arm on the European mainland. Second, its mass balance has been studied since 1970, and until 2000 it showed a considerable gain of ice, accompanied by an advance of its terminus. However, in the decade from 2000 to 2009, the glacier retreated 255m (840ft). The third notable feature is the laboratory beneath its surface (see panel, right).

GLACIER LABORATORY

Tunnels have been drilled in the bedrock under the Engabreen Glacier as part of a hydroelectric power scheme. At the side of these tunnels, a laboratory has been excavated under the glacier, where the ice is about 200m (660ft) thick. This has allowed researchers to install instruments that continuously record the stress on the bedrock and the speed, temperature, and pressures within the ice as it slips across the rock. The results are helping scientists develop mathematical models for predicting glacier movement.

EUROPE west
Glacier d'Argentière

LOCATION In the Savoie Alps, 15km (8 miles) northeast of Mont Blanc, France

TYPE Valley glacier

TERMINUS Terrestrial snout

AREA 8 square km (3 square miles)

LENGTH 9km (6 miles)

STATUS Retreating

The Glacier d'Argentière is one of numerous glaciers that descend from the flanks of the Mont Blanc Massif, a spectacular mountain chain that lies on the borders of Switzerland, France, and Italy. Surrounded by some of the highest mountains in the Alps, the glacier descends from a wide ice accumulation area at an altitude of around 3,300m (11,000ft). Attempts have been made to tap into the subglacial drainage of meltwater to provide hydroelectric power. To do this, tunnels were excavated under the glacier in the 1960s and a water intake put in place. The project was not entirely successful, due to changes in the course of the meltwater drainage, and the tunnels have now been closed. In 2005, a huge section near the snout of the glacier, containing some 400,000 cubic metres (11 million cubic ft) of ice, broke away from the rest of the glacier and disintegrated. Since

ALPINE PURSUITS

The glaciers around the Mont Blanc Massif are heavily used by alpine sports enthusiasts. Cross-country skiing is possible on the upper parts of some glaciers – including the Glacier d'Argentière, which is so smooth that light aircraft can land on it – although care is needed to avoid the crevasses. Other popular pursuits include snowboarding, ski-mountaineering, and ice-climbing. To facilitate this, night-time refuges have been set up in numerous, otherwise highly inhospitable, locations around the region.

then, the glacier has been in two parts. Of these, the main part terminates at a height of about 1,900m (6,200ft) at the top of a rock cliff, while lower down, a tongue of ice, covered in rock debris, continues down to a height of about 1,600m (5,200ft), which is a short but steep walk above the resort of Argentière. This lower part, which is rapidly shrinking, is occasionally replenished by avalanches of ice from the upper part.

NEW TERMINUS
Taken in 2009, this image shows the terminus of the main section of the Glacier d'Argentière.

EUROPE west
Mer de Glace

LOCATION In the Savoie Alps, 10km (6 miles) northeast of Mont Blanc, France

TYPE Valley glacier

TERMINUS Terrestrial snout

AREA 25 square km (10 square miles)

LENGTH 11km (7 miles)

STATUS Retreating

The Mer de Glace, or Sea of Ice, is so-called because of its alternating bands of light and dark ice. Although the glacier advanced 150m in the 1970s and 80s, it has since retreated over 500m (1,640ft), with a 30–40 per cent decline in the rate of flow.

MER DE GLACE, HAUTE-SAVOIE, FRANCE

EUROPE central
Aletsch Glacier

LOCATION In the Bernese Alps, 25km (16 miles) south of the Brienzer See, southwest Switzerland

TYPE Valley glacier

TERMINUS Terrestrial snout

AREA 80 square km (31 square miles)

LENGTH 23km (14 miles)

STATUS Retreating

EUROPE central
Tschierva Glacier

LOCATION In the Rhaetian Alps, close to the border with Italy, southeastern Switzerland

TYPE Valley glacier

TERMINUS Terrestrial snout

AREA 6 square km (2 square miles)

LENGTH 4km (2½ miles)

STATUS Retreating

The Tschierva is a medium-sized alpine glacier that descends steeply from a 4,049m (13,284ft) peak, Piz Bernina, on the Swiss–Italian border. The glacier is notable for its large and very clearly formed lateral moraines, which mark the glacier's furthest advance during the Little Ice Age in the 18th and 19th centuries (see p.373). Because of the Tschierva Glacier's retreat over the last 120 years or so, these moraines, which are about 40m (130ft) high, dwarf the lower parts of the glacier itself. As the glacier has retreated, it has revealed peat beds and ancient wood. Carbon dating of these samples shows that the tree-line in this region was much higher, and the glaciers far smaller, as recently as 5,000 years ago.

The Aletsch is the longest and largest valley glacier in Europe, descending from a saddle between the Jungfrau and Mönch peaks at 3,454m (11,300ft) and winding southwards towards the Rhône Valley. Along the way, it passes through the Konkordiaplatz ice plateau at the base of the Jungfrau, where it merges with other glaciers. It is up to 900m (2,950ft) deep, and the ice moves at speeds varying from about 200m (660ft) a year in the Konkordiaplatz to 10m (33ft) a year near the snout. The pattern of moraines below the snout indicates that the glacier has retreated about 5km (3 miles) since 1860.

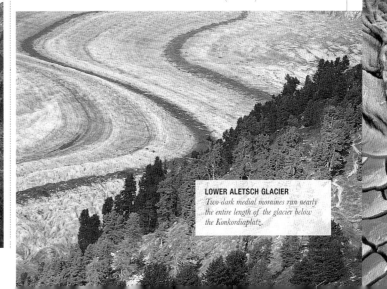

LOWER ALETSCH GLACIER
Two dark medial moraines run nearly the entire length of the glacier below the Konkordiaplatz.

LAND

LAND

Rhône Glacier

LOCATION At the head of the Rhône Valley, in the eastern part of the Bernese Alps, Switzerland

TYPE Valley glacier

TERMINUS Terrestrial snout

AREA 15 square km (6 square miles)

LENGTH 8km (5 miles)

STATUS Retreating

Recognized as the source of the River Rhône, the Rhône Glacier was once the largest in the Alps. Evidence from moraines shows that, 18,000 years ago, it reached as far as Lyons in France, more than 280km (175 miles) from its modern-day terminus. It has retreated 1,266m (4,153ft) between 1879 and 2010. About 1.5km (1 miles) wide on average, with a surface that is smooth in parts and deeply crevassed in others, the glacier was the subject of

GLACIER TERMINUS
The irregularly shaped snout of the Rhône Glacier can be seen today only by climbing up to an altitude of 2,200m (7,200ft).

one of the earliest studies into glacial ice movement. In a classic investigation, a straight line of stakes driven into the glacier was observed between 1874 and 1882. After a few years, the stakes had formed into a bow, proving that the ice in a glacier moves and that the movement is fastest in the middle.

Allalin Glacier

LOCATION In the Pennine Alps, southwestern Switzerland, close to the border with Italy

TYPE Cirque glacier

TERMINUS Terrestrial snout

AREA 8 square km (3 square miles)

LENGTH 6km (4 miles)

STATUS Retreating

Occupying the eastern flank of the Allalinhorn, the Allalin is a relatively small glacier, consisting of a bowl-shaped accumulation area at its top and a steeply descending ice-fall. In recent centuries, the glacier has been a hazard to people living nearby. Between the 16th and 19th centuries, during the Little Ice Age (see p.373), it repeatedly advanced into the nearby Saas Valley, blocking the flow of the River Saaser Vispa and creating a lake called the Gletscherrandsee. Whenever the glacier retreated again, the lake would suddenly drain in a flood that devastated the valley. Since 1900, the glacier has retreated over 1km (²⁄₃ miles). In 1965 a large piece of it broke off and cascaded into a dam construction site below, killing 88 people.

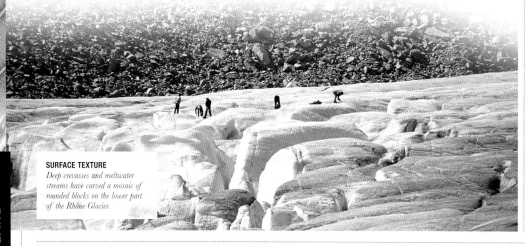

SURFACE TEXTURE
Deep crevasses and meltwater streams have carved a mosaic of rounded blocks on the lower part of the Rhône Glacier.

Kilimanjaro Ice-cap

LOCATION At the summit of Mount Kilimanjaro, northeastern Tanzania, close to the border with Kenya

TYPE Ice-cap

AREA 1.75 square km (³⁄₄ square mile)

STATUS Retreating

One of the few remaining glaciated areas in Africa is at the top of Mount Kilimanjaro (see p.131). Despite the mountain's proximity to the equator, a huge continuous ice-cap once covered most of its upper parts. As recently as 1912, the ice covered more than 10 square km (4 square miles). Since then, over 85 per cent of it has been lost, leaving just a small divided glacier inside the volcanic crater and some ice-fields on the northern flank of the peak. The ice-cap is predicted to disappear by 2060. Climate warming and greater regional aridity, with less new snowfall each year, are the most likely causes.

STEPPED ICE CLIFFS
Spectacular ice cliffs, about 25m (80ft) high, can still be seen at the edges of some of the ice fragments left on Kilimanjaro.

Bogdanovich Glacier

LOCATION Within the Kliuchevskoi volcano group, Kamchatka Peninsula, eastern Russia

TYPE Valley glacier

TERMINUS Terrestrial snout

AREA 14 square km (9 square miles)

LENGTH 10km (6 miles)

STATUS Uncertain

The Bogdanovich Glacier forms part of a large glaciated area in Kamchatka, nestling in a valley surrounded by three huge volcanoes. It slopes gently down from a height of 2,800m (9,200ft) and suffers occasional ash falls from the Kliuchevskoi volcano (see p.133).

KAMCHATKA PENINSULA
The Bogdanovich Glacier is located in the glaciated area visible just below and to the right of centre of this satellite image of the Kamchatka Peninsula.

South Inylchek Glacier

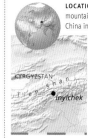

LOCATION In the Tien Shan mountains, extending from western China into eastern Kyrgyzstan

TYPE Valley glacier

TERMINUS Terrestrial snout

AREA 250 square km (96 square miles)

LENGTH 61km (38 miles)

STATUS Retreating

One of almost 8,000 glaciers in Kyrgyzstan, the Inylchek Glacier has two branches – North and South – which wind their way through separate valleys in the Tien Shan mountains before converging. The South Inylchek is one of the three longest valley glaciers in the world.

SOUTH INYLCHEK GLACIER

ASIA *south*
Baltoro Glacier

LOCATION In the central area of the Karakoram mountain range, northeastern Pakistan

TYPE Valley glacier

TERMINUS Terrestrial snout

AREA 150 square km (58 square miles)

LENGTH 50km (31 miles)

STATUS Stable

Northern Pakistan, in and around the Karakoram mountain range, contains the greatest concentration of ice in Asia, with glaciers covering more than 13,000 square km (5,000 square miles).

The Baltoro Glacier is one of the largest of these, occupying a long east–west valley running through the region. Up to 4km (2½ miles) wide in places, the Baltoro is fed by over 30 tributary glaciers, which form ice-falls where they meet the main trunk glacier. The valley walls above the glacier vary from very steep to precipitous. Much of the lower area of the glacier is covered in thick rock debris. Emerging from its snout is the fast-flowing and dangerous Braldu River, a tributary of the Indus. Unlike most Asian glaciers, the Baltoro does not seem to be in fast retreat. Between 1990 and 1997, it actually advanced slightly, and some of its tributary glaciers have displayed surge behaviour. A trek along the Baltoro provides the only possible land access to the base of K2 (see pp.110–11), so the glacier has been well-trodden by mountaineers.

EXPEDITION HIGHWAY
An expedition porter scrambles over the glacier's debris-strewn surface. Two tributary glaciers to the Baltoro can be seen in the background.

ASIA *south*
Durung Drung Glacier

LOCATION In the western part of the Zanskar Range of the Himalayas, Jammu and Kashmir, northern India

TYPE Valley glacier

TERMINUS Terrestrial snout

AREA 30 square km (12 square miles)

LENGTH 20km (12 miles)

STATUS Stable

One of the longest glaciers in the Himalayas, the Durung Drung is also one of the most accessible, from a road that crosses a pass, the Pensi-La, at 4,400m (14,435ft). Its surface consists principally of clean ice except for some thin rock debris at its snout and edges, and it has several tributary glaciers. From its deeply fissured snout arises the fast Stod or Doda river, a tributary of the Zanskar river.

ASIA *south*
Khumbu Glacier

LOCATION On the southern approach to the Mount Everest region of the Himalayas, Nepal

TYPE Valley glacier

TERMINUS Terrestrial snout

AREA 15 square km (6 square miles)

LENGTH 15km (9 miles)

STATUS Retreating

ICE FINS
These giant fin-like structures were squeezed up out of the side of the Khumbu Glacier as it was forced around a bend in its valley.

The Khumbu Glacier has two main segments. The upper segment consists of a steeply descending region of clean, deeply crevassed ice, the Khumbu Ice-fall. The world's highest glacier, this ice-fall is situated on the southwest flank of Mount Everest, immediately above the mountaineers' main base camp. At the bottom of the ice-fall,

the glacier turns past the base camp to the south, and then descends down a straight, steep-sided valley, 9–10km (5–6 miles) long, towards the Himalayan foothills. The glacier here has a relatively gentle downward slope and is covered in a thick layer of rock debris. Its snout has retreated a few kilometres since Everest was first climbed in 1953.

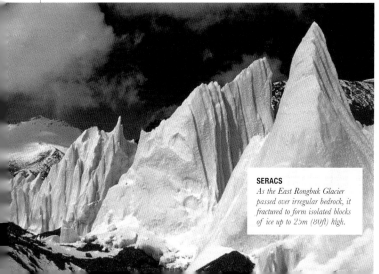

SERACS
As the East Rongbuk Glacier passed over irregular bedrock, it fractured to form isolated blocks of ice up to 25m (80ft) high.

ASIA *south*
East Rongbuk Glacier

LOCATION On the northern approach to the Mount Everest region of the Himalayas, Tibet

TYPE Valley glacier

TERMINUS Terrestrial snout

AREA 20 square km (8 square miles)

LENGTH 11km (7 miles)

STATUS Retreating

The East Rongbuk is part of a large, complex branching system of glaciers on the northern side of Mount Everest, and lies along one of the main routes

for reaching the summit from Tibet. Its upper part occupies a large arena, at an altitude of about 6,850m (22,500ft), below Everest's northeast ridge. From there, it descends in a northwesterly direction. The East Rongbuk used to merge lower down with the West Rongbuk glacier, but it now no longer does so, instead terminating at an altitude of about 5,600m (18,500ft). In common with several other glaciers in the region, the East Rongbuk has a large number of seracs, or ice pinnacles, on its surface. These can be up to 30m (100ft) high and are caused by successive fracturing of the ice as it passes over separate steep or irregular sections of bedrock. Each section produces a series of parallel cracks in the ice, and where these intersect, the pinnacles are formed.

RETREATING GLACIERS

Most of the world's glaciers have been melting and retreating for several decades, clearly due to the effects of global warming. Whatever the underlying causes of this warming (see pp.372–75), the undesirable results of glacier shrinkage are numerous – they range from acceleration of atmospheric warming due to reduced albedo (reflection of solar radiation back into space from ice), to sea-level rise and various other unwanted impacts on human life.

Thinning and retreating

Evidence that mountain glaciers are thinning and retreating worldwide comes from many different sources. These include ground observations, repeat aerial photography, and more recently satellite observations. Retreat has been occurring steadily since 1850, except for a slight slowing between 1950 and 1980 in some areas.

For some glaciers in the Americas, the cumulative losses in the past 50 years have been as high as 20,000–35,000kg per square metre, equivalent to thinning to a depth of 20–35m (65–115ft) over the whole surface of the glacier. Glaciers in the Himalayas have suffered large losses, as shown by widespread, rapid growth of lakes on the glacier surfaces. Some glaciers in Norway advanced in the 1990s due to increased precipitation but since around 2000 the trend has reversed and most are now in retreat. In Africa, glaciers that once existed on the tops of Mount Kilimanjaro and Mount Kenya are expected to disappear entirely within the next 30 to 50 years.

GRINNELL GLACIER
The view of Grinnell Glacier in Montana, USA, taken in 1940 (left) contrasts with the same view in 2006 (below). The meltwater lake has increased enormously.

HEAVY LOSSES
This graph shows cumulative losses of ice in seven regions of the world since 1960. The greatest losses have been in the Americas and high mountains of Asia.

Graph legend:
- Europe
- Andes
- Arctic
- Asian High Mountains
- NW USA and SW Canada
- Alaska and Coastal Mountains
- Patagonia

Y-axis: Average change in overall mass (1,000 kilograms per square metre)
X-axis: Year (1960, 1970, 1980, 1990, 2000)

Shrinking ice-sheets

In the past decade or so, many outlet glaciers flowing from the Greenland and West Antarctic ice-sheets have increased their flow rates, thinned, and retreated. For example, the rate of flow of the main trunk of Kangerdlugssuaq Glacier in Greenland jumped from an average of 15m (49ft) per day in the 1990s to 40m (130ft) per day in 2005. Events such as this have caused the Greenland ice-sheet to lose volume at a rate of about 150 cubic kilometres (36 cubic miles) a year since 1992. Evidence that the West Antarctic Ice Sheet (WAIS) is losing mass at an increasing rate comes from glaciers that drain into the Amundsen Sea, such as Pine Island Glacier. Recent satellite data show that these glaciers are losing mass much faster than it is being replaced by snowfall. A 2012 study estimated that the WAIS is losing volume at a rate of over 100 cubic kilometres (24 cubic miles) a year, mainly through losses at the Amundsen Sea Coast. In addition, since 1990 several large ice-shelves in Antarctica have either diminished considerably or disappeared entirely.

Dangerous consequences

Glacier melting and retreat are likely to have a number of unwelcome consequences for humans. These include sea-level rise (see p.374), loss of freshwater supply for irrigation, and loss of glacier runoff for hydropower. Melting of glaciers and ice-sheets is currently contributing about 1.5mm (1/16in) each year to global sea-level rise. This equates to a rise of about 13cm (5in) by 2100, which would cause considerable problems for some low-lying island nations. Loss of irrigation water would badly hit some countries in South America and Central Asia, such as Peru and Kyrgyzstan. A further problem is that in many parts of the world, mountain lakes formed from glacier meltwater are growing steadily larger. Such lakes may overwhelm the terminal moraines that hold them, potentially causing disastrous outburst floods down to the valleys below. Some valleys in Bhutan and Nepal have been identified as among those particularly at risk.

ICE-SHELF BREAK-UP
Part of the Wilkins ice-shelf in Antarctica is shown breaking up here during a series of major disintegration events in 2008–2009.

MELTWATER RIVER
Flowing meltwater has carved a deep, meandering canyon in the surface of this retreating glacier in the Wrangell-St. Elias National Park in Alaska.

ANTARCTICA
Antarctic Ice-sheet

LOCATION Covering most of the continent of Antarctica and extending over the sea as ice-shelves

TYPE Ice-sheet

AREA 13.7 million square km (5.3 million square miles)

STATUS Uncertain

The Antarctic Ice-sheet is by far the largest mass of ice on Earth. Its volume is over 30 million cubic km (7.2 million cubic miles), and it holds over 60 per cent of the Earth's fresh water. It weighs so much that it depresses the Earth's crust by about 900m (3,000ft). The ice-sheet consists of two parts, separated by the Transantarctic Mountains. The larger part, called the East Antarctic Ice-sheet (EAIS), covers most of the landmass known as Greater Antarctica. It is over 4.5km (2¾ miles) thick in places, and its base is mainly above sea-level. The West Antarctic Ice-sheet (WAIS), over Lesser Antarctica, has a maximum thickness of 3.5km (2¼ miles), and its base lies mostly below sea-level. The rate of ice formation is slow (Antarctica is the driest continent,

VEHICLE CONVOY
These vehicles are making their way across the ice-sheet close to the Adélie Coast of Greater Antarctica. The ridges of ice, called sastrugi, are caused by, and lie at right-angles to, the prevailing wind.

with snowfall averaging only a few centimetres per year), but once ice forms very little of it melts or evaporates while it is still part of the ice-sheet. Instead, under the force of its own weight, the ice slowly deforms and moves towards the coasts, where numerous large outlet glaciers and ice-streams carry it down to the sea. The rate of ice movement varies from less than a metre a year in parts of the ice-sheet domes, to several hundred metres a year nearer the coasts. In many places the outlet glaciers extend over the sea as ice tongues or merge to form vast platforms of floating ice called ice-shelves. Increasing fragmentation of the shelves and calving of huge icebergs causes ice streams on land to speed up. Many of the outlet glaciers draining Antarctica are immense. The largest, the Lambert, is 40km (25 miles) wide and over 400km (250 miles) long. Other notable features include the Byrd and Beardmore glaciers, which drain the

ANTARCTIC ICE-SHEET

ANTARCTIC COAST AND ICEBERG
Many icebergs form from glaciers flowing off the Antarctic Ice-sheet. The iceberg floating in the foreground is highly eroded, indicating that it has been drifting for several months.

ERNEST HENRY SHACKLETON

Irishman Ernest Shackleton (1874–1922) was one of the great Antarctic explorers of the early 20th century. In 1908–09, he and three companions walked to within just 156km (97 miles) of the South Pole before they had to turn back. After Roald Amundsen (see p.320) then Robert Falcon Scott reached the South Pole in 1911–12, he led another expedition to Antarctica in 1915, aiming to cross the continent. Unfortunately, his ship, *Endurance*, became locked in sea-ice and eventually sank. However, thanks to Shackleton's leadership, no lives were lost.

EMPEROR PENGUINS

The tallest and heaviest of all penguins, Emperors set up their breeding colonies on the newly formed sea-ice at the end of the Antarctic summer. The females lay a single egg then return to sea to feed, while the fasting males incubate the egg through the freezing winter. The down-covered chicks have to moult into their adult plumage before they can float out to sea on the ice as it melts and breaks up in spring.

EAIS into the Ross Ice-shelf, and the Rutford Ice-stream, which drains part of the WAIS into the Ronne Ice-shelf. The only ice-free areas in Antarctica are the peaks of the highest mountains and a few coastal areas. There are concerns that the ice-sheet is shrinking due to global warming – the WAIS is thought to be particularly vulnerable to accelerated iceberg-calving because its base is below sea-level. If it completely melted, it could raise global sea-level by 3.3m (10ft). A 2012 study, found that the WAIS lost about 70 cubic kilometres (17 cubic miles) of its volume per year between 1992 and 2011. The situation with the EAIS is less certain but it may also have lost some volume.

outline of lake visible by satellite as flat area on ice surface

direction of movement of ice-sheet

ice-sheet

upper layers of lake water freeze to the ice-sheet and are carried beyond the lake edge

lake buried 4km (2½ miles) beneath ice surface

bedrock

LAKE VOSTOK

The East Antarctic Ice-sheet overlies more than 360 lakes, the largest of which is Lake Vostok. Originally detected by ice-penetrating radar, the lake and any organisms in it are estimated to have been isolated for 15 million years.

ICE-CORE ANALYSIS

Ice accumulates in annual layers in ice-sheets, somewhat like the rings of a tree-trunk. By drilling down into the Antarctic Ice-sheet, extracting a long cylinder, or core, of ice, and examining how the ice changes with depth, scientists are able to find out a great deal about the Earth's past, including fluctuations in climate. The longest ice-core drilled so far provides a record that goes back 800,000 years. Tiny, trapped air bubbles reveal changes in the atmosphere, including rising levels of carbon dioxide. Changes in atmospheric pollution are also apparent in the ice-cores.

LAND

AUSTRALASIA *New Zealand*
Franz Josef Glacier

LOCATION	To the northeast of Mount Cook, in the Southern Alps, South Island, New Zealand
TYPE	Valley glacier
TERMINUS	Terrestrial snout
AREA	30 square km (12 square miles)
LENGTH	12km (7 miles)
STATUS	Retreating

Named in 1865, by a German geologist, after the Emperor of Austro–Hungary, the Franz Josef Glacier descends steeply from an altitude of 2,700m (8,860ft) in New Zealand's Southern Alps. The lower parts of the glacier used to flow through an evergreen forest near the coast. However, since 2008 the glacier's terminus has rapidly retreated, so by 2013 it only just reached below the tree-line. From the glacier's snout flows a fast and turbulent river, named the Waiho (Maori for "smoking water"; its name originates from the vapour rising from its ice-cold surface). The Franz Josef Glacier owes its existence primarily to a high rate of precipitation in the region – up to 30m (100ft) of snow falls on the glacier's ice-accumulation area every year. The glacier retreats and advances according to changes in regional climate change. Between 1983 and 2008, it advanced 1.5km (1 mile). From then until 2012, it retreated 500m (1,640ft).

GLACIAL STRIAE
Scratches like these on rocks in the valley below the glacier were caused by boulders dragged by the ice.

RAINFOREST AND GLACIERS
The combination of a temperate rainforest with large glaciers, such as the Franz Josef, flowing through it is unique to New Zealand.

AUSTRALASIA *New Zealand*
Tasman Glacier

LOCATION	Immediately east of Mount Cook, in the Southern Alps, South Island, New Zealand
TYPE	Valley glacier
TERMINUS	Lake-calving front
AREA	35 square km (14 square miles)
LENGTH	23km (14 miles)
STATUS	Retreating

The Tasman is the largest glacier in New Zealand, flowing down a long valley to the east of Mount Cook (also known as Aoraki). It is up to 600m (2,000ft) thick in places and up to 2km (1 miles) wide. It originates in a large ice accumulation area at an altitude of 2,800m (9,200ft), beneath Mount Elie de Beaumont, and two-thirds of the way down it is replenished by the Hochstetter Ice-fall. This drains an enormous amphitheatre of ice beneath Mount Cook and Mount Tasman. The upper Tasman Glacier receives regular heavy snowfalls and is smooth and relatively crevasse-free.

Further down are sections where it breaks up into a maze of crevasses, ice tunnels, and ice walls. The lower third of the glacier, which extends down to an altitude of about 700m (2,300ft), is covered in a 1m- (3ft-) thick layer of rock debris. This is the result of ice melting, which concentrates debris at the glacier's surface. At its bottom end, rapid melting since the 1960s has turned what were a few isolated craters and moulins in the centre of the glacier, and a small elongated lake along its eastern lateral moraine, into a large, melt-lake that extends for 6km (4 miles) from the glacier's terminus. The terminus itself has over the last few decades

BRAIDED STREAMS
Meltwater streams flow down a 15km- (9-mile-) long outwash plain below the glacier's terminus, converging as the Tasman River.

been retreating at an accelerating rate, thus extending the meltwater lake, which is now expected to lengthen to a maximum of 16km (10 miles) over the next several decades. The glacier has also thinned dramatically since the beginning of the 20th century. Today, lateral moraine walls almost 200m (650ft) high lie on both sides of the glacier; around 1900, the ice was above those walls. The meltwater lake at the foot of the glacier is now up to 250m (820ft) deep and maintains a steady temperature close to 0.3–0.5°C (32.5–32.9°F), largely because icebergs are continually calved into it from the glacier's terminus – a process that started in about 1991. Some of the icebergs, which are full of rock debris, weigh millions of tonnes – a particularly large calving event, in which more than 30 million tons of ice were dropped into the lake, was triggered in February 2011 by the devastating Canterbury earthquake. Occasionally, calving takes place underwater, causing icebergs to pop up in the middle of the lake. For reasons not fully understood, silt suspended in the water does not settle out, and gives the lake a uniform grey colour. A demonstration of why some glaciers carry so much rock debris inside them and on their surfaces was given in 1991, when a large part of the summit of Mount Cook broke off. Millions of tonnes of rock cascaded down the Hochstetter Ice-fall and then over the Tasman Glacier. The rubble is now being carried slowly down the glacier and will eventually be dumped into the meltwater lake.

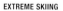

EXTREME SKIING
The upper parts of the Tasman Glacier provide one of the longest continuous ski runs in the world – about 11km (7 miles). These skiers were dropped off by helicopter.

ICY LAKE
This lake sits on top of part of the disintegrating lower end of the Tasman Glacier and is rapidly extending up the glacier.

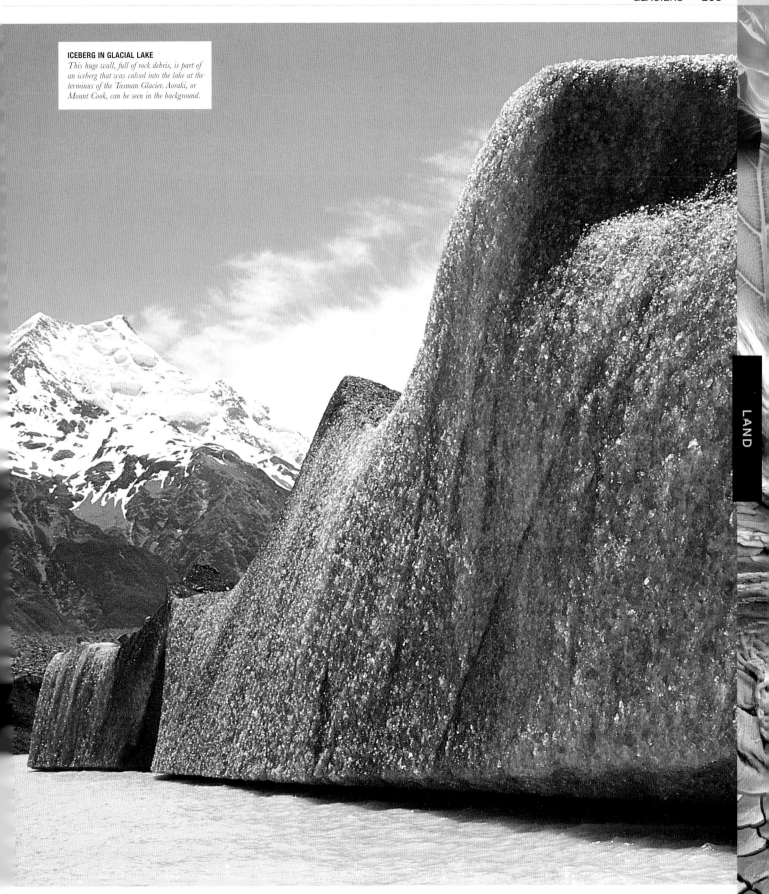

ICEBERG IN GLACIAL LAKE
This huge wall, full of rock debris, is part of an iceberg that was calved into the lake at the terminus of the Tasman Glacier. Aoraki, or Mount Cook, can be seen in the background.

LAND

SAHARA CROSSING
Air transport and roads have reduced the need for camel caravans in some parts of the Sahara, but here in Mauritania near the coastal settlement of Nouakchott they remain a vital means of communication.

DESERTS

THE TERM DESERT CONJURES UP vistas of rolling, featureless sand-dunes and intense, dry heat. While these conditions are certainly found in many places, the world's deserts are far more varied in character, with some having rocky landscapes, some occupying high plateaus, and others dominated by open, salty lake beds. Nor are deserts hot all of the time. In some "cold deserts" the winters may be snowy or frosty, in strong contrast to the hot, dry summers. The temperature range between day and night may also be marked, with temperatures falling rapidly from dusk until dawn, and sometimes even dropping below freezing. Conditions for life in a desert are challenging, with water scarce most of the time, except for occasional downpours, which can lead to destructive flash floods. Wind-blown sand and grit is another hazard in many deserts, and it also acts as a potent agent of erosion, shaping rocks and forming dunes.

LAND

Deserts

DESERTS ARE AMONG THE MOST HOSTILE places on Earth. They arise in regions that receive large amounts of sunshine, or where geographical features limit rainfall. High temperatures and dry winds quickly remove any moisture by evaporation. The dry ground becomes vulnerable to processes of erosion and weathering that shift sand and sculpt rock to produce beautiful but forbidding landscapes.

Types of Desert

Deserts have been classified in a number of different ways, but are usually defined according to their climate or their physical characteristics. Climatically, there are large differences between deserts. Subtropical deserts, such as the Sahara, have high temperatures all year and are described as "hot", whereas high-altitude or continental deserts, such as the Great Basin of North America and the deserts of Central Asia, experience cold winters and are described as "cold", although the summer temperatures may be high. Deserts may be just rocky or sandy, but several contain a mixture of surface features and textures. Where the occasional surface streams have no outlet, they evaporate, sometimes forming extensive deposits of salts. Many deserts are mainly or partly sandy, and the fine sand grains are easily moved and moulded by the wind, often into characteristic patterns or shaped dunes.

SEMI-ARID DESERT
In semi-arid deserts (right) the conditions are dry, but there is sufficient available moisture to sustain patches of vegetation.

COLD DESERT
Cold deserts are found in temperate latitudes, on high continental plateaus, and, as above, at high altitude in the rain-shadow of the Andes.

ROCKY DESERT
Many deserts are set in rocky terrain, such as the Colorado Desert shown left, where the rising sun is illuminating bare rock pinnacles and outcrops.

Weathering and Erosion

Desert landscapes are created and maintained by erosion and weathering acting over long periods. Both processes break down soft rocks into smaller particles, and sculpt hard rock formations. Erosion is the process of reshaping by moving agents, such as wind-blown sand, which scours the surface of exposed rocks and chips off small particles (see opposite). In some deserts, such erosion sculpts rounded structures called yardangs from the bedrock. They rise above the desert sands like the upturned hulls of ships. Erosion also forms pediments – gently sloping surfaces, at the foot of rocky highland areas, that are still being broken down by erosion. Sudden storms, though rare, are another major cause of erosion, since deserts tend to have little vegetation to protect their surfaces. Dry streambeds, or wadis, suddenly fill with water, and the loose gravel and sand they contain is swept away, to be deposited downstream. Weathering happens within rocks themselves – temperature variations can cause desert rocks to crack under the stress of thermal expansion and contraction. Moisture such as dew on a rock surface can also penetrate cracks, then expand or freeze, breaking the rock open. If salt water comes into contact with rock, then the growth of salt crystals within it may also crack the rock apart.

DESERT SCREE
As weathering eats into exposed rocky outcrops, a scree of boulders and stones litters the desert floor below.

SEA OF SAND
The Namib Desert in Africa is famous for the vast inland sea of majestic sand-dunes at Sossusvlei, which can reach heights of 200m (650ft).

Landforms

The processes of erosion that happen in desert climates produce distinctive small- and large-scale landforms. Large landforms include inselbergs – isolated hills that stand out above the surrounding flat desert surface, and are all that remain of long-eroded mountain ranges. Australia's Uluru (also known as Ayers Rock) is a famous example. Mesas and buttes are towering platforms topped by flat, erosion-resistant surfaces. They mark the former ground level – their surroundings eroded after their hard cap was penetrated, perhaps by an ancient stream. Gravels of various grades are commonly found in deserts, often as alluvial fans at the feet of raised plateaus or spreading over the surface of rock pavements. Gravelly or rocky surfaces with a finer material beneath are called desert pavements. The term erg, originating in the Sahara, refers to an almost sea-like expanse of sand. Flat desert basins may contain lakes, which are typically dry for part of the year, or even for many years. These are known as playas, and the soils here are usually high in a mixture of salts, mostly of calcium and sodium. Some desert rocks are covered with a black or brown glossy coating called desert varnish, which usually contains large amounts of iron and manganese oxides. How this forms is not fully understood.

DESERT VARNISH
The shiny coating found on some desert rocks is called desert varnish. In some regions the varnish has been used as a canvas for primitive rock art.

DESERT PAVEMENT
These antelope footprints in the Kalahari Desert have revealed the fine sand beneath the gravelly surface.

butte

rock pillar

rock broken down into scree

MESAS AND BUTTES
A mesa is the steep-sided, eroded remnant of a plateau, like the ones seen here rising up above the flat plain of Monument Valley, USA. A butte is simply a small mesa.

WIND-SCULPTED ROCKS
Wind is a powerful erosive force, especially if it contains sand particles. Here in Arizona, veins of calcite between bands of sandstone coloured with metal oxides emphasize the wave-like shapes of eroded sedimentary rock.

Wind and Dunes

Dunes are large accumulations of sand, forming hills, ridges, or other features in a desert landscape. Half of all dunes are linear or seif dunes – roughly parallel ridges of sand that can extend for 20km (12 miles) or more. They are a particular feature of the Kalahari and Simpson deserts. Barchan dunes are curved, with two arms trailing downwind, and are often found around the edges of sand seas. Star dunes have three or more arms, usually irregularly arranged. They can reach heights of more than 300m (1,000ft), and are found mainly in the eastern Sahara, the Namib, and in the deserts of Central Asia. Parabolic dunes are also large, with long trailing arms, and are a notable feature of the Thar Desert and many coastal dune regions. Crescentic dunes form ridges, with slightly wavy edges. These tend to form in areas with a narrow range of wind directions, and where there is little vegetation.

LAND

sparse sand

longitudinal, parallel dunes

wind direction varies slightly

LINEAR (SEIF) DUNE

variable winds

complex dune shape

STAR DUNE

constant wind direction

plentiful sand

asymmetrical dunes at right angles to wind

CRESCENTIC DUNE

BARCHAN DUNE

eddies on leeward side produce steep slip face

prevailing wind direction

horns advance more quickly than centre of crescent-shaped dune, as there is less sand to move

sand particles blown up gently sloping windward face

airflow diverted around side of dune

HOW DUNES FORM
Dune formation is a complex matter, still not fully understood, but in general dunes form where wind loses energy and drops the sand suspended within it. Wind-shifted sand soon becomes rippled, but over a longer period of time and with varied winds and textures of sand, distinctive dune shapes are created.

Water

Precipitation in deserts is scarce and unreliable. Average desert rainfall usually totals less than about 250mm (10in) a year, but in parts of the Sahara and coastal Chile, it is often exceedingly low – less than 1mm (¹⁄₁₆in) a year. Another key factor is that the dry, hot air soon removes water by evaporation, so that, even when the rains do fall, the water quickly turns to vapour, returning to the air before it can be used by animals or plants. In some deserts that experience cold winters, such as those of Central Asia, the main source of water is winter snow. Here again, availability of water is low, until the snows melt in the spring. Some coastal deserts, such as the Namib in southwest Africa and parts of the Atacama in Chile, receive moisture from fog, and this may be equivalent to as much as 130mm (5in) of rain annually. Dew is another important source of water, and if there is moisture in the air, it may form during the relatively cold, clear desert nights. In many deserts, such as the Thar on the India–Pakistan border, there are considerable stores of water underground, and these can be tapped by deep-rooted plants, and humans through drilling.

WADI
A wadi is a steep-sided watercourse, such as a stream, that was formed in an earlier, wetter climatic phase and now flows only irregularly.

WADIS IN THE YEMEN
This low-orbit satellite image of the Arabian Peninsula reveals a vein-like network of dry wadis, which are prone to flash floods after seasonal rains.

OASES

Most human activity in deserts has traditionally centred on reliable supplies of water, which guarantee plant growth for grazing livestock and enable the planting of staple crops, as well as offering drinking water. Many deserts contain large reserves of groundwater, particularly compared to surface stores, such as rivers and lakes. Sometimes, the water from these water-saturated rocks, or aquifers, comes to the surface in the form of springs. Most desert oases develop around natural permanent springs, and these produce a lush growth of plants, with palm trees a prominent feature in many regions. Even undeveloped oases provide vital supplies of water to local people, who often travel considerable distances to collect it.

SILGAU OASIS
At this oasis in the Thar Desert of Rajasthan, India, local women fill metal vessels with water and carry this precious resource back to their homes.

Animal Life

Although a desert may appear lifeless, night often reveals much activity from insects, reptiles, and small mammals in particular. These nocturnal animals avoid excessive water loss by sheltering from the heat of the day underground. Some species gain water from dew at night, or, in the case of the Darkling Beetle, from fog condensed on its body. Reptiles are perhaps the real desert specialists: they can withstand high temperatures and require little moisture, and when temperatures drop they become torpid until it warms up again. Snakes "swim" through sand by sinuous wriggling and burrow with ease, while many desert lizards use a tiptoe stance to raise themselves above the scorching surface. Large desert mammals, such as camels, are adapted for survival. Their woolly fur helps to slow down heating, and they can tolerate higher temperatures than other large mammals. They retain water by producing concentrated urine and dry dung, but can also lose large amounts of water without ill effect.

poisonous sting

exoskeleton retains moisture

claws

DESERT SCORPION
With a tough exoskeleton to help it retain moisture, this scorpion is well adapted for the dry desert climate.

SIDE-WINDING ADDER
Almost invisible, this desert-dwelling snake lies buried in the sand, waiting for a suitable victim to approach.

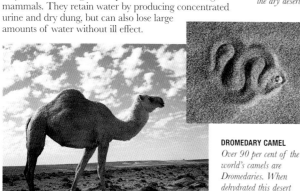

DROMEDARY CAMEL
Over 90 per cent of the world's camels are Dromedaries. When dehydrated this desert specialist can drink 50 litres (11 gallons) of water in a few minutes.

NAMAQUA SANDGROUSE
Male Namaqua Sandgrouses absorb water in their sponge-like breast feathers and carry it back to their chicks in the nest.

Plant Life

Desert plants are generally of two main types: ephemeral annuals, which survive arid conditions as seeds, and perennials, which continue to survive and cope with periods of water scarcity. The annuals grow, flower, and set seed rapidly when conditions are more suitable, such as after rare rains, and some can complete their lifecycle in as little as two weeks. The flowers are often brightly coloured and large, perhaps because potential pollinators are scarce. The perennials have various strategies for enduring drought, such as sending down deep roots to tap underground moisture, storing water in swollen tissues, as many succulents and cacti do, or by developing underground organs such as bulbs and sending out stems and leaves only when conditions allow. Many have tough, reduced leaves to reduce water loss through transpiration, and spines to resist grazing. Cacti are typical of the American deserts, and, as well as being spiny, many species are waxy or woolly to reduce water loss further. In the African deserts, various species of euphorbia occupy the same ecological niche as cacti – they are also succulent, and often spiny. Cacti and other succulents typically have large, attractive flowers, mainly pollinated by insects, although some, including the Saguaro, are pollinated by bats. In Australian deserts, the spiky spinifex grasses can play an important role in stabilizing dunes.

SONORAN DESERT IN DRY SEASON
Only the bright-red ripening fruits of the Prickly Pear Cactus stand out from the monotonous greys and greens of this parched desert landscape.

spine
(modified leaf)

waxy cuticle
retains water

water-storing
tissue

vascular cylinder
takes in water

roots

GOLDEN BARREL CACTUS
Native to the southwest USA and Mexico, this cactus sends its roots deep into the desert soil and stores water in its fleshy tissue, as revealed in cross-section. The outer cuticle helps to prevent water loss.

FOURWING SALTBUSH
The Fourwing Saltbush thrives in alkaline soils, and its leaves even taste salty. The first part of its name comes from the seed, which has four paper-like wings.

Desert distribution

The largest desert in the northern hemisphere is the Sahara. Further east, there are extensive deserts on the Arabian Peninsula, the Thar Desert in Pakistan and India, and the deserts of Central Asia, notably the Takla Makan and Gobi. In the USA, deserts are found mainly in California, Arizona, Nevada, and New Mexico, and in Mexico itself they occur in the northwest, especially in the states of Chihuahua and Sonora. The deserts of the southern hemisphere are mostly less extensive, occupying a narrow coastal belt in Chile and Peru, a swathe of southern Africa (mainly in Namibia, Botswana, and South Africa), and large patches of mainly central and western Australia.

LAND

SONORAN DESERT IN BLOOM
With the rain, the desert is transformed by the sudden flowering of ephemeral annuals, which have to bloom and reproduce in a short period.

DESERT PROFILES

The pages that follow contain profiles of the world's main deserts. Each profile begins with the following summary information:

TYPE Sandy, gravelly, stony, or rocky

AREA Surface area   **RAINFALL** Average annual rainfall

TEMPERATURE Summer maximum and winter minimum temperatures or average annual temperature

LAND

NORTH AMERICA *west*
Great Basin Desert

LOCATION	In the states of Oregon, Idaho, Nevada, Utah, Wyoming, Colorado, and California, USA
TYPE	Sandy, gravelly
AREA	409,000 square km (158,000 square miles)
RAINFALL	250mm (10in)
TEMPERATURE	Max: 38°C (100°F) Min: -7°C (-19°F)

The Great Basin is the largest desert in the USA, lying mainly in Nevada and Utah, with minor extensions into neighbouring states. Sandwiched between the Sierra Nevada range to the west and the rest of the Rocky Mountains to the east, it lies to the north of the Mojave Desert. It is classed as a cold desert, due mainly to its northerly position, but also because of its high altitude, ranging between 900m and 1,980m (3,000ft and 6,500ft)

prominent eyes with
vertical pupils

COUCH'S SPADEFOOT TOAD
This toad can survive a drought by lying dormant underground, encased within a watertight cocoon made of shed skin.

hindfeet used to burrow 1m (3ft) or more into sandy soil

above sea-level, although most of it is at 1,200m (4,000ft). The surface consists of broad valleys on a plateau, with remnants of earlier lakes. The winters are cold, but the summers are hot and mostly dry. Because it lies in the rain-shadow of the Sierra Nevada, the Great Basin receives little rain, and about 60 per cent of the precipitation falls as winter snow. The gradual melting of the snow in spring seeps into the mostly fine-textured desert soils and only then is available to the plants. The Rocky Mountains also prevent most of the continental weather fronts from reaching the Great Basin, although there are occasional summer storms. Playas (temporary lakes) are a feature of the landscape, and their salty soils support vegetation dominated mainly by Saltbush. The vegetation tends to consist of shrubs, such as Sagebush, Blackbrush, a few cacti, and the bristlecone pine, which is one of the longest-living plants (up to 4,900 years). Among these plants live animals including jackrabbits, the Great Basin Rattlesnake, and the Desert Horned Lizard. In some areas, the concentration of sodium and calcium salts is so high that no plants can survive.

HARDY PLANTS
On the low hills of eastern Nevada, the dominant vegetation is the state flower, Sagebrush. This woody shrub has narrow, grey-green leaves and small yellow blooms.

NORTH AMERICA *southwest*
Mojave and Sonoran deserts

LOCATION	Mojave: predominantly in southern California, USA, Sonoran: mostly in Arizona, USA
TYPE	Sandy, rocky
AREA	Mojave 140,000 square km (54,000 square miles) Sonoran 275,000 square km (108,000 square miles)
RAINFALL	Mojave 50–125mm (2–5in), Sonoran 250mm (10in)

TEMPERATURE Mojave Max: 48°C (119°F) Min: -13°C (8°F), Sonoran Max: 48°C (119°F) Min: -13°C (119°F)

The Mojave lies in southern California, southeast of the Sierra Nevada range. This is a high desert, lying mostly at more than 600m (2,000ft) above sea-level. Death Valley in the north is an

JOSHUA TREE
Something of a symbol of the Mojave Desert, this large member of the yucca family thrives in cooler sites on the higher ground.

exception – at 86m (282ft) below sea-level, it is the lowest place in the USA, and it is also the hottest, reaching 57°C (134°F) in 1913. The plant life of the northern Mojave resembles that of the Great Basin, with a range of drought-tolerant shrubs (the extremely arid Death Valley has very little vegetation). The Sonoran Desert lies to the south of the Mojave, at lower altitude. This is a hot desert, but has winter rains that stimulate the growth and flowering of colourful annual plants. Cacti are also a prominent feature, and include species that grow to 12m (40ft) high. Trees with nitrogen-fixing bacteria in their roots make an important contribution to the fertility of the soil. Fauna of the region include the Desert Tortoise, Desert Scorpion, and a large lizard called the Chuckwalla.

VOLCANIC CRATER
Explosive volcanic activity during the Pleistocene Epoch created this huge maar crater in the southern part of the Sonoran Desert, north Mexico.

DEATH VALLEY SALT FLATS
These strange polygons were created when high summer temperatures cracked the salt flat crust, allowing the water trapped below to evaporate and precipitate salt crystals.

NUCLEAR STORE

Yucca Mountain, which lies within an active volcanic field in Nevada, has been earmarked as a suitable site for the storage of spent nuclear fuel and waste. Having conducted a series of scientific studies over two decades at a cost over $4 billion, experts concluded that it will be safe to store the materials, which will remain highly radioactive for thousands of years, sealed in canisters in tunnels about 200–300m (650–970ft) below the surface. However, other interest groups remain concerned about the area's tectonic stability.

AT THE END OF THE TUNNEL

A specially adapted machine emerges after boring an 8km- (5-mile-) long investigative tunnel underneath Yucca Mountain.

NORTH AMERICA *south*

Chihuahua Desert

LOCATION Between the Sierra Madre mountain ranges, Mexico, extending north into the USA

TYPE Sandy, stony

AREA 453,250 square km (175,000 square miles)

RAINFALL 250mm (10in)

TEMPERATURE Max: 40°C (104°F) Min: -30°C (-22°F)

Named after the Mexican province near its centre, the Chihuahua is a high-altitude desert, lying mostly at 1,000–1,500m (3,240–4,860ft). It is the

WESTERN DIAMONDBACK RATTLESNAKE
This highly venomous viper locates warm-blooded prey with the two heat-sensitive pits above its nostrils.

largest desert in North America, sandwiched between the Sierra Madre ranges of Mexico, and extending north into New Mexico, Texas, and Arizona. Winters here are cool, with frosts occurring at night, but summers are very hot, and rain falls mainly during the summer, when it is least effective. In the lower sites, the soils are quite porous, with a calcareous base overlain by sand and gravel, and Creosote Bush and Tarbush grow here. On higher ground, such as the smooth-

sided slopes known as bajadas, the thick-leaved, frost-hardy yuccas dominate. The bajadas have a rough surface of eroded rocks, boulders, and stones, and they also trap pockets of soil, in which plants are able to thrive. Higher still, where more water is available, the vegetation changes from desert grassland to a high-altitude scrub. These varied habitats allow the Chihuahua to support a wide range of animal life, from tarantulas to bats. Desertification over the last few thousand years and grazing by large herds of cattle have led to the loss of the original desert grasslands.

TULAROSA BASIN
The shining white gypsum sand-dunes of this beautiful valley at the northern end of the Chihuahua Desert cover about 712 square km (275 square miles).

SOUTH AMERICA *south*

Patagonia Desert

LOCATION East of the Andes in the southern provinces of Chubut and Santa Cruz, Argentina

TYPE Gravelly

AREA 670,000 square km (260,000 square miles)

RAINFALL 100–260mm (4–10¼ in)

TEMPERATURE Average: 5–13°C (41–55°F)

This cold semi-desert lies in the rain shadow of the Andes, and consists mainly of a series of dissected plateaus. Precipitation falls mostly in the long, bleak winters, with frosts likely any time between June and September. The region is subject to strong, steady, westerly winds, which severely restrict the vegetation and erode the soil.

BLEACHED BONES IN THE DESERT

SOUTH AMERICA *west*
Atacama Desert

LOCATION Along the coast of northern Chile, west of the Andes, between Arica and Vallenar

TYPE Rocky, salty

AREA 105,200 square km (40,600 square miles)

RAINFALL Less than 15mm (⅗ in)

TEMPERATURE
Max: 35°C (95°F)
Min: -4°C (25°F)

The Atacama is the driest of all deserts, with some places having recorded no rain at all in living memory. It occupies a narrow coastal strip in northern Chile, averaging less than 160km (100 miles) in width, but extending about 960km (600 miles) south from the border with Peru, forming a huge strip of arid, hostile beach. Coastal fogs form in a few areas, providing moisture that allows the development of some plant communities, including cacti. On the eastern side, however, where the foothills of the Andes rise up, there is a small amount of rainfall in winter. Large deposits of salt are a feature of several parts of the Atacama, often in large salt basins, known as salars. When the salt flats flood after a storm they can support specialist invertebrates like the Brine Shrimp, whose eggs can survive several years of drought, and they are also home to large numbers of birds, including three species of flamingo. The Atacama has significant deposits of rare and valuable minerals, notably saltpetre (nitrates of potassium and sodium), which were formed in chemical reactions between the salty waters and volcanic debris. These are mined and extracted in a number of sites. The desert's dry climate, in which very few decomposing bacteria can exist, has preserved many features of archaeological interest, including Incan artefacts (500 years ago, this was the southern limit of their empire) and mummified remains from the Paleo-Indian civilization, thousands of years older.

SALT FORMATIONS
Many areas of the Atacama Desert are dominated by deposits of various salts, which sometimes accumulate into strange crystalline shapes.

SATELLITE VIEW
Snow-capped volcanoes tower above the Atacama Desert in northern Chile. This is the driest place on Earth, as the dry lake beds at top right illustrate. On the left, the Atacama Fault runs from north to south.

COPPER MINING

Many deserts contain valuable deposits of minerals, including precious metals. Chuquicamata, the world's largest copper mine in terms of size and production, lies in the Atacama, near Calama in northern Chile. First mined more than 500 years ago, blasting of terraces for most of the last 100 years has produced a huge pit, currently 2km by 3km (1¼ miles by 1¾ miles) across and 810m (2,624ft) deep.

CHUQUICAMATA MINE
As much as 600,000 tonnes of ore and waste are mined each day and removed by a fleet of over 300 trucks.

VALLEY OF THE MOON
The Valle de Luna in northern Chile is a remarkable spectacle. Here salt, sand, and varied rock formations are set against the dramatic backdrop of the Andean peaks.

ASIA west
Arabian Peninsula

LOCATION Stretching from Syria in the north to Yemen and Oman in the south, east of the Red Sea

TYPE Sandy, gravelly

AREA 2.3 million square km (900,000 square miles)

RAINFALL 50–200mm (2–8in)

TEMPERATURE
Max: 49°C (120°F)
Min: 0°C (32°F)

In many ways the deserts of the Arabian Peninsula are an extension of the Sahara (see pp.246–47), separated from it only by the Red Sea. The desert is very arid, with less than 100mm (4in) rainfall in most years, and has very hot summers and mild winters. It shares many features with the Sahara, such as large expanses of monotonous sand seas, which are difficult to traverse. Indeed, there are no permanent roads in this desert, making it impossible to drive over. The most famous expanse of sand is the Ar Rub 'al Khali, or

long tail aids balance when hopping

very long hindlegs

tall ears

JERBOA
Exclusively nocturnal, the Jerboa emerges from its burrow at night to feed on seeds, roots, and leaves. Its very long hind legs enable it to hop at speed over the desert sand – despite growing to only about 10cm (4in) long, it can leap as far as 3m (10ft).

Empty Quarter, in the south, which covers an area the same size as France. Mountain ranges run along much of the Red Sea coast and also near the Gulf coast in Oman. Some gravel plains are found in the foothills, such as in the Hajar Mountains in the east. These ranges comprise some of the finest exposed rocks of the oceanic crust and contain fossils up to 300 million years old. The gravel plains

often have a sparse cover of scrub, with species such as Ghaf, a leguminous tree that is an important source of fodder and firewood. In many places, the sands lie above oil-rich sedimentary rocks on which the famous Gulf oilfields have been developed. Parts of the landscape bear evidence of less hostile conditions in the past. These include wetter climates, savannah vegetation, and river systems. Fossil remains of animals such as elephants, hippos, turtles, crocodiles, and freshwater molluscs have been recovered. Some parts of the desert have extensive salt flats, known locally as sabkha, and here the surface has a hard crystalline crust. This is often impervious and floods easily when the rare rains occur, creating temporary salty lakes. The Arabian Peninsula is used as a flight path by birds migrating between Asia and Africa, and the coastal lagoons, desert pools, and wadis provide vital refreshment. Recent human activity has caused the extinction of many animal species and the ecoregion is now listed as critical/endangered by the World Wildlife Fund.

WILFRED THESIGER

Born in Addis Ababa, Ethiopia, Wilfred Thesiger (1910–2003) studied in England before returning to Africa to work in the Sudan. An intrepid explorer, he was one of the first Europeans to visit the Ar Rub 'al Khali, where between 1945 and 1950 he lived among the local nomadic people, the Bedu. He described his experiences in the desert in his first book, *Arabian Sands*.

ROCK AND SAND
*Remnants of a former landscape, eroded
volcanic rocks rise above the shifting sands
near the Ahaggar Massif in southeast
Algeria, at the heart of the Sahara Desert.*

Sahara Desert

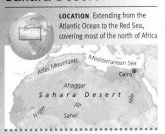

LOCATION Extending from the Atlantic Ocean to the Red Sea, covering most of the north of Africa

TYPE Sandy, gravelly, stony

AREA 9 million square km (3.5 million square miles)

RAINFALL 20–400mm (⅔–16in)

TEMPERATURE Average: 16–37°C (61–97°F)

The world's largest desert, the Sahara covers an area about the size of the USA. Although it contains many distinct geographical features, such as gravel surfaces (regs) and rocky floors (hammadas), its most famous features are the large ergs, or sand seas. Saharan sand tends to have a reddish colour, and the average thickness

PLANT LIFE
Spiny shrubs dominate the vegetation in the rocky desert on the fringe of the Sahara in Morocco. Their thorns protect them from grazing animals.

of the sand in the ergs ranges from 20m to over 100m (65–325ft). The ergs consist of dunes of different types. Some are true giants, and these megadunes may reach 300m (970ft) in height, with a crescentic, pyramidal, or linear shape. The Saharan landscape is moulded in large part by the wind. It creates the dunes and moves and shapes the sand, and also sculpts yardangs in the hammada areas, notably in Egypt west of the Nile, as well as in Libya and Chad. The overall net movement of the sands is more or less clockwise, from west to east along the Mediterranean side and the reverse in the Sahel region (the boundary between desert and savanna) to the south, where it is driven mainly by the harmattan (northeasterly) winds. In the eastern, central, and southern Sahara there is an overall loss of sand from the ergs towards the Sahel, where the sand is generally accumulating and the desert extending, partly due to overgrazing. There are regular patterns to the prevailing winds, which can be strong and persist for days, carrying sand, soil, and dust and obscuring the landscape for miles

CAMEL CARAVAN
Dromedary camels have long been domesticated in the Sahara. They eat a wide variety of plants and, given the chance, will also feed on bones.

APE OR HOMINID?

In 2002, the Sahara yielded one of its most intriguing secrets: a fossil skull found in the Djurab Desert in Chad, which some scientists are claiming to be the oldest known human-like remains. The skull, thought to be between 6 and 7 million years old, combines both ape and early human (hominid) features, such as a chimp-like brain case and a prominent brow ridge. The new species has been named *Sahelanthropus tchadensis*, after the Sahel region of the southern Sahara where the fossil was discovered.

human-like brow ridge   *chimp-like cranium*

vertical face

DESERT ROSE
The mineral gypsum is often found in sand-dunes, deposited by the evaporation of mineral-rich groundwater. The growth of the gypsum crystals is affected by the grains of sand, resulting in petal-like shapes clustered in "flowers".

around. Although vegetation is scant, oases, wadis, and other drainage channels support tough shrubs and palm trees. Several oases are found in moats, which are depressions, about 40–60m (130–195ft) deep, around inselbergs. Although there are low regions such as the Qattara Depression in northern Egypt, which is below sea-level, most of the Sahara occupies a tableland with an average altitude of 400–500m (1,300–1,600ft), and there are clusters of high ground in the centre, such as the massifs of Aïr, Ahaggar, and Tibesti. Rainfall is scant and intermittent, and some areas may see no rain at all for years at a stretch. Storms develop from time to time, but these are localized, and can cause rapid erosion. Periodic droughts and famines have occurred every 40 years or so, especially across the southern Sahara – most recently in the Sahel in 2010 – caused by changes in the surface temperatures of the North Atlantic Ocean. Animal species endemic to the Sahara show various adaptations to the intense heat. They include the Desert Horned Viper, which has strong, keeled scales that enable it to slip below the sand, where it lies protected from the heat of the day. At night, it waits in ambush for lizards, birds, and rodents. Another nocturnal desert specialist, the Fennec Fox, has furry soles that enable it to walk on soft, hot sand.

white spots warn off predators

long legs

sensitive antennae

DOMINO BEETLE
This ground beetle has unusually long legs, which raise its body clear of the hot desert sands when out hunting insects for food.

NOMADS OF THE DESERT

The Sahara is inhabited by diverse groups, known as Tuareg, who share a common language and culture. The men wear a veil, or tagilmust, that covers almost their entire face. This is for spiritual reasons, but it also protects them from the desert sand and winds. The women wear a smaller veil, and the Tuareg refer to themselves as Kel Tagilmust, or "people of the veil". Traditionally nomadic or semi-nomadic herders of goats, sheep, cattle, and camels, for centuries, the Tuareg also

provided guides for the camel caravans of the trans-Saharan traders. The advent of roads and mechanized transport means that this source of external income has largely been lost, and today many Tuareg have been forced to settle in towns.

TUAREG OF THE SAHARA
The flowing blue dress of the Tuareg men absorb more heat than white, but this creates a cooling breeze through the robes.

LAND

DESERTIFICATION

Geological evidence – such as fossilized dunes and lake beds – shows that deserts change in the course of time. They shrink when the climate becomes more moist, and expand when it turns dry. Desertification, on the other hand, is the spread of desert-like conditions through the mismanagement of land. More than a quarter of the Earth's land surface is currently affected by this phenomenon, or at risk from it.

Living with Drought

In many parts of the world, rainfall follows a predictable pattern, with only minor variations from year to year. In arid regions, the climate is much more unreliable: just occasionally, heavy rain falls in sporadic storms, but years can then go by with little or no rain at all. Wild plants and animals are well adapted to these conditions, but, for humans, they are a major problem.

Where rainfall is scant and haphazard, shifting agriculture is a widespread way of life. By keeping on the move, nomadic herders can react to changing conditions, leading their animals to places where food can be found. In regions such as the Sahel – the belt of dry land south of the Sahara – this form of shifting exploitation has continued for several thousand years, but in recent decades several factors have put extra demands on arid land worldwide. One of these is a rise in the human population. With more people to feed, animal stocks tend to rise, until they strip away vegetation faster than it grows. This overexploitation leads to soil erosion, and at that point the desertification process sets in. Left unchecked, it can cause permanent changes in the landscape, and the original vegetation is unable to recover. Desertified landscapes sometimes resemble natural desert, but the remnants of soil – and the lack of balanced ecology – often reveal its recent origins.

The Sahel is particularly vulnerable to desertification, and so is much of southern Africa. But this is not solely an African problem, nor is it confined to the developing world. It currently threatens the southern USA, from California to western Texas, the southern fringes of Europe, as well as a wide expanse of south and Central Asia.

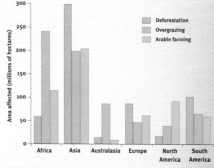

GROWING LOSSES
Desertification affects all the world's inhabited continents, but typically areas near existing deserts. In Africa, the main cause is overgrazing, while in Asia deforestation occupies first place.

Causes and Effects

Like global warming (see p.376), desertification has been the subject of intense debate among scientists. Most accept that overexploitation is a contributory factor, but opinions differ about whether it is the sole one. Some researchers think that the main trigger is local climate change, while others believe that human factors are largely to blame. The evidence is not easy to assess, because – just as with global warming – long-term trends can easily be masked by short-term change. Despite these differences, there is no disagreement about the effects: desertification can put land permanently out of action for farming.

According to the United Nations, more than 250 million people are directly affected by desertification, and 1 billion more are potentially at risk. As well as causing food shortages, desertification gives rise to other health problems, and it can displace entire populations, turning people into environmental refugees.

Combating Desertification

Despite headlines about "rolling back deserts", naturally expanding deserts cannot be stopped. Desertification, however, can be slowed and even halted by adopting measures designed to protect plant cover. Reducing livestock and planting drought-resistant trees and shrubs help to hold the soil in place, and, in regions where wood is used for fuel, they relieve the pressure on trees that grow in the wild. Paradoxically, improving the water supply does not necessarily relieve the problem. Extra wells can allow livestock numbers to increase beyond the land's carrying capacity, while excessive irrigation may increase salinity of the soil. In the Fertile Crescent, from Lebanon through to Iran, where agriculture began in the Middle East, irrigation in early recorded history damaged arid land so much that it remains unproductive today.

STORM WITHOUT RAIN
Caught by a sudden dust-storm, a group of women huddles together in Rajasthan, northwest India. Desertification is a major threat in this part of Asia (see graph).

RAINFALL IN THE SAHEL
Records from 1900 onwards show that rainfall in the Sahel is extremely variable. Since 1967, the annual departure from the long-term average has switched from being largely positive to almost entirely negative. This trend towards drier times has aggravated desertification.

DESERT FRONTIER
A giant sand-dune threatens to engulf a palm plantation in Libya, on the edge of the Sahara Desert. Since the end of the last ice age, the Sahara has advanced and receded several times.

LAND

AFRICA *south*

Kalahari Desert

LOCATION Centred upon southern Botswana, extending west into Namibia and south into South Africa

TYPE Sandy

AREA 712,250 square km (275,000 square miles)

RAINFALL 125–500mm (5–20in)

TEMPERATURE
Max: 47°C (117°F)
Min: -13°C (10°F)

Ranging in altitude from about 900m (3,000ft) to 1,200m (4,000ft), the Kalahari Desert lies between the Orange River in the south and the Zambezi River in the north. Dominated by sandy ridges, the desert is also studded with lake beds and salt pans, which are usually dry. The soil is mostly fine-grained sand – bright red in some areas, and grey in others – and the dune systems are largely fixed and inactive. Parts of the Kalahari, notably the southwest, are known for their extensive

linear dunes, many of which are partly vegetated. The vegetation is characterized by thorny scrub, with acacia trees and spiny shrubs, and the southern Kalahari, in particular, has a park-like landscape. Large herds of game, such as Springbok, Gemsbok, and Wildebeest, roam the Kalahari, moving long distances in search of occasional flushes of fresh vegetation. One of the commonest small mammals is

the Meerkat, a highly social mongoose. Expert diggers, Meerkats are well adapted to the desert, creating elaborate communal burrows in the sand. The salt pans occasionally flood after heavy rains, attracting large numbers of birds, including both the Greater and Lesser Flamingo. The Kalahari is also home to the nomadic San people, about 40,000 in number.

AFRICAN WHITE-BACKED VULTURE
This impressive scavenger is a common sight in the Kalahari, either soaring overhead on its large, broad wings or feeding at a carcass.

SANDSTORM IN THE KALAHARI
Thorn trees provide the Gemsbok (centre) and Springbok with some shelter from sandstorms, which occur frequently in dry, sandy areas.

AFRICA *southwest*

Namib Desert

LOCATION On the Atlantic coast of Namibia, extending into southern Angola in the north

TYPE Gravelly, sandy

AREA 31,000 square km (81,000 square miles)

RAINFALL 15–100mm (½–4in)

TEMPERATURE
Max: 25°C (77°F)
Min: 10°C (50°F)

A long, narrow strip mostly less than 160km (100 miles) wide, the Namib stretches some 1,300km (800 miles) along the coast of southwest Africa. This is a dramatic coastline, with high dunes bordering the sea in some places. It receives very little direct precipitation – a mere 15mm (⅗in) a year near the coast – but coastal fogs

provide much more moisture in the form of condensation. The dune systems are mostly active, with star dunes accounting for 10 per cent of all their number. Another unusual geological feature is the presence of rounded rock yardangs. Further inland, the Namib rises across a plain to an escarpment towards the east. The flora includes a large number of lichens (some brightly coloured), which are able to absorb moisture from the humid air when coastal fogs roll inland. A surprising number of animals survive in this hostile environment, ranging from small rodents to African Elephants.

WELWITSCHIA MIRABILIS
A speciality of the northern Namib Desert, this plant produces just two leaves during its entire lifespan of several hundred years.

GRANT'S GOLDEN MOLE
This unusual burrowing insectivore is found only in the Namib Desert and nearby areas. Covered in long, silky fur, it feeds on insects, such as termites and beetles, and larger prey like geckos, as above.

leaf shredded by wind

small, salmon-pink cones indicate that this is a male plant

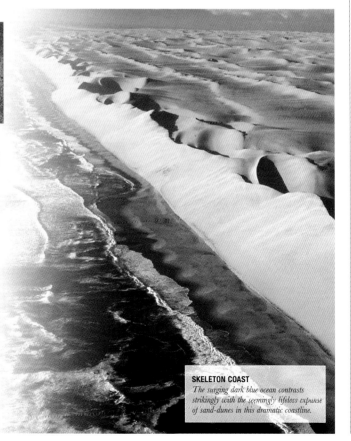

SKELETON COAST
The surging dark blue ocean contrasts strikingly with the seemingly lifeless expanse of sand-dunes in this dramatic coastline.

Thar Desert

LOCATION In the province of Rajasthan in northwest India, extending into southeast Pakistan

TYPE Rocky, sandy

AREA 446,000 square km (172,200 square miles)

RAINFALL 100–500mm (4–20in)

TEMPERATURE Max: 42°C (108°F) Min: 3°C (37°F)

needle-like leaves

plumes of small flowers

TAMARISK
This heath-like small shrub is widely distributed in the Thar and many other desert regions in Asia. Its small, scale-like leaves help it conserve water.

The Thar (or Great Indian) Desert is centred on the province of Rajasthan, extending eastwards to the Aravali Hills. The landscape is mixed, with areas of sandy or gravel plains, broken rocks, and dune systems. Although most of the dunes are fixed and inactive, there are some regions of shifting sands. Parabolic dunes are a special feature of this desert. U-shaped, with fronts 10–70m (33–230ft) high and trailing, partly vegetated, parallel arms up to 2km (1¼ miles) long, such dunes are unusual inland and are caused by

unusually consistent prevailing winds. There is a marked absence of oases, but some areas, especially in the west, have been irrigated by the River Sutlej. Vegetation is generally sparse, and tends to be dominated by tough grasses and shrubs or small trees, such as tamarisks and acacias. The Thar is one of the last haunts of the highly endangered bird, the Indian Bustard.

SAND SCULPTURES
Undulating patterns have formed along the ridge of this linear dune in the Thar Desert. Such sculpting is the result of complex interactions of sand and wind.

Kara Kum Desert

LOCATION Occupying most of Turkmenistan, east of the Caspian Sea, south of the Aral Sea

TYPE Sandy

AREA 297,900 square km (115,000 square miles)

RAINFALL 100–200mm (4–8in)

TEMPERATURE Average: -14–32°C (7–90°F)

Kara Kum means "black sands" in the language of Turkmenistan. It lies to the east of the southern end of the Caspian Sea, and west of the Amu Darya River. The landscape here is of cracked clay surfaces and crescentic

dune systems. There is normally little or no rain between May and October, and dust-storms are a frequent occurrence. Crops, such as cotton, are grown in oases and in areas irrigated by the Kara Kum Canal, which takes water about 800km (500 miles) from the Amu Darya River west across the desert to Ashgabat. Black Saxaul trees are part of the dominant vegetation here, their very narrow leaves helping to reduce water loss by transpiration. The Sand Boa snake is also especially adapted to life in the desert: it has a flat head with eyes that face upwards, enabling it to keep watch for prey even when submerged in the sand.

DESERT GRAZING
The edge of the Kara Kum Desert has enough grass in spring to support grazing animals, although the grass quickly becomes parched.

Takla Makan Desert

LOCATION North of the Kunlun Mountains in Xinjiang Province in the west of China

TYPE Sandy, gravelly

SIZE 327,000 square km (126,250 square miles)

RAINFALL 40–100mm (1⅗–4in)

TEMPERATURE Max: 38°C (62°F) Min: -9°C (16°F)

The Takla Mahan is the second largest shifting sand desert in the world. Surrounded on three sides by snow-capped mountains, it lies

between 500m and 2,000m (1,600ft and 6,600ft) and is internally drained by the Tarim river system, which flows into the Lop lowlands, depositing gypsum and salty sand there. The numerous rivers that enter the desert are fed by snowmelt from the mountains and are fringed with reeds, tamarisks, and even groves of poplars. However, away from the rivers, the plant life is sparse, with drought-resistant shrubs, such as Saxaul, helping to stabilize the dunes.

DESERT MOUNTAINS
An inhospitable mixture of stony plains and areas of shifting sand-dunes, this desert is aptly named: Takla Makan means "place of no return".

LAND

ASIA north

Gobi Desert

LOCATION Stretching across southern Mongolia and the north of China as far as the Great Wall

TYPE Stony, gravelly, sandy

AREA 1.3 million square km (500,000 square miles)

RAINFALL 10–250mm (²/₅–10in)

TEMPERATURE Max: 45°C (113°F) Min: -40°C (-40°F)

The largest desert in Asia, the Gobi takes its name from the Mongolian word for desert. To the north it grades into steppe, and stretches to the Altai Mountains in the west, while its southern limit is set by ranges such as the Qilian Shan, forming part of the northern rim of the Plateau of Tibet. The landscape ranges from rocky massifs to wide valleys and plains, but very little of the Gobi is covered by sand. The central part consists of stony pavement, with sparse vegetation. It is extremely arid in the west, with no surface groundwater. Most rain falls during the summer, and the annual rainfall gradually diminishes across the region from about 250mm (10in) in the east to 10mm (²/₅in) in the west. The flora of the Gobi lacks the spring ephemeral annuals of many other deserts, probably because winter and spring here are very dry. One of the most ecologically important plants of the Gobi is Saxaul, a hardy, almost leafless woody shrub which is resistant to drought, and which grows as scattered clumps in the desert. Saxaul grows to 2–4m (6¹/₂–13ft) in height, and it can survive even where the soil is sandy and unstable, helping to prevent further erosion. The shrub forms groves or woods on some of the adjacent mountain slopes, although in many places it is threatened by being overused for

BACTRIAN CAMELS
Bactrian (or two-humped) Camels are native to the deserts of Central Asia and have long been domesticated, although about 300 still roam wild in a protected area of the Gobi Desert.

firewood. The sandy areas of the Gobi are home to the Long-eared Desert Hedgehog and small rodents such as the Dwarf or Desert Hamster. Several large mammal species are also found here. The last remaining wild Bactrian Camels roam the desert, mainly protected in a reserve in the Southern Altai area (above), and wild asses still live in the Gobi (below left), as do small herds of Blacktailed and Mongolian Gazelles. The world's only desert-dwelling bear, the Mazaalai (or Gobi Bear) is also found in the Altai region, but it is critically endangered. Reptiles endemic to the desert include the Gobi Gecko and the Tatar Sand Boa. There is increasing desertification of the Gobi, especially along its southern edge, with grasslands being overwhelmed by dust storms as a result of increasing human activity, including deforestation and grazing.

GRAVEL DESERT
Gravel covers large areas of the Gobi Desert. Most of the central regions, such as this area in China, are so arid that vegetation is extremely sparse and grazing animals must travel long distances to find adequate supplies of food.

ASIATIC WILD ASS
The Khulan is a subspecies of Asiatic wild ass, which is the most horse-like of asses. It lives in the desert and desert steppes of Mongolia, particularly in the Gobi, in herds of up to 500 animals.

LIVING WITH THE GOBI

Mongols are the indigenous semi-nomadic people of the Gobi Desert region. Mongol tribes once herded their grazing animals (sheep, goats, cattle, and camels) over a wide area of the desert and steppe country, moving camp several times a year to avoid using up the desert's limited resources. They depended almost entirely on these animals, which yielded milk, sour cream, and yoghurt, as well as meat, skins, and wool. The Mongols also domesticated wild horses, using them to round up their flocks. The herdsmen and their families live in a type of lightweight, easily transportable tent, called a *ger*, which has a wooden frame and traditionally is covered in animal skins and woollen felt.

BEASTS OF BURDEN
Camels are the favoured means of transport for the Mongols, and they are also sheared for their thick wool.

GOBI GURVANSAIKHAN
The Gobi Gurvansaikhan ("Three Beauties")
National Park protects a large area of desert in
southern Mongolia, seen here with the eastern
Altai Mountains in the background.

AUSTRALASIA *Australia*
Great Sandy Desert

LOCATION In the north of Western Australia, extending as far as the Indian Ocean in the northwest

TYPE Gravelly, sandy

SIZE 340,000 square km (130,000 square miles)

RAINFALL 250–300mm (10–12in)

TEMPERATURE
Max: 42°C (108°F)
Min: 25°C (77°F)

More than 40 per cent of Australia's land is classed as desert, and the Great Sandy Desert is one of the largest, occupying a vast, almost uninhabited area towards the north of Western Australia, southwest of the Kimberley Plateau. This is the only Australian desert to extend to the coast, forming the long sweep of Eighty Mile Beach where it meets the Indian Ocean. The sands here, as in most of Australia's deserts, are bright red, due to a coating of iron oxides on the sand grains. Rainfall is relatively high, with most rains arriving in the form of occasional thunderstorms. Daytime temperatures are in the range 38–42°C (100–108°F), and the short winter is warm, with temperatures averaging 25–30°C (77–86°F). The heat means that much of the moisture is lost by evaporation and is therefore not available to plants, with spinifex grasses among the few able to survive. Reserves of oil have been found beneath the sands and gravels of this desert, but these have yet to be exploited on any large commercial scale.

GREATER BILBY
Also known as the Rabbit-eared Bandicoot, this highly endangered marsupial digs a burrow up to 3m (10ft) long and shelters there during the day, emerging at night to feed on seeds, fruit, and insects.

INTRODUCED SPECIES

Dingoes were introduced to Australia from Southeast Asia some 3,500 years ago. They are regarded as a pest because they attack livestock, and they have been excluded from parts of Australia by the erection of fences. Along with more recently introduced species such as foxes and domestic cats, Dingoes pose a severe predatory threat to small native marsupials such as the Greater Bilby (see above). Another alien pest, the European Rabbit, has displaced native fauna and destroyed vegetation, permanently changing the landscape in arid areas.

DINGOES
Now readily associated with Australian fauna, the Dingo is probably descended from the Indian Wolf.

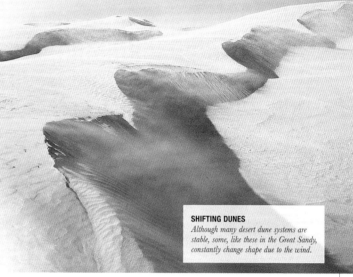

SHIFTING DUNES
Although many desert dune systems are stable, some, like these in the Great Sandy, constantly change shape due to the wind.

AUSTRALASIA *Australia*
Tanami Desert

LOCATION In the centre of the Northern Territory, north of Alice Springs, Australia

TYPE Rocky, sandy

SIZE 37,500 square km (14,500 square miles)

RAINFALL 200–400mm (8–16in)

TEMPERATURE
Max: 42°C (108°F)
Min: 25°C (77°F)

Lying to the east of the Great Sandy Desert, the Tanami Desert contains a large area of red sandy plains, with intermittent ranges of hills. The plant life here is a combination of tough spinifex grasses and small shrubs, such as Saltbush, as well as occasional Spiny Acacias. A surprising feature of the Tanami, and the rest of Australia's arid interior, is the presence of Dromedary Camels, which were brought over by the early colonizers of the outback as pack animals. They became redundant with the arrival of motor transport, and today's feral herds are their descendants. The Tanami also has the largest population of the endangered Rufous Hare Wallaby. In the early 20th century, the discovery of gold led to the establishment of small mining communities, but the harsh, dry climate made economic extraction difficult.

AUSTRALASIA *Australia*
Simpson Desert

LOCATION In the southern Northern Territory, western Queensland, and northern South Australia

TYPE Sandy

SIZE 145,000 square km (56,000 square miles)

RAINFALL 175–200mm (7–8in)

TEMPERATURE
Max: 50°C (122°F)
Min: 0°C (32°F)

Located in central Australia, the Simpson Desert is the world's largest sand dune desert, famous for its parallel red coloured dunes, growing to 38m (125ft) high and up to 120km (75 miles) long. Summer daytime temperatures average 35–40°C (95–104°F), and the winters are mild (18–23°C/64–74°F) with occasional night frosts. The rainfall is low and irregular, usually from thunderstorms, and the dominant vegetation is spinifex grasses and shrubs.

ULURU
Rising 348m (1,142ft) above the desert floor, Uluru (also known as Ayers Rock) is a vast mass of 300-million year old sandstone.

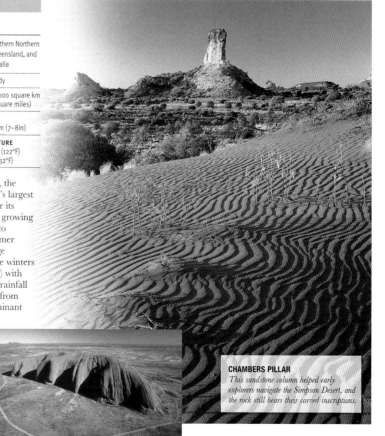

CHAMBERS PILLAR
This sandstone column helped early explorers navigate the Simpson Desert, and the rock still bears their carved inscriptions.

AUSTRALASIA *Australia*
Gibson Desert

LOCATION In the centre of Western Australia, extending eastwards into Northern Territory

TYPE Gravelly, sandy

SIZE 156,000 square km (60,250 square miles)

RAINFALL 200–250mm (8–10in)

TEMPERATURE Max: 42°C (108°F) Min: 18°C (64°F)

The Gibson Desert lies between the Great Sandy and Great Victoria deserts. It takes its name from the Australian explorer Alfred Gibson, who attempted to cross it in 1874, but perished while searching for water. The landscape is mainly one of undulating beds of gravel, with areas of red sandhills, known as buckshot plains. Some parts are rocky, and in others

ALEXANDRA'S PARROT
This nomadic, slender bird is unusual among parrots in being adapted to survive in the desert. Its diet consists mainly of small seeds gathered from the ground and tree blossoms.

inselbergs protrude from flat plains. In the west lies Lake Disappointment, a large salt lake that attracts great numbers of waterfowl. Daytime temperatures in the Gibson average 33–42°C (91–108°F) in summer, and 18–23°C (64–73°F) in winter. The rains are very unreliable in this region, coming mostly from the occasional thunderstorm, of which there are some 20 to 30 each year, and the vegetation is patchy. Alongside the usual spinifex grasses are mulgas (species of acacia, or wattle), which lend a green tint to the landscape, and colourful flowers such as the Yellow Coneflower appear after the rains. Red Kangaroos are a common sight.

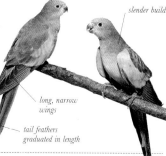
slender build / *long, narrow wings* / *tail feathers graduated in length*

AUSTRALASIA *Australia*
Great Victoria Desert

LOCATION In the southeast of Western Australia, extending east to the centre of South Australia

TYPE Sandy, gravelly

SIZE 338,500 square km (150,000 square miles)

RAINFALL 150–250mm (6–10in)

TEMPERATURE Max: 40°C (104°F) Min: 18°C (64°F)

Protected as a World Wildlife Fund Ecoregion, this desert borders Western Australia and South Australia, north of the Nullabor Plain. Mainly a sandy desert with extensive dune fields, it also includes gibber plains, on which the soil is covered by closely packed pebbles that are often glazed by iron oxides. They usually lack vegetation, although ephemeral annual species may appear after rains. In addition to the more familiar types of sand-dunes, another kind, known as lunette dunes,

also occurs here. Lunette dunes are a special feature of the Australian deserts, especially in the south. They are crescent-shaped, consist mostly of clay, and are formed at the downwind edges of temporary lakes from dry, wind-blown lake-floor sediments. Although the summers are hot, winter frosts are not infrequent in parts of the Great Victoria Desert, especially on the higher ground. But the winters are short, with temperatures rising quickly again by late September. Many parts of this desert have sufficient moisture to support open woodland, with eucalypts, common mulgas, and an understorey of grass hummocks. The Great Victoria Desert is

STURT'S DESERT PEA
The floral emblem of South Australia, this striking plant is able to survive the extremes of the inland desert climate.

famous for its reptiles, which number over 100 species, with geckos and skinks being particularly diverse. Many of the reptiles are active during the day, such as the bizarre Thorny Devil, whose camouflaged pattern makes it hard to spot against the stones and sand of the desert. Equally striking are the Parentie and Gould's Goanna, both of which can exceed 1.8m (6ft) in length. Little farming takes place here, although there are several Aboriginal reserves and some sheep and cattle ranches around the more fertile edges.

THORNY DEVIL
Despite its fearsome appearance, the desert-dwelling Thorny Devil is harmless to all except ants, and relies on its sharp spines for protection.

SAND DUNES AFTER RAIN
Although arid, the Great Victoria Desert can support scattered bushes along temporary watercourses, as here.

LAND

EASTERN GIBSON DESERT
Rock-strewn hills, spinifex grass, and mulgas are characteristic of the eastern Gibson Desert.

CLOUDFOREST
*Epiphytes such as Spanish Moss clothe
the damp branches and trunks of trees in
this Costa Rican cloudforest, providing
niches for a vast number of species.*

FORESTS

FORESTS COVER 30 PER CENT of the Earth's land surface and provide some of the richest of all habitats, offering an abundance of sites for plant germination as well as food and shelter for a wide range of woodland animals. Different types of forest are found in different regions of the world, from the dark boreal forest (taiga), which extends to the edge of the Arctic tundra, to the lush mixed broadleaf forests of temperate North America, Europe, and Asia and the dense rainforests of the humid tropics.

Forests also play a vital role in the global water and carbon cycles: in improving air quality, and in preventing soil loss through erosion. They were central to early human evolution, and even today the rainforests, in particular, are still home to many native peoples. Now, many of the world's natural forests are threatened with destruction as land is cleared for housing, roads, timber, or agriculture, and some forests survive only in inaccessible areas or in enclaves on protected sites.

LAND

Forests

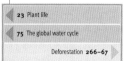
FORESTS ARE CATEGORIZED in various ways, usually according to the dominant type of tree. An important distinction is that between broadleaved and coniferous (usually needle-leaved) trees. Most coniferous trees are evergreen, which means that they retain a full complement of leaves throughout the year, but many broadleaved trees are also evergreen, and a few coniferous trees (such as larch) are deciduous. Deciduous trees shed all their leaves during the part of the year that is unfavourable for growth. This is the cold winter in temperate latitudes, but in the seasonal tropics, it may be the regular dry season.

Forest Vegetation

Forest vegetation is dominated by the major tree species that form a high canopy. Conifers and their allies bear naked seeds. They have needle-like, scale-like, or blunt linear leaves, usually with a resinous coating that helps them survive cold winters. Broadleaves bear ovules in an ovary that develop into seeds only after fertilization. They have a variety of larger leaf shapes to better collect sunlight to drive photosynthesis. Coniferous forests have less ground vegetation than broadleaved forests, since they are darker, and the resinous shed leaves produce an acid soil. In deciduous forests, the shed leaves form a nutrient-rich humus that fosters many more ground-cover plants. These are often adapted to grow and flower quickly in the spring, taking advantage of the brighter conditions before the trees above unfold their foliage.

BROADLEAF

CLUSTER OF CONIFER LEAVES

LEAF TYPES
Broadleaves offer a large, flat surface area for light-gathering and gaseous exchange. Narrow conifer leaves reduce water loss by transpiration.

CONIFEROUS CONES
The "fruit" of most conifers, such as this Norway Spruce, is a cone, consisting of woody scales that turn brown when ripe.

cluster of small flowers

FLOWERS AND LEAVES

compound leaf with five distinct leaflets

spiky husk splits when it hits ground, releasing nut

shiny brown seed (or nut)

SEEDS

BROADLEAVED FLOWER AND SEED
Many broadleaved trees, like Horse Chestnut, have showy flowers to attract pollinators such as insects, and some produce large, edible seeds.

Tropical Forests

Growth is rapid and lush in many tropical forests, and their complex structure offers niches for a multitude of animals and plants other than trees. Mature tropical rainforest is a multi-layered habitat. The canopy is composed of trees whose crowns almost meet. Beneath it lies a more broken understorey of young trees, and an often-dense ground cover of saplings and undergrowth. Tall trees whose crowns stick out above the canopy are known as emergents. In many tropical rainforests, the moisture levels remain high year-round, whereas in others the rainfall is seasonal, as in the forests of Southeast Asia, where the monsoon brings sudden high levels of rain. Some tropical forests are dry, such as those of eastern South America.

EMERGENTS

CANOPY

UNDERSTOREY

GROUND LAYER

RAINFOREST STRUCTURE
Distinct layers can be seen in a mature rainforest. The mid-level canopy is overtopped by lone emergent giants, and there is a loose understorey beneath.

RAINFOREST CANOPY
The dense canopy of almost interlocking crowns is clearly visible in this Madagascan tropical forest.

LAND

Temperate Forests

Temperate regions contain a wide variety of forest types. Many temperate forests are broadleaved deciduous, especially where the winters are hard, as in continental Europe, eastern North America, and many parts of eastern Asia. In such forests, there is a huge contrast between the forest in summer, at the height of the growing season, and in winter, when all the leaves have been shed and have accumulated on the forest floor. In China, Japan, and Korea, evergreen broadleaved trees are more common in the temperate forests, and sometimes form mixed stands with conifers. However, as these parts of the world have long been settled, many of the original forests have been destroyed, at least in part, and their rich, fertile soils used for agriculture. The remaining temperate broadleaved forests are nearly all managed in one way or another, although some are protected and are being allowed to revert to a more natural state.

SUMMER AND AUTUMN
Deciduous forests change dramatically with the onset of autumn, when the trees lose all their leaves in a short time.

yellow pigment from chloroplast remains

CHANGING LEAVES
As they die, some leaves change colour from green to yellow, orange, or red, following the breakdown of the chloroplasts that contain their chlorophyll.

green colour from chlorophyll

Coniferous Forests

There are several different kinds of coniferous forest, but the most extensive, and the best known, are the boreal forests of northern North America and northern Eurasia (taiga). These are dominated mainly by evergreen coniferous trees, such as species of spruce, pine, and fir, although larches, which are deciduous, are a prominent feature of some areas. Coniferous forests are also commonly found in many mountain regions, where they tend to develop above the highest levels of broadleaved woodland, with spruces and pines being the main trees present. An unusual type of coniferous forest is found in the high-rainfall coastal zone of the Pacific Northwest of North America. This temperate rainforest boasts several very tall species, such as Douglas Fir and Coast Redwood, while California's coniferous forest is home to the famous Giant Sequoia.

SUMMER AND WINTER
In northern or mountain coniferous forests, the trees retain a full covering of needles through the harshest winters. In fact, individual leaves are shed and replaced, but not all at the same time.

GREEN AND GOLD
Larch is an unusual conifer in that it is deciduous. Here, in France, its beautiful autumn colours stand out against the dark green of the evergreen conifers.

LAND

NORTH AMERICA *north*

North American boreal forest

LOCATION Extending from central Alaska, USA, in the west to central Labrador, Canada, in the east

TYPE Boreal forest

AREA 6.25 million square km (2.4 million square miles)

Boreal forest is one of the largest global biomes, covering more than 16 million square km (over 6 million square miles). It dominates much of northern North America, covering one-third of Canada's landmass. It is a counterpart to the Eurasian boreal forest or taiga (see p.270). The climatic conditions under which the boreal forest develops are generally cool and humid, with very cold winters, lasting from seven to nine months. Snow covers the ground

BLACK SPRUCE
Here, in the northern boreal forest of Alaska, scattered Black Spruces tower above the willow scrub. This is the dominant tree in the open woodlands at the forest–tundra edge, from Alaska, across Canada to Newfoundland.

for much of the year, often into the summer months. Coniferous trees, such as Black and White spruce, are well adapted to survive such rigorous conditions, and they dominate the North American boreal forest. The drooping branches shrug off the weight of heavy snow, and the waxy needles allow good control of water loss. Although conditions may be wet and boggy in summer, for much of the year water is frozen and therefore largely unavailable to the trees. To the north of its range, the boreal forest changes gradually into Arctic tundra as conditions become too harsh to support tree growth. The tall, closed coniferous forest thins out, with the trees becoming shorter (the three-month

growing season limits their height to 3–4.5m/10–15ft) and scattered. To the south, the transition is to prairie grassland in the central part of the belt, and to mixed forest in the west and east. Many of the forests in the north are known as lichen woodland, as lichens dominate the ground flora, replacing the mosses that are more common further south where water is more available. The Alaskan forest is the most varied, largely due to the influence of the mountain ranges and oceans on the climate. In the central region around the Canadian Shield, the forest is more uniform, with spruces tending to dominate, while in the east Balsam Fir is a key species. Around the Great Lakes, the boreal forest is mixed, with deciduous species including Sugar Maple and Yellow Birch. Quaking

ALASKAN FOREST
The deep northern boreal forests are broken up in some places by rivers, streams, and boggy lakes, as here in Alaska.

Aspens thrive on poor soil and are often found at montane levels. Mammals of the forest include the Canada Lynx and its prey, the Snowshoe Hare (trapping records have revealed their population cycles to be closely linked), and the Northern Flying Squirrel. Great Grey Owls are found here and also in the Eurasian boreal forest, and feed on voles, mice, and small birds.

QUAKING ASPENS
The slender white trunks of Quaking Aspens add to the beauty of the boreal scenery here, in British Columbia.

CANADIAN BOREAL FOREST
Mount Robson Provincial Park in British Columbia protects over 2,170 square km (840 square miles) of unspoilt boreal forest close to Canada's highest peak.

NORTH AMERICA *west*

Pacific Northwest rainforest

LOCATION Along the Pacific Coast from the Gulf of Alaska to northern California, USA, and Canada

TYPE Temperate rainforest

AREA 1.2 million square km (480,000 square miles)

These remarkable forests, the only temperate rainforests in the northern hemisphere, occupy a relatively narrow strip along North America's northern Pacific Coast. The rainfall is high (800–3,000mm/31–118in, mostly between October and March) and is supplemented in some areas by coastal fogs. These conditions are ideal to support the growth of some of the giants of the plant kingdom, notably conifers such as the Redwood, which can grow to over 110m (355ft) in height, Douglas Fir, Sitka Spruce, and Western Hemlock. Douglas Firs

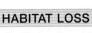

WESTERN HEMLOCK
These shade-tolerant trees thrive in low light conditions, enabling them to slowly replace pioneer tree species, such as the Douglas Fir.

dominate in the Coast Ranges, Olympic Mountains, and northern Cascade Range, up to about 1,000m (3,300ft). Redwood forests are a feature of northern California and southern Oregon.

HABITAT LOSS

The Northern Spotted Owl is found only in the natural coniferous forests of the Pacific Northwest, where its habitat is under threat from logging activities, to which it is particularly sensitive. Each pair of owls requires about 11 square km (4 square miles) of unspoilt old-growth forest or heavily wooded canyons for successful breeding. Its population is now estimated at about 5,000 pairs in the USA and a mere 25 pairs in British Columbia (it is Canada's rarest bird).

HIGH RAINFOREST
Washington State's famous temperate rainforest receives a staggering 3,350mm (132in) of rain a year, resulting in lush vegetation, including many epiphytes.

SURVIVING THE WINTER
The thick, spongy bark of the Giant Sequoia, seen here in Sequoia National Park, protects the tree from the winter cold as well as from the effects of fire.

NORTH AMERICA *west*

California coniferous forest

LOCATION Along the western slopes of the Sierra Nevada, central California, USA

TYPE Evergreen temperate forest

AREA 43,600 square km (16,800 square miles)

These forests are famous for being the home of the world's largest tree species (in terms of bulk), the Giant Sequoia, or Big Tree. This is a high-altitude community, found mainly between 1,400m and 2,300m (4,540ft and 7,450ft). There are about 75 separate groves where the Giant Sequoias grow, often associated with White Fir, Sugar Pine, and Incense Cedar. Although not quite as tall as the Redwood or Douglas Fir (see above), Giant Sequoias may grow for over 2,000 years and reach almost 100m (325ft) in height. Fire is an important ecological factor in these coniferous forests. The cones of Giant Sequoias require the heat of forest fires before they can open to shed their seeds. Fire also burns the soil surface,

GENERAL SHERMAN
This, the largest living Giant Sequoia, is about 2,200 years old. It is 84m (275ft) tall and 9m (30ft) across at its base.

exposing the mineral-rich layers lying beneath, which are essential for seedling growth. The fully grown trees are protected by their spongy bark, up to 45cm (17½in) thick, which gives them an asbestos-like insulation from fire damage. Other trees in the region include Douglas Fir and Ponderosa and Lodgepole pines, with Engelmann Spruce and Bristlecone Pine at subalpine levels. The latter species is very slow-growing and includes the world's oldest-known living plant specimen – referred to as the Old Man, it is nearly 4,770 years old. Mammals of these forests include Black Bears and Mountain Lions (Cougars).

YOSEMITE
Equally famous for its meadows, mountains, and waterfalls, Yosemite National Park also boasts three groves of ancient Giant Sequoias.

LAND

DEFORESTATION

Humans have had a greater impact on forests than on any other land habitat. Forest clearance began with the development of agriculture, 10,000 years ago, and since then nearly a quarter of the world's tree cover has disappeared. Deforestation is now occurring most rapidly in the tropics, where it poses a major threat to plant and animal life and to the atmosphere, but the temperate world has actually lost far more of its natural forest cover – the difference is that it happened longer ago.

Temperate Deforestation

Trees are the natural vegetation across most of the temperate world, apart from arid areas. Deciduous forest once covered much of Europe, eastern Asia, and eastern North America, while coniferous trees grew on mountains and in the far north. That coniferous forest is still largely intact, but almost all deciduous forest has been cut down. In Europe, clearance was gradual, but in North America it was more abrupt. When European colonists arrived in the early 1600s, forests stretched from the Atlantic coast to the Mississippi. By the mid-1800s, most of this had gone.

Forest cover is now generally stable. In North America, the deciduous forest has partially regenerated, because land fell into disuse when cereal farming moved westwards, onto the open plains. But in most parts of the temperate world, remaining forests are managed as a resource. This is particularly true in the coniferous zone, where an area is totally cleared of trees and then replanted, a practice known as clear-cutting. As a result, natural "old growth" forest – with its varied wildlife – is becoming increasingly rare.

In the American northwest, conservationists have waged a long campaign to save the virgin coniferous forest that remains. In western Australia, a similar struggle centres on the region's unique eucalypt forests, which contain some of the continent's tallest and oldest trees.

1950 **1985** **2000**
2005 **2010** **2020 (projected)**

▨ Forest area

BORNEO TREE LOSS
Borneo's rainforests are 130 million years old, the oldest in the world. But, since the 1985 alone, the proportion of the island covered by forest has dropped from 73.7 per cent to 44.4 per cent.

clearance for cropping by local people. Global demand for timber is a major pressure, too. In Borneo in the 1980s and 1990s, up to 240 cubic metres of wood were being taken from every hectare (3,400 cubic feet per acre). This compares with 23 cubic metres (812 cubic feet) in the Amazon. Rainforest soils are generally poor, so the cleared ground is often unproductive when used for agriculture. Despite many initiatives to protect it, tropical rainforest continues to disappear. At least half its original area has been cleared, and a further quarter may vanish by 2050.

Mangrove Forests

As well as rainforests, the tropics are home to mangroves – trees that grow in the zone between high and low tides. Mangrove forests develop on muddy shores, and, depending on local topography, they can be narrow and ribbon-like or they can reach far inland. They stabilize the coast, and they are also important breeding grounds for molluscs, fish, and wetland birds.

Mangrove wood is used for timber and charcoal, and in some parts of the tropics it is an important and sustainable resource. In recent years, the world's mangrove forests have suffered large-scale clearance, mainly to make way for aquaculture (see p.345). Mangrove removal has a direct impact on fisheries, and it also weakens the coast's natural defences against hurricanes and typhoons. However, commercial pressure means that these unique ecosystems are disappearing even faster than forests on land.

HISTORY IN THE HILLS
Scotland's Southern Uplands were once covered with natural forest. Centuries of deforestation, followed by recent replanting, have created the landscape that exists today.

Tropical Deforestation

In populous parts of the tropics, such as India and southern China, most of the original tree cover was cleared several thousand years ago, and remaining trees are now heavily exploited as a source of fuel. But in the humid equatorial belt, deforestation began in earnest only in the mid-20th century, and it is now happening at an unprecedented rate, especially in rainforests.

In some regions, the principal cause is agricultural. In Borneo, for instance, much of the continuing loss of forest cover can now be blamed on the growth of both palm oil plantations and

COASTAL RETREAT
Scarlet Ibises use mangroves as overnight roosts and as a place to raise their young, from Venezuela southwards to Brazil.

LAND

TREE HARVEST
In Canada, trees are usually removed by completely clearing an area. Although efficient, such clear cutting harms wildlife and accelerates erosion.

EUROPE AND ASIA *north*

Eurasian boreal forest

LOCATION Stretching from western Scandinavia, across northern Europe and Asia to the Pacific Ocean

TYPE Boreal forest

AREA 8.75 million square km (3.4 million square miles)

Part of the world's second largest biome and one of the least disturbed by human activity, the Eurasian boreal forest, or taiga, extends over 10,000km (6,210 miles) from Scandinavia to the east coast of Russia. It is broadest in Siberia, where it stretches from 49°N to 72°N. In Europe, the main tree species is Norway Spruce, although Scots Pine dominates in some parts of the boreal forest here, especially in the more oceanic west. Further east, Siberian Spruce, Siberian Fir, and Siberian Stone Pine also occur. Although evergreen conifers cover large stretches of the boreal forest, deciduous trees flourish in some areas, often mixed with the conifers. These trees include larch, birch, alder, and rowan, with larch prevalent in a vast expanse of the Yakutiya region of north-central Russia. Towards its northern limit, the taiga starts to thin out, with trees more widely spaced or restricted to sheltered sites such as valleys, and eventually the trees give way to tundra vegetation. To the south, the taiga grades into mixed woodland or, further east, into steppe habitats. In Russia, the northern taiga is interspersed with expanses of bogs and marshland, where

impeded drainage produces conditions too wet for forest. Dwarf shrubs such as Bilberry, Cranberry, and Crowberry flourish here. The trees of the boreal forest survive very harsh conditions, with winter temperatures in Siberia plunging to -60°C (-76°F). These mainly dense, dark forests tend to have a rather sparse ground flora but abundant mosses and lichens. The taiga still has stable populations of mammals such as Sable and Eurasian Brown Bears, and typical birds include Capercaillie and Siberian Jays.

WOLVERINE
This powerful member of the weasel family is found in both boreal forest belts. It takes a wide range of food, from eggs and birds, to lemmings and berries, and can even kill reindeer.

SIBERIAN BIRCH FOREST
Silver Birch is especially prevalent at the interface between the taiga and tundra. Birch forest is less dense than coniferous forest, and the light reaching the forest floor encourages a thick layer of herbs to develop.

BOREAL FOREST, FINLAND
The autumn colours of birch, Finland's national tree, brighten the landscape of the boreal forest in Lapland. Birch rapidly colonizes disturbed soil, and often grows near rivers and lakes.

NENETS

The Nenet people, who number about 10,000, live in the northern boreal forests and tundra of Siberia in Russia, where they herd Reindeer, on which they depend for food, clothing, tools, and transport. Each summer, they move north with the Reindeer herds to fresh grazing lands in the tundra as it becomes free of ice, and then return to the protection of the taiga during the autumn and long winter. The Nenet have perfected the art of exploiting the harsh environments of the Siberian boreal forests and adjacent tundra. Their diet of Reindeer meat is supplemented by sea and river fish, seals, and wildfowl. However, in the face of increased links with modern society, the Nenet are now struggling to retain their traditional lifestyle.

TAIGA
These mammal tracks are preserved in snow beneath a stand of tall conifers in the Russian boreal forest. In many areas, snow covers the ground for several months.

LAND

AFRICA central

Central African rainforest

LOCATION From the coasts of Cameroon, Equatorial Guinea, and Gabon to Uganda and Burundi

TYPE Tropical rainforest

AREA 1.9 million square km (1.2 million square miles)

The rainforests of central Africa account for more than 80 per cent of the continent's rainforest, but 2 per cent of this has been removed by human acitvity since the 1990s. The forest is centred on the basin of the Congo River (see p.178). The rainforests of the Democratic Republic of Congo (DRC), in particular, are the richest in the whole of Africa, with about 11,000 plant species, including relatives of impatiens and begonias, and over 400 species of mammal, such as the Bonobo and African Forest Elephant. The trees include valuable timber species such as Sapele, Iroko, and African Mahogany.

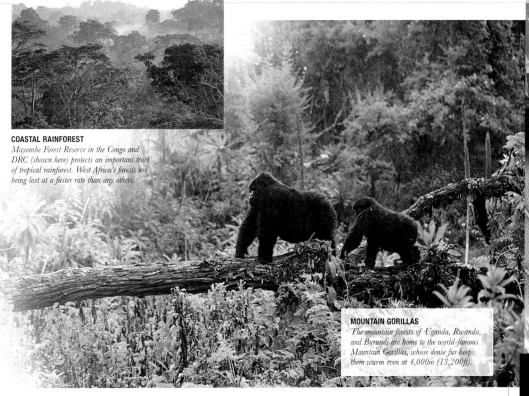

COASTAL RAINFOREST
Mayombe Forest Reserve in the Congo and DRC (shown here) protects an important tract of tropical rainforest. West Africa's forests are being lost at a faster rate than any others.

MOUNTAIN GORILLAS
The mountain forests of Uganda, Rwanda, and Burundi are home to the world-famous Mountain Gorillas, whose dense fur keeps them warm even at 4,000m (13,200ft).

AFRICA southeast

Madagascan rainforest

LOCATION On the Masoala Peninsula in the northeast, and on hills in the east, Madagascar

TYPE Tropical rainforest

AREA 38,000 square km (14,670 square miles)

Most of Madagascar's rainforests lie on the eastern side of the island and are now restricted to a narrow, broken strip following the hills just inland from the coast. Some of the best-preserved of the lowland forests are on the Masoala Peninsula in the northeast. The canopy

leaf-shaped body

fused toes for gripping branches

prehensile tail

PARSON'S CHAMELEON
This chameleon lives mainly in trees, is slow-moving, and so relies on camouflage to avoid predators.

of the forest is low (about 25m/81ft) and, in addition to hardwood trees such as ebony, there are many palms, as well as epiphytes including orchids and ferns, with 80 per cent of the plant species being endemic. However, due to illegal logging, the forest was listed in 2010 as a World Heritage Serial Site in danger. Of the 300 species of reptiles identified, 95 per cent are endemic, including two-thirds of the world's chameleons. Madagascar is renowned for its lemurs, which are found only there and on some nearby islands. Those species that inhabit the rainforest include the Ruffed Lemur (see p.261) and the nocturnal Aye-aye. Over 500 species of Madagascar's plants have medicinal uses, most famously the Rosy Periwinkle, which is now used worldwide for treating some types of childhood leukaemia.

MASOALA NATIONAL PARK
This reserve, covering about 2,175 square km (840 square miles), protects Madagascar's largest remaining rainforest, as well as nearby coral reefs.

ASIA east

Asian mountain mixed forest

LOCATION In eastern China, from Shaanxi Province to the Pacific coast and in southern Japan

TYPE Deciduous temperate and evergreen temperate forests

AREA 1.9 million square km (760,000 square miles)

The mixed forests of Asia tend to be restricted to mountain sites, partly because much of the lowland has been cultivated. In China's Sichuan Province, the forests consist of a mixture of needle-leaved evergreen trees such as hemlock and spruce, with many broadleaved deciduous trees such as birch, maple, and cherry. In the Qin Ling Mountains the forests are largely of oaks, pines, and firs. A notable feature of these forests is the abundance of bamboo in the understorey. In Japan, the mountain forests contain Japanese Beech and Cedar, while at higher altitudes conifers such as Nikko Fir dominate, along with Erman's Birch.

BAMBOO FOREST
Bamboo forests are found in several parts of China, notably in the east. In some areas, the bamboo is cropped to provide a wide range of products, from poles to food and medicine.

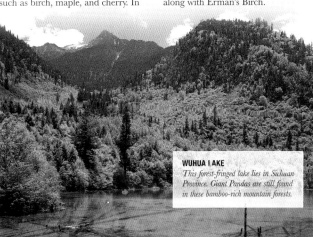

WUHUA LAKE
This forest-fringed lake lies in Sichuan Province. Giant Pandas are still found in these bamboo-rich mountain forests.

LOWLAND RAINFOREST IN BORNEO
Occasional tall, emergent trees rise above the general level of the canopy in this rainforest, while the gap created by the river encourages rapid growth of young trees and climbers.

Indonesian rainforest

LOCATION From the island of Sumatra in the west to Papua New Guinea in the east

PACIFIC OCEAN

Borneo
Jakarta
New Guinea

INDIAN OCEAN

TYPE Tropical rainforest

AREA 1.43 million square km (540,540 square miles)

Indonesia's extensive rainforests form about 10 per cent of the world's forest, but some 1,000 square km (386 square miles) were being removed each year by logging, until 2010, when a moratorium on new logging was imposed. With more than 500 mammal species, around 1,500 bird species, 1,000 reptiles and amphibians, and 20,000 plant species, they are also some of the richest habitats in existence. In lowland areas, a mixed rainforest usually develops below about 950m (3,100ft). Typically this has three main layers of trees, of up to 100 different species. Many belong to the family Dipterocarpaceae, which is virtually absent from the tropical forests outside Asia. About 18m (60ft) tall, with trunks that are branch-free for most of their length, many trees rise into the canopy, a few overtopping it as emergents. Many species flower during the same season, having been free of flowers for several years. The ground vegetation is made up of young trees, shrubs, palms, and ferns. The palms are more diverse than anywhere else in the world, with 975 species, but the largest family are the orchids, numbering 6,500 species. Some plants that grow here are remarkable, such as the Rafflesia (see below). Swamp forests are widespread in Indonesia, occurring where the ground is waterlogged for much of the year, such as close to rivers that are prone to flooding or on wet, peaty ground. Many of the coasts have mangrove forests in the tidal zones, and these show a transition towards inland rainforest. Above about 950m (3,100ft), montane forest develops. Here the trees are mostly less than 15m (50ft) tall and have smaller, more leathery leaves. Such habitats are rich in epiphytes, including mosses, ferns, orchids, and lichens. Cloud and mist often form, and it is this aerial moisture that supports the epiphytes.

ORANG-UTANS

The orang-utan, one of our closest relatives, uses its long arms and large hands to help it clamber through the tangled tropical forest.

LAND

MANGROVE FORESTS
Thriving in marine or brackish mud around many tropical coasts, some species of mangrove produce "knees" (pneumatophores), special aerial growths that bring air into the root tissues.

RAINFOREST FIRES

Fires are a major threat, even to moist rainforest, and Indonesia has suffered badly, both from natural fires and from those started deliberately as an aid to logging operations or for clearing trees to make way for alternative land-use. Once a forest fire has taken hold, particularly in dry conditions, such as those of the drought in 1997, the proximity of the trees allows it to spread rapidly, destroying not only the trees themselves but virtually all the associated wildlife.

FIGHTING THE FIRE
This villager is attempting to douse a brush fire in Kalimantan, the Indonesian part of Borneo, in 1997.

petals resembling rotting flesh attract insects

centre of flower releases carrion-like scent

RAFFLESIA ARNOLDII
This species produces a single flower that is larger than that of any other plant. The flower of one individual weighed 11kg (23lb) and measured 1m (3ft) in diameter.

ASIA northeast

Northeast Asian mixed forest

LOCATION From northeast China, through Korea, southeast Russia, and northern Japan

TYPE Deciduous temperate and evergreen temperate forests

AREA 3.2 million square km (1.2 million square miles)

A typical example of this type of mixed forest is that found on the foothills of the Sikhote-Alin' Range in Ussuriland, southeast Russia. It is mostly composed of Cedar Pine, Black Fir, and local species of spruce, ash, linden, maple, and walnut. Lush undergrowth includes plants such as wild vines and ginseng. Mammals include Musk Deer and, in some parts, the rare Siberian Tiger.

LOWLAND FOREST, USSURILAND, RUSSIA

ASIA southeast

Southeast Asian rainforest

LOCATION In Burma (Myanmar), Laos, Thailand, peninsular Malaysia, Cambodia, and Vietnam

TYPE Tropical rainforest

AREA 1.7 million square km (655,000 square miles)

Like those of Indonesia (see p.273), the rainforests of mainland Southeast Asia are dominated by dipterocarp trees, which account for 40 per cent of the understorey and about 80 per cent of emergents. The tallest trees reach heights of 40–50m (130–162ft). The valuable timber tree Teak is native to Burma, Thailand, and Laos, where it is usually found mixed with other trees. But logging has greatly reduced the natural stands, and Teak plantations in various Asian countries, Africa, and the Americas now help to meet

MONTANE RAINFOREST
The forests surrounding Thailand's highest peak, Doi Inthanon, range from tropical to a more temperate cloudforest towards the summit.

RAJAH BROOKE'S BIRDWING
Both sexes of this large butterfly feed on flowers, and the males (shown here) often drink from wet mud on the forest floor.

distinctive contrast of green on black base

jet-black body

elongated forewing typical of birdwing butterflies

LOWLAND RAINFOREST
These tropical trees in southern Thailand have typically straight trunks, branching mainly towards the crown.

the incessant demand. In peninsular Malaysia, the rainforests contain large numbers of rattans. These palms are harvested for thatching, matting, and basketry materials, and are a source of dyes and medicines. Many familiar tropical fruits originate from the Southeast Asian forests, such as bananas and mangoes, and also durian.

AUSTRALASIA New Zealand

New Zealand mixed forest

LOCATION Throughout New Zealand's South Island, from the coast to submontane levels

TYPE Deciduous temperate and evergreen temperate forests

AREA 110,000 square km (44,000 square miles)

Temperate forests still cover a large area of New Zealand's South Island. Common trees include Southern and Silver beech and members of the podocarp family, long-lived conifers that were widespread in the Mesozoic Era but which today are mostly confined to the southern hemisphere. Deciduous trees such as Tawa and Kamahi often dominate in the forest canopy, and these tend to be overshadowed by tall podocarps, such as Kahikatea, Rimu (or Red Pine), and Totara.

COASTAL FOREST
New Zealand has large areas of well-preserved coastal lowland forests, as here in Catlins, in the far south of South Island.

AUSTRALASIA Australia

Australian eucalypt forest

LOCATION In northern, eastern, southwestern, and southeastern Australia, including Tasmania

TYPE Evergreen temperate forest

AREA 1.49 million square km (575,000 square miles)

Eucalypt forest is scattered through various regions of Australia, but not in the interior, which is too arid for tree growth. Australia has about 450 species

JOSEPH BANKS

Englishman Joseph Banks (1743–1820) was one of the great botanical explorers and collectors. Aged 25, he joined James Cook's expedition to the South Pacific on the *Endeavour*. In 1770, they landed in eastern Australia, where Banks amassed a vast collection of botanical specimens then unknown to Europeans. Appropriately, Captain Cook named their landing place Botany Bay.

of eucalypt, nearly all of which are evergreen. Different species dominate in different areas: Karri in the north and southwest; Sydney Blue Gum in the east; and Australian Mountain Ash in the southeast. Fires are frequent during dry weather, and most gum trees have fire-resistant bark. They can also regenerate rapidly from seed or by sending up suckers. Koalas spend nearly all their lives up in the trees in the forests of east Australia, feeding on gum leaves at night. One of the

BLUE MOUNTAINS
The Blue Mountains, to the west of Sydney, get their name from the bluish haze created by sunlight filtering through a mist of eucalypt oil released by the gum trees covering their slopes.

smallest possums, the Honey Possum, is only found in the forests of the southwest. The eucalypt forest is being threatened by plant dieback disease, alien species, and human activity, with 15,000 square km (580 square miles) cleared between 2000 and 2004.

OLD-GROWTH RED GUM TREES
Many species of eucalypts shed old bark as they grow, revealing lighter new bark underneath, as seen in these old red gums in Victoria.

AUSTRALASIA *Australia*

Northeast Australian rainforest

LOCATION In the coastal ranges of northeast Queensland, from Cape York south to the Connors Range

TYPE Tropical rainforest

AREA 10,500 square km (4,050 square miles)

The largest expanse of Australia's remaining tropical rainforest is found between Cooktown and Townsville, centred on Cairns. The forests are best developed on the eastern slopes of the coastal ranges, where the average annual rainfall is highest, at more than 1,500mm (59in). The canopy is uneven, varying from 20m to 40m (65ft to 130ft) in height, and the undergrowth features clambering vines and epiphytes, as well as Walking Stick Palms, ginger, and aroids. The trees include valuable timber species such as Queensland Maple, kauri pines, and Red Cedar (though logging is now illegal in much of the forest), and strangler figs. At the highest altitudes, over 1,000m (3,300ft), the trees are shorter, and these cloudforests have a dense growth of ferns and mosses. Australia's geographical isolation means that it has a high number of ancient and unique species, and Queensland's tropical rainforests account for much of the country's biodiversity. About 20 per cent of Australia's cycads (see p.23) are found here, as is Idiot Fruit, a primitive flowering plant that originated 120 million years ago. Two species of tree kangaroo, Lumholtz's and Bennett's, live in the rainforest, along with many other endemic mammals, birds, reptiles, and frogs.

LUMHOLTZ'S TREE KANGAROO
This nocturnal marsupial is a highly agile climber, using its cushioned, rough-soled feet to cling to branches and its long tail as a counterbalance.

SATIN BOWERBIRD
To attract the female, the glossy black male builds an elaborate bower on the rainforest floor, which it decorates with any blue object it can carry in its beak.

DAINTREE RAINFOREST
This rainforest, a major part of the Wet Tropics World Heritage Site created in 1988, clothes the coastal hills near Cairns and stretches right down to the sea.

ABOVE THE CANOPY

Skyrail is a cableway near Cairns that runs for 7.5km (4⅔ miles) from the base of the MacAllister Range to Kuranda, a village high up in the rainforest. There are 114 gondolas, from which tourists can gaze down at the forest and its inhabitants with the minimum of disturbance. There are also two stops where the cableway descends through the canopy and people can get out and walk through the forest on boardwalks.

FAST-FLOWING STREAM
This stream is in the Daintree rainforest, North Queensland. The forests in this area contain 41 per cent of Australia's freshwater fish species.

LAND

SEASONAL FLOODING
Waterlilies bloom near the mouth of the River Limmen, which lies in the northeast of Australia's Northern Territory. This river has extensive areas of seasonally inundated floodplains along its banks.

WETLANDS

WETLANDS ARE FOUND ALL OVER the world, in places where drainage of water is impeded or in areas adjacent to the floodplains, deltas, and estuaries of large rivers. A wetland is any waterlogged or flooded terrestrial area that has a covering of water plants, either rooted or free-floating. The water is often just 1m (3ft) deep. Not all wetlands are flooded all the year round – for example, some wetlands occur in areas that are seasonally flooded by rivers; others form where spring meltwater cannot drain away because of underlying permafrost. Wetlands are highly important ecosystems, supporting a wide variety of specially adapted plants and animals, most notably vast numbers of water birds. They may act as reservoirs of water for nearby human populations, and are also important in many regions as a source of fish and for recreational activities. Many of them are increasingly threatened by encroachment – with large areas being drained for housing or agricultural use – and also by pollution.

Wetlands

WETLANDS CAN BE DIVIDED INTO freshwater wetlands, where the water is mainly derived from rainfall, and saltwater wetlands, which are generally coastal and influenced by sea water. Inland saltwater wetlands occur where evaporation has concentrated salts in the surface layers of the soil. Many freshwater wetlands occur at lake and river margins, especially along the floodplains of lowland rivers, and soil saturation can be highly seasonal.

FOSSILS IN PEAT

Bogs preserve material because wet peat contains little oxygen and so slows down the processes of decay. The peat bogs of northern Europe, particularly those in Denmark, have yielded some remarkably well-preserved human bodies, about 2,000 years old, still with their hair, skin, and fingernails intact. These include the remains of the man shown here, thought to have been the victim of ritual sacrifice.

Freshwater Wetlands

The main types of freshwater wetland are fens, bogs, swamps, and marshes. Fens and bogs, known collectively as mires, are habitats rich in wet, peaty soils. Bogs receive water from rainfall alone, and form acid peat. Fens receive groundwater as well as rainfall – they are generally wetter, and form neutral or alkaline peat. Mires are most widespread in temperate regions with high rainfall, as in the north and west of North America and Europe. They also occur at high altitudes if conditions are cool and damp. There are many gradations between fens and bogs, with mixed mires or intermediate mires occurring in some areas. The terms swamp and marsh classify wetlands by the plants that grow in them – a swamp is a wetland forest, while a marsh is a wet grassland.

WICKEN FEN
This wetland reserve in Cambridgeshire protects a vital remnant of the once widespread fens of eastern England.

PEAT CUTTING
Large areas of Ireland are covered in bogs, especially in the west, as here in County Clare. The peat is traditionally cut, dried, and used for fuel, but is a non-renewable resource.

aquatic vegetation takes root in shallows | impervious bedrock | accumulating mud
lake clay

WETLAND SUCCESSION
Freshwater wetlands often occur on peat bogs, which form as lakes are infilled by sediment. In the first stage of this process, mud collects on an impervious lake bed.

trees grow on new peat | fen peat collects and fills up lake

INTERMEDIATE STAGE
Fen peat develops above the lake mud as the partly decomposed remains of plants, such as sedges and rushes, gather under the influence of mineral-rich (alkaline) groundwater.

bog-mosses | bog peat

PEAT BOG
As fen peat fills the lake, the surface is isolated from alkaline groundwater, and slowly becomes more acidic. This encourages the growth of bog-mosses, whose remains gather as bog peat.

Saltwater Wetlands

Most saltwater wetlands occur at the interface of land and sea, where fresh and salt water mix. A range of habitats forms where large rivers with wide floodplains braid to create extensive deltas. These include brackish (slightly salty) and saltwater lagoons, and salt marshes with salt-tolerant vegetation covering the rich estuarine mud. In warm climates, salty lagoons are often managed by people as a method of salt production. In the tropics, mangrove swamps are often found in tidal creeks and gullies. Mangrove trees germinate fast in the mud, their stilt-like roots stabilizing the soil and allowing the plants to survive tidal sea-level changes. Saltwater wetlands also occur inland, frequently in arid regions, and even in some deserts, where intermittent flooding creates temporary water bodies.

SALT MARSH
Salt marshes develop in flat, coastal regions that are regularly flooded at high tide, such as here in the Chincoteague Inlet, USA.

Plant Life

Wetlands present a variety challenges and opportunities to plants. Many aquatic or marsh plants have light, spongy stems and leaves, adapted to transport atmospheric oxygen to the roots, allowing the plant to keep respiring. Some, such as Water Hyacinth and Water Fern, also have waxy or hairy leaves, which resist waterlogging. By contrast, salt-marsh plants often display features shared by desert plants, such as a thick cuticle and narrow leaves. Salt water is not easily absorbed by plants (as salt solutions tend to draw water out of plant tissues by osmosis), so many salt-marsh plants suffer effective drought conditions, at least some of the time. Some plants growing at the edges of creeks, ponds, or lagoons, such as reeds, are held above the water by woody stems and can survive short-term changes in water level.

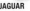

bright, open trap attracts insects

trigger hair near hinge of trap

teeth interlock to close trap

VENUS FLYTRAP
Insects caught in this plant's leaves provide essential nutrients that are rare in the soils of the eastern USA, where it grows.

SPHAGNUM MOSS
This fast-spreading inhabitant of bogs and fens grows half-submerged. Its decomposing remains form many types of peat.

MARSH MARIGOLD
The Marsh Marigold, which is common in temperate freshwater wetlands, produces brightly coloured flowers in spring and summer.

Animal Life

Fish and many aquatic invertebrates thrive in wetlands where there is sufficient water available, and in turn they provide food for a host of other animals, most notably a wide range of water birds. Herons and egrets stalk their prey in shallow water, ducks filter-feed at the surface or dive for food, while waders are adept at snatching invertebrates at or just below the surface of the wet mud. A large number of reptiles, including crocodiles, alligators, and freshwater turtles, are at home in wetlands. Grass snakes often swim in search of frogs, and tropical wetland species include the world's largest snake, the Anaconda. The mammals have produced many wetland specialists, especially among the rodents, such as beavers, Muskrats, and Capybaras. Larger herbivores that are at home in wetlands include the Asian Water Buffalo and hippopotamuses.

ATLANTIC MUDSKIPPER
Mudskippers are a unique fish that can climb out of water, using its fins to grasp.

JAGUAR
The Jaguar's preferred habitat is swamps or seasonally flooded forests. It is a strong swimmer, and its diet includes Capybaras, fish, and crocodiles.

COMMON BLUE DAMSELFLY
Damselflies are voracious aerial predators as adults, but the long juvenile stage of their life is spent underwater.

LAND

SEASONAL GATHERING
Wetlands such as Botswana's Okavango Delta burst into life in the wet season, when herds of game such as these Burchell's Zebras gather.

WETLAND PROFILES
The pages that follow contain profiles of some of the world's main wetlands. Each profile begins with the following summary information:

TYPE	Marsh, bog, fen, swamp, mire, delta, or lagoon
WATER	Fresh, acid fresh, brackish, or salt
AREA	Surface area

LAND

Pantanal

LOCATION In the Mato Grosso and Mato Grosso do Sul states of Brazil, extending into Bolivia and Paraguay

TYPE Swamp, marsh

WATER Fresh

AREA 129,500 square km (50,000 square miles)

VICTORIA WATER LILY
This magnificent aquatic lily has large floating leaves, about 1–2m (3–6ft) in diameter, which can support the weight of a child.

At around 13 times the size of the Everglades, the Pantanal is the world's largest and most biologically diverse freshwater wetland. However, it now has critical/endangered status because of wildlife poaching, the contamination of its waters by pesticides, and gold-mining effluent. A low-lying floodplain with rich alluvial soil, the Panatanal occupies about one-third of the basin

CAPYBARAS
The Capybara is at home on land and in water. Its ears, eyes, and nostrils are set on top of the head, so it can remain alert while swimming.

of the upper Paraguay River. It is a dynamic ecosystem governed by the annual flooding of the river, for which it acts as a sponge. Each year the waters rise by several metres, transforming a vast area of dry grasslands and forests into temporary swamps, islands, pools, and water channels. Floating aquatic plants, such as Water Hyacinth and Water Ferns, often carpet the water, in which piranhas, caimans, and anacondas are to be found. Caranda Palms grow on the flooded land, while on the higher ground the mixed forest includes fig trees and Acuri Palms. The Pantanal is home to the endangered Jaguar, the Capybara – the world's largest rodent – tapirs, and Capuchin and Howler monkeys. Birds include the rare Hyacinth Macaw, and there are thousands of species of butterfly.

MARSH AND FLOODED FOREST
This aerial view shows the complex of inter-related habitats that make up the Pantanal, with vegetation-covered waterways cutting between forested embankments.

Llanos wetlands

LOCATION Centred upon the River Orinoco and its tributaries in western Venezuela

TYPE Swamp, marsh

WATER Fresh

AREA 10,000 square km (3,860 square miles)

The Llanos is a term used to describe the huge expanse of savanna plains that stretch across Colombia and Venezuela from the Andes to the Orinoco Delta. Within this region, the Llanos wetlands comprise large areas of swamps and seasonally flooded savanna around the River Orinoco (see p.169) and its tributaries. The heaviest rains fall in May, at the end of the dry season, causing the rivers to overflow and transform the surrounding forests and grasslands into temporary wetlands. These support about 70 species of water birds, including around 90 per cent of the world's population of the endangered Scarlet Ibis.

SCARLET IBIS
This brightly coloured bird breeds in treetop colonies, often over water, and feeds in flocks in lagoons, swamps, and estuaries.

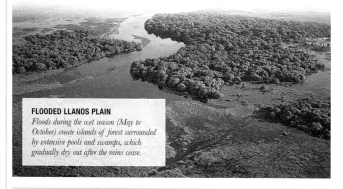

FLOODED LLANOS PLAIN
Floods during the wet season (May to October) create islands of forest surrounded by extensive pools and swamps, which gradually dry out after the rains cease.

Flow Country

LOCATION In the counties of Caithness and Sutherland in the far north of Scotland

TYPE Bog

WATER Acid fresh

AREA 4,000 square km (1,540 square miles)

The Flow Country is a landscape of huge, rolling peatlands in the extreme north of Scotland, and it contains some of the best-developed blanket bogs in the world. Blanket bogs are wet peat formations that hug the contours of the land and which grow very slowly, as little as 1mm (¹⁄₂₅in) a year, under the influence of a cool, wet climate. Sphagnum mosses, which ultimately create and sustain the bogs (see p.279), thrive, and ridges, hummocks, and small pools are rich in a variety of other plants.

BOGBEAN
The white flowers of Bogbean stand out from the dark, peaty waters in which it grows.

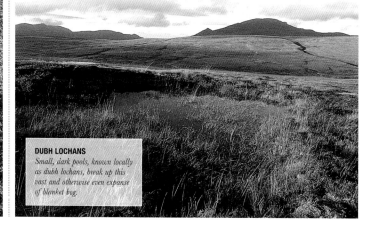

DUBH LOCHANS
Small, dark pools, known locally as dubh lochans, break up this vast and otherwise even expanse of blanket bog.

Biebrza Marshes

LOCATION Centred on the Biebrza River Valley, in Suwalki, Lomza, and Bialystok provinces, northeast Poland

TYPE Bog, fen, marsh

WATER Fresh

AREA 1,000 square km (390 square miles)

Biebrza Marshes • Bialystok
• Warsaw

The Biebrza Marshes are a complex mixture of habitats, including river channels, lakes, extensive marshes, wooded areas on higher ground, and peat bogs that are some of the best preserved in the world. Many parts show a classic succession from riverside fen through raised bog,

GREAT SNIPE

This wader breeds on the Biebrza Marshes, where male birds gather in groups called leks to attract females by posturing and making croaking and bubbling calls.

grading into wet woodland. These varied habitats support a wide range of wildlife. The birds found here include many species of waders, gulls, terns, and both White and Black storks. Mammals include wetland specialists such as Elk, Muskrats, and Eurasian Beavers.

WATER MEADOWS

The water meadows of these marshes are regularly flooded, and the resulting rich alluvial soil supports a varied community of wetland plants.

Hortobágy

LOCATION Centred on the upper reaches of the River Tisza on the Great Hungarian Plain, Hungary

TYPE Lagoon, marsh

WATER Fresh, salt

AREA 115 square km (44 square miles)

Hortobágy
Budapest • Danube / Tisza

Hortobágy lies in the Hungarian steppe region, known as the Puszta, an area consisting mainly of semi-arid grassland. Regular flooding by the River Tisza has turned part of this otherwise dry landscape into a wetland

COMMON CRANES

Large flocks of these migratory birds often stop over at Hortobágy to feed on insects, frogs, and plants.

encompassing streams, lakes, lagoons, salt marshes, and river-valley woodland. The region became Hungary's first National Park in 1973 and a World Heritage site in 1999. Now recognized as one of the world's best wetland reserves, it hosts over 300 bird species. Regulation of the flow of the River Tisza has reduced flooding, and the park authorities now use canals to preserve some of the wetland habitats.

REED-BEDS

The lakes of Hortobágy are fringed by dense beds of reeds, which are used for shelter by ducks, herons, and other birds.

LAND

Camargue

LOCATION Lying within the Rhône Delta, on the northwest shore of the Mediterranean Sea, France

TYPE Lagoon, marsh

WATER Fresh, salt

AREA 850 square km (330 square miles)

Camargue • Rhône
Marseille •

The Camargue is based on sediments deposited by the River Rhône (see p.173) as it braids to form a huge delta, just to the west of Marseille. This diverse wetland comprises salt marshes,

saltwater and brackish lagoons, freshwater ponds, rivers, grazed flooded meadows, reed-beds, and dunes. The plants found here include salt-tolerant tamarisk bushes, Sand Crocuses, and the white-flowered Sea Daffodil, as well as many orchids. But, aside from its white horses and black bulls, it is for its birds that the Camargue is best known. The breeding birds include its famous colony of Greater Flamingos (now numbering about 10,000), as well as Black-winged Stilts and Avocets. Its location also gives it great significance as a refuelling stop for migrating birds

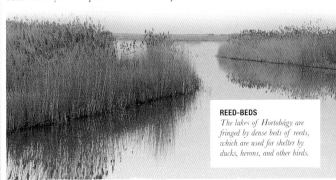

BRINE SHRIMP

These translucent crustaceans thrive in temporary salt lagoons, providing food for flamingos and other birds.

flying between Europe and Africa. Much of the original wetland has been drained for conversion to agriculture (see panel, right), and a series of dykes and canals control the flow of the water. This, along with pollution of the Rhône, has led to a deterioration of some of the habitats. In 1970, the entire Camargue was designated a Regional Natural Park, and some smaller areas have since been given greater protection as nature reserves.

RICE CULTIVATION

Large areas of the Camargue, especially in the north, have been drained and are used to grow cereals, fruit, and vegetables under irrigation. Rice, which has been cultivated here since the Middle Ages, in particular thrives in the region's rich alluvial soil. The small plots of land in which the rice is grown are flooded with water from the irrigation canals in spring, and the crop is harvested mechanically during September and October, once the rice-fields have been drained.

FERAL HORSES

The Camargue's famous white horses are actually grey when young, only becoming white when four or five years old. For centuries they have been used by local farmers and breeders to round up the black bulls that also roam the salt marshes.

WILDEBEEST MIGRATION
Mass migrations to follow the best grazing, such as that undertook by the Blue Wildebeest in east Africa, is common among large herbivores.

GRASSLANDS AND TUNDRA

VAST AREAS OF THE EARTH'S SURFACE are covered by apparently unchanging expanses of natural grassland. In fact, this uniformity is often an illusion, for grasslands vary widely: they may be hilly or punctuated by rocky outcrops; they include both lush and semi-arid areas; and some, especially in the tropics, are dotted with trees, pools, and marshes. Despite experiencing harsh weather, grasslands are one of the world's most productive biomes. Tundra is another open biome that covers a large part of the Earth's land, mainly in the Arctic. Conditions in this desolate, treeless terrain are even more extreme, with long, cold, perpetually dark winters followed in spring by an explosion of life.

NORTH AMERICA *central*

Great Plains

LOCATION Occupying much of North America between the Rocky Mountains and River Mississippi

TYPE Temperate

AREA 3 million square km (1.2 million square miles)

By far the largest expanse of grassland in North America, the Great Plains stretch from the southern Canadian provinces of Alberta, Manitoba, and Saskatchewan, through the USA's Midwest, and south almost to northern Mexico. As recently as the early 19th century, this immense area was covered by grasslands known

WESTERN MEADOWLARK
One of the most characteristic prairie birds, the meadowlark perches on a fence post or large bush to deliver its rich, flute-like territorial song.

as prairies, but most of the fertile land is now under intensive agriculture. It is especially suitable for growing cereals, such as wheat and corn (maize), and has become the main grain-producing region of North America. Only one per cent of the natural grassland survives, divided into three main types: short-grass prairie, mixed-grass prairie, and tall-grass prairie. Short-grass prairie occurs mostly in the west in the rain-shadow of the Rocky Mountains, where the annual rainfall is about 250mm (10in). Here, most grasses are 20–50cm (8–19in) high. Tall-grass prairie is found in the eastern districts of the Great Plains, with an annual rainfall of 650–1,000mm (26–39in). Some of the

COMMON SUNFLOWER
This is the wild ancestor of the popular garden plant. It flourishes in the rich, dark soils of the Great Plains.

FOXTAIL GRASS
In summer, Foxtail Grass produces long, feathery flower-heads. Later in the season, its seeds are eaten by a wide variety of rodents and birds.

grasses growing here, such as Indian Grass, Big Bluestem, and Cordgrass, may reach 1.5m (5ft). In central areas, mixed-grass prairie forms a zone of transition between short- and tall-grass prairie. The open prairie landscape used to be preserved partly by grazing by native herbivores, which included Bison, Pronghorn, and prairie dogs, but in places the steady decline of these animals has led to changes in the length and composition of the turf. Before European colonization, the prairies were also home to North American tribes such as the Lakota and Pawnee.

ROLLING PLAINS
Undulating hills and wide, grassy plains are typical of many parts of the prairies, as here in Nebraska, USA. The harsh winters and strong winds prevent all but a handful of trees from gaining a hold.

RETURN OF THE BISON

Until the early 1800s, up to 60 million Bison (or Buffalo) roamed the short-grass prairie in huge herds. Hunting by settlers from the USA's east coast reduced the Bison population to just 2,000 by 1885. Today, there are more than 350,000, mainly in National Parks and cattle ranches. There are plans to create a "buffalo commons", allowing herds to move freely over the prairies of Montana, the Dakotas, Nebraska, Kansas, and Oklahoma.

BADLANDS NATIONAL PARK
Named after its strange rock formations sculpted by wind and rain, this reserve in South Dakota protects the largest area of mixed-grass prairie in the USA.

South American tropical grasslands

LOCATION In eastern Colombia and Venezuela, south-central Brazil and Paraguay, and northern Argentina

TYPE Tropical

AREA 2.7 million square km (1 million square miles)

MANED WOLF
Neither wolf nor fox, this member of the dog family lives in Brazil, Paraguay, and northern Argentina. Its stilt-like legs help it to move through long grass, and to leap on rodent prey.

South America has two enormous savannas: the Llanos and the cerrado. Lying either side of the River Orinoco in Venezuela and eastern Colombia, the Llanos is a wilderness of rough grassland interspersed with marshy areas (see p.282) and light woodland. Various species of tussocky *Trachypogon* grass are dominant, while typical animals include Savanna Rabbits and Carpenter Ants. Today, the Llanos is a major cattle-ranching region. The cerrado occupies much of Brazil and Paraguay, covering an area the size of western Europe. It borders the Amazon Basin (see pp.171 and 265) to the north, with the Pantanal wetland (see p.283) to the west and the Atlantic forests in the east. As many as five per cent of the world's animal species live in this savanna, including the Giant Anteater and tall, flightless birds called rheas. The cerrado's ecological richness is due in part to its mosaic of habitats, ranging from grasslands to dry forests (see p.268). But agriculture is rapidly encroaching on the cerrado; less than two per cent of it is protected. To the south, in Argentina's arid chaco region, there are sandy, desert-like grasslands.

BRAZILIAN CERRADO
Open grassland shades into scrub and palm forest in the cerrado, creating a marginal habitat rich in species.

Pampas

LOCATION In northern Argentina and Uruguay, extending from the Andes foothills to the Atlantic Ocean

TYPE Temperate

AREA 700,000 square km (270,000 square miles)

Named after a Quechua Indian word meaning "flat surface", the Pampas is a huge plain in the southeastern corner of South America. It is centred on the lowlands of the River Plate (see p.168).

Apart from a few low hills, most of the region is just above sea-level. Deposits of volcanic ash provide a rich soil. The eastern Pampas, which includes much of Uruguay and the Argentinian province of Buenos Aires, enjoys a year-round mild climate, with cool summers and an annual rainfall of up to 1,200mm (47in). Snow and frosts are very rare. The original vegetation of coarse grasses, including the famous Pampas grass (see p.228), has greatly reduced, as ranching developed and other non-native grasses more suitable to cattle and horses were introduced. Clusters of trees cling to the damper hollows or drainage channels.

PAMPAS NEAR BUENOS AIRES
Much of the Pampas has been converted to fertile agricultural land or is used for settlement. It is the most densely populated part of Argentina.

Animals of the Pampas include the endangered Pampas Deer, Geoffroy's Cat, and the Argentine Tortoise. Further west, in the Argentine provinces of La Pampa and Córdoba, the landscape is different. Here, the rainfall is half that of the eastern Pampas, and the sandier soil supports a semi-arid grassland made up of feather grasses and other species. Towards the Andes, the land rises and becomes increasingly dry, eventually turning into semi-desert.

CATTLE RANCHING

Millions of cattle are raised on the Pampas, and gauchos, or cowboys, still follow the herds on horseback. To some extent, their livestock have replaced the ecosystem's natural grazers and fulfil a similar function. However, the mix of native grasses has largely been replaced by a smaller number of introduced fodder species.

PATAGONIAN PAMPAS
Blasted by an icy, dry wind known as the pampero, this desolate plateau in southern Argentina provides a contrast to the lush Pampas further north.

LAND

ASIA *central*

Central Asian steppe grasslands

LOCATION Extending from Ukraine, east through southern Russia and Kazakhstan, to Mongolia and China

TYPE Temperate

AREA 2.5 million square km (975,000 square miles)

The steppes of Central Asia stretch almost a third of the way around the world and include some of the least populated areas on Earth. In the west,

SAVING A SPECIES

Built like a heavy pony, Przewalski's Horse is the only truly wild horse. At home on steppes and in semi-deserts, it once ranged from the Urals to northern China. It was extinct in the wild by 1969, but more than 1,000 survived in zoos. Small herds bred in captivity are now being reintroduced to suitable sites.

the steppes reach the northern shores of the Black Sea, while they extend east in an irregular band almost to the mountains of China's northeastern provinces on the Pacific. This immense grassland zone is bordered to the north by the Eurasian boreal forest (see p.270), and to the south by the Central Asian deserts (see pp.251–53). Dramatic swings in temperature are a defining feature of the steppes; on the grassy upland plateaus of Mongolia, it may reach 40°C (104°F) in summer and plunge to -20°C (-4°F) in winter. The annual rainfall of 200–600mm (8–23½in) is sporadic, with prolonged droughts and sudden thunderstorms. Thick snow blankets the ground in winter. When the snow melts in spring, the steppes are briefly ablaze with a profusion of flowers, including irises, hyacinths, crocuses, and tulips. During the short summer, feather and fescue grasses and sedges dominate the turf. Apart from a few stunted trees confined to the sheltered valleys, the steppes are bereft of tall vegetation, although in northern China there is a more park-like landscape, with a scattering

of trees such as elms. Animals of the steppes are adapted to the extreme climate in various ways. The Saiga Antelope has a bulbous, trunk-like nose that warms and moistens the cold, dry air it breathes, while rodents such as the Steppe Lemming, susliks, and gerbils dig burrows for shelter.

SOUTHERN RUSSIAN STEPPES
Many of the steppes in Russia, Ukraine, and Kazakhstan have been converted to semi-natural grasslands due to heavy grazing by cattle.

MAKING HAY

Steppe soils are fragile, and attempts at cultivation for cereals in the 1950s were disastrous and soon abandoned. However, use of grasses for haymaking is a vital, labour-intensive activity, in which even children play a part. Hay provides fodder for cattle, sheep, goats, and horses during the long winter months, when the ground is frozen solid and grazing impossible. A poor harvest could easily lead to a crippling loss of livestock.

NORTHERN MONGOLIAN STEPPES
The mountains of southern Siberia rise above this high-altitude plateau near Ulan-Uul. A sparse covering of dusty turf is often all that distinguishes the high steppes from semi-desert.

LAND

ASIA south

Indian savanna grasslands

LOCATION Within a zone stretching northwards from south-central India to the Himalayan foothills

TYPE Tropical

AREA 35,000 square km (13,515 square miles)

Forming a discontinuous area and with few large expanses remaining, Indian savanna grasslands occur mainly in inland regions, around the fringes of

deserts, and in hilly country. Those Terrai-Duar grasslands remaining after the encroachment of agriculture represent one of the most threatened grassland ecoregions in the world. They form a narrow strip along the southern margin of the Himalayas, from Nepal east to Bhutan and India. The hot, humid summers and monsoon rains enable tall grasses, including giant reeds and canes, to grow. These "grass forests" have the highest densities of Tigers in India. Further south, the much lower rainfall of the Deccan Plateau gives rise to coarser, semi-arid pastures with a scattering of trees such as Sandalwood. This is the haunt of numerous reptiles, among them the highly venomous Indian Cobra.

GRASSLAND PLATEAU
The interior uplands of southern India are known as the Deccan Plateau. Pockets of wooded savanna form a patchwork with dry forest, farmland, and villages in this highly populated region.

DEW-COVERED GRASSES
Morning dew clings to grasses in the Corbett National Park in the Indian Himalayan foothills. Torrential monsoon downpours create swampy conditions here, in which annual grasses thrive.

ELEPHANT GRASS
In the grasslands of Nepal, this relative of sugar-cane grows up to 8m (26ft) high. It provides the Indian Rhinoceros with both shelter and the bulk of its diet.

AUSTRALASIA Australia

Australian savanna grasslands

LOCATION Stretching from the far north of Western Australia, through Northern Territory, into Queensland

TYPE Tropical

AREA 1.2 million square km (463,500 square miles)

Australia's savanna grasslands are one of the largest, most unique, and unspoiled grassland ecoregions in the world, but they have been threatened by invasive non-native weeds and pests. They form a wide band between the hot interior deserts and northern coastal forests, with the Great Dividing Range to the east. It is hot and

AUSTRALIAN BAOBAB
Although mainly found in Africa, and particularly Madagascar, one species of baobab is endemic to northwest Australia.

humid during the wet season (December to March), but little or no rain falls during the cooler dry season (May to August). Wooded savanna is mainly found in the wetter north and east, but gum trees, also known as eucalypts, are present in most areas. One group of uniquely Australian grasses are the spinifex, which bristle with spear-like leaves that minimize water loss, allowing them to thrive in the desert too.

RED KANGAROO
The largest of the kangaroos, this marsupial is common in wooded savannas. Its numbers double in years of high rainfall.

short forelegs

large, muscular hindlimbs

very long, strong tail

TOUGH GRASSES
Scattered clumps of hardy grasses such as spinifex typify these grasslands, as here in the Barkly Tableland, Northern Territory.

LAND

Ocean Water

THE OCEANS OF THE WORLD contain about 1.35 billion cubic kilometres (a third of a billion cubic miles) of seawater. This vast quantity of water is not uniform but varies in several physical attributes, including temperature, salinity, pressure, and level of illumination. The variation in these properties is mainly vertical, dividing the oceans into layers, each of which has specific attributes. However, there is also horizontal variation – between tropical and temperate latitudes, for example – and seasonal changes as well.

Light

Light cannot penetrate far through ocean water. However, different colours, or wavelengths, of light penetrate to varying extents. White light, such as sunlight, contains a mixture of wavelengths, ranging from red and orange (long wavelength) at one end of the spectrum to blue and violet (short) at the other. Ocean water strongly absorbs the longer wavelengths, and the amount of very short wavelength (violet) light in sunlight is small. As a result, only a little light in the blue area of the spectrum reaches much beyond a depth of 45m (150ft), and divers who descend into this zone see everything as a blue-grey colour. Below a depth of about 200m (650ft), even this blue light has been absorbed, and so the ocean is almost completely dark. Because they rely on light to photosynthesize, phytoplankton are restricted to the upper layers of the oceans, and this in turn affects the distribution of other marine organisms. A few organisms that live at depth are able to generate their own light.

COLOBONEMA
This small jellyfish lives at depths of 100–800m (330–2,650ft). It has bioluminescent (light-producing) tentacles.

Red Orange Yellow Green Blue Violet

Depth (m): 0, 30, 60, 90

LIGHT PENETRATION
Visible light in the red/orange area of the light spectrum is absorbed in the top 10–15m (33–50ft) of even the clearest seawater. Most other colours of the spectrum are absorbed in the next 30m (100ft), so only a little blue light reaches deeper than 45m (150ft).

WITH FLASH

WITHOUT FLASH

TRUE COLOURS
Even at 20m (65ft) depth, features such as coral reefs appear blue-grey under ambient light conditions. Only by illuminating the reef with a torch or photographic flash are the real colours of reef organisms revealed.

Salinity

The salinity, or saltiness, of the oceans averages about 35 grams of salt per litre (1,000 grams) of water, often expressed as 35ppt (parts per thousand). This concentration varies, being highest at the surface of warm seas, due to water evaporation from the surface, and lowest in polar oceans near the mouths of rivers, where there is a high rate of freshwater inflow. The salts in the oceans came originally from minerals that dissolved from rocks into rain-water and were then carried in rivers to the sea. The dissolved salts exist in the form of ions (charged particles), the most important being sodium, chloride, magnesium, and sulphate ions, although there are many others in smaller quantities.

HALITE (ROCK SALT) CRYSTAL
Analysis of seawater trapped in ancient salt crystals has shown that its ion content has varied a little over millions of years.

other 0.3g
calcite ($CaCO_3$) 1.2g
sylvite (KCl) 7.4g
gypsum ($CaSO_4.2H_2O$) 15.4g
magnesium salts ($MgCl_2$, $MgSO_4$, $MgBr_2$) 56g
halite ($NaCl$) 273g

OCEAN WATER SALTS
If 10 litres (17½ pints) of seawater were evaporated, about 353g (12½oz) of salts would be obtained, of the types shown left. The largest component is halite (sodium chloride, or table salt).

Pressure

The units by which oceanographers measure pressure are called bars (one bar is equal to 100,000 Newtons per square metre). At sea-level, all objects are subject to atmospheric pressure, which averages about one bar. Underwater, pressure increases at the rate of about one bar for every 10m (33ft) increase in depth, due to the weight of the overlying water. This means that at 90m (300ft), the total pressure is 10 bars or 10 times the surface pressure, while at 4km (2½ miles), the pressure is over 400 times that at the surface. The huge pressures pose a considerable challenge to human exploration of the deep ocean, and animals living there exhibit special adaptations.

COMMON OCTOPUS

COPING WITH PRESSURE
The Dumbo Octopus lives as deep as 1,500m (5,000ft), compared with a maximum of 200m (650ft) for the Common Octopus. Its adaptations include a semi-gelatinous body, webbed arms, and fins above the eyes.

DUMBO OCTOPUS

USA

Gulf of Mexico

Mexico

South America

KEYS TO NORTH ATLANTIC MAP

This 3-D map shows the variation in early summer temperatures in part of the North Atlantic (the vertical scale has been exaggerated). The map shows that temperatures vary much more at the surface than at depth. The variation in salinity and density with depth at tropical and high latitudes is shown in the bars on the opposite page. (In the key, salinity values are expressed in practical salinity units, or psu, a measure obtained by comparing a seawater sample's electrical properties to that of a standard salt solution. The psu equates roughly to ppt, or parts per thousand.)

Density (kg/m³): 1,050, 1,040, 1,030, 1,020

Salinity (psu): 38, 37, 36, 35, 34

Temperature: 90°F/32°C, 30°C, 70°F/20°C, 50°F/10°C, 30°F/0°C

Sound

Sound travels further and faster in seawater than in air – its speed in seawater is about 1,500m (5,000ft) per second, more than four times faster than in air. The velocity is decreased by a decrease in temperature and increased by an increase in pressure (depth) of the water. The effects of vertical variations in temperature and pressure on sound velocity mean that in most ocean areas there is a layer of minimum sound velocity at about 1,000m (3,300ft) depth. This layer is called the SOFAR (Sound Fixing and Ranging) channel. It is exploited for long-distance communication underwater by people using hydro-acoustic and sonar listening devices, and, it is believed, by whales and dolphins.

THE SOFAR CHANNEL
Low-frequency sounds generated in the SOFAR channel are "trapped" in it, by refraction or bending of the sound waves towards the centre of the channel. As a result, sounds can travel for long distances in this ocean layer, a phenomenon that has been exploited by submarines.

CETACEANS AT RISK

There is growing evidence that human use of sound underwater, such as military use of sonar for submarine detection, can damage the sensitive hearing apparatus of whales and dolphins, which forms part of their own sonar-based navigation system. This can cause the animals to become disoriented, often with fatal results.

HIGH LATITUDES (65–70°N)
Here, there is only a small and gradual change in temperature with depth. Salinity is usually lowest at the surface, due to high freshwater input.

TROPICAL LATITUDES (0–22°N)
Here, the ocean surface is warm and very saline due to high water evaporation. There is a sharp decline in temperature and salinity, and rise in density, down through the first 1,000m (3,500ft).

Temperature

Temperature varies significantly over the surface of the oceans, but there is little variation at depth. In tropical and subtropical regions, intense solar heating warms the upper ocean to produce a broad band of water with temperatures higher than 25°C (77°F). Below the surface, from a depth of about 300m (1,000ft) down to about 1,000m (3,300ft), the temperature steeply declines to about 8–10°C (46–50°F). This region of steep decline is called a thermocline. Below 1,000m (3,300ft), the temperature decreases more gradually to a uniform 2°C (35.6°F) throughout the deep oceans. In mid-latitudes (40–50°N and S), the temperature structure of the ocean is similar to that in the tropics, except that the seasonal variation in surface temperature is much more marked, from about 17°C (63°F) in summer to 10°C (50°F) in winter, and there is a more gradual thermocline. In high latitudes and polar oceans, surface temperatures are in the range 0–5°C (32–41°F), although the temperatures in some parts and at some times may drop below 0°C (seawater freezes at a few degrees below zero, the exact temperature depending on its salinity). Below the surface, there is a gradual change to the uniform deep-water temperature of 2°C (35.6°F).

OCEAN

Ocean Tectonics

THE SEA FLOOR LIES AT DEPTHS ranging from zero to more than 11,000m (36,000ft) below the surface of the oceans. In many places, this surface is a flat, monotonous expanse – the abyssal plains. Elsewhere, it has been heavily shaped by a combination of tectonic and volcanic activity to form features such as massive mountain ranges, seamounts, deep trenches, and basins. It is also worth noting that the ocean floor is comparatively young – no part is greater than 200 million years old – because it is continuously reworked by the plate-tectonic processes of sea-floor spreading and subduction.

OCEAN

Mid-ocean Ridges

Mid-ocean ridges are the largest features of the sea floor. In fact, they are the largest single geological feature on the Earth's surface. They consist of an interconnected chain of mountains that twists and branches for about 65,000km (40,000 miles) over the floor of the world's oceans. These mountains occur at divergent plate boundaries (see p.54), where new oceanic lithosphere is created from magma that wells up from Earth's mantle, then cools and hardens. Overall, the ridges rise several thousand metres above the general level of the sea floor. In some places, volcanoes rising from the ridges break the surface of the sea; Iceland, in the North Atlantic, is an example of this. Two different types of ridge are recognized: fast- and slow-spreading. Slow-spreading ridges, such as the Mid-Atlantic Ridge, form new oceanic lithosphere at a rate of only about 2–5cm (1–2in) a year. They have deep depressions (rift valleys), which are 10–20km (6–12 mile) wide, running down their centres. Fast-spreading ridges, which include the East Pacific Rise, spread at 10–20cm (4–8in) a year, and lack rift valleys.

MID-ATLANTIC RIDGE
A section of the Mid-Atlantic ridge reaches the sea surface in Iceland, where it is visible as a series of deep cracks running through an area known as the Thingvellir Rift valley.

Hydrothermal Vents

Located on or near the mid-ocean ridges, at an average depth of about 2,100m (7,000ft), are some spectacular features called hydrothermal vents. These vents are like hot springs (see p.161), continuously spewing out copious amounts of mineral-rich seawater at temperatures as high as 400°C (750°F). Some of the vents have tall chimneys, formed from dissolved minerals that precipitate out when the hot vent water meets cold deep-ocean water. Black smokers are vents in which a dark cloud of sulphides precipitates out of the vent water as it exits the chimney. The minerals dissolved in the water, and bacteria that thrive on these substances, support a diverse community of organisms, including giant tubeworms and clams.

LIFE AT VENTS
These blind Rift Shrimps and the Vent Crab are found in large numbers around mid-Atlantic hydrothermal vents.

SUBMERSIBLES

Manned submersible vehicles have played an important part in unlocking the secrets of the sea floor. In 1977, for example, scientists aboard the submersible *Alvin* discovered the previously unknown phenomenon of hydrothermal vents in the Pacific Ocean. *Alvin* has a maximum depth of 4,500m (14,764ft). *Johnson Sea-Link II*, shown here, operates at shallower depths and is used to study continental slopes.

Submarine Volcanoes

Volcanic activity occurs under the sea surface in a number of different settings, including on or near mid-ocean ridges, above hotspots beneath the Earth's crust, and within volcanic island arcs (see p.117). It can take hundreds of thousands of years for a submarine volcano to grow to the point where its summit reaches the surface. Many become extinct before this happens and end up as seamounts that then gradually erode away. When one does reach the surface, a spectacular eruption can result. Examples are the sudden surface appearance of a volcano called Kick'em Jenny in the Caribbean in 1939, and the eruptions that built up the island of Surtsey, south of Iceland, in 1963. In most cases where volcanic islands are formed by such eruptions, they tend not to last long, as they are quickly eroded by wave action – a number of submarine volcanoes in the southwest Pacific are known to have created whole series of short-lived islands. In a few cases, if the underlying volcanic source is strong, a submarine volcano may grow into a large, long-lived volcanic island.

FUKUTOKU-OKANOBA
This submarine volcano in the west Pacific has erupted at, or just under, the sea surface on several occasions, most recently in 2010. The eruptions sometimes leave rafts of hot, steaming pumice floating on the surface, as here.

WEST MATA
Located near Tonga, this volcano's summit currently lies about 1,150m (3,800ft) underwater. In 2009, a robotic submersible filmed it erupting huge amounts of lava, seen here with surface splits that reveal the hot magma inside.

HAWAIIAN ISLANDS
This satellite photograph shows several of the Hawaiian Islands, including Hawaii at bottom right and Oahu at top left. Hawaii is composed of five merged volcanoes, only two of them still active.

Island Chains and Seamounts

Some submarine volcanoes are erupted onto the sea floor at some distance from any plate boundaries, above what are known as hotspots. Many scientists think that these hotspots lie at the top of mantle plumes – streams of magma rising up from deep in the mantle (see p.39). As oceanic lithosphere passes over a hotspot, magma erupting up through it creates a subsea volcano that will grow as long as it remains over the hotspot. If the plate moves in a straight line, and the hotspot stays in the same place, periodic eruptions may form a line of volcanic features called a hotspot chain. Depending on the persistence of a hotspot, the strength of the magma eruptions, and the speed of plate movement, different types of hotspot chains may develop. They range from chains of substantial volcanic islands, such as the Hawaiian Islands, to linear chains of seamounts, the conical remains of extinct volcanoes that lie below the ocean surface. Guyots, slightly different phenomena with flat tops, are volcanoes that broke above the surface before later subsiding. The Hawaiian Island chain, together with a line of seamounts that extends to its northwest (the Emperor Seamounts), constitute a single hotspot chain that stretches for 6,000km (3,700 miles) across the Pacific.

Niihau 391m (1,283ft)
Kauai 1,598m (5,243ft)
Oahu 1,227m (4,025ft)
Molokai 1,512m (4,961ft)
Lanai 1,026m (3,366ft)
Maui 3,055m (10,023ft)
Hawaii 4,205m (13,796ft)
sea-level

ISLAND CHAIN
Each of the Hawaiian Islands is volcanic in origin and rises several kilometres from the ocean floor (the vertical scale in this depiction has been exaggerated). The chain was created by a hotspot, currently underneath Loihi, a submarine volcano.

Kahoolawe 1,598m (5,242ft)
Loihi submarine volcano

BLACK SMOKERS
Hydrothermal vents, such as these on the Mid-Atlantic Ridge, are among the most extreme environments in which living organisms can survive.

OCEAN

Ocean Trenches and Island Arcs

The deepest parts of the ocean are found in arc-shaped depressions in the ocean floor called deep-sea trenches. These trenches form at the convergent plate boundaries called subduction zones where one plate descends beneath another (see p.55). Where oceanic lithospere is subducted beneath oceanic lithosphere, the result is the development of an arc of volcanic islands above the overriding plate and parallel to the trench. One example of a trench–island arc combination is the Java–Sunda Trench and Indonesian Island Arc on the edge of the Indian Ocean. Most of the world's deep-sea trenches descend to depths of over 6,000m (20,000ft). The very deepest, the Mariana Trench, plunges to 11,034m (36,201ft). Despite the total darkness, high pressure, and near-freezing temperatures, a surprising variety of life-forms are able to live in the trenches, including some limpets and clams.

OCEAN FLOOR CONVERGENCE
Where oceanic lithosphere subducts under a neighbouring plate, escaping water lowers the melting point of the mantle rock above. Magma forms and rises to the surface, eventually creating a gentle arc of volcanic islands.

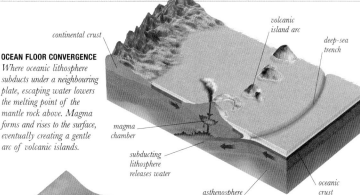

continental crust / volcanic island arc / deep-sea trench / magma chamber / subducting lithosphere releases water / asthenosphere / oceanic crust

ANAK KRAKATAU
This small island is part of the Indonesian Island Arc, a classic volcanic island arc lying on the northeastern edge of the Indian Ocean.

AMPHIPOD
Shrimp-like animals such as this small crustacean have been found in even the deepest ocean trenches.

Wave origination
At the sea surface, a series of high-energy waves is triggered. These move off in two directions.

wave movement

block of sea floor suddenly shoots up several metres, pushing up the column of water above it

powerful shockwaves spread out in all directions

Sea floor rupture
A massive rupture rips across the sea floor. At the same time, a huge block of seabed is suddenly thrust upwards.

rupture line may be hundreds of kilometres long

epicentre – the spot on the sea floor above the point in the Earth's interior where the rupture started

in the open sea, tsunami waves are evenly spaced with a long wavelength

Tsunami Generation

Subduction zones, where oceanic lithosphere descends beneath a neighbouring plate (either oceanic lithosphere or continental lithosphere), are common sites for earthquakes. A powerful earthquake occurring at a subduction zone, particularly if it involves a rupture that causes a large section of sea floor suddenly to be thrust upwards or to sink, may trigger a tsunami – a series of high-energy waves that spread out from the ocean area above the disrupted sea floor. Not all tsunamis are caused by large earthquakes at subduction zones – other possible causes include cataclysmic volcanic eruptions close to the sea, mass downslope movements of sediment underwater, big landslides into the sea, or impacts of large objects from space. However, subduction zone earthquakes are the most common cause of the largest, most serious tsunamis, such as the Indian Ocean Tsunami of 2004 and the 2011 tsunami that devastated part of Japan

oceanic crust / uplift / subduction zone / plate movement / hypocentre / shockwaves / asthenosphere

Amplification
As a tsunami wave approaches shore, it slows and its height increases. These changes are caused by movements of seawater under the wave interacting with the sea floor.

EARTHQUAKE TRIGGER
A large earthquake occurring at a subduction zone may cause a massive slab of sea floor to be thrust upwards. This in turn pushes up the overlying column of water, triggering a tsunami.

passage of each wave is accompanied by a circular movement of seawater under it

tsunami wave grows higher as the sea floor slopes upwards

OCEAN

Tsunami Propagation and Impact

The series of high-energy waves that comprise a tsunami spreads out in all directions if it is caused by a disturbance at a single point. The waves travel in two opposite, directions if – as is often the case – the cause is a linear rupture in the sea floor. In the open ocean, these waves travel at about 800kph (500mph) and have a very long wavelength – with the distance between wave crests as much as 200km (125 miles). The waves can propagate thousands of kilometres across oceans, only gradually losing energy. The initial signs of a tsunami about to hit shore depend on whether a wave trough or crest arrives first. If a trough arrives first, the sea recedes dramatically, whereas in the case of a crest, the incoming wave appears offshore. As the wave nears the shore and interacts with the sea bottom, it slows to less than 80kph (50mph), and its height increases. Usually, it does not break like a normal wave but surges forwards powerfully. A large tsunami can lift and smash boats, buildings, and vehicles. After about 15 minutes, the water pulls back strongly, drawing vast amounts of debris out to sea. The cycle can repeat several times over an hour or so.

INDIAN OCEAN TSUNAMI
The Indian Ocean tsunami of 26 December 2004 left a colossal amount of destruction on coasts across the region, including here at Banda Aceh in Indonesia.

TSUNAMI CHARACTERISTICS
Out at sea, tsunami waves have a low amplitude (height) and may pass unnoticed. Once it reaches the shore it surges forwards, causing massive destruction. The first wave is usually followed by others, typically at intervals of about 20 minutes.

WARNING SYSTEMS

Tsunami warning systems are in place in the Pacific, Atlantic, and Indian oceans. These systems have three main components: a network of seismometers for detecting tremors that might trigger tsunamis; a means of detecting tsunamis in the open ocean – usually pressure sensors on the sea floor linked to surface transmitters; and procedures for quickly sending alerts to affected populations. This map, created moments after the 2011 Japanese tsunami was detected, shows predicted wave heights across the Pacific; red indicates the greatest height.

World Distribution

This map shows the distribution of mid-ocean ridges, hydrothermal vents, deep-sea trenches (marking convergent boundaries associated with subduction zones), and major zones in which seamounts are found. Subduction zones, the sites of the types of earthquakes that most commonly cause destructive tsunamis, are found mainly around the Pacific.

— Mid-ocean ridges
— Deep-sea trenches
▦ Seamount zones
• Hydrothermal vent zones

OCEAN

Inundation
When a tsunami wave hits a shore, it usually does not break and collapse. Instead it continues forwards, flooding the coast and smashing buildings.

few buildings can survive being hit by a large tsunami wave; many are destroyed

Shelves and Plains

40–41	The crust
52–53	Tectonic plates
54–55	Plate boundaries
190–91	Freshwater quality
	Fishing 344–45

AWAY FROM THE TECTONICALLY ACTIVE regions of the sea floor are other large and relatively tranquil areas of ocean, where disturbances are few apart from a constant gentle rain of sediment from above. These regions fall into two main types: the continental shelves, which themselves form part of larger zones around the edges of the world's landmasses called continental margins; and the abyssal plains, which occupy deep-sea regions between the continental margins and the mid-oceanic ridges. Both the continental margins and abyssal plains are inhabited by a diverse range of organisms.

Continental Margins

The continental margins consist of three parts: the continental shelf, slope, and rise. The continental shelves are areas that were dry land during the last ice age and have since been flooded. They slope gently away from modern-day shorelines to a depth of about 200m (660ft). Past the edge of the continental shelf, called the shelf break, is the more steeply descending continental slope, and beyond that the continental rise, which stretches down to the abyssal plain. Many continental shelf areas are rich in deposits of oil and natural gas and also methane hydrate. The latter, a solid but volatile substance, is potentially a highly valuable energy source, but the question of how to extract it safely from the sea floor has yet to be answered.

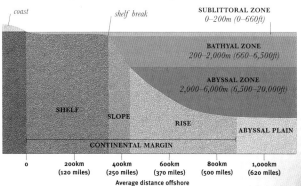

coast — shelf break

SUBLITTORAL ZONE
0–200m (0–660ft)

BATHYAL ZONE
200–2,000m (660–6,500ft)

ABYSSAL ZONE
2,000–6,000m (6,500–20,000ft)

SHELF — SLOPE — RISE — ABYSSAL PLAIN

CONTINENTAL MARGIN

| 0 | 200km (120 miles) | 400km (250 miles) | 600km (370 miles) | 800km (500 miles) | 1,000km (620 miles) |

Average distance offshore

LOBSTERS
Lobsters inhabit the sublittoral zone. Some species migrate from place to place, often in groups, as here.

BRITTLESTAR
Brittlestars, relatives of starfish, inhabit the bathyal and other depth zones, often in huge numbers.

ANGLERFISH
Anglerfish swim in the bathyal and abyssal zones. Females have a luminescent organ that attracts prey.

CONTINENTAL MARGIN
This is a typical continental margin profile. Each part (shelf, slope, and rise) is associated with a depth zone, and each zone (sublittoral, bathyal, and abyssal) is associated with different types of organisms.

LIGHT TRAPS

The Sea Mouse is an unusual type of floor-dwelling worm that lives in the sublittoral and bathyal zones at depths of up to 2,000m (6,600ft). The animal has numerous iridescent spines on its surface that are so efficient in handling light they have attracted the attention of experts in fibre optics. The Sea Mouse itself is thought to use the spines for defence, their colour acting as a warning to predators.

Submarine Canyons

At many locations on the continental margins, the continental slope has been eroded into deep, V-shaped valleys, called submarine canyons. The upper part of these canyons is often close to the point on the continental shelf where a large river runs into the sea. The canyons are excavated by a combination of sediment slumping down the slope and turbidity currents, which are large-scale movements of water and silt, like underwater avalanches, triggered by earthquakes or floods. Once they have formed, the canyons continue to act as passageways for sediment, which flows through them and finally comes to rest on the abyssal plain in a wide fan shape. The largest of these fans are associated with major sediment-carrying rivers, such as the Ganges and Amazon.

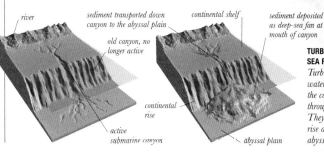

river

sediment transported down canyon to the abyssal plain

old canyon, no longer active

continental rise

active submarine canyon

continental shelf

sediment deposited as deep-sea fan at mouth of canyon

abyssal plain

TURBIDITY CURRENTS AND DEEP-SEA FANS
Turbidity currents are masses of water and silt that flow down the continental slope, often through submarine canyons. They move past the continental rise and deposit sediment on the abyssal plain as a deep-sea fan.

WRECK OF RMS RHONE
The world's continental shelves are littered with shipwrecks, such as this one in the Caribbean Sea. The ship sank in a hurricane in 1867.

OCEAN

GLOBIGERINA
This is a foraminiferan, a simple organism with a calcium-carbonate shell.

PTEROPOD
Pteropods are tiny molluscs with shells of calcium carbonate.

Ocean Sediments

Most of the ocean floor is covered in layers of sediment. In some places, these are over 5km (3 miles) thick and have taken more than 100 million years to accumulate. On the continental shelf, most sediments are gravels, sands, and muds that are derived from the erosion of rocks on land and transported by rivers to the sea. Deep-sea sediments come from many different sources. Some are fine silts that have migrated down from the continental shelf through mechanisms such as turbidity currents. Others derive from sand and dust that has been blown by winds off the continents, or from icebergs that carry rock particles away from glaciers in polar regions and then drop the particles as they melt. Authigenic sediments are precipitates of chemicals, such as iron oxide, from seawater, in forms such as manganese nodules (see below). Another important type of sediment is biogenic ooze, the skeletal remains of microscopic organisms that once lived in the ocean. There are two major varieties: calcareous oozes consisting of calcium carbonate; and siliceous oozes consisting of silica. Oozes composed of the shells of different foraminiferan species (see p.372) have been used to obtain information about ocean surface and floor temperatures and climatic conditions in the past, going back over 100 million years.

SEA-BED SEDIMENTS
This map shows the distribution of the different sediments found on the floor of the Atlantic Ocean. Oozes are composed of the shells of countless millions of tiny organisms, such as those shown at far right.

Clay — Pteropod ooze
Globigerina ooze — Diatom ooze
Radiolarian ooze

RADIOLARIAN
Radiolarians are single-celled, floating, animal-like organisms with silica shells.

DIATOMS
Diatoms are delicate, photosynthesizing life-forms with silica shells.

Abyssal Plains

The abyssal plains begin where the continental margins end. They occupy extensive areas of the seafloor at depths of 4,000–6,000m (13,000–20,000ft) and are the deepest parts of the oceans apart from the deep-sea trenches. They are the flattest, and some of the most featureless, places on Earth, with a gradient of just 1:1,000. Despite the pitch blackness of the water, the huge pressure, and the freezing cold, many different animals live on the abyssal plains, including several species of worms, shrimps, brittlestars, sea cucumbers, and some extraordinary fish.

MANGANESE NODULES
These potato-sized lumps litter wide areas of the abyssal plains. They contain many valuable metals, but so far no satisfactory way has been devised for mining them.

World Distribution

Areas of continental shelf (light purple on the map below) exist around the edges of all continents but vary greatly in their width, from just a few kilometres off the west coast of much of the Americas to up to 900km (560 miles) off the coast of Siberia, Russia. The narrowest shelves are found at convergent plate margins. Abyssal plains (dark purple on the map) are most common in the Atlantic and Indian oceans, but are relatively rare in the Pacific.

OCEAN

Reefs

CORAL REEFS ARE WAVE-RESISTANT structures built from the remains of small marine organisms. They are found in many shallow warm-water seas. The main bulk of a reef is a mass of limestone, consisting of the build-up of cemented skeletons and shell fragments of animals that once inhabited the reef. On the surface of this limestone is a thin skin of living organisms. When these organisms die, their hard parts remain as part of the reef structure, helping the reef to grow in size over time. Coral reefs support a highly diverse fauna and flora, and protect shorelines from erosion. But they are also vulnerable to changes in environmental conditions such as water temperature, salinity, oxygen content, and pollution.

JAMES DWIGHT DANA

From his observations on various coastlines in the South Pacific, the American geologist James Dana (1813–95) found evidence to support Charles Darwin's ideas on how atolls form (see right). Dana also developed a theory explaining how the shapes of atolls are related to wind and wave patterns, which affect the supply of nutrients to reef-building organisms.

How Coral Reefs Form

The main reef-forming organisms, known as hard or stony corals, belong to a group of animals called cnidarians. Individual animals are called coral polyps. As it grows, a coral polyp secretes limestone, building on the rock underneath. Some reef-building corals consist of single large polyps, but the majority live as colonies that, as they grow, create community skeletons in a variety of shapes. An important contributor to the life of coral polyps is the presence within their tissues of unicellular algae called zooxanthellae. Although polyps use their tentacles to capture plankton for food, most of their nutrition comes from these algae. The algae use photosynthesis to convert the carbon dioxide produced by the polyps' respiration into the nutrients that polyps need for growth and so for production of limestone.

POLYP OF A HARD CORAL
This reef-building species, called a plate or mushroom coral, consists of a single large polyp with many green, pink-tipped tentacles. Often mistaken for anemones, mushroom corals inhabit shallow reefs.

They also provide oxygen for the polyps. Other organisms that add their skeletal remains to reefs include molluscs and echinoderms. Further contributions are made by boring and grazing organisms. These fragment some of the coral skeletons into sand, which fills the gaps in the skeletons. Algae and encrusting bryozoans cement the coral fragments and other debris into a solid reef.

tentacle *mouth*

gut cavity

connecting tissue between adjacent polyps *limestone exoskeleton*

HARD CORAL POLYP ANATOMY
The polyp's gut cavity sits within a fluted, cup-like limestone exoskeleton. Food is taken in, and some waste products are expelled, through the mouth. The tissue around the gut cavity lays down limestone, which helps to build the reef.

Fringing Reefs

Fringing reefs form a fringe of coral around a tropical island or along part of the shore of a large landmass, with little or no lagoon between the reef and shore. They are the most common type of reef worldwide. Fringing reefs consist of several zones that are characterized by their depth, structure, and coral communities. The reef crest is the part the waves break over, marked by a line of breaking surf. In front of the reef crest is an area called the buttress zone, where there are spurs of coral growing out into the sea separated by grooves. This is the region of most active coral growth. Shoreward of the reef crest is the reef flat, a shallow, flat expanse of limestone, sand, and coral fragments that may become partly exposed at low tide.

REEFS IN PALAU
This aerial view shows a large area of fringing reefs (the light coloured areas) around islands and exposed coral flats in the Republic of Palau in the western Pacific.

CORAL SPUR
In this area on the surface of a spur at the front of a fringing reef, several colonies of stony coral are growing in about a metre of water.

BORA BORA
Bora Bora lies in the south-central Pacific Ocean. It consists of a volcanic island surrounded by a lagoon and a necklace of submerged reefs and elongated islands that constitute a barrier reef.

OCEAN

Barrier Reefs

A barrier reef is a coral reef that parallels the shore but is separated from it by a sizeable lagoon. Large and continuous barrier reefs occur in association with continental land-masses. The largest in the world are the Great Barrier Reef off the coast of Queensland, Australia, and the Belize Barrier Reef in the Caribbean. Smaller barrier reefs can also be seen around sinking volcanic islands.

Barrier reefs contain the same zones as fringing reefs, but with some additions. In front of the buttress zone, there is frequently a steeply descending wall called a reef face, or drop-off, which is usually rich in coral formations. The main bulk of the reef behind the reef crest is often several kilometres wide and may include patch reefs separated by submerged areas.

REEF FACE
A diver swims around the top of the reef face on part of Australia's Great Barrier Reef.

GREAT BARRIER REEF
This satellite image of part of the Great Barrier Reef shows that it is an assemblage of reefs rather than a single structure.

Atolls

An atoll is a ring of coral reefs, or low-lying islands made of coral, that encloses a shallow central lagoon. Atolls are often elliptical in shape, but many are irregularly shaped. The process by which they form was first explained in the 1840s by the English naturalist Charles Darwin. Darwin proposed that fringing reefs can transform into barrier reefs and barrier reefs into atolls. He theorized that these transitions result from the upward growth of coral on the edge of a gradually sinking volcano, and that the ring-like appearance of an atoll with a central lagoon result from the total submergence of the summit of the volcano. Other scientists have contributed to Darwin's theory, especially on the importance of temperature restraints in reef formation and the contribution of wave patterns to atoll shapes. Today, it is realized that sea-level rise may contribute to atoll formation as much as volcanic subsidence.

MALDIVES ATOLL
This example of a small atoll is in the North Male' island group in the Indian Ocean.

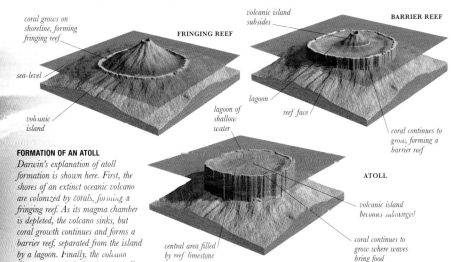

coral grows on shoreline, forming fringing reef

sea-level

volcanic island

FRINGING REEF

volcanic island subsides

BARRIER REEF

lagoon

reef face

coral continues to grow, forming a barrier reef

lagoon of shallow water

FORMATION OF AN ATOLL
Darwin's explanation of atoll formation is shown here. First, the shores of an extinct oceanic volcano are colonized by corals, forming a fringing reef. As its magma chamber is depleted, the volcano sinks, but coral growth continues and forms a barrier reef, separated from the island by a lagoon. Finally, the volcano disappears entirely, leaving an atoll.

central area filled by reef limestone

ATOLL

volcanic island becomes submerged

coral continues to grow where waves bring food

CROWN OF THORNS STARFISH
The large Crown of Thorns Starfish, which eats coral polyps, has become a blight on coral reefs throughout the Indo-Pacific region.

Dangers and Stresses

Many different types of stress can damage and destroy coral reefs. Some damage is due to human activity (see p.329), and a significant threat is posed by rising sea-levels due to global warming (see p.377). Natural disturbances include various coral diseases, tropical storms, and an increase in predation by animals such as parrotfish, snails, and the Crown of Thorns Starfish. The latter has been a particular concern since the 1960s. One theory for its emergence is that there has been a loss of some of its natural predators. Another is that the addition of nutrients from human use of the coastal zone has increased the availability of planktonic food for young starfish.

Coral Reef Distribution

Reefs cover about 600,000 square km (230,000 square miles) of the world's marine areas. Reef-building corals can grow only in shallow, clear water, where there is plenty of sunlight, water temperatures of at least 18°C (64°F) but preferably 25–29°C (77–84°F), average salinity of 36ppt, and not too much wave action, turbidity, or silting. The right conditions for reef growth are found mainly within tropical areas of the Pacific, Indian, and Atlantic oceans, and predominantly in the western parts where the waters are warmer than in the eastern parts. Coral reefs are absent from any coastal areas where there is a large amount of sedimentation from river run-off. There are no reefs near the mouths of the large rivers of east Asia, for example.

OCEAN

Polar Oceans

THE POLAR OCEANS COMPRISE THE Arctic Ocean in the northern hemisphere and the Southern Ocean in the south. They differ from other oceans in several respects, not least the vast amounts of ice that float on them in various forms, although parts of the Atlantic and Pacific oceans are also covered with ice for some of the year. This ice coverage has helped stabilize world climates, insulating polar oceans from solar radiation in summer and preventing heat loss in winter. However, this balance is threatened by global climate change. The polar oceans are less stratified by temperature and density than other oceans and have different water circulation patterns.

PANCAKE ICE
These scientists in Antarctica are investigating the properties of pancake ice, circular pieces of sea-ice up to several metres in diameter and 10cm (4in) thick.

Ice-Shelves

Ice-shelves are extensions of ice-sheets and other glaciers over the sea. Although there are a few in the Canadian Arctic, most of the world's ice-shelves, including two enormous ones, the Ross and Ronne-Filchner ice-shelves, exist around the coasts of Antarctica (see p.231). Because they originate from snow, ice-shelves contain fresh water. At their seaward edges, they are marked by cliffs that are up to 60m (200ft) high and may extend up to 900m (3,000ft) underwater. Underneath the ice-shelves, there is some circulation of seawater. Water drawn in from beyond the edge of the shelf freezes underneath the ice, rejecting salt as it does so. This creates a layer of cold, salty, dense water that sinks and flows away from the continental shelf area beneath the ice to deeper water. Since the early 1990s, some of the smaller Antarctic ice-shelves have completely broken up (see p.373). This has raised concerns for the future of the ice-sheets covering Antarctica, with implications for possible accelerated sea-level rise, as ice-shelves appear to provide a barrier to ice flow off the ice-sheets.

BRUNT ICE-SHELF, ANTARCTICA
The edge of an ice-shelf is usually marked by ice cliffs. Here the cliffs are fronted by sea-ice on which some Emperor Penguins are gathered.

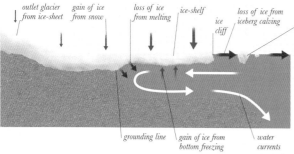

outlet glacier from ice-sheet · *gain of ice from snow* · *loss of ice from melting* · *ice-shelf* · *ice cliff* · *loss of ice from iceberg calving* · *iceberg*

grounding line · *gain of ice from bottom freezing* · *water currents*

ICE-SHELF GAINS AND LOSSES
Ice-shelves gain ice from glaciers flowing into them, from seawater freezing to their undersurface, and from new snowfalls. They lose ice mainly by icebergs calving (breaking off) from their front edges.

Icebergs

Icebergs are pieces of ice that have broken off the edges of ice-shelves or from the fronts of glaciers where they reach the sea. They range from tabular icebergs, hundreds of square kilometres in area, to yacht-sized chunks of ice (called bergy bits), and car-sized ones (called growlers), which are just as dangerous to shipping. In the Southern Ocean, most icebergs have broken off ice-shelves around Antarctica. They initially drift westward in a coastal current around the continent and many become trapped in bays. A few drift several hundred kilometres from Antarctica, some reaching as far north as 40°S. In the northern hemisphere, most icebergs have originated from glaciers flowing off Greenland, Ellesmere Island in the Canadian Arctic, or Alaska. A few reach as far south as 45°N. Because of their glacial origin, icebergs contain fresh water. The average density of icebergs is about 87 per cent of the average density of seawater. As a result, an iceberg typically floats with about 87 per cent of its volume underwater

ICEBERG TYPES AND SHAPES
Icebergs come in various regular shapes, including pinnacle, pyramid, wedge, and blocky, but there are also many irregularly shaped icebergs. Striated icebergs contain layers of rock debris from the glacier from which they were calved.

STRIATED

BLOCKY

DRY DOCK

IRREGULAR

PINNACLE

Circulation in Polar Oceans

The circulation of water in polar oceans is influenced by factors such as changes in the surface temperature and salinity of the water caused by the formation and melting of sea-ice. Both polar oceans are sources of cold, dense bodies of water that sink towards the ocean floor and then continue towards the Equator. These flows are key drivers of the Earth's deep-water circulation. In the Arctic, there is a constant flow of cold water and sea-ice across the North Pole from Siberia towards Greenland in a current called the Transpolar Drift. To the east and southwest of Greenland, this cold water dips under warmer Atlantic water. Further north, the Atlantic water plunges beneath less saline Arctic water then moves through the Arctic Basin. An equivalent circulation operates in the Southern Ocean (see p.346).

ARCTIC CURRENTS

This map shows the basic pattern of surface currents and downwellings in the Arctic and North Atlantic oceans. Observations of ice drift have indicated the surface flows. One of the most pronounced currents is the southerly movement of cold water to the east of Greenland.

➡ Warm surface current
➡ Warm sinking current
➡ Cold surface current
➡ Cold sinking current

Sea-Ice

Unlike icebergs and ice-shelves, sea-ice is seawater that has frozen. It contains little salt as most is rejected as it forms, and it floats on the sea because it is less dense than seawater. About 7 per cent of the world's oceans are covered in sea-ice, nearly all of it in polar regions. New sea-ice forms in distinct stages. Early on, a viscous, slushy layer of ice crystals, called grease ice, develops at the sea surface. The ice thickens and hardens, and is broken up by wave action into platelets. As these collide the result is a mosaic of platter shapes with curling edges, called pancake ice. Later stages include first-year ice, which is more than 30cm (12in) thick, and multi-year ice, which has survived at least two summers' melt and can be 3–10m (10–35ft) thick. Fast ice is sea-ice that is securely frozen to the shore or an ice-shelf, while pack ice is any other area of sea-ice.

GREASE ICE
A Crabeater Seal surfaces through grease ice – an early stage in sea-ice formation – in the Weddell Sea.

ICE LEAD
A lead is a narrow fracture or passageway through sea-ice, which makes the ice navigable by surface vessels and some marine mammals.

POLYNYA
Polynyas are ice-free areas within a region of sea-ice. Upwelling of warm water in a localized area is one way they are formed.

Oceans of the World

IT IS GENERALLY ACCEPTED TODAY that the Earth has five oceans, although the Southern Ocean was officially recognized only in 2000. Three long-recognized oceans, the Atlantic, Indian, and Pacific, extend northward from the Southern Ocean, separating the world's major landmasses. The fifth and smallest ocean, the Arctic Ocean, caps the north polar region. Around the edges of these oceans are smaller regions called seas, bays, and gulfs. Some of the seas, such as the Sargasso Sea, are only vaguely defined, but others, such as the Mediterranean Sea and the Caribbean Sea, are almost completely surrounded by land or by arcs of islands.

MEDITERRANEAN SEA
An offshoot of the Atlantic Ocean, the Mediterranean Sea was the centre of the classical world. This coast is on the volcanic island of Santorini, in the Cyclades Islands, Greece.

ATLANTIC OCEAN
A major area for marine commerce and fishing, the Atlantic is known for its storms, though lighthouses on its coasts, such as this one at Minots Ledge, USA, help to protect shipping.

CARIBBEAN SEA
The warm waters of the Caribbean Sea support large numbers of marine species, such as these Bottlenose Dolphins.

YELLOW SEAHORSE
Seahorses are fish that swim upright and have prehensile tails. This species is common in the Indian Ocean.

INDIAN OCEAN
The Indian Ocean is littered with clusters of coral islands, the best known being the Seychelles and the Maldives. The Maldive Islands lie to the southwest of Sri Lanka and consist of more than a thousand islands, of which two are shown here. Most of them are uninhabited.

OCEANS AND SEAS
This map shows the range of depths in the world's oceans and seas. Surrounding all the landmasses are shallow areas of continental shelf (the lightest shade of blue). Beyond the shelves, the ocean basins fall into two main depth zones: a deeper, mostly flat region at about 5,000m (16,400ft) and a more elevated, rugged zone at 1,000–5,000m (3,300–16,400ft), lying mainly around the mid-ocean ridge areas.

0–500m
500–1,000m
1,000–2,500m
2,500–5,000m
over 5,000m

OCEAN

ARCTIC OCEAN

Greenland

Baffin Bay

Greenland Sea

Barents Sea

Kara Sea

Norwegian Sea

White Sea

Hudson Bay

Gulf of St. Lawrence

North Sea

Baltic Sea

EUROPE

ASIA

NORTH AMERICA

Bay of Biscay

Bay of Fundy

Black Sea

Mediterranean Sea

Persian Gulf

Gulf of Mexico

Sargasso Sea

Red Sea

Arabian Sea

Caribbean Sea

AFRICA

Bay of Bengal

ATLANTIC OCEAN

SOUTH AMERICA

INDIAN OCEAN

Mozambique Channel

Scotia Sea

SOUTHERN OCEAN

Weddell Sea

ANTARCTICA

ARCTIC OCEAN
The Arctic Ocean consists of a deep basin surrounded by a ring of seas, which partly cover continental shelves. The volcanic island of Jan Mayen, seen here, lies on the edge of one of these marginal seas, the Greenland Sea.

WALRUS
Walruses are insulated from the Arctic cold by a thick, subcutaneous layer of blubber. When sunbathing, their heavily creased skin flushes deep pink.

FERDINAND MAGELLAN

The Portuguese explorer Ferdinand Magellan (1480–1521) led the first expedition to circumnavigate the globe, though he died during the voyage. Magellan embarked on the enterprise in 1519 hoping to discover a new route to the Spice Islands (now the Maluku Islands or Moluccas) by finding a passage from the Atlantic into the Pacific. In November 1520, he discovered such a passage near the tip of South America, today called the Straits of Magellan.

PACIFIC OCEAN
By far the largest of the oceans, the Pacific is dotted with thousands of islands, many formed from (or on) the tops of undersea volcanoes, and fringed with coral reefs. This little island in the Solomon Islands group in the western Pacific is a typical example.

CRIMSON ANEMONE
Anemones are found worldwide, in all seas and at various depths. This species lives in the northeastern Pacific.

SOUTHERN OCEAN
Covered in ice for much of the year, the Southern Ocean is whipped by high winds in winter, producing mountainous seas. Despite the severe conditions, an amazing diversity of wildlife thrives there. It is home to some of the world's great whales and large numbers of birds, such as these Chinstrap Penguins drifting on sea-ice in the Weddell Sea.

OCEAN AND SEA PROFILES

The pages that follow contain profiles of the world's oceans and major seas, bays, and gulfs. Each profile begins with the following summary information:

AREA Surface area

MAXIMUM DEPTH Depth of the deepest part of the ocean, sea, or gulf

INFLOWS Major inflows including oceans, basins, seas, rivers, fjords and glaciers

OCEAN

ARCTIC OCEAN
Arctic Ocean

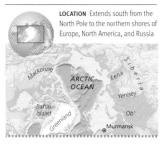

LOCATION Extends south from the North Pole to the northern shores of Europe, North America, and Russia

AREA 14 million square km (5.4 million square miles)

MAXIMUM DEPTH 4,665m (15,305ft)

INFLOWS Atlantic Ocean, Pacific Ocean; rivers Mackenzie, Ob', Yenisey, Lena, Kolyma

The Arctic Ocean is the smallest of the world's oceans. It is also the least studied, partly because about a third of its surface is permanently covered in ice. The ocean comprises a central region around the North Pole and several marginal seas. Most of the Arctic is in continuous darkness from November to February and continuous daylight from May to August. The floor of the Arctic Ocean has two distinct parts: an extensive depression (the Arctic Basin) in the centre, with an average depth of about 4,000m (13,500ft), and an area of continental shelf around the edges. The central basin is divided by a long submarine ridge, the Lomonosov Ridge, into two large sub-basins. These are called the Amerasia Basin (on the North American side) and the Eurasia Basin (on the European side). The continental shelf area is much wider on the Eurasian than the Amerasian side. Many islands and archipelagoes sit on the shelf area. Sea-ice covers the Arctic Ocean more or less permanently above a latitude of about 75°N. In most of the rest of the ocean, sea-ice occurs in winter but retreats in summer. The permanent ice-cap is composed of pack ice – pieces of sea-ice that may be more than 10m (33ft) thick. Wind and currents (see p.312) keep the pack ice in continuous motion, forming cracks and open pools. Since the 1960s, the Arctic ice-cap has

TEMPORARY NORTH POLE
Although the North Pole is in a geographically fixed position, signs stuck in the ice to mark its position can be accurate only temporarily because the ice drifts a few kilometres per day.

thinned considerably, causing loss of habitat for some of the fauna, especially polar bears. It has also allowed increased navigation, bringing with it consequent economic exploitation and sovereignty issues. Melting of the ice-cap in itself would not affect sea-levels (because it is already afloat) but would strip the ocean of its reflective cover, allowing the water to absorb and retain more solar heat. Warmer waters would, in turn, speed melting. In addition to sea-ice, the Arctic Ocean contains thousands of icebergs and larger bodies called ice islands. These have broken off glaciers and ice-shelves, mainly around Greenland and the Canadian Arctic. The main input of water into the Arctic Ocean comes from the Atlantic Ocean (see p.317). A second input of water enters from the Pacific Ocean through the shallow Bering Strait.

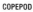

COPEPOD
Small crustaceans called copepods are a key component of the Arctic food chain. They are herbivores, feeding on phytoplankton, and are themselves eaten by fish, squid, sea birds, seals, and some whales.

BOWHEAD WHALE BREACHING
The Bowhead Whale is found only in Arctic and subArctic waters. Its broad back has no dorsal fin, which may make it easier for it to swim beneath the polar ice, to which it stays close all year round.

ICE-BREAKERS

Ice-breakers are ships that combine powerful engines, heavy displacement (weight) for their size, and reinforced hulls. A modern ice-breaker can break through sea-ice that is 1.8m (6ft) thick at a steady 6kph (3¾ mph), or through 6.5m (21ft) of ice by ramming. The bow of an ice-breaker is shaped so that when the ship is driven forward, momentum causes it to ride up on top of the ice, which is crushed by the weight of the ship. Today, ice-breakers are involved in the supply of remote settlements, creation of navigation channels for commercial ships, scientific exploration, and tourism.

ROALD AMUNDSEN

The Norwegian Roald Amundsen (1872–1928) is best known for leading the first expedition to reach the South Pole, but his accomplishments in the Arctic were equally illustrious. Between 1903 and 1906, on the sloop *Gjoa*, he led the first expedition to negotiate the Northwest Passage, a long sought-after sea route through the Canadian Arctic Archipelago, linking the Atlantic Ocean to the Pacific. As part of the expedition, Amundsen also established the position (at the time) of the North Magnetic Pole

ICE FACTORY
Disko Bay in northern Greenland, 300km (185 miles) north of the Arctic Circle, contains one of the most productive ice floes in the northern hemisphere, averaging 20 million tons of ice per day. Icebergs are towed from here into harbours to be chipped into ice cubes.

ARCTIC OCEAN *south*

Barents Sea

LOCATION North of Norway and European Russia, and south of Svalbard and Franz Josef Land

AREA
1.4 million square km (542,000 square miles)

MAXIMUM DEPTH
600m (2,000ft)

INFLOWS Norwegian Sea (Atlantic Ocean), Arctic Basin

Of all the Arctic seas, the Barents Sea is unique in that a substantial part of it is ice-free all year round. A predominantly shallow sea, it covers an area of continental shelf cut by several trenches. Ice encroaches into northern parts of the sea during the winter, and a cold current flows from the north all year round. The combination of mixing warm and cold currents and changes in surface density over the year causes frequent upwellings of nutrient-rich water, and this leads to strong plankton blooms in spring and summer. The plankton support large populations of fish, which in turn sustain other animals and a productive fishing industry.

UNDERWATER LIFE
The floor of the Barents Sea is rich in invertebrates, including feather stars, anemones, sea cucumbers, and starfish, as shown here.

SOUTHERN COAST
The Barents Sea coast of northern Norway and Russia contains many shallow bays and inlets, though in the west it is deeply indented with fjords.

ARCTIC OCEAN *south*

White Sea

LOCATION Forms an inlet adjacent to the Barents Sea in the northern part of European Russia

AREA 90,000 square km (35,000 square miles)

MAXIMUM DEPTH
340m (1,115ft)

INFLOWS Barents Sea; rivers Onega, Northern Dvina

The White Sea is an almost completely landlocked body of water with an average depth of 60m (200ft). Its floor, which consists of continental shelf, is broken up by various troughs and ridges. The White Sea connects to the Barents Sea through a narrow strait known as the Gorlo ("throat") and to the Baltic Sea via canals and Lake Onega to its southwest. The sea can be navigated year-round, albeit with the help of ice-breakers in winter. It is on a key route linking the economically active parts of northwestern Russia with the rest of the world.

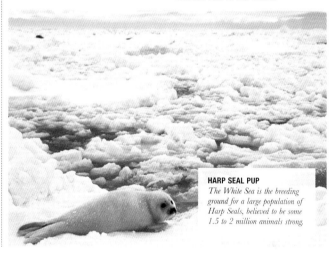

HARP SEAL PUP
The White Sea is the breeding ground for a large population of Harp Seals, believed to be some 1.5 to 2 million animals strong.

ARCTIC OCEAN *south*

Kara Sea

LOCATION Bounded by the islands of Novaya Zemlya in the west, and Severnaya Zemlya in the east

AREA 880,000 square km (340,000 square miles)

MAXIMUM DEPTH
620m (2,035ft)

INFLOWS Barents Sea, Laptev Sea; rivers Ob', Yenisey

The Kara Sea formed as a result of deglaciation after the last ice age. Most of the sea sits over continental shelf with depths of less than 200m (655ft). The sea floor contains many broad terraces that step down from the southeast (where it is very shallow) to the north and west. Two deep troughs cut through the shelf. A huge volume of fresh water pours into the Kara Sea during the summer from rivers along the Siberian coast. Because of this, surface

DEEP INLETS
Several deep inlets of the Kara Sea cut into the mainland. Those visible at the foot of this satellite image are estuaries at the mouths of the rivers Ob' and Yenisey.

salinity varies considerably, from about 34ppt throughout most of the sea in winter down to 10–12ppt near the mouths of the rivers Ob' (see p.193) and Yenisey in early summer. From December to June, most of the sea is ice-covered. In contrast, between July and October, over 90 per cent is ice-free, although surface temperatures never rise above 4–5°C (39–41°F). During the summer, the Kara Sea is an important route for transport of goods into and out of western Siberia, including oil and natural gas since large deposits were discovered in the Ob'-Yenisey region. The sea is also an important fishing ground, but there are concerns about the threat to marine life posed by the dumping of nuclear waste in the recent past.

ARCTIC OCEAN *south*

Laptev Sea

LOCATION Bounded by Severnaya Zemlya in the west and the New Siberian Islands in the east

AREA 714,000 square km (276,000 square miles)

MAXIMUM DEPTH
2,980m (9,775ft)

INFLOWS Kara Sea, Arctic Basin; rivers Lena, Khatanga

Of the various Arctic seas, the Laptev Sea is one of the coldest and most inhospitable. It has been called the ice factory of the Arctic, as it produces most of the ice transported by the Transpolar Drift, a current that carries water and sea-ice from the coasts of Siberia and Alaska across the North Pole to the Fram Strait, east of Greenland. Almost all of the Laptev Sea is ice-covered from October to May. In winter there are gales and blizzards; in the summer, frequent fogs. Much of the sea covers a shallow continental shelf, which breaks off abruptly to depths of 2,000m (6,600ft) or more in the far north. The sea is influenced by large amounts of run-off from large Siberian rivers, several of which form extensive deltas.

TIKSI HARBOUR
Tiksi is the main port on the Laptev Sea coast but is active only from June to October. For the rest of the year, the harbour is frozen over. Timber is the main cargo that goes through the port.

East Siberian Sea

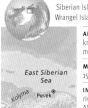

LOCATION Bounded by the New Siberian Islands in the west and Wrangel Island in the east

AREA 936,000 square km (361,000 square miles)

MAXIMUM DEPTH 155m (510ft)

INFLOWS Laptev Sea; rivers Kolyma, Indigirka, Alezeya

The East Siberian Sea is the shallowest of the Arctic seas. Its average depth is just 10–20m (35–65ft) in its western and central parts and 30–40m (100–130ft) in the east. Freshwater

BROKEN, DRIFTING SEA-ICE (TOP RIGHT)

input from the Kolyma River runs as high as 10 million litres (2.6 million gallons) per second in the spring. The salinity of the sea ranges from almost zero near the river-mouth to 33ppt in the north. It is ice-covered for most of the year, and navigation through it is possible only in August and September.

Chukchi Sea

LOCATION Lying to the northeast of eastern Siberia and to the northwest of northern Alaska

AREA 582,000 square km (225,000 square miles)

MAXIMUM DEPTH 110m (360ft)

INFLOWS Bering Sea (Pacific Ocean), East Siberian Sea, Arctic Basin

The Chukchi Sea is a mostly shallow sea situated between Alaska, Siberia, and the central Arctic Basin. The sea is fed by low-salinity waters from the Pacific Ocean via the narrow, shallow

Bering Strait. This water mixes with colder and more saline water in the Chukchi Sea; the mixed water then moves into the Arctic Basin. In the northeast, a submarine channel feeds some of the mixed water into the Beaufort Sea. The Chukchi Sea is totally iced over between December and May. It supports large populations of walrus and several species of seal.

A SUMMER FOGBOW

Baffin Bay

LOCATION Southwest of northern Greenland and northeast of Baffin Island in the Canadian Arctic

AREA 689,000 square km (266,000 square miles)

MAXIMUM DEPTH 2,100m (6,900ft)

INFLOWS Arctic Basin, Labrador Sea (Atlantic Ocean); glaciers of West Greenland

Separated from the Arctic Basin by Ellesmere Island and parts of the Canadian Archipelago, Baffin Bay is a mostly deep-water Arctic sea. From mid-August to October, the bay is

ICEBERGS IN DAVIS STRAIT
Many icebergs calved from glaciers in western Greenland drift across Baffin Bay. From there, the Baffin Current moves them into the Labrador Sea.

largely free of sea-ice, but in winter an ice cover forms and moves southeast under the prevailing winds. Combined with Arctic pack ice entering through the northern sounds, and icebergs that have broken off glaciers in northwestern Greenland, this makes the bay unnavigable for much of the year. A significant feature is the North Water polynya, an area of open water where thick ice cover would be expected. Its presence may be related to the warming effect of the West Greenland Current, which enters the bay from the south.

Beaufort Sea

LOCATION North of northern Alaska and northwestern Canada, bounded in the east by the Amundsen Gulf

AREA 476,000 square km (184,000 square miles)

MAXIMUM DEPTH 4,680m (15,350ft)

INFLOWS Chukchi Sea, Arctic Basin; rivers Mackenzie, Colville

The Beaufort Sea has a shallow coastal area and a deep offshore area, the Beaufort Deep. Ice covers the sea for most of the year, but it is navigable near the coast from August to October. The Mackenzie River deposits billions of tons of fresh water and 15 million tons of sediment into the sea each year.

MELTING SEA-ICE

Greenland Sea

LOCATION Bounded by the Arctic Basin to the north, Svalbard to the northeast, and Iceland to the south

AREA 1.2 million square km (465,000 square miles)

MAXIMUM DEPTH 4,800m (16,000ft)

INFLOWS Arctic Basin, Norwegian Sea (Atlantic Ocean)

Sandwiched between the Arctic Basin to the north and the Atlantic Ocean to the south, the Greenland Sea is an important exchange region for different bodies of water moving in the global system of ocean circulation. A constant current of warm and salty Atlantic water flows north through the eastern part of the sea into the Arctic Basin. Simultaneously, enormous amounts of shallow fresh water and ice move south via the Fram Strait between Greenland and Svalbard and down the western part of the sea as the East Greenland Current. As they pass through, these

waters are modified by cooling (Atlantic water) and melting (Arctic ice). In each case, the water subsequently sinks to the sea-floor when it meets the less dense water masses. From November to July, ice covers most of the sea and includes drifting Arctic pack ice, locally formed sea-ice, and icebergs. Surface water temperatures range from -1°C (30°F) in the north in February to 6°C (43°F) in the south in August. Moderately dense populations of a variety of plankton thrive in the Greenland Sea during spring and summer.

BLACK-LEGGED KITTIWAKES
Seen here perched on an iceberg in the western part of the Greenland Sea, Black-legged Kittiwakes are one of the main gull species that breed on the Greenland coast.

OCEAN

OCEAN

NORTH ATLANTIC STORM
Cyclonic storms and rough seas are common in the North Atlantic above the latitude of 30°N. These wave-battered rocks are at Porto do Moniz on the island of Madeira.

ATLANTIC OCEAN
Atlantic Ocean

LOCATION Between North and South America to the west and Europe and Africa to the east

AREA 77 million square km (29.7 million square miles)

MAXIMUM DEPTH 8,605m (28,230ft)

INFLOWS Arctic Ocean, Southern Ocean; rivers St. Lawrence, Mississippi, Orinoco, Amazon, Paraná Congo, Niger, Loire, Rhine; Mediterranean Sea

The Atlantic Ocean is the second largest of the world's oceans, and it has several tributary seas. An immense mountain range extends from north to south along the Atlantic sea floor, covering almost a third of its area. Known as the Mid-Atlantic Ridge, this began to form about 180 million years ago, and during the Mesozoic Era sea-floor spreading on either side of the ridge opened up the Atlantic by separating the Americas from Europe and Africa. Rising from the ridge system and its flanks are several islands,

ROCKY SHORELINE
The Atlantic Ocean has many rocky coasts, such as this shoreline of eroded pink granite, on Mount Desert Island, Maine, USA. The glacier-sculpted island is the home of Acadia National Park.

including Iceland, the Azores, and Ascension Island. On either side of the Mid-Atlantic Ridge lie basins that are smooth and flat in some areas, but disrupted in others. Some large volcanoes are found singly or in rows in the Atlantic basins. These rise to form sea mounts and, in some places, islands (such as Bermuda). The surface waters of the Atlantic Ocean move in two large gyres, a clockwise one in the North Atlantic and an anticlockwise one in the South Atlantic. In addition, there is a distinct deep-water circulation. Dense cold water formed at the poles sinks to the bottom and moves slowly at depth towards the Equator. These water masses converge and mix in the South Atlantic, where a portion of the water wells up, bringing nutrients to the surface. Prevailing weather in the Atlantic Ocean varies with latitude. The higher latitudes are characterized by variable westerly winds, changeable weather, and frequent storms. Closer to the Equator, there are belts of higher pressure systems, and constant easterly trade winds. This region has few intense storms, though in late summer/early autumn, the low latitudes of the North Atlantic are affected by hurricanes, which arise in the mid- and eastern Atlantic and move west and northwest.

ISOLATED ISLAND
Tristan da Cunha in the South Atlantic is the most remote inhabited island in the world. A volcano rising from 3,700m (12,140ft) below sea-level, it is almost entirely surrounded by high cliffs.

LIGHTHOUSES

The Atlantic Ocean has been the most heavily travelled of the world's oceans for hundreds of years, and many of its coasts are prone to storms and fog. To safeguard the large numbers of passing ships, thousands of lighthouses have been constructed on Atlantic coasts since the 1700s. Today, over 200 lighthouses are in active use on the eastern US seaboard alone. Lighthouses are constructed at important points on a coastline: at entrances to estuaries or harbours, and on isolated or sunken rocks or shoals. Today, most lighthouses are automated – the days of permanent lighthouse-keepers are almost gone.

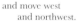

ATLANTIC COD
Cod is an important commercial fish species of the North Atlantic, but overfishing has severely depleted stocks in several regions.

BASKING SHARK
Basking sharks range throughout Atlantic waters. They swim with their mouths wide open, trapping small crustaceans in their comb-like gill rakers.

LIVING REEF
Like a forest on land, this coral reef at
Milne Bay, Papua New Guinea, has a
complex structure that provides homes
and food for a wealth of animals.

THREATS TO CORAL REEFS

Coral reefs are extremely rich marine habitats and by far the largest structures created by living things. However, because they grow slowly and have stringent environmental requirements, they are easily harmed by human activity. At least 20 per cent of the world's coral reefs have been so badly damaged that they are effectively dead. Without urgent action, about 40 per cent of the reefs may disappear in the next 30 years – a prospect that conservationists are fighting hard to prevent.

Reefs in Danger

Corals are soft-bodied animals that protect themselves by building chalky skeletons. The skeletons last far longer than the animals themselves, and they build up to form reefs. The surface of a reef is like a living skin. It contains millions of coral animals, or polyps, and even larger numbers of microscopic algae called zooxanthellae. These live inside the polyps, and they help to nourish their hosts by harnessing the energy in sunlight (see pp.314–15).

In a healthy reef, some branching corals grow more than 20cm (8in) a year. Their upward spread is limited only by the sea itself, because few corals can stand more than an hour of exposure at low tide. This growth offsets the damage caused by storms and by coral-eating animals, so the reef expands or maintains its size. But if anything harms either the polyps or their zooxanthellae, this delicate balance is upset. Growth is no longer maintained, and the surface of the reef begins to erode. If the coral does not recover, the entire ecosystem begins to decline, because corals provide reef animals with food and habitats.

DEAD ZONE
Staghorn corals are the fastest-growing coral and among the most easily damaged. They are seen here littering the sea bed in the Caribbean.

Causes of Decline

Coral reefs have always been used as a local resource, and they can be seriously harmed by overfishing or by removing the coral itself for personal or commercial gain. They can also be affected by pollution from an area far away.

Coral requires clear, nutrient-poor water, because this favours their zooxanthellae and keeps competing free-living algae in check. Conversely, anything that makes seawater more turbid or more fertile can suppress their growth. In many parts of the tropics, farming and logging have increased soil erosion, producing sediment-laden run-off, which finds its way into the sea. This shades the coral, robbing it of the light that its zooxanthellae partners need to survive. Reefs are also affected by coastal and tourist development, because sewage raises water nutrient levels, causing overgrowths of algae. Sewage treatment can prevent this, but adequate funds are often lacking. Even in developed countries, many coastal communities still discharge raw sewage into the sea.

STRANGERS ON THE SHORE
In coastal areas with coral reefs, tourism has to be carefully managed to avoid creating environmental damage.

Raised Sea Temperatures

Despite these threats, local reef damage can be reversed. In protected areas, some reefs have been quick to recover when pollution and fishing are controlled. But coral reefs are also threatened by global warming (see pp.376–77) – a worldwide phenomenon that is far harder to control.

When sea temperatures are raised, coral reefs are harmed. Coral polyps are put under stress, and so they respond by expelling their algae – in a process called coral bleaching. Bleaching reverses itself if the water then cools, but, if raised temperatures continue for a prolonged period, the coral polyps die.

Human addition of carbon dioxide to the air also turns the oceans more acidic. This could severely impair corals' ability to grow their skeletons.

SCATTERED REMAINS
Fragments of old coral litter a beach at Puako, Hawaii, and contrast with the black volcanic sand.

BLEACHING EVENTS
This graph shows the incidence of coral bleaching across the world over three decades. There has been a general upward trend and a year of catastrophic bleaching in 1998.

OCEAN

Mediterranean Sea

LOCATION To the south of Europe and western Turkey and to the north of North Africa

AREA 2.5 million square km (970,000 square miles)

MAXIMUM DEPTH 4,900m (16,000ft)

INFLOWS Atlantic Ocean; Black Sea; rivers Nile, Rhône, Po, Ebro

OCEAN

The world's largest inland sea, the Mediterranean occupies an elongated depression between Europe and Africa that originally formed tens of millions of years ago. About 6 million years ago, a fall in sea-level cut the Mediterranean off from the Atlantic Ocean to the west. During the next 2 million years, the depression repeatedly reflooded and dried out, leaving some thick salt deposits. Finally, a rise in sea-level allowed Atlantic waters to flood back in. Today, the Mediterranean Sea remains linked to the Atlantic Ocean via the Straits of Gibraltar in the west, a channel just 13km (8 miles) wide and 320m (1,050ft) deep. It also connects to the Red Sea via the Suez Canal in

OCTOPUS ON SEA FLOOR
Although Mediterranean marine life has been depleted over the past 40 years through human activity, some species, such as octopuses, remain common.

the southeast (see p.336) and to the Black Sea in the northeast.

Underwater, the Mediterranean sea floor is composed of a series of moderately deep basins separated by sills (see p.139). One of the main sills runs between the island of Sicily and Cape Bon in Tunisia, dividing the sea into a western half and a larger eastern half. The Mediterranean Sea also contains many smaller regions lying over shallower water, such as the Adriatic Sea to the east of Italy and the Gulf of Gabes off the eastern coast of Tunisia. Large islands in the Mediterranean include Crete and Cyprus in the eastern half, Sardinia, Corsica, and Majorca in the western half, and Sicily at the toe of Italy. The Aegean Sea, between Greece and Turkey, is dotted with the many islands

JACQUES COUSTEAU

As the inventor of SCUBA, and through his films and books about the underwater world, the Frenchman Jacques Cousteau (1910–97) made a huge contribution to subaquatic exploration in the 20th century and to public awareness of the marine environment. The Mediterranean Sea was the site of both Cousteau's original experiments with SCUBA and some important discoveries, such as the unearthing in 1957 of an ancient Greek wine freighter, buried beneath the seafloor off Marseilles.

LAVA FORMATIONS
Along with some other Aegean Islands, Lesbos has seen considerable volcanic activity in the past, as evidenced by these lava formations on its coast.

STRAITS OF GIBRALTAR
Two series of solitons, or large pulses of water travelling in the open sea, can be seen above, propagating from the Straits of Gibraltar at the top of this picture. They are triggered by inflowing Atlantic water accelerated by its passage through the straits.

ALEXANDRIA
One of the busiest Mediterranean ports is Alexandria, located on the edge of the Nile Delta. A former capital of Egypt, Alexandria now handles over 80 per cent of the country's exports and imports.

SEA FLOOR TREASURE

Trading has been conducted by sea in the Mediterranean for over 3,000 years. As a result of navigational errors, storms, and wars, the present-day sea floor is littered with ancient wrecks, providing many sites of archaeological interest. Here, a diver brings a basket from the surface to collect the remains of bowls, bottles, and cups from a wreck that sank off the coast of Turkey in the 11th century CE. The oldest known shipwreck in the Mediterranean (at Ulu Burun, also off the coast of Turkey) dates from the 14th century BCE.

of the Greek Archipelago. Although a large amount of fresh water flows into the Mediterranean Sea from rivers, the total amount is only about a third of the water lost by evaporation. As a result, the sea is highly saline. There is also a continuous inflow of surface waters of normal salinity into the Mediterranean from the Atlantic via the Straits of Gibraltar, and to a lesser extent, from the Black Sea. These inflows are partly offset by outflows of saltier water at depth. The dominant current in the Mediterranean Sea is eastward, flowing along the north of the African coast, a continuation of the current that brings seawater in from the Atlantic. This current is most powerful in summer, when evaporation is at its strongest. Tides are generally weak throughout the whole region, two exceptions being the Gulf of Gabes and the Adriatic Sea. The Mediterranean Sea has long been important as a route for trade, (see panel, right) and remains so today, particularly since the opening of the Suez Canal. Marine mammals, fish, sponges, corals, and other invertebrates were once plentiful. However, a rise in population and the expansion of industry and tourism over the past 40 years have led to severe pollution of many of the coastal areas. This, together with overfishing, has severely depleted some fish stocks and other marine life.

OCEAN

INDIAN OCEAN

Indian Ocean

LOCATION Between Africa and Australia, extending from southern Asia to the Southern Ocean

[map showing Calcutta, Bombay, INDIAN OCEAN, Cape Town, Perth]

AREA 69 million square km (26.5 million square miles)

MAXIMUM DEPTH 7,258m (23,812ft)

INFLOWS Rivers Ganges, Indus, Tigris, Euphrates, Zambezi, Limpopo, Murray

The Indian Ocean is one of the youngest of the world's ocean basins and the most complex in terms of the structure of its floor. Both the Indian and Southern Oceans have formed over the past 120 million years following the break-up of the ancient continent of Gondwana. The Indian Ocean narrows towards the north, where the Indian Peninsula divides it into two large bodies of water, the Arabian Sea on the west and the Bay of Bengal on the east. The most

BANDED SEA SNAKE
These snakes are common in shallow lagoons in the eastern part of the Indian Ocean. Their tails act like rudders, making them highly efficient swimmers.

MACARONI PENGUINS
The Indian Ocean extends as far south as 60˚S. On a remote southern island, Kerguelen, there are many colonies of mammals and birds, including this colourful species of penguin.

striking feature of the ocean floor is a massive mid-ocean ridge, shaped like an upside-down Y, which occupies about a fifth of the ocean's total floor area (see p.319). One arm runs to the south of Africa and joins the Mid-Atlantic Ridge. The other runs to the south of Australia, where it eventually joins the Pacific–Antarctic Ridge. The two ridge arms join roughly in the centre of the ocean and continue north as the Mid-Indian Ridge. Creation of new oceanic crust at the various ridges is continuing to separate Africa, Antarctica, and Australia from each other. Along an extensive arc at its northeast margin, the Indian Plate is subducting beneath the southeast

edge of the Eurasian Plate to form the Indonesian volcanic arcs of Sumatra and Java. A continental shelf extends to an average distance of about 120km (75 miles) from the landmasses around the ocean. In places, the shelf and continental slope are penetrated by deep canyons carved by outflows from the Ganges, Indus, and Zambezi rivers, which have also deposited vast amounts of sediment onto the abyssal plains. The

SCULPTED ROCKS
These curious granitic rock formations, on the coast of the island of La Digue in the Seychelles, have been carved by a combination of wind, rain, and seawater erosion.

northern part of the Indian Ocean has a monsoon climate, characterized by rain-bearing winds that change direction twice yearly (see p.383). These changes are accompanied by twice-yearly reversals in the pattern of ocean currents, something that distinguishes the northern part of the Indian Ocean from all other oceans. The monsoon zone is also prone to destructive tropical storms that form over the open ocean and head in a westward direction. South of the monsoon zone lies the trade-winds zone, characterized by steady southeasterlies that prevail throughout the year. A third zone lies in the southern part of the Indian Ocean, between the latitudes of 30°S and 60°S. Here, there are light and variable winds in the northern part, and strong westerlies in the south. The warm waters that persist throughout much of the Indian Ocean provide an ideal environment for a rich variety of marine life. Some 4,000 species of fish live near the shores, many unique to this ocean. Coral reefs are abundant around all islands in the tropical areas, as well as along the western coasts of Thailand and Burma (Myanmar) and the east coast of Africa.

ZHENG HE

One of the first explorers to travel widely across the Indian Ocean was a Chinese Admiral, Zheng He (1371–1435). Accompanied by a huge fleet of ships, he visited most parts of the region, including India, Arabia, and east Africa, during 7 separate voyages in 1405–1433. His objectives included trading in goods, gathering knowledge about the region, and extending the sphere of Chinese political influence.

STILT FISHING
This method of fishing is still practised today in parts of Sri Lanka and Thailand. The fishermen and -women perch on poles in shallow water to avoid scaring away the fish.

Red Sea

LOCATION Between the northeastern corner of Africa and the Arabian Peninsula

AREA 450,000 square km (175,000 square miles)

MAXIMUM DEPTH 3,040m (9,975ft)

INFLOWS Arabian Sea (via the Gulf of Aden)

One of the warmest of the world's seas, the Red Sea occupies a depression formed by the Great Rift Valley (see p.88), the primary branch of the East African Ridge System, which has developed over the past 50 million years. Hydrothermal vents on the sea floor are evidence of continuing tectonic activity. The Sinai Peninsula splits the northern end of the sea into two arms: the shallow Gulf of Suez on the west; and the deeper Gulf of Aqaba on the east. Hardly any rain falls on the Red Sea and no rivers flow into it, but water evaporates at a high rate owing to the strong solar radiation. As a result, the Red Sea is highly saline. To make up for evaporation losses, surface water flows in from the Gulf of Aden in the south and continues as a northward-moving surface current. The Red Sea contains a rich marine life based on extensive coral reefs. Since the 1970s, this marine life has attracted increasing numbers of recreational scuba-divers, whose activities have caused great damage to the reefs.

SEA ROSE
This curious flower-like object, commonly seen attached to rocks at shallow depths, is actually a ribbon of eggs that was laid by a nudibranch, or sea slug.

SUEZ CANAL

First opened to shipping in 1869, the Suez Canal connects the Gulf of Suez at the northern end of the Red Sea to the Mediterranean Sea. One of the busiest waterways in the world, the 163km- (101-mile-) long canal provides a short cut for maritime traffic travelling between ports in North America and Europe and those in the Middle East, southern Asia, East Africa, and Oceania. The canal has no locks because the Gulf of Suez has roughly the same sea-level as the Mediterranean Sea.

GULF OF SUEZ
The turquoise waters of the Red Sea are completely surrounded by desert and, behind a coastal plain, mountains that rise as high as 2,000m (6,500ft).

ANEMONE GARDENS
The thousands of animal species found on Red Sea reefs include many Giant Anemones. The clownfish swimming close by secrete a mucus that protects them from the stinging tentacles.

OCEAN

OCEAN

INDIAN OCEAN *northwest*
Persian Gulf

LOCATION Forms an inlet of the Arabian Sea, between Iran and the Arabian Peninsula

AREA 241,000 square km (93,000 square miles)

MAXIMUM DEPTH 110m (360ft)

INFLOWS Rivers Tigris, Euphrates, Karun

Sometimes called the Arabian Gulf or just the Gulf, the Persian Gulf is best known for the large deposits of oil and natural gas that lie around its shores and beneath its thin floor. The region contains approximately two-thirds of the world's proven oil reserves and a third of its proven natural gas reserves. A warm and salty sea, the gulf receives a large inflow of both water and sediments from the Shatt al 'Arab, a river formed from the confluence of the Tigris and Euphrates rivers in the northwest (in Iraq). Its eastern shore is mountainous but its western shore is low-lying, with many islands, lagoons, and tidal flats. After oil, fishing is the most important industry in the Persian Gulf.

DESALINATION

The Gulf region receives little rainfall so water is scarce, though there are limited groundwater reserves. To avoid water shortages, over 20 desalination plants have been built on the western side of the Persian Gulf. Together they produce over 5,000 million litres (1,300 million gallons) of desalinated water per day. They return warm, concentrated seawater back into the Persian Gulf.

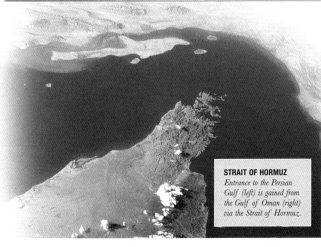

STRAIT OF HORMUZ
Entrance to the Persian Gulf (left) is gained from the Gulf of Oman (right) via the Strait of Hormuz.

INDIAN OCEAN *north*
Arabian Sea

LOCATION To the east of the Arabian Peninsula and to the southwest of the Indian Peninsula

AREA 3.9 million square km (1.5 million square miles)

MAXIMUM DEPTH 5,803m (19,038ft)

INFLOWS Rivers Indus, Narmada

The Arabian Sea occupies the western part of the northern Indian Ocean. Two northern extensions, the Gulf of Aden and Gulf of Oman, connect it to the Red Sea and Persian Gulf respectively. Various island groups lie around its margins, including the Seychelles to the southwest and the Maldives to the southeast. The sea supports an extensive fishing industry.

FISHERMEN ON DHOWS

INDIAN OCEAN *west*
Mozambique Channel

LOCATION Between Mozambique on the African mainland to the west and Madagascar to the east

AREA 1 million square km (386,000 square miles)

MAXIMUM DEPTH 3,000m (9,800ft)

INFLOWS River Zambezi, Rio Lúrio

An important shipping route for the countries of east and southern Africa, the 1,000km- (620-mile-) long Mozambique Channel is fed by the waters of the Zambezi and all the major rivers of Madagascar. For many decades, it was believed that a continuous warm current, the Mozambique Current, passed down through the channel. Recently it has been shown that no such current exists. Rather, water movements in the area are dominated by a series of anticlockwise eddies that reach to the channel bottom.

THE COELACANTH

The Mozambique Channel is one of just two places in the world with an identified population of Coelacanths, primitive fish that were believed to have been extinct for 65 million years until, in 1938, one was caught off the east coast of South Africa. Coelacanths live at depths greater than 150m (500ft), where they feed on small bottom-dwelling fish and cuttlefish.

PIROGUE BEACHED ON NOSY BE
The island of Nosy Be lies just off mainland Madagascar, on the eastern side of the Mozambique Channel. Pirogues are boats of a simple construction, typically used by Madagascans for fishing.

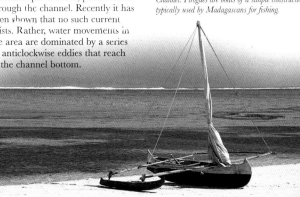

INDIAN OCEAN *north*
Bay of Bengal

LOCATION To the east of the Indian Peninsula and to the west of Burma (Myanmar) and the Malay Peninsula

AREA 2.9 million square km (1.1 million square miles)

MAXIMUM DEPTH 4,695m (15,400ft)

INFLOWS Rivers Ganges, Mahanadi, Godavari, Krishna, Kaveri, Irrawaddy

The Bay of Bengal occupies the northeastern corner of the Indian Ocean. Its smaller eastern part, the Andaman Sea, is separated from the rest of the bay by two island groups, the Andaman and Nicobar islands. The Bay of Bengal is bordered by a wide area of continental shelf cut through by canyons, and its floor is a vast abyssal plain. A distinctive feature at its northern extremity is the wide and thick fan of sediments from the River Ganges (see p.182). Intense tropical storms with high winds and torrential rain occur in spring and autumn. Combined with inflow from rivers during the summer monsoon, these markedly reduce the surface salinity of the bay's waters.

LIMESTONE ROCK OUTCROPS
On the Andaman Sea coast of Thailand, at Phang-Nga, there are many spectacular undercut limestone cliffs.

KO PANYEE, THAILAND
This picturesque fishing village rests precariously on wooden piles driven into the floor of the bay.

OCEAN

Pacific Ocean

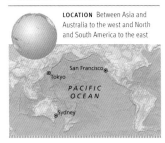

LOCATION Between Asia and Australia to the west and North and South America to the east

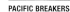

AREA 156 million square km (60 million square miles)

MAXIMUM DEPTH 10,924m (35,840ft)

INFLOWS Southern Ocean; rivers Yukon, Columbia, Amur, Yellow, Yangtze, Mekong

By far the largest ocean, the Pacific covers more than a third of the Earth's surface and holds more than half of its liquid water. It also contains the deepest point in the world's oceans, the Challenger Deep in the Mariana Trench. About three-quarters of the Pacific Ocean lies over a single tectonic plate, the Pacific Plate. Marking the boundary between this and the adjacent oceanic Nazca Plate in the southeastern Pacific is a large mid-ocean ridge, the East Pacific

MARINE IGUANA
One of many unusual animals found in the Galápagos Islands, the Marine Iguana is the only lizard that forages underwater for food.

ARTIFICIAL ISLANDS

Faced with a severe shortage of suitable land for building, Japan has turned to its Pacific coastal areas as potential construction sites, and created several artificial islands. There are now several in Tokyo Harbour and two near the port city of Kobe. Artificial islands are usually built by enclosing an area of shallow water with a seawall and then filling it in. Similar projects are now planned in other parts of the world, including the Baltic and Mediterranean seas.

KANSAI AIRPORT
This airport was constructed on an island built some 5km (3 miles) off the coast of Osaka, Japan, between 1987 and 1993.

Rise. Associated with plate movements away from this ridge, and occurring all around the Pacific Ocean's Ring of Fire (see p.117), are various deep-sea trenches marking subduction zones with abundant volcanic and earthquake activity. The eastern part of the Pacific Ocean has high mountain ranges on the continental side for most of its length. It has a narrow continental shelf, few large rivers discharging into it, and a regular coastline, except for fiords in the extreme north and south. In contrast, the western Pacific has an irregular continental boundary, many large marginal seas, huge rivers flowing in off the Asian mainland, and some wide areas of continental shelf. The surface waters over most of the Pacific Ocean move in two large gyres (see p.312). The main deep-water circulation is a northward spread of cold water at depth. This reaches as far north as Japan and then moves to the east. The main winds of the Pacific are twin belts of westerlies (blowing from west to east) between latitudes of 30° and 60°, both north and south of the Equator. Between the westerlies are the more predictable trade winds, which blow towards the Equator. Typhoons affect two large areas of the western Pacific in late summer and early autumn. There are numerous islands in the Pacific Ocean, many of them part of volcanic island arcs. Under the Nazca Plate off Ecuador is a volcanic hot spot that created the Galápagos Islands. Over millions of years, a remarkable collection of animals and plants reached this isolated spot from South America and then diversified on the different islands. Charles Darwin's study of this unique fauna and flora in the 1830s influenced the formation of his ideas about evolution.

GIANT KELP FOREST
The northeastern coasts of the Pacific are covered in forests of Giant Kelp. Among the world's fastest-growing plants, they thrive along rocky reefs.

PACIFIC BREAKERS
The Pacific has the world's largest fetch, the area over which wind can interact with surface water to create waves. This results in some immense breakers, like these ones in Hawaii.

RED TIDE
A red tide is seawater discoloured by a bloom of certain types of plankton, some of which produce toxins. Red tides occur in many parts of the Pacific, including the coasts of California (seen here).

ISLANDS IN PALAU, MICRONESIA
Consisting of coral structures built on top of a submarine ridge, these are typical islands of the west Pacific, except for the way they have been uplifted and eroded into humped shapes.

PACIFIC OCEAN north
Bering Sea

LOCATION Between western Alaska, USA, and the northeastern extremity of the Asian landmass

AREA
2.3 million square km (890,000 square miles)

MAXIMUM DEPTH
4,097m (13,442ft)

INFLOWS Central North Pacific Ocean; rivers Yukon, Anadyr'

The Bering Sea is the most northerly marginal sea of the Pacific Ocean, connecting to the Arctic Ocean in the north via the Bering Strait. In the south, the sea is fringed by an arc of volcanic islands, the Aleutians. In the southwest, the sea floor is separated by ridges into three basins. The Bering Sea has a severe climate, and in winter its northern part is covered in ice. It has a high biological productivity, however, with explosions of plankton growth occurring twice each year. The plankton supports large numbers of fish, mammals such as Sea Otters, and on the continental shelf area in the northeast, invertebrates such as molluscs, starfish, and sponges.

SEA-ICE BREAKING UP IN SPRING

PACIFIC OCEAN northeast
Gulf of Alaska

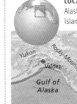

LOCATION Lying to the south of Alaska, USA, between Kodiak Island and Cape Spencer

AREA
1.5 million square km (592,000 square miles)

MAXIMUM DEPTH
5,000m (16,500ft)

INFLOWS Rivers Susitna, Copper; numerous large iceberg-producing glaciers

The Gulf of Alaska is a roughly triangular-shaped body of water, the apex of which is in Prince William Sound near the port of Valdez, which is North America's northernmost ice-free harbour. Two sides of the triangle extend from there to Cape Spencer (near the entrance to Glacier Bay) in the southeast and to Kodiak Island and the Alaskan Peninsula to the southwest. A warm current, the Alaska Current, moves through the gulf up the southeastern coast of Alaska, and a continuation, the Alaska Stream, runs out past the Alaskan Peninsula towards the central North Pacific. The southern part of the gulf lies over a deep abyssal plain, and in the southwest this plunges into the eastern part of the Aleutian Trench, to the southeast of Kodiak Island. There are several deep fiords and inlets along the Alaskan Gulf Coast. Many large glaciers, such as the Hubbard Glacier (see p.216), discharge icebergs into these inlets, from where they slowly float out to sea.

THE EXXON VALDEZ

The *Exxon Valdez* disaster of 1989, caused when an oil tanker went aground in Prince William Sound, was the world's worst-ever oil spill in terms of damage to the environment. Fourteen years later, toxic chemicals were still seeping into the Gulf of Alaska from contaminated beaches.

BREACHING ORCA
Orcas, or Killer Whales, are a common sight in the Gulf of Alaska, preying upon seals, sea lions, fish, squid, and occasionally sea birds and Sea Otters.

PACIFIC OCEAN northeast
Gulf of California

LOCATION Between the west coast of mainland Mexico and the peninsula of Baja California

AREA 160,000 square km (62,000 square miles)

MAXIMUM DEPTH
3,050m (10,000ft)

INFLOWS Rivers Fuerte, Sonora, Yaqui, Colorado

BALL OF JACK FISH
Various types of jack are among the 800 species of fish found in the gulf. The balling behavior seen here is thought to be a defence against predators.

Also known as the Sea of Cortés, the Gulf of California is a 1,200km- (750-mile-) long inlet from the Pacific Ocean into the west coast of Mexico. It lies over the boundary between the Pacific and North American plates and is thought to have formed by sea-floor spreading over the past 6 million years. The Gulf of California consists of two distinct regions. The northern part is mostly shallow – due to the accumulation of silt transported by the Colorado River (see p.166) over thousands of years – and has a large tidal range. The southern part is much deeper and less affected by tides, and it includes the Guaymas Basin, which has many hydrothermal vents. The large amount of sunlight in the region, combined with the nutrients provided by upwelling, allow high plankton growth, which supports some rich fishing grounds. Unfortunately, the gulf's environment is now threatened by overfishing, unregulated tourism development, and insufficient freshwater flow (most water from the Colorado River is now diverted for residential and agricultural use).

BAHIA DE LOS ANGELES
This area of the Gulf of California, surrounded by desert, has been compared to the Galápagos Islands because of its diverse marine life.

Sea of Okhotsk

LOCATION Off the far eastern coast of Russia, to the west of the Kamchatka Peninsula

AREA
1.6 million square km
(611,000 square miles)

MAXIMUM DEPTH
3,372m (11,063ft)

INFLOWS Sea of Japan; rivers Amur, Uda, Okhota, Penzhina

The Sea of Okhotsk is a large, cold sea that freezes over during the winter months and is frequently covered with fog. Except where it laps the northern-most Japanese island of Hokkaido in the south, it is surrounded by Russian territory: the Kamchatka Peninsula in

THE WORLD'S LARGEST EAGLE
The coasts of the Sea of Okhotsk are a breeding ground for Steller's Sea Eagle.

the east; the Russian mainland and the island of Sakhalin in the west; and the Kurile Island arc in the southeast. The floor of the sea slopes gently from north to south and then plunges to depths greater than 3,000m (10,000ft) to the northwest of the Kuriles. Tides and currents in the sea are strong, with a tidal range reaching 13m (43ft) in some locations. The Sea of Okhotsk is exceptionally important to Russia as a fisheries resource. Oil and gas deposits have also been found on the continental shelf area in the northern part of the sea.

ISLAND IN THE KURILES
The volcanic origin of Ushishur Island is clear in this view of its lake-filled central crater.

Sea of Japan

LOCATION To the northwest of Japan and to the east of the Korean Peninsula and southeastern Siberia

AREA 978,000 square km (377,600 square miles)

MAXIMUM DEPTH
3,742m (12,276ft)

INFLOWS East China Sea; rivers Tumen, Ishikari, Shinano, Agano, Mogami, Teshio

The Sea of Japan is almost completely enclosed by mainland Asia and the islands of Japan. A current of warm water (the Tsushima Current) flows into the sea from the East China Sea to the south. Outflow is mainly into the Sea of Okhotsk in the north, via

the La Pérouse Strait, and into the Pacific Ocean to the east through the Tsugaru Strait. The northern part of the sea freezes in winter. Occasional upwellings of nutrient-rich water encourage strong plankton blooms.

RUGGED COASTLINE
The coasts around the Sea of Japan are mostly rocky, as here on the island of Honshu.

FISHING FOR SQUID

During summer and autumn, large fishing fleets set off into the Sea of Japan to fish for squid. Bright halogen lamps, specially waterproofed, are lowered underwater or floated on the surface to attract the squid, which feed at night. The lights are so brilliant that the fleets can be seen from space.

OCEAN

Yellow Sea

LOCATION To the southwest of the Korean Peninsula, extending to the coast of east-central China

AREA 530,000 square km (205,000 square miles)

MAXIMUM DEPTH
103m (338ft)

INFLOWS Rivers Yellow, Yangtze, Liao He, Luan He, Yalu, Han

The Yellow Sea is a shallow, flat-bottomed, and partly enclosed inlet of the Pacific Ocean. Its main bulk lies to the southwest of the southern part of the Korean Peninsula (see p.92). Further north, there are two extensions of the sea: Korea Bay in the northeast; and the Gulf of Bo Hai in the north-west, into which flows the waters of

the Yellow River. The Yellow Sea derives its name from the colour of the silt-laden water that is discharged into it from the Yellow River, the Yangtze, and other major rivers. Most of the Yellow Sea floor is continental shelf that only 10,000 years ago was dry land or the estuary of the Yellow River. There are many sand shoals near the coast of China, and several small islands lie off the coast of Korea. A warm current flows from the southeast into the middle of the Yellow Sea, and there are southward-flowing currents along the coasts. Tides in the sea are considerable, especially along the west coast of the Korean Peninsula, with a maximum tidal range of 8m (27ft). The surface temperature of the sea varies remarkably, from close to freezing in the north in winter to as high as 28°C (82°F) in some of the shallower parts during the summer. The Yellow Sea is particularly rich in bottom-dwelling fish, and this is exploited by fleets of trawlers from China, Japan, and North and South Korea.

GREEN TURTLE
The Yellow Sea is the northern limit of the range of the Green Turtle, which lives near coasts and grazes on algae and sea grass.

SILT-LADEN WATERS
In this satellite image of the Yellow Sea, the Yellow River can be seen discharging its load of silt at top left, as can the Yangtze at bottom left.

PACIFIC OCEAN *west*

East China Sea

LOCATION Between east-central China and the Ryukyu Islands, extending south to Taiwan

AREA 751,000 square km (290,000 square miles)

MAXIMUM DEPTH 2,717m (8,912ft)

INFLOWS South China Sea, Philippine Sea; River Yangtze

The East China Sea is a shallow sea with an average depth of just 349m (1,145ft). It is separated from the Yellow Sea (see p.341) to the north by an imaginary line that runs from Cheju Island, off the tip of the Korean Peninsula, to the mouth of the River Yangtze in mainland China. To the south, it connects to the South China Sea (see below) through a shallow strait, the Taiwan Strait, between mainland China and the island of Taiwan. Much of the western part of the sea covers an area of continental shelf. Its deepest section, the Okinawa Trough, stretches for several hundred kilometres along the western side of the Ryukyu Islands in the east. A warm current (a branch of the Kuroshio Current) enters the East China Sea to the east of Taiwan and moves north, with branches penetrating into the Yellow Sea and into the Sea of Japan (see p.341) to the northeast. During summer, warm, moist winds from the western Pacific bring heavy rain to the East China Sea, sometimes accompanied by typhoons (hurricanes). In winter, cold, dry winds blow across the sea from the Asian mainland. Fishing is one of the major sources of income in the region, with the main catches being anchovy, tuna, shrimp, mackerel, and the eel-like Cutlass Fish. The East China Sea serves as the main shipping route from the South China Sea to ports in Japan and elsewhere in the North Pacific.

MANTA RAY
Manta Rays are most often encountered near the surface of lagoons. These gigantic fish, measuring up to 7m (23ft) across, swim by flapping their large pectoral fins.

TYPHOON
Hurricanes in the western Pacific are known as typhoons. Many form to the east of the Philippines and then move northwest over the East China Sea.

HYOPCHAE BEACH ON CHEJU
This idyllic beach is on the west coast of Cheju Island in the northern part of the East China Sea. Offshore are some of the world's most northerly coral reefs.

PACIFIC OCEAN *west*

South China Sea

LOCATION Bounded by southern China, eastern Southeast Asia, the Philippines, and Indonesia

AREA 3.7 million square km (1.4 million square miles)

MAXIMUM DEPTH 5,016m (16,457ft)

INFLOWS Rivers Xi Jiang, Mekong, Red, Tha Chin, Chao Phraya

The largest marginal sea of the western Pacific, the South China Sea stretches for over 2,700km (1,700 miles) around the southeast edge of the Asian mainland. Two offshoots of the sea, the Gulf of Tongking and the Gulf of Thailand, indent Southeast Asia. The northeastern part of the sea, close to the Philippines, lies over a deep, diamond-shaped submarine basin, of which the most southerly part is called the South China Basin. North of this lies a broad area of continental shelf that extends for up to 240km (150 miles) from the coast of China and Vietnam and includes the Taiwan Strait and Gulf of Tongking. To the south, off southern Vietnam, the shelf narrows and then connects with the Sunda Shelf, one of the largest areas of continental shelf in the world, which underlies the whole of the southern part of the South China Sea. This shelf is dotted with many small islands and island groups. The weather in the South China Sea is marked by monsoons and summer typhoons. Annual rainfall is as high as 4,000mm (160in) on parts of the Sunda Shelf. Both fishing and shipping are of high economic importance. Fish caught in the South China Sea supply as much as 50 per cent of the animal protein consumed by the people of Southeast Asia. The major ports and commercial centres around the sea include Hong Kong, Manila, Hô Chi Minh City, Singapore, and Bangkok.

WHALE SHARK
The world's largest fish at over 12 tonnes, these plankton feeders are commonly sighted in some areas of the South China Sea, such as in western parts of the Philippines.

TEK SING PORCELAIN

A famous shipwreck in the South China Sea is that of the *Tek Sing*, an unusually large Chinese junk that ran aground on a coral reef about 500km (300 miles) southeast of Singapore in 1822, while en route to Java. The ship was carrying about 350,000 pieces of Chinese porcelain, much of which has been salvaged by divers and subsequently auctioned, following discovery of the wreck site in 1999.

ANG THONG NATIONAL PARK
Lying in the Gulf of Thailand, this marine park consists of 42 forest-topped islands that were created by sea-level rise.

PACIFIC OCEAN *west*
Sulu Sea

LOCATION Between northeastern Borneo (Malaysia) and the central islands of the Philippines

AREA 260,000 square km (100,000 square miles)

MAXIMUM DEPTH 5,600m (18,400ft)

INFLOWS Celebes Sea

The Sulu Sea is one of several warm seas around Borneo. It connects in the northwest to the South China Sea via passages on either side of the island of Palawan, part of the Philippines. In the southeast, the Sulu Sea is fringed by the Sulu Archipelago, comprising over 4,000 small coral islands. Pearl fishing is often carried out from stilt houses built on top of the reefs.

LIMESTONE CLIFF, PALAWAN

PACIFIC OCEAN *west*
Banda Sea

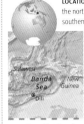

LOCATION Bounded by Sulawesi to the northwest and the central and southern Maluku Islands to the east

AREA 470,000 square km (180,000 square miles)

MAXIMUM DEPTH 7,440m (24,410ft)

INFLOWS Molucca Sea, Arafura Sea

The Banda Sea is a warm sea that laps the shores of the Maluku Islands or Moluccas, formerly the Spice Islands, of Indonesia. It connects to numerous other marginal seas, including the Molucca Sea in the north, and the Arafura Sea in the southeast, via straits between various island groups. The people of these islands are still involved in the cultivation of spices such as cloves and nutmeg, as well as fruit, coconuts, and tapioca.

NEIJALAKKA ISLAND, MALUKU, INDONESIA

PACIFIC OCEAN *southwest*
Tasman Sea

LOCATION Lying between New Zealand and the southeastern coast of Australia

AREA 2.3 million square km (900,000 square miles)

MAXIMUM DEPTH 5,945m (19,500ft)

INFLOWS Southern Ocean; Coral Sea

The most southerly of the marginal seas of the Pacific, the Tasman Sea lies in the belt of westerly winds known as the roaring forties and is noted for its storminess. The sea merges with

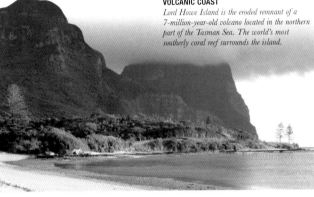

the Coral Sea (see below) in the north, and in the southwest connects to the Indian Ocean via the Bass Strait (see p.312) between Tasmania and Australia. Its southern part overlies a broad, deep basin, the Tasman Basin, while the northeastern part covers an elongated trough, the New Caledonia Depression. These two deep areas are separated by a ridge called the Lord Howe Rise. Lord Howe Island lies near the boundary of this rise and the Tasman Basin. A dominant current in the western part of the sea is the warm, southward-moving East Australia Current. During winter and spring, colder water moves up from the south. The Tasman Sea's resources include oil deposits in the Gippsland Basin at the eastern end of Bass Strait.

VOLCANIC COAST
Lord Howe Island is the eroded remnant of a 7-million-year-old volcano located in the northern part of the Tasman Sea. The world's most southerly coral reef surrounds the island.

PACIFIC OCEAN *southwest*
Coral Sea

LOCATION To the southeast of Papua New Guinea, east of northeast Australia and west of Vanuatu

AREA 4.8 million square km (1.8 million square miles)

MAXIMUM DEPTH 9,165m (30,070ft)

INFLOWS West Central Pacific Ocean; rivers Fly, Purari, Kikori

The Coral Sea is a large marginal sea that extends from northeastern Australia some 1,300km (800 miles) east to the island chain of Vanuatu (formerly the New Hebrides). A major feature is the Great Barrier Reef, the world's largest coral reef, which stretches for 2,010km (1,250 miles) along the east coast of Queensland. However, the reef occupies only a small area of the whole Coral Sea. To its east, and north of latitude 20°S, there are many individual

CLOSED ANEMONE
This giant anemone, with attendant clownfish, is one of several thousand species of cnidarians (corals, sea anemones, jellyfish, and hydroids) that are found in the Coral Sea.

reefs and small islands, known collectively as the Coral Sea Islands Territory, which rise from an area called the Coral Sea Plateau. To the northeast of the Coral Sea Plateau lies a large, deep basin, the Coral Sea Basin, and there are other deep basins much further east towards Vanuatu. Tectonic plate boundaries lie at the northern and eastern margins of the sea, where the Indian and Australian plates are being forced beneath adjoining plates. These boundaries are marked by deep trenches, notably the Vanuatu Trench. The main current in the Coral Sea is the South Equatorial Current, which flows from the east. As it approaches Queensland, it splits into two branches, one of which moves down the east coast of Australia as the East Australia Current while the other deflects north towards Papua New Guinea and then back east across the northern part of the Coral Sea. The sea has a subtropical climate and is subject to typhoons, especially from January to April. The Coral Sea's marine life is highly diverse and includes hundreds of species of stony (reef-building) corals, over 4,000 types of mollusc, and thousands of species of fish.

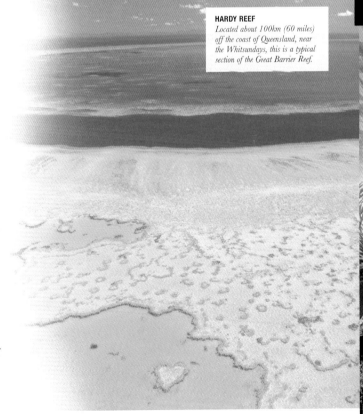

HARDY REEF
Located about 100km (60 miles) off the coast of Queensland, near the Whitsundays, this is a typical section of the Great Barrier Reef.

OCEAN

EROSIONAL COASTLINE
These cliffs pounded by Atlantic waves are near the village of Port, County Donegal, Ireland. They show features typical of long-term marine erosion.

COASTS

COASTS ARE THE PLACES WHERE the Earth's oceans and seas meet the land. Within these regions can be found a great variety of different landforms, which are shaped by the interaction of breaking waves, the rise and fall of tides, the effect of currents, and slow changes in the levels of land and sea. Coasts can also be affected by land-based phenomena – such as glacier advance and retreat, lava flows, and the discharge of sediment from rivers – and weathering by wind, rain, or frost.

Variations in these processes and factors over time and along the length of shorelines cause constant change, sometimes eroding coasts and sometimes building them up. Last but not least, the activities of people also influence coastlines – about half of the world's human population lives on or within 100km (60 miles) of a coast. These activities include the building of coast defences such as sea-walls and groynes, the reclaiming of land from the sea, and the creation of artificial islands.

Coasts and Sea-Level

A COAST IS A STRIP OF LAND in immediate contact with the sea, extending from the shoreline inland to the first major change in terrain. Coasts are dynamic rather than static. They quickly alter in response to natural forces such as wave action and tides, land-based processes, and sea-level change. These forces and processes constantly push and pull at coastlines, and, as a result, their shape and location changes. There are also many different types of coasts. The types and the processes that shape them are in turn determined by the various causes of sea-level change.

Emergent Coasts

Emergent coastlines result from land being uplifted faster than sea-level has risen since the last ice age. The causes are either tectonic activity (for example, on the USA's Pacific Coast) or slow glacial rebound (such as in parts of Scandinavia and New England, USA). On emergent coasts, areas that were formerly sea floor may become exposed above the shoreline, and former beaches may become the tops of cliffs. Emergent coasts are typically rocky, but usually have a smooth shoreline.

RAISED BEACH
The tops of these cliffs in the Bay of Fundy, Canada, are former beaches that were raised by glacial rebound.

Sea-Level Change

Changes in sea-level are of two different types, regional and global. The most important cause of a global change in sea-level is an increase or decrease in the extent of the world's ice-sheets and glaciers (see below). When these grow larger, sea-level drops because water becomes locked up in the ice; and when they melt, sea-level rises. Two other parameters that affect global sea-level are ocean temperature and the size of ocean basins (see right). Regional sea-level change occurs when a specific area of land rises or falls relative to the general sea-level. Two of the main causes are tectonic uplifting of land, which is common in regions where oceanic crust is being forced beneath continental crust, and glacial rebound, which is a slow rise of an area of land after an ice-sheet that once weighed it down has melted. Sea-levels have constantly fluctuated throughout the Earth's history, not least in the recent past. For example, about 15–18,000 years ago, during the last ice age, sea-levels were about 120m (400ft) lower than they are today.

OCEAN BASIN CHANGE
A rise in sea-level can occur when new crust is produced at a fast-spreading ridge. The new crust swells because it is relatively hot and buoyant, pushing the ocean water upwards.

CHANGES IN SEA-LEVEL OVER GLACIAL CYCLES
When temperatures rise, glacial ice melts and flows into the sea and seawater expands, raising sea-levels. The rise is partially offset by depression of oceanic crust and, in some regions, by land rising following glacial rebound.

Types of Coasts

Coasts are either primary or secondary. Primary coasts are relatively young ones that have been created by terrestrial processes or by sea-level change. Examples of primary coasts are volcanic coasts, where lava has flowed to the sea and solidified, and deltas, where a river deposits sediment as it enters the sea. Coasts in which sea-level change has played a significant part include drowned and emergent coasts. Other types of primary coast are those dominated by glaciers or glacial moraines, and karst coasts, where a region of limestone has been eroded and later inundated by the sea. Secondary coasts are older ones that have been shaped by marine erosional and depositional processes (see pp.354–55) or the activities of marine organisms (see Reefs, pp.314–15).

VOLCANIC COAST
This coast on the Snaefellsnes Peninsula, Iceland, was created by lava from a nearby volcano. Since the coast formed, it has started to undergo some wave erosion.

DROWNED KARST
This coast of eroded limestone in Ha Long Bay, Vietnam, has been inundated by a rise in sea-level.

DELTA COAST
A delta, such as this one, the Wadi al-Mujib on the Dead Sea, Jordan, is the result of sediment deposited by a river.

Drowned Coasts

Drowned coasts (sometimes called submergent coasts) are formed as a result of a global or regional rise in sea-level. Several types are recognized. A ria coast is a river-eroded hilly landscape, with valleys running perpendicular to the coast, that has been partly drowned. The coast usually has deep bays or estuaries, intervening headlands, and many offshore islands. There are examples in southwest Ireland and Great Britain, northwest Spain, and the eastern USA (such as Chesapeake Bay, see p.68). A fiord coast, seen in Norway, Chile, and New Zealand's South Island, for example, develops when a glaciated mountain landscape becomes partly drowned, forming long deep bays with steep sides. A Dalmatian coast, named after the coast of Dalmatia, Croatia, is a series of valleys formed by folds running parallel to the coast that has been almost completely submerged.

COASTLINE PAST AND PRESENT
The eastern coast of North America has changed a lot in the past 15,000 years. Sea-level rise has drowned many ancient valleys.

- - - - Eastern coastline of North America 15,000 years ago

DALMATIAN COAST
This satellite photograph shows the classic drowned Dalmatian coast in the Adriatic Sea.

RIA COAST
Southwest Ireland, in the counties of Cork and Kerry, contains a series of elongated bays typical of a ria coast.

OCEAN

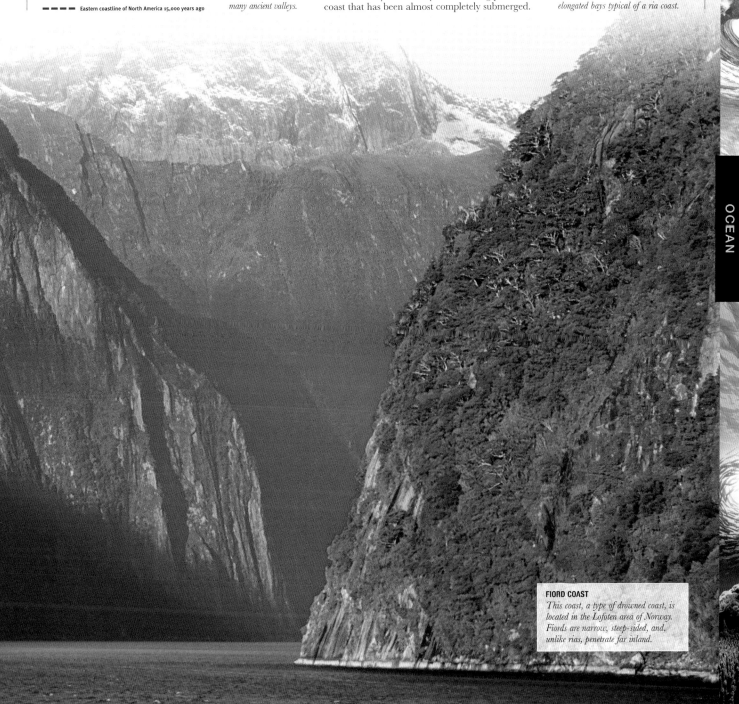

FIORD COAST
This coast, a type of drowned coast, is located in the Lofoten area of Norway. Fiords are narrow, steep-sided, and, unlike rias, penetrate far inland.

Erosional and Depositional Coastlines

EROSIONAL AND DEPOSITIONAL coastlines are two forms of secondary coast, which have been shaped primarily by marine processes. Erosional coasts occur where land is being eroded by the sea faster than sediment can be deposited. They are typically associated with emergent coasts (see p.352), where the land is being lifted by tectonic processes. Depositional coasts occur where sediment is being deposited on a coast faster than it is eroded. They are often associated with tectonically inactive continental margins, where the coast is slowly subsiding.

Processes of Erosion

Energy for the processes of coastal erosion is supplied mainly by waves and currents. As they beat against cliffs, waves compress air within cracks in rocks, and on re-expansion the air can shatter the rock. Mechanical erosion refers to waves hurling beach material against cliffs and abrading the rock. Where waves encounter headlands, a significant factor is refraction (bending) of the wave fronts, which causes their erosive energy to be directed towards the headlands and away from the bays. Waves arriving on a coast at an angle also generate a longshore drift (movement of sediment along a shore), which shifts material eroded from the headland towards adjacent bays. Groundwater that has emerged at the surface and surface-water run-off also gradually wear channels through the headland.

REFRACTING WAVE
The bending of the wave front towards the headland can be seen clearly here in this bay in southern Ireland.

part of wave front opposite bay continues

bay

beach deposits

headland

erosion divides headland into stacks

lobe of sediment

energy concentrated on headland as wave front refracts

part of wave front opposite headland slows as it encounters shallower water

wave front (extended crest of wave)

CONCENTRATION OF WAVE ENERGY
When a wave front reaches a shore, the parts opposite headlands slow down before the parts opposite bays. As a result, the wave front refracts (bends) and this concentrates its energy on the headlands.

Erosional Landforms

At headlands subjected to wave erosion, various distinctive features develop in a classic sequence. First, sea caves form at the bases of the cliffs on the sides of the headlands, usually along faults and joints (planes of weakness in a rock, see p.82). Wave action gradually deepens and widens the caves until they penetrate right through the headland to form an arch. Next, the roof of the arch collapses to leave an isolated rock pillar called a stack. These are ultimately worn down to stumps. Along cliffs, wave action cuts into the base of the cliff. This produces a horizontal platform at sea-level called a wave-cut platform, which provides some protection from further erosion by dissipating wave energy. Tectonic uplift sometimes raises the land in short bursts, and it is then worn into a series of wave-cut platforms called marine terraces.

CAVES
The coast of Cornwall, England, is dotted with numerous erosional features, including these caves at Nanjizel, near Land's End.

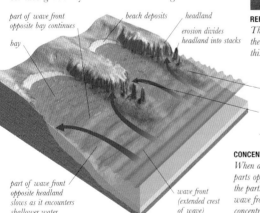

ARCH
This spectacular example of a wave-eroded arch is at Loch Ard Gorge (named after a ship that was wrecked there) on the coast of Victoria, Australia.

OCEAN

Processes of Deposition

Like coastal erosion, coastal deposition is brought about primarily by wave action. However, whereas erosion occurs in areas of high wave energy, deposition happens in environments where most of the energy has been dissipated before it reaches the shore, allowing sand or other material in the water to settle out. The deposited sediment comes mostly from rivers, but some comes from eroded headlands or from offshore. An important mechanism of transport and deposition is that of longshore drift. When wind and waves strike a shore obliquely, the movement of surf (swash) propels water and sand up the shore at an angle, but backwash drags them back down at a right angle to the shore. The overall effect is to move water and sand gradually along the shore. Eventually, where the sediment-carrying water arrives at a lower energy environment, the sediment settles out and builds up to form features such as spits, sand bars, and barrier islands. Some depositional processes modify one type of landform into another. For example, the development of a beach may lead to a spit, which may eventually extend across the mouth of a bay to create a baymouth bar.

SPIT
This spit at Hurst Castle is one of the most prominent depositional features on the southern coast of England.

river current   spit   dune   old coastline   movement of sand along beach   swash

salt-marsh   headland   backwash

second most dominant wind

direction of longshore drift   prevailing winds

LONGSHORE DRIFT AND FORMATION OF A SPIT
In this coastline, sand and water is carried past the headland by longshore drift, but the sand settles out at the mouth of an estuary where the waves are opposed by a sluggish current. There, it forms a slowly growing spit.

Depositional Landforms

Depositional processes form a number of characteristic features around coasts. A spit is a sandy peninsula with one end attached to land. An offshore bar is an unattached sand bar (a general name for any sand deposit) that lies parallel to the coast. About 13 per cent of the world's coasts have offshore bars. Where a spit extends right across the mouth of a bay, or two spits have merged, the result is called a baymouth bar. A tombolo is a sand bar that connects an island to land or to another island. Barrier islands are sand bars that coalesce to form long, linear islands parallel to the coast. They are typical of the eastern and Gulf coasts of the USA, and often slowly migrate shorewards. Other types of depositional landform include salt-marshes, which often develop on the landward sides of spits and bars, and mudflats, which form from the deposition of fine silt in sheltered tidal water, particularly in estuaries.

TOMBOLOS
This example of a tombolo (a sand bar between two islands) is in Puget Sound, near Seattle, USA.

ALASKAN MUDFLAT
Large mudflats on the Alaskan coast are the result of glacial erosion of nearby mountains.

STACKS
Stacks – such as the Twelve Apostles off Victoria, Australia – represent an advanced stage in the erosion of a headland.

OCEAN

Structure of the Atmosphere

THE ATMOSPHERE FORMS distinct layers around the Earth. These layers are remarkably uniform in chemical composition, but their density decreases with altitude. Within each layer there is a constant temperature change with height that alters abruptly at its boundaries. The lowest layer, called the troposphere, is where life exists and weather occurs because of the heating effect of the Sun. The Sun's rays pass through the atmosphere and warm the Earth's surface, causing the air to move and water to evaporate or condense. This causes weather and creates the different climate regions. Harmful ultraviolet rays are filtered out by the ozone layer, a gas that forms a thin layer in the stratosphere.

Layers

The lowest layer in the atmosphere is the troposphere, where air moves vertically and horizontally, and is thoroughly mixed. Air temperature decreases with height. As warm air rises, it loses some of its energy and becomes cooler. Eventually, it reaches a level at which it cools no further. The air above it is no denser, and so it rises no further. This level marks a boundary, called the tropopause. It is the first of several such boundaries that divide our atmosphere into its distinct layers. It separates the troposphere from the stratosphere, which itself ends at the stratopause. Above lies the mesosphere, and the thermosphere. At the top of the thermosphere, the temperature rises to about 1,000°C (1,800°F) due to the absorption of ultraviolet radiation. The upper limit of the thermosphere, the thermopause, extends up to 1,000km (625 miles). This outermost layer gradually merges with the vacuum of the Sun's atmosphere (which we call space), so Earth's atmosphere has no distinct upper boundary.

AURORA
The Northern and Southern Lights, also known as the Aurora Borealis and Australis, appear in the thermosphere.

RADIATION FOG
The troposphere is warmed by the Sun during the day but at night it cools again by radiating heat. The cool early morning air may contain fog.

LIVING AT HIGH ALTITUDE

Air pressure decreases with altitude, and above about 4,000m (13,200ft) there is insufficient oxygen for people to sustain strenuous activity – unless they are acclimatized. These tea pickers in Darjiling, India, have greater lung capacity and breathe more deeply than lowlanders. Their blood has a greater affinity for oxygen and can absorb it faster. These unique adaptations are genetic and are therefore passed on from one generation to the next. It allows the tea pickers to work on the upper slopes and carry heavy loads all day without becoming unduly breathless.

THERMOSPHERE
This layer extends up to the thermopause, as high as 1,000km (625 miles). The temperature in the lower part of this layer remains constant with height, but increases rapidly above 88km (55 miles).

MESOSPHERE
The temperature of the mesosphere remains constant with height through the lower mesosphere, but above about 56km (35 miles) it decreases with height to about -80°C (-112°F) at the mesopause.

STRATOSPHERE
Temperature in the stratosphere remains stable up to about 20km (12 miles), then increases, due to absorption of ultraviolet radiation. This layer's upper boundary, called the stratopause, is at about 48km (28 miles).

TROPOSPHERE
The upper limit, called the tropopause, is about 16km (10 miles) at the equator, and 8km (5 miles) over the poles. Temperature at high altitude drops to about -30°C (-22°F) at the poles and -65°C (-85°F) at the Equator.

LAYERS OF THE ATMOSPHERE
The atmosphere consists of layers, principally the troposphere, stratosphere, mesosphere, and thermosphere. Each is defined by the way temperature changes within its limits. The layers are separated by clear boundaries.

Height above sea-level

130km / 80 miles
120km / 74 miles
110km / 68 miles
100km / 62 miles
90km / 56 miles
8km / 50 miles
70km / 42 miles
60km / 36 miles
50km / 30 miles
40km / 24 miles
30km / 18 miles
20km / 12 miles
10km / 6 miles
Sea-level

aurora caused by collisions between protons and electrons from the Sun, and nitrogen and oxygen atoms in the atmosphere

meteor burning up in the atmosphere

mesopause

stratopause

tropopause

Average pressure

negligible
1 mb
3 mb
10 mb
50 mb
200 mb
1000 mb

Average temperature

60°C
140°F

-10°C
14°F

-80°C
-112°F

-90°C
-130°F

80°C
-112 °F

-50°C
-58°F

-30°C
-22°F

-10°C
-14°F

-20°C
-4°F

-40°C
-40 °F

-60°C
-80°F

-60°C
-80°F

15°C
59°F

above this level the air is so thin that each molecule may have a different temperature

noctilucent clouds, which appear when ice crystals form on meteoric dust at high levels, reflect the sunlight

thin layer of ozone gas absorbs harmful radiation from the Sun

all weather occurs in the lowest layer of the atmosphere

SAMPLING THE AIR

Balloons are used to sample the more inaccessible parts of the atmosphere. The Jimsphere seen here is an inflatable weather balloon, which is used to determine wind speed and direction prior to the launch of space vehicles, and missiles. Its shiny surface enhances radar signals, and the conical "spikes" on its surface help to stabilize its flight. Other types of weather balloons are released daily from weather stations all over the world.

Composition

Air consists mainly of three gases: nitrogen, oxygen, and argon, in constant proportions. It also contains water vapour, but in variable amounts. In addition to these principal constituents, there are minute quantities of 10 other gases. These are carbon dioxide, neon, helium, methane, krypton, hydrogen, nitrous oxide, carbon monoxide, xenon, and ozone. These form about 0.04 per cent of the atmosphere by volume. Air also contains even smaller amounts of gases that come from the surface, such as ammonia, nitrogen dioxide, hydrogen sulphide, and sulphur dioxide. Finally, there are dust and smoke particles.

NITROGEN 78.08%

OXYGEN 20.95%

ATMOSPHERIC GASES
The major constituents of air are nitrogen, oxygen, and argon, which total 99.96 per cent by volume. The composition is the same in the troposphere and stratosphere.

OTHER GASES:
ARGON 0.93%
CARBON DIOXIDE 0.037%
NEON 0.018%
HELIUM 0.005%
WATER VAPOUR VARIES FROM 0–4%

Airborne Water

Water evaporates from the surfaces of oceans, lakes, rivers, and from wet ground. It also evaporates from cloud droplets and raindrops, many of which fail to reach the ground. Water vapour is a gas, and it is present in all air. The amount of water vapour varies widely. Desert air often contains almost no water vapour, but even the moist air of the humid tropics seldom contains more than about four per cent of water vapour by volume. The humidity of the air is a measure of the amount of water vapour it contains. However, the most often quoted measure is relative humidity, which is the amount of water vapour present expressed as a percentage of the amount of water vapour needed to saturate the air. This varies according to the amount of water vapour and the temperature of the air. Warm air can hold more water vapour than cold air.

NOCTILUCENT CLOUDS
This type of cloud is sometimes seen on summer nights in high latitudes. Unlike other clouds, it forms in the mesopause, and shines by reflecting light from the Sun

THE SNOWLINE
At altitude, low temperatures stop snow from melting even in summer. The lower limit of the permanent snow, seen here on Cotopaxi in Ecuador, is called the snowline.

RAINBOW
This rainbow in Idaho, USA, is produced when light is refracted, on entering raindrops, then reflected from their rear, and refracted again as it leaves.

Atmospheric Particles

Air contains solid particles, called aerosols, that are so small they remain temporarily suspended. They fall so slowly that upcurrents repeatedly carry them aloft. Nevertheless, individual particles do not remain airborne for very long. Large particles return to the ground within minutes, and small particles, such as smoke, within a few hours. Some fall to the ground and some collide with surfaces as they are carried horizontally by the wind, but most are washed to the ground by rain and snow. Many particles are lifted into the air as a result of natural events. Volcanic eruptions eject vast quantities of ash and dust, while desert winds carry sand and dust over great distances – for example, Saharan dust occasionally falls in North America. Fires, ignited by lightning or humans, release smoke and ash that can be carried upwards by rising hot air. Even pollen and spores released from plants, fungi, and bacteria become airborne, along with the aerosols produced by various agricultural and industrial practices. Water vapour in the atmosphere condenses onto certain minute particles, including dust, smoke, and sulphate. Some aerosols reflect sunlight back towards space, partially offsetting the effects of global warming. These cloud condensation nuclei, as they are known, allow clouds to form.

VOLCANIC ASH
This is a magnified image of a particle of volcanic ash. Many tonnes of ash are produced during a volcanic eruption.

POLLUTION
Clouds of aerosol particles are seen here in the skies along the southern edge of the Himalayas in northern India, streaming south over Bangladesh. This type of industrial and urban pollution now affects much of southern Asia.

ETNA ERUPTION
Mount Etna, Sicily, erupted in 2002. This satellite image shows a cloud of ash travelling southwards across the Mediterranean Sea.

ATMOSPHERE

Energy in the Atmosphere

THE SUN SUPPLIES THE ENERGY to produce our weather. The Sun's radiant heat is absorbed by the land and sea surface, and air is warmed from below by contact with it. Air movements transport this heat throughout the troposphere. Warmth from the Sun also provides energy for water to evaporate. Water vapour enters the air, and when it condenses to form clouds the water molecules release the latent heat that was absorbed when the water first evaporated. A huge amount of energy is involved in this process: an average summer thunderstorm releases as much energy as burning 7,000 tonnes of coal in less than one hour; and a tornado releases enough energy to light the streets of New York City for one night.

SOLAR POWER

The Sun's energy can be used to heat homes and generate power. Solar collectors on the roof can heat water and solar cells can convert sunlight into electrical power. A solar furnace, seen here, uses hundreds of mirrors to focus light and heat onto a target in a central tower. It heats to more than 2,000°C (3,600°F), raising steam for power generation or for research.

Solar Budget

The balance between the amount of solar energy received by the Earth's surface, its atmosphere, or the clouds, and the amount of energy reflected or radiated back into space, is known as the solar budget. The temperature at the visible surface of the Sun is about 5,800°C (10,472°F). It radiates its heat into space, but in all directions. The Earth, which is about 150 million km (93 million miles) away, receives only a tiny proportion of it. The amount of solar energy arriving as shortwave radiation at the topmost level of the atmosphere is known as the solar constant. Of the solar energy that reaches the top of the atmosphere, about 30 per cent is lost due to backscatter by air molecules, and reflection by clouds, land, and sea. Reflection will vary both with the amount of cloud cover and the nature of the Earth's surface (see opposite). About 70 per cent of all incoming radiation is absorbed, mostly by the land and sea, but also by the air and clouds. The surface radiates the energy it has absorbed as longwave radiation, maintaining the balance between heat gains and losses. About 45 per cent of the radiation reaching the Earth is visible as light.

THE SOLAR BUDGET
Just over half the sunlight reaching the Earth penetrates to the surface, and almost one-fifth is absorbed by the atmosphere. The remainder is reflected by clouds and the surrounding surface or scattered back into space by air molecules.

energy reflected by Earth's surface (4 per cent)

energy scattered back from atmosphere (6 per cent)

energy reflected by clouds (20 per cent)

total incoming energy from Sun

Sun sends out shortwave radiation in all directions

energy absorbed by the clouds (19 per cent)

energy reaching surface diffusely, after being re-radiated from atmosphere (26 per cent)

energy absorbed by land and sea surface (25 per cent)

SOLAR ACTIVITY

The solar flare, shown right, is produced by a sudden release of the Sun's energy. It creates a huge amount of radiated heat, which has a direct effect on our climate.

WAVELENGTHS

Incoming solar radiation is emitted at shorter wavelength than that which is radiated back into space. Ultraviolet wavelengths are absorbed by oxygen and ozone, and the longer infra-red wavelengths are absorbed by carbon dioxide and water vapour.

radiation from Sun

radiation from land and sea

Energy

Ultraviolet

Visible light

Infra-red

Microwave

Wavelength

Greenhouse Effect

Radiation from the Sun is most intense at short wavelengths. The atmosphere is almost completely transparent to this radiation, which passes through the air and is absorbed by the Earth's surface. When the land and sea are warm, they radiate the energy they have absorbed, but at longer wavelengths. Some of the longwave radiation is absorbed and re-radiated back to the Earth by atmospheric gases, including water vapour, carbon dioxide, methane, and ozone. This warms the gases, and although the Earth's radiation eventually escapes into space, it is retained long enough to warm the atmosphere. This is the greenhouse effect, and the gases causing it are called greenhouse gases. Without the natural greenhouse effect, temperatures would be 30°–40°C (54–72°F) cooler. However, since 1900, the concentration of carbon dioxide in the atmosphere has increased by about 30 per cent due to an increase in the burning of fossil fuels, atmospheric pollution, and deforestation (trees absorb carbon dioxide). Many scientists agree that the addition of carbon dioxide and other greenhouse gases to the air is changing the temperature balance, producing an enhanced greenhouse effect and increasing average temperatures over the Earth as a whole.

some heat emitted by greenhouse gases escapes to space

some heat emitted by greenhouse gases heats surface

greenhouse gases absorb longwave radiation

escaping longwave radiation

diffused incoming radiation

solar radiation deflected back into space

incoming solar radiation

SUNFLOWERS
The Sun's energy is important to most living things. Green plants, such as these sunflowers, need sunlight to photosynthesize food. The flowers turn to follow the path of the Sun.

GLOBAL WARMING
The lower atmosphere gradually becomes warmer when longwave solar radiation emitted by the Earth's surface is trapped in the atmosphere by carbon dioxide, water vapour, methane, and other greenhouse gases.

Absorption Variables

Different surfaces reflect different proportions of the radiation falling on them. This is because pale colours reflect light and heat, and dark colours absorb them. The percentage of the radiation that a surface reflects is known as the albedo of that surface. Freshly fallen snow is highly reflective. It has an albedo of 75–95 per cent, usually written also as 0.75–0.95. Bright cloud is also very reflective. Its albedo is 0.70–0.90. So, surfaces with a high albedo absorb very little heat, while dark surfaces absorb solar radiation much better. A broad-leaved forest, with an albedo of 0.10–0.20, absorbs 80–90 per cent of the radiation falling on it. A coniferous forest absorbs even more. If the surface of a large area is changed, the albedo may be altered. Removing forest and replacing it with farm crops, for example, increases the albedo from about 0.10 to about 0.20, and so more sunlight is reflected. When grassland is replaced with concrete, the albedo increases from about 0.15 to 0.22. Changes of this kind can affect the local climate, because increased reflection reduces convection in the air, and this in turn affects the amount of cloud cover.

ICE AND SNOW
Most of Antarctica is covered by ice and snow. This reflects almost all of the sunlight, so the layers beneath the surface remain cold.

DARK CANOPY
This forest canopy in the Amazon Basin is dark and will absorb sunlight. This affects the air temperature in the forest and the rate at which water evaporates.

Changes in State

Water exists in three different forms (or phases). It occurs as liquid water, as solid ice, and as water vapour, which is an invisible gas. Most substances can exist in these three phases, but water is remarkable in that it can exist in all three states at temperatures commonly experienced at the Earth's surface. For example, in winter, the surface of a pond may partly freeze over. Here water is present as ice (solid) and water (liquid), and in the air above the pond, there is water vapour (gas). All three are present in the same place, at the same time. When ice melts or changes directly into water vapour, and when liquid water evaporates, energy is needed to break the bonds holding the water molecules together. The molecules absorb this energy, but it does not change the temperature of the ice or water. The energy is latent (or hidden) heat. The same amount of heat is released when water vapour condenses, or changes directly to ice, and when liquid water freezes into ice. The release of latent heat when water vapour condenses provides the energy that fuels the growth of huge storm clouds. These clouds usually have great vertical depth due to unstable atmospheric conditions. This instability occurs because latent heat is released from water vapour as it condenses from the air, making the rising air warmer than the surrounding air, so it continues to rise.

HEAVY RAINSTORM
Warm air rises and cools over the hills around Lake Shastina, California, USA, causing water vapour to condense and resulting in a rainstorm.

WATERSPOUT
This waterspout, off the Bahamas, is visible because low pressure inside the wind funnel causes water vapour to condense into droplets.

TROUBLED SKIES
High-altitude polar clouds – seen here over Lapland – indicate unusually low temperatures in the stratosphere. Ozone thins rapidly in these conditions.

THE OZONE LAYER

Ozone is a natural component of the atmosphere, and a gas that plays a crucial part in the survival of life on Earth (see p.363). In the stratosphere, the ozone layer screens out short-wave ultraviolet (UV) radiation – a form of solar energy that can damage or kill living cells. During the 20th century, the ozone layer was seriously thinned by atmospheric pollutants, but, following concerted international action in the late 1980s, the damage is gradually being reversed.

Ozone and Life

Toxic and highly reactive, ozone is a relatively rare form of oxygen that has three atoms in each of its molecules (O_3), rather than the normal two (O_2), which many organisms breathe. Most of the world's ozone is found in the ozone layer, which is 20–25km (12–16 miles) above the Earth's surface. Here, ozone is continually formed from O_2, and it reverts back into O_2 when it breaks down again.

In the ozone layer, ozone molecules absorb UV-B and UV-C radiation – short-wavelength forms of ultraviolet that carry high levels of energy. They re-emit this energy as heat. As a result, the ozone layer acts as a screen, preventing most of this radiation from reaching the ground. Any depletion of the ozone layer is potentially dangerous for life, because UV-B and UV-C radiation can disrupt organic molecules, producing cancerous changes in living cells.

Ozone Depletion

The ozone layer has been stable around the Earth for millions of years, but that situation ended in the late 1920s, when chemists synthesized the first chlorofluorocarbons (CFCs). These non-flammable gases turned out to have many uses: as solvents, aerosol propellants, and industrial cleaners, and also as coolants in refrigerators and air-conditioners. Unfortunately, CFCs can destroy ozone if they escape into the atmosphere. They can continue to do damage for decades or even centuries after they have been released, because they are stable and do not dissolve in rain.

During the early 1970s, two American chemists – Mario Molina and Sherwood Rowland – identified the theoretical threat of ozone depletion. Initially, reaction was sceptical, but, when in 1983 scientists at the British Antarctic Survey discovered an ozone "hole" over the South Pole, the abstract threat suddenly became real.

SOUTHERN EXPOSURE
The Antarctic ozone hole forms during the southern winter and reaches a maximum each spring. In this composite satellite map, the zone of greatest deficiency is shown in red.

International Action

The reality of ozone depletion prompted a rapid response. In 1987, two dozen industrialized countries signed the Montreal Protocol, which committed them to phase out CFC production by 1996. In the period leading up to this deadline, "ozone-friendly" products were developed to take their place. In 1990, a further agreement was

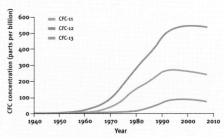

ATMOSPHERIC CFC CONCENTRATIONS
Since the 1950s, levels of CFC-11, CFC-12, and CFC-13 have risen steeply before flattening out in response to a production ban. The concentrations are highest in the northern hemisphere, where most of the world's production was based.

drawn up to include most developing nations, with a ten-year extension to allow them to adopt ozone-friendly technology. As a result of these measures, atmospheric CFC levels have reached a plateau and may already be starting to fall.

How long the ozone layer takes to repair itself will depend on the residence time of different CFCs – the period that an average molecule stays in the atmosphere – and also on the amounts originally released. For example, CFC-11, which was widely used in refrigeration, aerosols, and plastic foams, has a residence time of 45 years, while that of CFC-115 is 500 years. Current data suggest that the ozone layer might be near normal by 2050, though scientists remain wary of newly synthesized substances that may also have ozone-depleting effects.

TASK FORCE
To prevent CFCs escaping into the atmosphere, old refrigerators and freezers here in southern England have their coolant removed before being scrapped.

Ground-Level Ozone

Ozone can be dangerous when it is near the ground. Such ozone is created by lightning, by any kind of machinery that creates electric sparks, and also by internal combustion engines. The exhaust gases of internal combustion engines include nitrogen oxides and organic compounds, and these can form ozone when they react – particularly in the presence of sunlight. In traffic-dense urban areas, such photochemical reactions can raise the air's ozone content to ten times its normal background level.

Ground-level ozone is toxic to plants, and it irritates the lining of the lungs, causing asthma and bronchitis. This form of pollution can be reduced by improvements in engine design, and by the use of catalytic converters in car exhausts.

Atmospheric Circulation

AIR IS CONSTANTLY MOVING. Worldwide, this movement constitutes the general circulation of the atmosphere, transporting warmth from equatorial areas to high latitudes, and returning cooler air to the tropics. It comprises three sets of "cells". These cells produce wind systems called prevailing winds, which drive the surface waters of the ocean, creating currents. The winds are deflected in opposite directions north and south of the Equator by the Coriolis effect. In the upper troposphere, fast-moving jet streams form due to differences in temperature and pressure at the boundaries of air masses. They can increase the intensity and movement of low-pressure systems, resulting in climate cycles, or oscillations. El Niño is one such oscillation that affects weather patterns on a global scale. The behaviour of the atmosphere is unpredictable, so it is difficult to know when these climatic events will take place.

polar easterlies blowing away from high-pressure system over the North Pole

inner core of jet stream flows much faster than outer shell

polar-front jet stream

subtropical jet stream flows at about 30°N all year round

Coriolis Effect

Air flowing towards, or away from the Equator invariably follows a curved path that swings it to the right in the northern hemisphere and to the left in the southern hemisphere. The reason for this was discovered in 1835 by Gustave-Gaspard de Coriolis (see panel, below). It used to be called the Coriolis force and is still abbreviated as CorF, but no force is involved, and nowadays it is known as the Coriolis effect. It occurs because the Earth is rotating anticlockwise about its axis, so as air moves across the surface, the surface itself is also moving beneath it but at a different speed. The magnitude of the Coriolis effect depends on the latitude, and the speed of the moving air. The Coriolis effect is greatest at the poles.

initial direction

deflected right

HOW CORIOLIS EFFECT WORKS
All points on the Earth's surface complete one revolution every 24 hours, so a point at the Equator travels further and faster than a point at higher latitude. This rotation causes the air to shift to the right north of the equator and to the left south of the equator.

deflected path

normal path

direction of Earth's rotation

DEFLECTING AIR
Air moving over the Earth's surface travels at a different speed to the Earth's rotation, so when plotted on a map, it appears to be deflected.

STORM BUILDUP
These storm clouds, forming off the south-east coast of the USA, are in the northern hemisphere, and so rotate anticlockwise.

direction of Earth's rotation

cloud indicating position of intertropical convergence zone

GUSTAVE-GASPARD DE CORIOLIS

The mathematician and mechanical engineer Gustave-Gaspard de Coriolis (1792–1843) was born in Paris, France. In 1816, he became a tutor at the École Polytechnique, where he carried out research on friction and hydraulics. He went on to discover the Coriolis effect, publishing his results in 1835. He died in Paris aged only 51.

Fluid Circulation

The air in the Earth's atmosphere moves in response to heating by the Sun. When a fluid is heated, its molecules absorb energy. This allows them to move faster, so they move further apart, and the fluid expands. Expansion makes it less dense, because a given volume contains fewer molecules than before. Denser fluid, which is heavier, then sinks beneath the less dense fluid, pushing it upwards. Air acts like a fluid when it is heated by contact with the Earth's surface that has been warmed by the Sun. As warm air rises, air pressure decreases, as there is a smaller amount of air above it, pressing down. This allows the air to expand, but this uses energy, so it also cools. When the air reaches a level where its density equals that of the air immediately above it, it stops rising. If the air then subsides, the pressure on it increases. It absorbs energy and its temperature rises. These changes give rise to the different cells of the Earth's circulation system.

cool air subsides at the South Pole, flowing towards mid-latitudes as the polar easterlies

HOW AIR MOVES IN CELLS

Atmospheric circulation in each hemisphere consists of three cells. At the Equator, warm air rises, moves north and south, and subsides at the tropics. The air that flows back to the Equator creates the Hadley cells. Cold air subsides over the poles, flows to mid-latitudes, where it meets air from Hadley cells, so rises, and returns to the poles, forming polar cells. Rising mid-latitude air divides, flowing to the poles and to the Equator, forming Ferrel cells.

polar-cell air circulation is caused by subsiding air at the pole flowing south towards the Equator. On meeting Hadley-cell air, it rises

air in Ferrel cells rises to the tropopause and then divides, some air flowing to the pole and some towards the Equator

winds in mid-latitudes produced by Ferrel cells flow from the west

northeasterly trade winds deflected to right by Coriolis effect

air within Hadley cells rises moist at the Equator and subsides dry at the subtropics

southeasterly trade winds

roaring forties

Jets and Waves

Jet streams are narrow, winding ribbons of strong wind in the upper troposphere. They occur at the top of fronts, marking the boundary between air masses at different temperatures (see pp.380–81). As they are produced by a temperature difference, they are also known as thermal winds. Sometimes waves form in jet streams, and travel along with them. Wind speed at the centre of a jet stream is about 105kph (65mph), but speeds of 500kph (310mph) have been recorded. Polar-front jet streams flow in temperate latitudes, between 30 and 50°N and S, depending on the season. The subtropical jet stream is at about 30°N and S all year round. These jet streams blow with cold air on their left in the northern hemisphere, and on their right in the southern hemisphere. They blow therefore from west to east in both hemispheres. In summer, there is a jet stream that blows from east to west at about 20°N, crossing Asia, southern Arabia, and northeastern Africa.

STORM DAMAGE

During the night of 16 October 1987, there was a severe storm in the UK, caused by an unusual northwards shift of the jet stream.

JET STREAM

These bands of cirrus cloud mark the position of the jet stream over the Red Sea and Egypt. The cloud forms in air that is lifted as it is drawn into the core of the jet stream.

Prevailing Winds

Although the wind may blow from any direction, when directions at a particular place are compared over a long period, it is usually found that the wind blows from one direction more than it blows from any other. This is the prevailing wind. The general circulation of the atmosphere produces belts of prevailing winds around the world. In the tropics, wind blowing towards the equator, as part of the Hadley cells, is deflected to the right, and forms the northeasterly and southeasterly trade winds. Air flowing away from the high pressure over the poles is deflected to the right and forms the polar easterlies. Between these, in middle latitudes, the Ferrel cells produce westerly winds. Over the world as a whole, the force of the easterly winds is precisely balanced by the force of the westerlies. If this were not so, the rotation of the Earth would either speed up or slow down. In sandy deserts, and in polar regions, prevailing winds produce dunes, and drifts, with characteristic shapes. Sand and snow grains are blown up a slope, and tumble down the far side. This creates high dunes and snow drifts, with sharp, sinuous crests, extending for great distances. Knowing about prevailing winds is important for locating structures such as airport runways. Sailors used to depend on prevailing winds to cross oceans and would avoid places, such as the doldrums, where there is little wind.

HIGH DUNES

The sinuous crest of these Namibian Desert dunes shows that the prevailing wind flows along the dune, sometimes a little to the left or to the right.

WIND SYSTEMS

Global wind belts result from the way air circulates. Seasonal differences in the northern hemisphere are due to large landmasses where pressure systems change from high in January to low in July.

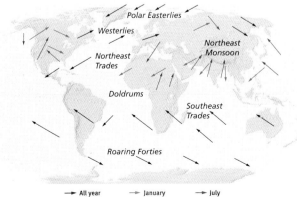

Polar Easterlies
Westerlies
Northeast Trades
Northeast Monsoon
Doldrums
Southeast Trades
Roaring Forties

→ All year → January → July

INTERTROPICAL CONVERGENCE ZONE

In equatorial regions, the meeting of trade winds at the Equator is known as the intertropical convergence zone. Here, a band of cloud indicates its position.

Moisture and the Oceans

Oceans cover about 70 per cent of the surface of the Earth, and they play a major part in the formation and regulation of climates. Because water warms and cools much more slowly than dry land, the oceans moderate temperatures, making summers cooler and winters warmer than they would be on a completely dry planet. Ocean currents (see p.312) also transport heat from the Equator into high latitudes. The North Pole has a much warmer climate than the South Pole because it lies at the centre of the Arctic Ocean, rather than the centre of the continent of Antarctica, and there is always liquid water beneath the sea-ice. Precipitation – rain, snow, hail, fog, dew, and frost – consists of water that came originally from the ocean, and that returns there through rivers and groundwater. This is an obvious contribution to climate, but it is not the only one. The condensation of water vapour in rising air releases latent heat (see p.365) that makes the air continue to rise. This is how storm clouds form. The energy of tornadoes and hurricanes is provided mainly by condensation. Clouds also shade the surface by reflecting incoming sunlight, which has a cooling effect. The climatic importance of the oceans is most evident when rains fail and food crops wither in a drought.

GULF STREAM
This satellite image of the east coast of the USA shows temperature differences in the ocean due to warm (orange and yellow) and cool (blue and green) currents. The warm current is the Gulf Stream, which transfers heat polewards.

ICEBERGS
These icebergs near Cuverville Island, Antarctica, provide information about ocean currents as they move north into warmer waters and then melt.

WATERSPOUT
When a tornado moves over water, it is called a waterspout. This one occurred off the coast of Spain and killed six people. The spray ring at the base consists of water whipped up from the surface.

Winds and Currents

Prevailing winds, blowing over the ocean, drive the surface water along particular paths to form ocean currents. The trade winds drive equatorial currents westwards in both hemispheres. As they approach land, they turn away from the Equator into higher latitudes. Here the Coriolis effect swings the currents further, until they enter the middle latitudes, where prevailing winds come from the west. They then form currents flowing eastwards, but the Coriolis effect continues to deflect them. Finally, they head back toward the Equator. This circular movement forms gyres, one in each major ocean, apart from the Southern Ocean. On the western sides of oceans, currents are narrow, deep, fast-flowing, and carry warm water; on the eastern side, they are wide, shallow, slow-moving, and carry cool water. In the Southern Ocean, there is no land to deflect the Antarctic Circumpolar Current. It is the only current to flow all the way around the world. Currents do not flow precisely in the direction of the wind. This is because friction between the surface layer of water and the layer below, combined with the Coriolis effect, deflect the current at about 45° to the right of the wind direction in the northern hemisphere, and to its left in the southern hemisphere.

TYPHOON
Typhoon Odessa (left) formed in the tropical trade-wind belt of the western Pacific. It moved northwards until it met the mid-latitude westerlies.

EDDY OFF JAPAN
The winds around pressure systems drive eddies (small currents), such as this one, visible as a green spiral below the white streaks of cloud.

Variation and Oscillation

Climates change due to cyclical variations in the distribution of pressure over varying periods. An example of a climate cycle is the North Atlantic Oscillation (NAO), which results from pressure differences between the Azores high and Iceland low. When pressure is higher than average over the Azores, and lower over Iceland, the NAO index is said to be positive (high). At this time the jet stream flows strongly over the Atlantic, bringing mild, wet winters to Europe and warm, dry winters to the Mediterranean. When the pressure difference is small, the NAO index is said to be negative (low). This blocks the jet stream, so in winter cold air enters Europe from Asia, and rainfall increases in the Mediterranean region. The NAO is unpredictable, but tends to occur every couple of years.

HARSH WINTER IN CANADA
Tuktoyaktuk, northwest Canada, shown here experiences harsher than normal winters due to climatic oscillations.

weak low-pressure system

cold weather with snow

dry weather

weak high-pressure system

NORTH ATLANTIC OSCILLATION (NEGATIVE)
A negative (low) North Atlantic Oscillation exists when pressure systems are weak, bringing mild winters to the northwestern Atlantic, cold weather with snow to northeastern North America, cold, dry winters to northern Europe, and wet weather to the Mediterranean.

cold, dry weather

stronger than usual high pressure

weaker than normal low-pressure system

warm, wet winters

cloud track

NORTH ATLANTIC OSCILLATION (POSITIVE)
A positive (high) North Atlantic Oscillation index brings cold winters to the northwestern Atlantic and northeastern North America, mild winters and higher rainfall to northern Europe, and dry weather to the Mediterranean region.

El Niño

El Niño is a reversal in the normal flow of the South Equatorial Current in the Pacific that brings dramatic changes in the weather at intervals of between two and seven years. The effects of El Niño become evident in late December, and are associated with a change in the distribution of air pressure over the South Pacific. This change is known as the Southern Oscillation. The full cycle is called an El Niño–Southern Oscillation (ENSO) event and includes La Niña, the opposite of El Niño. Ordinarily, pressure is high over the eastern South Pacific and low in the west. This produces the trade winds that drive the South Equatorial Current, carrying warm water away from South America and toward Indonesia. This pattern produces heavy rain over Indonesia and extremely arid conditions along the coast of Peru and northern Chile. During an ENSO event, the pressure difference weakens or reverses, as do the trade winds. Heavy rain falls over Peru and Chile, causing deserts to bloom, while Indonesia experiences drought, sometimes leading to serious forest fires.

FLOODING
Heavy rains caused by El Niño cause extensive damage. Here, a mudslide in California, USA, has flowed down a slope and covered a section of road, blocking it to traffic. Other risks include floods and landslides.

rising warm moist air associated with heavy rainfall and low pressure

southeast trade winds

descending warm air associated with dry conditions and high pressure

accumulation of warm water

South Equatorial Current

upwelling of cold nutrient rich waters as warm surface waters are shallow

NORMAL CLIMATIC CONDITIONS
Ordinarily, a low-pressure system over Australia draws the southeast trade winds across the eastern Pacific from a high-pressure system over South America. These winds drive the warm South Equatorial Current towards the coast of Australia. Off the coast of South America, the warm water layer is only 100m (300ft) deep, so upwellings of cold water bring nutrients to the surface.

descending air and high pressure brings warm, dry weather

southeast trade winds reversed or weakened

low pressure and rising air associated with rainfall

warm water flows eastwards, accumulating off South America

upwelling blocked by warm water

EL NINO EFFECT
During El Niño, the pressure systems that normally develop over Australia and South America are much weaker or reversed, which is reflected by the flow of the trade winds and ocean currents. Warm water to a depth of about 152m (500ft) flows eastward, blocking the normal upwelling of nutrients along the west coast of the Americas, and devastating fish stocks.

EL NINO HUMAN IMPACT

El Niño brings drought to Indonesia and northeastern South America. Soils dry out and crack. This farmer must hope there is enough irrigation water to keep his crop alive, and that the rains will soon return. Indonesian farmers commonly clear the ground by burning off old, dead vegetation in preparation for planting. In El Niño years, the fires may blaze out of control, as they did during the unusually severe El Niño of 1997–98. When subsistence crops, such as rice and corn, fail, the government has to purchase the shortfall of food from elsewhere. In 1997, when over 105 million people in Indonesia were still dependent on agriculture to make a living, over five billion tonnes of rice were imported. The cost puts considerable additional strain on the country's economy.

Climate Change

THE WORLD'S CLIMATES are changing constantly. In the past they have been both warmer and cooler than they are now, due to catastrophic events and cycles that have natural causes. At present, the average global temperature is increasing, but the rise is not spread evenly around the Earth and some regions are becoming cooler. Several factors are contributing to the present warming. Most climatologists agree that part of it is due to an enhanced greenhouse effect, which is caused by the release of certain gases when fossil fuels – coal, oil, and natural gas – are burned.

Past Evidence

Reliable written climate records are available for about the last 200 years, but until recently there were few weather stations in much of Africa, Asia, the Middle East, and South America, so scientists must reconstruct past climates from other types of evidence. Tree rings, for example, vary in width, depending on growing conditions, and details of climate over more than 8,000 years have been obtained from bristlecone pines in California, USA. Many beetles live only within a narrow temperature range and their wing cases, which are sometimes preserved in the soil, can provide evidence about the climate in which the insects lived. Plant pollen also preserves well, and can reveal the plant communities that inhabited a particular area and, thus, the climate at the time. Scientists also study cores drilled from sea-bed and lake-bed sediments, and from polar ice-sheets, in search of clues to water temperatures, rainfall, and the composition of the gases in the atmosphere.

POLLEN GRAIN
Scientists use pollen to reconstruct past climates. It is extracted from cores drilled in sediment or peat.

temperature   carbon dioxide
Age (thousands of years ago)

CARBON DIOXIDE VARIATION
From this graph, using data from Vostok Station in Antarctica, it can be seen that the amount of carbon dioxide in the atmosphere and temperature have varied together over the past two ice age cycles.

UNICELLULAR FORAMINIFERAN
This is a magnified image of the shell of a temperature-sensitive animal found in sedimentary rocks.

DESERTIFICATION
Deserts increase in area when climates become hotter and drier, as here in the Sahel, where the desert has encroached on a village.

Orbital Cycles

Fluctuations in the Earth's orbit around the Sun and rotation on its axis over time are reflected by cyclical changes in the climate. When these fluctuations coincide, temperatures fall sufficiently to trigger an ice age. The Earth's orbital path extends from almost circular to slightly elliptical over a cycle of about 100,000 years, altering the distance between the Earth and the Sun. The tilt of the Earth's axis varies over 42,000 years, altering the area directly exposed to the Sun. The rotational axis of the Earth wobbles over 25,800 years, causing the dates of the solstices and equinoxes to move.

ORBITAL VARIATIONS
The orbit and rotation of the Earth is not constant, but changes cyclically over time. Its orbit fluctuates from elliptical to circular (when the orbit is described as more or less eccentric), and it is also subject to tilt about its axis, and wobble through movement of the axis. Over time, these changes in the Earth's orbit affect temperature and can be correlated to specific events, such as ice ages.

MILUTIN MILANKOVICH

Serbian mathematician and climatologist Milutin Milankovich (1879–1958) was determined to test a suggested link between climate and the levels of solar radiation reaching the Earth. He identified three cyclical changes (see left) that might be relevant, and calculated the dates when these combined to minimize and maximize solar radiation over hundreds of thousands of years. The dates coincided with the ice ages.

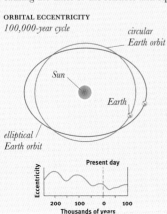

ORBITAL ECCENTRICITY
100,000-year cycle

circular Earth orbit

Sun

Earth

elliptical Earth orbit

Present day

Thousands of years

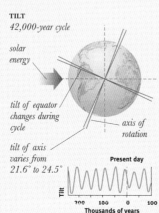

TILT
42,000-year cycle

solar energy

tilt of equator changes during cycle

axis of rotation

tilt of axis varies from 21.6° to 24.5°

Present day

Thousands of years

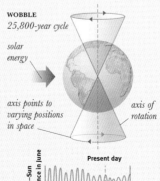

WOBBLE
25,800-year cycle

solar energy

axis points to varying positions in space

axis of rotation

Present day

Thousands of years

ATMOSPHERE

Other Causes

The present climatic warming may be due, in part, to changes other than higher concentrations of greenhouse gases. It may be a natural trend as the Earth emerges from the Little Ice Age, a cold period that lasted from the 15th to the mid-19th century. Warming may also be caused by natural oscillations. The North Atlantic Oscillation (see p.371) has been mostly positive since 1990, bringing mild winters to Europe and possibly increasing the flow of warmer water into the Arctic Basin, melting the sea-ice in places. One of the two hottest years on record (2010) may partly have been due to a strong El Niño event. Warming may not be a predominant, or even the main, cause of the shrinkage of glaciers in tropical Africa – factors such as reduced snowfall may be equally or more important. Changes in solar output may also affect climate. Throughout history, periods when few sunspots were recorded have coincided with cold conditions. A period of low sunspot activity called the Maunder Minimum was the coldest part of the Little Ice Age. An intensification of the solar wind, which happened during the 1990s, may go some way to explaining the warming that occurred in that decade – a stronger solar wind reduces cloudiness, allowing more radiation to enter and be absorbed by the atmosphere (see p.365). However, most climate scientists have not been convinced by these arguments. The overall consensus is that global warming and associated climate change are at least partly and in all likelihood predominantly the result of human activity and not just part of some natural cycle.

SOLAR ACTIVITY
Sunspots reflect variations in solar activity. They have two distinct regions: a dark centre, called the umbra, and a brighter, hotter surrounding area – the penumbra.

FOREST FIRES
Scientific evidence suggests that there is a link between climate and fire. Burning vegetation releases carbon dioxide into the atmosphere, and the smoke screens out solar radiation. Here, flames and smoke engulf Northfork in Wyoming, USA.

The Current Trend

At present, average global temperature is rising. The temperature is recorded in three ways. Surface weather stations record temperatures at least twice each day – there are about 10,000 stations on land and 7,000 at sea. Weather balloons monitor air temperature at different altitudes. Finally, satellites monitor atmospheric temperature above about 2km (6,500ft). The most reliable data indicate that average global temperature rose by about 0.8°C (1.44°F) between the early 20th century and 2012. Since 1975, the increase has been at a higher rate of about 1.5°C (2.7°F) per century. When temperature data obtained with modern instruments is compared with paleoclimatic data (from past evidence such as tree rings), it is clear that not only has there been a sharp recent temperature rise, but also the Earth is warmer today than at any time in the past 1,500 years.

TEMPERATURE CHANGES
The graph shows estimated variations in global temperature going back 1,500 years using palaeoclimatic data up to 1850 and data from modern instruments thereafter. The shaded areas denote uncertainty in the historic data.

VOLCANIC ERUPTIONS
Clouds of fine dust and ash particles rise from Cerro Negro, a volcano in Nicaragua, Central America. Most of the particles will fall to the ground in a matter of hours, but any that enter the stratosphere will remain airborne much longer, shading the Earth's surface and slightly reducing the temperature.

Changes in the Arctic

Since the 1970s, when it first became possible to study the phenomenon accurately using satellites, a highly significant decline has occurred in sea-ice coverage in the Arctic Ocean. This shrinkage has been faster than that predicted by climate models. The sea-ice coverage reaches a minimum in September each year, and this minimum plumbed new record lows in 2002, 2005, and 2007, followed by an all-time record low on 16 September 2012. The loss of sea-ice provides evidence of global warming, separate from other ice-related evidence such as the retreat of glaciers (see p.228). One of the possible adverse effects of the loss of Arctic sea-ice may be increased warming due to reduced albedo (see p.365). However, it is likely that average plankton mass will increase in the Arctic Ocean, which could lock up more carbon.

METHANE RELEASE
A likely effect of higher temperatures in the Arctic is increased release of the greenhouse gas methane from thawing permafrost. Here, escaping methane has just been ignited.

SEA-ICE SHRINKAGE
Images of Arctic sea-ice coverage in 1980 (left) and 2012 (below), as measured by satellites, show the marked shrinkage in "core" ice coverage (the bright white areas) remaining each September.

Rising Sea-level

Since the late 19th century, most of the world's glaciers have retreated, and their melt water has contributed to a rise in global sea-level. In a warming planet, sea-level has also increased due to thermal expansion, because, above 4°C (39°F), warm water is less dense than cold water. Over the past 100 years, global sea level has risen at an average rate of about 1.5mm (¹/₁₆in) a year, but since 1993 the rise has been faster, at a rate of about 3mm (¹/₈in) per year. If melting were to start breaking up the West Antarctic Ice-sheet (see pp.230), the rise could accelerate considerably. Projections of future sea-level rise vary widely, because some conditions may accelerate the change, while others could dampen it. Climate models based on the current rate of increase in greenhouse gases indicate that global sea-level may rise by 20–50cm (8–20in) above its 2013 level by 2100.

RISING TREND
This graph traces changes in sea-level. It combines instrumental data from the past 140 years with a range of estimates for earlier times and the future.

ISLANDS AT RISK
Many small coral islands, such as this one in the Maldives, have a maximum height of less than 1m (3ft), making them highly vulnerable to sea-level rise.

LOSS OF HABITAT
The Arctic Ocean is now expected to be almost entirely ice-free for part of the year by about 2035. As sea-ice is used by polar bears when they hunt, its decline threatens their survival.

Extreme Weather

A predicted feature of climate change resulting from global warming includes more frequent occurrence of extreme weather events such as heat waves, droughts, and episodes of heavy rainfall causing major floods. Over the past few decades, this prediction has turned into reality. One study compared the incidence of extreme weather events from 1951 to 1980 and from 1981 to 2011. The researchers found that only about 0.2 per cent of the world's land area was hit by extreme weather in the former years, but about 10 per cent was affected in the latter period. Some examples of the types of events that most scientists think have been made more likely by global warming include the extended heat wave that hit Europe in 2003; Cyclone Nargis, which devastated Myanmar (Burma) in 2008; the 2010 floods in Pakistan and Australia; and the 2012–2013 North American Drought, which was one of the costliest natural disasters in US history. Although no specific weather event can be said with complete certainty to be a direct effect of climate change, the trend of more frequent extreme weather events can be. The trend is so pronounced that it is no longer realistic to ascribe the majority of extreme weather events to chance or to natural climate cycles, such as El Niño and La Niña.

DROUGHT
River levels dropped to an all-time low during a drought that affected the Amazon basin in 2010. Tree deaths caused the rainforest to release an estimated 8 billion tons of carbon dioxide.

STORMS
Hurricane Isaac, part of one of the most destructive Atlantic hurricane seasons of all time, batters Gulfport, Mississippi, USA, in August 2012.

FLOODING
People use a boat to transport a motorcycle down a flooded street as Typhoon Ketsana passes through the central Vietnamese city of Hue in 2009.

Changing Biomes and Habitats

Over time, climate change is likely to alter the distribution of natural biomes and habitats. As parts of the world become warmer, woodland will encroach into grassland, for example, while coniferous forests will spread into the tundra zone. In some areas, the movement may be to higher altitudes rather than to higher latitudes. The distributions of both plant and animal species will gradually alter. A study of some 2,000 species published in 2011 found that this is already been happening, with species migrating northwards at an average rate of 17.6km (11 miles) per decade and to higher elevations at an average of 12.2m (40ft) per decade. The extent of some biomes may become diminished rather than altered by side-effects of climate change, for example mangrove swamps and other types of coastal wetland may shrink as sea-levels rise. For some plants and animals, particularly those that occupy expanding biomes, the changes will open up new opportunities, but for others survival will become more difficult. Where a habitat is gradually being lost, or where there is no higher ground to move to, or where changes are taking place too quickly for a species to adjust, losses and even extinctions are likely to occur.

SHRINKING SWAMPS
Mangrove swamps, such as the Sundarbans in Bangladesh and northeastern India, are shrinking worldwide. This threatens the survival of animal inhabitants, such as tigers in the Sundarbans.

CETTI'S WARBLER
The distribution of this small songbird, which first bred in the UK only in 1961, has been moving steadily north through England and Wales in recent years, probably as a result of milder winters and perhaps more subtle climatic shifts.

SOLAR POWER
The use of solar panels to generate electricity, as here at Nellis Air Force Base, Nevada, USA, is an example of using renewable energy to reduce carbon emissions and thus global warming.

GLOBAL WARMING

Since the early 1800s, carbon dioxide levels in the atmosphere have risen by nearly 50 per cent, chiefly through the increased use of fossil fuels. This has accentuated the greenhouse effect (see p.365), making the Earth warm up, and during the coming century global warming is likely to accelerate still more. For the world's human population, this represents a huge and momentous change.

Changing Climates
Scientists generally agree that global warming is a phenomenon caused by human activity rather than the result of a natural climate cycle. Forecasting the effect of global warming is extremely difficult, because many variables are involved. Earth's dynamic systems, such as its atmosphere and oceans, also mean that warming will not be felt equally all over the world. According to current computer forecasts, areas at high latitudes will experience the most rapid warming over the next 50 years. This phenomenon can already be seen in the Antarctic Peninsula, where average summer temperatures have risen by about 2°C (3.5°F) since the 1970s. Paradoxically, warmer parts of the world may also experience some abnormally cold periods as weather patterns shift.

Agriculture and Health
Global warming and accompanying climate change can affect agriculture in a number of ways, such as through the direct influence of higher temperatures on crop yields, changes in the amount and pattern of rainfall, and the impact of a rising sea-level on land availability. Effects may include the expansion of subtropical deserts and reductions in crop yields in tropical regions, though agricultural yields are predicted to rise in many temperate regions. Another area likely to be affected is human health. Projected impacts range from excess deaths due to heat waves to alterations in the distribution of some infectious diseases. Climatic conditions strongly affect diseases transmitted by snails and insects, altering their geographic range. For example, the area of China where the snail-borne disease schistosomiasis occurs is expected to enlarge, and changes are also predicted in the distribution of mosquito-borne diseases such as malaria and dengue fever.

DISEASE VECTOR
Mosquitoes of the genus Aedes *transmit dengue fever and several other infectious diseases. By altering their distribution, global warming is expected to expose several hundred million additional people to dengue.*

Coastal Populations
The sea-level rise expected to occur this century as a result of global warming (see p.374) greatly increases the risk of flooding of coastal areas, and so is likely to affect the approximately 23 per cent of the world's population who live on or near a coast. Many of these people live on river deltas, which are particularly vulnerable to flooding. A serious consequences of flooding from the sea will be the contamination of both surface and underground freshwater

CITY AT RISK
Severe flooding hits Dhaka, the capital of Bangladesh. It is feared that projected sea-level rise in the 21st century will displace millions of the low-lying city's population.

supplies, worsening existing shortages. In some areas, extensive areas of farmland, especially rice paddies, will be lost to the sea. Some wealthier countries will be able to protect their coastal populations by building higher sea defences, but eventually this approach is likely to become impractical.

Tackling Global Warming
Possible responses to global warming include attempts to control greenhouse gas emissions and geoengineering solutions. Examples of emissions control include obtaining more energy from non-polluting, renewable resources (such as solar and wind power) and individuals reducing their energy use. Geoengineering solutions, which at present are mostly only in the research stage, fall into two main categories. First are solutions that concentrate on capturing carbon dioxide from the atmosphere, whether by artificial or natural means, and turning it into a form that can be permanently stored away. A second set of suggested approaches attempt to reduce solar heating of the atmosphere. These range from the relatively simple, such as putting solar reflective surfaces on the tops of buildings, to much more expensive and speculative ones, such as installing orbiting mirrors in space to reflect solar radiation.

THE KEELING CURVE
Named after the American scientist who first plotted it, this graph shows the rise in atmospheric carbon dioxide – thought to be a major cause of global warming – since 1958.

ATMOSPHERE

Air Masses and Weather Systems

AN AIR MASS is a body of air with uniform characteristics. Different air masses meet and interact along boundaries called fronts. There is a close link between air masses and patterns of circulating air known as pressure systems: warm air masses are associated with low-pressure systems and cool air masses with high-pressure systems. Over the course of a year, the distribution of air masses and pressure systems changes. These shifts can have significant effect on the weather. For example, continental air is hot in summer, causing low pressure over the land, and bitterly cold in winter, resulting in high pressure.

Air Masses

An air mass is a volume of air that covers most of a continent or ocean and acquires characteristics from the surface below it. Air over a continent will be drier than air over the ocean, and it will be warmer in summer and cooler in winter, because of the different rates at which the land and sea warm and cool with the seasons. Once it has acquired these characteristics, the almost homogenous air constitutes an air mass. Air masses extend from the surface all the way up to the tropopause (see p.362). Air masses have names that describe their origins: those that form over land are continental, and those forming over the sea are maritime. Depending on the latitude in which they form, air masses may be arctic, polar, tropical, or equatorial. These names can then be combined to produce six types of air mass: continental arctic; continental polar; continental tropical; maritime arctic; maritime polar; maritime tropical; and maritime equatorial. There is no continental equatorial type, because there is no continental land mass in equatorial regions that is large enough to produce continental equatorial air. Arctic and polar air are essentially identical at surface level, but they differ in the upper atmosphere. When two air masses meet, they do not simply merge together, because they are at different temperatures. This means that the density of the air is different in the two air masses. Instead of mixing, the denser air moves beneath the less dense air, lifting it from the surface. The boundary between two air masses is known as a front, named for the air behind it: as a warm front passes, warm air replaces cool air; a cold front brings cooler air.

VILHELM BJERKNES

The Norwegian Vilhelm Bjerknes (1862–1951) is one of the founders of scientific meteorology. He established the Bergen Geophysical Institute in 1917, and set up a series of weather stations throughout Norway. Using the data they provided, Bjerknes and his team discovered the existence of air masses, separated by fronts, and proposed a theory to describe the formation and dissolution of weather fronts.

polar continental air mass

polar maritime air mass

polar maritime air mass

tropical continental air mass

tropical maritime air mass

tropical maritime air mass

NORTH AMERICAN AIR MASSES
The weather at a particular place is usually influenced by several air masses. For example, North American weather is influenced by the six air masses shown above: cool polar air flows from the north, and warm tropical air from the south. In winter, tropical maritime air comes in from the Pacific Ocean.

DEEP CLOUD
When two air masses meet along a cold front, air is forced upwards and becomes unstable, resulting in the formation of deep cumulus clouds.

Pressure Systems

Warm, rising air produces an area of low surface pressure (or cyclone). Dense, subsiding, cool air forms an area of high surface pressure called an anticyclone. The difference in pressure between the centre of a pressure system and the air outside it is called a pressure gradient. Air flows along this gradient from areas of high to low pressure – the steeper the gradient, the stronger the wind. The moving air is deflected by the Coriolis effect (see p.368), so in the northern hemisphere air flows anticlockwise around cyclones and clockwise around anticyclones.

HIGH AND LOW PRESSURE
Air spirals into a low-pressure area (cyclone), then rises, perpetuating the low pressure below, but creating high pressure above, where air diverges. In high-pressure areas (anticyclone), the situation is reversed.

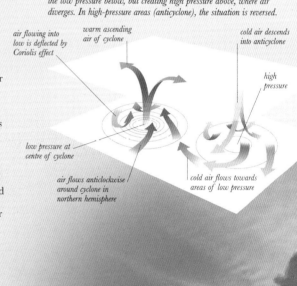

air flowing into low is deflected by Coriolis effect

warm ascending air of cyclone

cold air descends into anticyclone

high pressure

low pressure at centre of cyclone

air flows anticlockwise around cyclone in northern hemisphere

cold air flows towards areas of low pressure

Fronts

On a weather map, the position of a front is indicated where it meets the ground, but fronts also extend upwards, often all the way to the tropopause, the boundary between the troposphere and the stratosphere (see p.358). Fronts are 100–200km (60–120 miles) wide, and they form along the edges of air masses. They also slope, so a frontal system, comprising a warm and cold front with warm air between them, is shaped rather like a bowl, but with uneven sides. A warm front slopes at about 0.5°–1°, and a cold front at about 2°. Cold fronts travel at an average speed of 35kph (22mph), and warm fronts at 24kph (15mph). At a cold front, cool air undercuts warm air, forcing it steeply upwards along the line of the front. Strong convection currents develop, leading to the formation of storm clouds and heavy rainfall. Cold fronts are often associated with low-pressure systems and unsettled conditions blowing away from a high-pressure region. At a warm front, warm air rises over cold air more gradually.

Moisture condenses in the rising air, producing clouds and precipitation, the type depending on how rapidly the air rises. Because it moves more quickly, a cold front will eventually overtake a warm one, lifting it clear of the ground. This is known as an occlusion. A warm occlusion occurs when the cold front rises over the warm one, and a cold occlusion occurs when the cold front undercuts the warm front.

GRADUAL SLOPE OF A WARM FRONT
This warm front over Illinois, USA, has produced layered, stratus-type cloud. It meets the ground about 300km (186 miles) away.

STORM FRONT
A fast-moving cold front may "shovel up" warm air, producing huge storm clouds. Each cloud dissipates quickly, but another forms, creating a squall line, as seen here.

COLD FRONT
A cold front advances into the warm air ahead of it, forcing air to rise up the relatively steep frontal slope. This triggers the formation of cumulus-type clouds.

dense cumulus cloud of considerable height

warm air

steep gradient

cold front

area of low pressure

area of high pressure

area of high pressure

heavy rain ahead of front

thin, stratus-type cloud

thick rain-clouds

WARM FRONT
Air rises more slowly up the shallow slope of a warm front and produces stratus-type clouds. The clouds warn people of its approach as the front overhangs the region ahead of it.

warm front

shallow gradient

rain at base of front

area of low pressure

Jet Streams

Jet streams are narrow ribbons of fast-moving air that circle the Earth, close to the tropopause, at 100–500kph (60–310mph). They are produced by the difference in temperature between air masses. Because warm air is less dense than cold air, pressure decreases with height more rapidly in a column of warm air than in cold air. This difference in temperature is reflected in a difference in pressure that increases with height. It is this difference that generates the wind, which blows with the cold air on its left in the northern hemisphere and on its right in the southern hemisphere. This means the jet streams blow from west to east in both hemispheres. The exception is a jet stream that develops in summer over India and Africa, which flows in the opposite direction.

JET-STREAM VARIATION
Jet streams do not blow in a constant direction. Shallow waves, known as Rossby waves, develop, which become bigger over about three weeks and then disappear as a steady flow resumes.

shallow Rossby wave forming in jet stream

polar jet stream

cells break away and form depressions

EARLY WAVES

ENLARGED WAVES

Atmosphere

High- and Low-Pressure Weather

As cold air sinks, it becomes warmer, creating an area of high pressure at the surface and bringing settled weather with cloudless skies. It is usually dry and sunny in summer and cold and frosty in winter. However, if the descending air traps warmer air beneath it, fog may form. Warmth at the surface causes air to rise, producing low surface pressure. Moisture condenses in the rising air, producing both cloud and precipitation, the type depending on how rapidly the air rises. Winds blowing into low-pressure regions are generally stronger than the winds blowing away from high-pressure regions because the pressure gradient is usually steeper around low-pressure systems. The very high winds and heavy rain of a tropical cyclone are extremely destructive. In temperate areas, low-pressure cyclones bring less severe weather and are known as depressions.

HIGH-PRESSURE SYSTEMS
Clear skies, dry air, and fine weather indicate anticyclonic (high-pressure) systems, such as seen here in the Namib Desert. Air flowing outwards prevents moister air from entering.

CLEAR SKIES
This satellite image of South Australia shows anticyclonic conditions in summer, which bring high temperatures and almost no rain.

STORMY WEATHER FRONT
A cold front is lifting warm, moist, unstable air, causing these storm clouds to form over Norfolk, England. The clouds will produce heavy rain.

LOW-PRESSURE SYSTEMS
Cyclonic (low-pressure) weather, as seen here in Brazil, is usually dull, with grey cloud, often accompanied by persistent, light rain.

Mid-Latitude Depressions

Between polar and tropical regions, low-pressure areas, called mid-latitude depressions, travel from west to east, usually with one depression following another. They are caused by horizontal waves in the jet stream, called Rossby waves, at the top of the front between tropical and polar air. Rossby waves produce similar waves at surface level. A crest in a Rossby wave, projecting into cold air on the polar side of the jet stream, produces a ridge of high pressure. A trough in the jet stream, projecting into warm air on the equatorial side, produces low pressure. These ridges and troughs are where the winds are fastest. At the surface, anticyclones usually occur downwind of the ridges and cyclones downwind of the troughs. A mid-latitude depression tends to develop a characteristic arrangement of warm and cold fronts. The system begins as a simple boundary between warm and cold air, with the air on either side flowing in opposite directions. As it travels eastwards, separate fronts develop. Because cold fronts move more quickly than warm ones, they eventually merge, form an occlusion, and then dissipate.

DEPRESSION DIARY
These illustrations show the development, movement, and decay of a mid-latitude depression. A front develops, and then deepens. Over time, the cyclonic circulation results in occlusion of the front, which then dissipates.

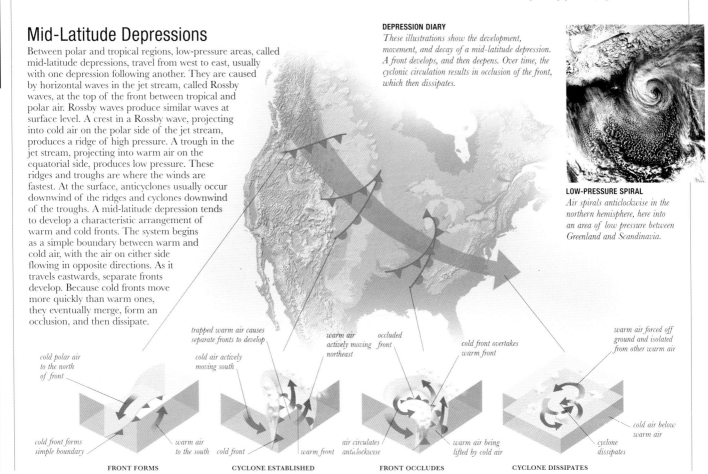

LOW-PRESSURE SPIRAL
Air spirals anticlockwise in the northern hemisphere, here into an area of low pressure between Greenland and Scandinavia.

trapped warm air causes separate fronts to develop

warm air actively moving northeast

occluded front

cold front overtakes warm front

warm air forced off ground and isolated from other warm air

cold polar air to the north of front

cold air actively moving south

cold front forms simple boundary

warm air to the south

cold front

warm front

air circulates anticlockwise

warm air being lifted by cold air

cyclone dissipates

cold air below warm air

FRONT FORMS   **CYCLONE ESTABLISHED**   **FRONT OCCLUDES**   **CYCLONE DISSIPATES**

Tropical Cyclones

A tropical cyclone, known also as a hurricane or typhoon, is a low-pressure system that develops only where a large area of the sea's surface has a temperature no lower than 27°C (80°F) and the wind direction or speed changes with height, to remove rising air. The Coriolis effect makes the winds spiral. These conditions occur mainly in late summer, when the sea is warm, between latitudes 5° and 20°. A disturbance in the wind pattern starts the air turning, producing low surface pressure with air accelerating into it. The high temperature causes high evaporation, so the rising air is very moist. As it cools, condensation releases latent heat, increasing instability and generating towering storm clouds.

HURRICANE PAULINE
This hurricane struck Mexico in October 1997. Wind speeds in the cloud wall surrounding the eye reached over 200kph (125mph).

ANATOMY OF A HURRICANE
Warm, sinking air forms the calm area known as the eye, around which there is a cloud wall where the strongest winds and the heaviest rain occur. Rising air produces high pressure aloft, while subsiding air produces spiral bands of cloud with clear skies in between. Strong convection and condensation inside the clouds power the hurricane.

high-level winds spiral outwards

fastest winds spiral round eye wall

dry air descends

sea surface rises in area of storm surge

spiralling bands of wind and rain

TYPHOON ODESSA
The eye of typhoon Odessa, over the western Pacific, is evident from the "hole" where warm, dry air is sinking, causing cloudless skies.

ATMOSPHERE

HURRICANE TRACK
Hurricanes travel westwards, and swing to the right as they approach land. How soon this happens will determine whether or not they cross land. This is the track of Mitch, which struck Central America in October 1998. Its winds blew continuously at 290kph (180mph) for 15 hours.

end of hurricane track

start of hurricane track

Monsoon Systems

Monsoon weather occurs in some parts of the tropics due to a seasonal change in the direction of the prevailing wind. During the winter, very dry air flows outwards from high pressure in the continental interior. In summer, as the land warms, the high pressure gives way to low pressure. Over the ocean, however, pressure remains relatively high because water warms much more slowly. The winds reverse direction, bringing moist air over the land. As it crosses onto the land, the air rises, producing huge clouds and the torrential rains of the monsoon.

high-pressure system over Tibetan Plateau

WINTER
In winter, a high-pressure system develops over the Tibetan Plateau, giving rise to very dry winds that flow towards a low-pressure system over the Indian Ocean.

cool, dry northeast winds

low-pressure system over Tibetan Plateau

intertropical convergence zone

low pressure over Indian Ocean

SUMMER
In summer, low pressure over the Tibetan Plateau and northward movement of the intertropical convergence zone draw in moist air from the Indian Ocean over Asia.

high pressure over Indian Ocean

warm, wet southwest winds

intertropical convergence zone

THE ONSET OF THE MONSOON

People in India and elsewhere in Asia are dependent on the monsoon for growing their crops. If the monsoon is early, the fields may not be ready for planting, but if it is late, planting is delayed and the crop yield is poor. This can be devastating for subsistence farmers. In drought years, people go hungry and their stock starves. Today, the increasing accuracy with which the onset of the monsoon is predicted allows some farmers to plan which crops to plant. If they know when the rains will arrive, they also know the length of the growing season. The monsoon starts with a spectacular thunderstorm, and torrential rain that lasts for a week or more. Heavy rain can cause flooding, but the people still celebrate the first rains of the monsoon.

LIVING WITH HURRICANES

Although tropical cyclones – also known as hurricanes and typhoons – are generated at sea, they can inflict widespread devastation and loss of life if they reach coasts and travel inland. These storms also trigger storm surges, flooding, and catastrophic landslides. Attempts to defuse hurricanes by cloud-seeding – a method of inducing rain – have met with limited success. In recent years, however, improvements in hurricane and typhoon warning systems have saved thousands of lives.

Wind and Water

Hurricane strength is measured using the Saffir-Simpson scale, which has a maximum rating of five. In a category-five hurricane, wind speeds can reach over 240kph (155mph), and, because the wind's impact increases exponentially with its speed, it can tear off roofs and smash wooden buildings apart. This destructive power is made worse by the fact that the wind blows in the opposite directions on either side of the hurricane's centre, or eye. As the eye passes overhead, the wind stops and then reverses, ripping out anything that has been loosened in the initial blast.

Violent though it is, wind takes second place to water as a cause of cyclone-related deaths. Where land is low-lying, seawater is forced inland in storm surges, which can be more than 8m (26ft) high. Such surges are a hazard in the Gulf of Mexico, where they played a deadly role in the hurricane that hit the Texan port of Galveston in 1900, but they can also strike the USA's Atlantic coast, from Florida to the Carolinas. They are also a particular risk in the Ganges delta, in the northern reaches of the Bay of Bengal. This region is densely populated, and the land is only a few metres above sea-level during a normal high tide. To make matters worse, the gentle slope of the sea bed increases the chance of large storm surges forming when winds blow towards the coast. Since 1980, storm surges in the Bay of Bengal have claimed over half a million lives.

When Hurricane Katrina struck New Orleans in August 2005, it was also the storm surge that did the real damage. However, investigations show that flood control measures can make the problem worse if not well-maintained. New Orleans is cut through by a channel to take shipping from the river to the sea, flanked by levees. Some of the levees were all too quickly breeched to swamp parts of the city as the channel became superhighway for the surge.

STORM SURGE
This town in the Dominican Republic was flooded in 1998 by Hurricane George, which caused millions of dollars' worth of damage.

Advance Warning

Geostationary and polar-orbiting satellites are used to track developing storms in cyclone-generating regions. Once a potential threat has been identified, regional forecasting systems estimate a storm's strength, path, and eventual arrival on land. Hurricanes and typhoons make slow progress across the sea, so storm alerts can give several days' advance warning – vital preparation time for people likely to be affected.

It is relatively easy to track storms, but much more difficult to forecast their future path. Hurricanes and typhoons follow curving tracks, moving outwards from the tropics, but local conditions such as surface-temperature variations often make them deviate from their original course. Autumn 2012's Hurricane Sandy, which blasted the NE USA, looked like a weak tropical storm when it was in the Caribbean, but turned suddenly into a giant as it merged with a mid-latitude depression.

CLOSING IN
Seen by satellite, Hurricane Fran spirals near the USA's Atlantic coast in 1996. The hurricane inflicted extensive damage in North Carolina.

Warming of The Seas

Hurricanes develop best in hot conditions, and form in regions where the sea's surface temperature exceeds about 26°C (79°F). In the North Atlantic, heat stored during the summer produces a peak hurricane season from August to October, while off northern Australia the cyclone season reaches its height between January and March. Once the sea starts to cool, violent cyclonic storms are rare, but with an increase in global warming (see pp.370–71), zones of warm surface water will become larger and more persistent. As a result, the threat from hurricanes and typhoons is almost certain to grow.

With more heat available to generate rising air, cyclonic storms are likely to become more frequent, and the strength of each storm may increase. The amount of moisture that it carries will grow. Hurricanes may also wander further from the tropics than they do now, threatening areas as far north as New England relatively often. Hurricane Sandy gave an uncomfortable warning that it may well be happening already.

WIND AND WATER
Storm surges are related to a hurricane's wind speed, and to the topography of the coast. A hurricane of strength 5 on the Saffir-Simpson scale (shown here) may produce a surge of 8m (25ft).

Typical storm surge height (ft) / Typical storm surge height (m)

25 — 8

20 — 6

15 —

10 — 4

5 — 2

0 — 0

1   2   3   4   5

120 (75)   155 (95)   180 (115)   205 (135)   240 (155)   275 (175)

Wind speed in kph (mph)

SANDY'S AFTERMATH
In 2012, a tropical cyclone, Hurricane Sandy, merged with fast-moving cold air in the north Atlantic. When the resulting superstorm came ashore, it caused great damage, as seen here at Breezy Point, New York, USA.

Precipitation and Clouds

CLOUDS FORM WHEN water vapour in rising air condenses into droplets or freezes directly into ice crystals. The height at which this occurs depends on the stability of the air and the amount of moisture present. A typical cloud droplet, or ice crystal, is about 0.01mm (0.0004in) across. Cold clouds formed at high altitude contain only ice crystals, lower-altitude warm clouds contain only water droplets, and mixed clouds contain both. Snowflakes form if ice crystals and water droplets cool to below freezing. Water evaporates from the droplets and is deposited on the ice crystals, which collide and form snowflakes. Fog and dew form when condensation occurs at ground level, but if temperatures fall below freezing, dew is replaced by frost and rime.

Stable and Unstable Air

Air is warmed when it is in contact with the ground. This causes it to become less dense than the cooler air above and so it starts to rise. As air moves upwards, its temperature falls at a set rate, the lapse rate, making it denser and heavier as its height increases. Eventually the rising air reaches a point at which it is more dense than the surrounding air and it starts to sink again. This air is said to be stable. As air rises and cools, the amount of water vapour it can hold decreases until it becomes saturated and water droplets form. The temperature at which this happens is referred to as the dew point. The height of the dew point is not fixed and varies according to air temperature. When water vapour condenses into water droplets, it releases latent heat (see below). If the saturated air is cooling at a slower rate than the surrounding air, it will also be warmer and so it will continue to rise. This air that rises without being forced is referred to as unstable. Clouds form at the dew point and may attain great depth under these conditions.

warm air continues to rise	°C	°F		°C	°F	
						5,000m (16,500ft)
	-8	18		8	46	4,000m (13,000ft)
clouds form at dew point	4	39		14	57	3,000m (10,000ft)
air pocket less dense than environment	16	61		20	68	2,000m (6,500ft)
air cools as it rises	28	82		30	86	1,000m (3,300ft)
pocket of air at ground temperature	40	104		40	104	0

UNSTABLE CONDITIONS
In these conditions, a rising pocket of air is always warmer than that surrounding it. At the dew point, the air becomes saturated with water vapour and clouds start to form.

STORM CLOUD
Clouds like this form in unstable air. Water vapour condenses, releasing latent heat so the air continues to rise. Violent vertical currents in the cloud may produce a thunderstorm.

Condensation

Condensation is the change that takes place when a gas, such as water vapour, changes into a liquid, such as water. A water-vapour molecule consists of elements, two hydrogen and one oxygen, that move freely among the molecules of the other atmospheric gases. When two water molecules collide, they bounce off each other. However, as the temperature falls, the molecules have less energy and move more slowly. When they reach the dew-point temperature, at which water condenses, water-vapour molecules join together when they meet. A hydrogen bond forms between one of the hydrogen atoms of one molecule and the oxygen atom of another, forming them into short strings. The water vapour has then condensed into a liquid. As they join, the molecules fall into a state that requires less energy to sustain it, and so they give up some of their energy as heat. This is called latent heat. Its release warms the surrounding air and may be absorbed by liquid molecules, allowing them to vaporize. Thus groups of water molecules are constantly breaking and re-forming. If the water droplets grow large enough, they eventually fall as rain.

RAINBOW IN HAWAII
Light is refracted (bent) as it enters a raindrop and again as it leaves it. This separates the light into its constituent colours and forms the rainbow.

STORM CLOUD
Cumulonimbus clouds are among the largest of all clouds and have great vertical height, but they are short-lived, rarely lasting for more than an hour.

ATMOSPHERE

Lifting and Rainfall

Clouds form when moist air cools to its dew-point temperature. Air becomes cooler if it is made to rise, and so cloud often forms in rising air. The height at which water vapour condenses in rising air marks the cloud base. Air can be made to rise in three ways. If it is heated from below, due to contact with a warm surface, air rises by convection, forming small fair-weather cumulus or cumulonimbus clouds. If moving air has to pass over a mountain, it must rise. This is called orographic lifting and results in orographic cloud formation. Warm air also rises when cooler air pushes beneath it at a weather front. This is frontal lifting, producing frontal clouds. If clouds are thick enough, water droplets and ice crystals link together until they are heavy enough to fall as precipitation. Convection produces showers, and brief storms. Orographic and frontal clouds produce more persistent rain and drizzle.

FRONTAL RAIN — rain falls along front
CONVERGENCE RAIN — clouds form
air forced upwards
warm air rising over cold air
converging air
OROGRAPHIC RAIN
airflow continues in lee of mountain
mountains force air to rise and cool, resulting in rain on windward slope
leeward slope receives little rain

LAKE EFFECT CLOUDS
In winter, large lakes, such as Lake Superior, USA, are slow to freeze. Air crossing them gathers moisture that condenses into clouds as it passes over cold land.

OROGRAPHIC CLOUD
Clouds form in the rising air passing over this mountain in Greenland. Orographic clouds often form a cap shrouding the mountain summit and extending a short distance downwind.

RAIN-CLOUD FORMATION
Moist air that is made to rise above the dew point forms clouds. They form where warm air rises over cool air at a front (frontal rain); where air rises by convection over warm ground, producing a local area of low pressure into which air converges and rises (convergence rain); and where air rises over mountains (orographic rain).

No-Freeze Rainfall

Rain feels warm if it falls from a cloud that consists entirely of water droplets. Such clouds, which form only in air that is above freezing point, are known as warm clouds, and the rain they produce is called no-freeze rainfall. The lower parts of clouds are often warm, but outside the tropics the freezing level is rarely high enough for deep warm clouds to form and produce rain. Raindrops form in warm clouds by the merging of cloud droplets, which vary greatly in size. Bigger ones, being heavier, fall faster than small ones and overtake them. When droplets of similar size collide, they merge and break into two again, but when a big droplet meets a small one, they coalesce. The droplet grows bigger, collects more small droplets, and finally falls as rain.

HEAVY RAIN
Warm clouds produce big, heavy raindrops. Regular, heavy rainfall is a feature of regions with tropical climates.

TROPICAL RAINSTORM
Water evaporates quickly in the tropics. It rises fast, forming warm clouds that produce frequent rainstorms.

SATELLITE DATA

This is a false-colour image produced as part of a project called the Tropical Rainfall Measuring Mission. The aim of the project is to measure the energy released by tropical rainfall, and to calculate the effect of this energy on the global climate. Data is gathered using instruments carried on satellites, including radar to measure raindrop formation in clouds, and microwave receivers to measure air temperature. When the images are received, computers colour parts of them differently to enhance any variation. In this image, pale blue indicates light rainfall. Areas of heavy rainfall are coloured orange and red.

ATMOSPHERE

Rain

Water that reaches the ground as droplets is known as rain or drizzle. Drizzle consists of drops that are less than 0.5mm (¹⁄₅₀in) in diameter and very close together. These droplets form near the base of stratus cloud, in which there are no upcurrents that would allow them to coalesce with other droplets and grow larger. They sink slowly, but because the cloud base is so low they have no time to evaporate before reaching the ground. Drops larger than those of drizzle fall as rain. Raindrops vary in size, but within limits. The smaller the drop, the more slowly it falls, and therefore the longer it has to evaporate in the air between the cloud base and the ground. This means that a raindrop must be at least 0.5mm (¹⁄₅₀in) in diameter if it is to reach the ground. Most raindrops are 2–5mm (¹⁄₂₅–¹⁄₅in) in diameter. This is between 1 million and 2.5 million times bigger than an average cloud droplet, so many cloud droplets must merge together before they are big enough to fall as rain. Raindrops fall at 23–33kph (14–20mph). Friction with the air breaks up drops over 5mm (¹⁄₅in).

RAINY SEASON
Seasonal rainfall, such as this in the Serengeti in Tanzania, triggers the regrowth of plants, which in turn supports a wide variety of wildlife.

DISTANT RAINFALL
Rain seen falling in the distance looks like a grey curtain under cloud. Sometimes the curtain does not reach the ground, because raindrops evaporate in the dry air beneath the cloud.

SAHEL DROUGHT

The semi-arid Sahel region lies along the southern edge of the Sahara Desert. Usually there is a short rainy season in summer, when the intertropical convergence zone moves north, which revives the pasture for livestock and allows some crop cultivation. However, the rains are unreliable, and the region has endured many droughts. The worst drought of modern times began with light rains in the 1960s and complete failure of the rains in 1972 and 1973. Rainfall did not return to normal until the 1980s. Up to 200,000 people and 4 million cattle died.

Hail and Snow

Most hailstones are hard, roughly spherical pellets of ice, 5–50mm (¹⁄₅–2in) across. Soft hail forms when rime (see opposite page) collects on snow crystals, producing pellets up to 5mm (¹⁄₅in) in diameter that flatten when they hit the ground. A hailstone begins as a raindrop near the bottom of a large cumulonimbus cloud. Carried aloft by air currents, it freezes when it is above the freezing level, then falls in downcurrents near the top of the cloud. The hailstone grows by encountering supercooled water droplets that freeze onto it. Its final size depends on the number of circuits it has made between the top and bottom of the cloud. Snowflakes form when ice crystals adhere to one another, and they are 1–20mm (¹⁄₂₅–¹⁄₅in) across. The biggest snowflakes develop between 0° and -5°C (32–23°F). At this temperature, water coats the crystals and freezes as soon as another crystal touches it. All snowflakes are six-sided, but the random way they form ensures no two are identical. Ice pellets, or sleet, are melted snowflakes or raindrops, 2–5mm (²⁄₂₅–¹⁄₅in) across, that freeze between the cloud base and the ground in air that is below freezing temperature. Ice particles smaller than 1mm (¹⁄₂₅in) are called snow grains.

SHAPED BY THE WIND
An ice storm in New Hampshire, USA, has decorated this sign. Freezing raindrops, driven by a strong wind, struck the sign, spread out, and then froze. Later drops spread over earlier ones, producing this shape.

SNOWFLAKE
Snowflakes, such as the one shown here, form when ice crystals collide with one another. Each has a unique shape, but all are six-sided.

INSIDE A HAILSTONE
In this section through a hailstone, viewed in polarized light, the alternating layers of clear ice and opaque rime that form the hailstone are clearly evident.

HAILSTONES
Hailstones form only in large cumulonimbus clouds, where they are carried up and down repeatedly, growing all the time. The bigger the cloud, the larger the hailstones become.

BLIZZARD CONDITIONS
Heavy snow, low temperatures, and strong winds are characteristic of blizzards. Here emperor penguins sit out a blizzard in Antarctica.

ATMOSPHERE

Fog and Dew

Fog and mist occur when a layer of moist air, near ground level, cools to below its dew-point temperature. On high ground, fog and mist are often stratus cloud with a base lower than the hilltops. Dew forms late at night, when objects on the ground lose the warmth they absorbed by day. If the air is moist, contact with cold surfaces can cause water vapour to condense, coating them with liquid droplets. Cooling the surface also produces radiation fog because the ground cools by radiating away its warmth. Valley fog is a type of radiation fog. Advection fog forms if a wind carries warm, moist air over a cold surface.

RADIATION FOG

Early-morning fog on the Vermilion Lakes, Canada, formed by condensation when the Earth's surface cooled and reached the dew point.

ICE DEPOSITS

Freezing raindrops fell onto these pine needles, which were below freezing temperature, and froze almost instantly into clear ice.

RIME ON FORESTED HILLSIDE

These trees near Bamboo, North Carolina, USA, are coated with sparkling, white rime frost.

Frost and Rime

Frost is a layer of ice crystals that covers objects such as plants, parked cars, and windows. It also forms on the surface of fallen snow and in the air spaces inside it. If the dew-point temperature is below freezing, water vapour will be deposited on surfaces as ice crystals. This is how hoar frost, the commonest type of frost, forms. Dew may also freeze if the temperature falls. It may form clear ice, with rounded surfaces, or fern frost, which covers windowpanes with patterns resembling fern fronds. Fern frost develops when the dew on the window cools below freezing, but remains liquid. Ice crystals form between the droplets, then the droplets freeze onto the crystals, rapidly covering the window with frost. Rime frost is white and rough to the touch, forms thicker layers than hoar frost, and may grow into feathery shapes. It forms in cold, foggy conditions when supercooled water droplets in freezing fog or drizzle freeze on contact with a very cold surface, or when water vapour is deposited directly as ice crystals. Once the surface is coated with ice crystals, more water freezes onto the existing crystals. If a wind is blowing, rime frost forms only on the side of structures, such as radio and ships' masts, that are facing into the wind.

LUKE HOWARD

Luke Howard (1772–1864) was an English pharmacist with a keen interest in meteorology. He began keeping weather records when he was 11 years old. Howard wrote the first study of urban climate and the first book on meteorology. His cloud classification was strongly influenced by the system of two-part names used for biological classification.

GLOBAL CLOUD COVER

This satellite image shows that clouds occur worldwide, but are not uniform. Different clouds form under different climatic conditions.

Cloud Types

Clouds differ in appearance and in the height at which they develop. These differences provide the basis for an international system for classifying them. The classification is derived from the one proposed in 1803 by Luke Howard (see panel, left), and it uses the names he coined: combinations of cirrus (curl), stratus (layer), nimbus (rain), and cumulus (heap). It groups clouds as high, middle, or low level, according to the height at which the cloud base most often occurs. In middle- and high-level clouds, this varies with latitude, the height and range being lower at the poles than in temperate latitudes and highest at the equator. Clouds are grouped into ten basic types: cirrus, cirrostratus, and cirrocumulus (high clouds); altocumulus and altostratus (medium clouds); and nimbostratus, cumulonimbus, cumulus, stratus, and stratocumulus (low clouds). Some cloud types are further subdivided using 14 specific terms, such as humilis and congestus (with cumulus), which refers to the character of the cloud, or lenticularis and undulatus (with altocumulus), which further defines the shape.

cirrus	Tropopause
cirrocumulus	high level, above 6,000m (20,000ft)
cirrostratus	
altocumulus	middle level, 2,000–6,000m (6,500–20,000ft)
altostratus	
stratocumulus	
stratus	low level, 0–2,000m (0–6,500ft)
cumulus nimbostratus	cumulonimbus
	Height of cloud base

CLOUD TYPES

The ten basic types of cloud, which are classified by their appearance, are shown here. There is a clear division between high-, middle-, and low-level clouds. Only the cumulonimbus cloud has great vertical height.

ATMOSPHERE

GLOSSARY

In this glossary, terms defined within a larger entry are highlighted in **bold** type, while references to terms defined in other entries are identified with *italic* type.

A

ABLATION The loss of ice from a glacier due to melting, evaporation, or calving. The region of a glacier where there is a net loss of ice is known as the **ablation area**. See also *accumulation area*.

ABYSSAL Relating to the deep ocean floor and its environment, beyond the continental shelves and slopes. Abyssal depths are deeper than bathyal depths but not as deep as deep-sea trenches. The **abyssal plain** is the flat, sediment-covered plain at about 4,000–6,000m (13,000–20,000ft) depth that forms the bed of most of the world's oceans. See also *bathyal, deep-sea trench*.

ACCRETION The gravitational coming-together of small particles, for example in the early Solar System, resulting in the formation of the planets.

ACCUMULATION AREA The part of a glacier where snowfall exceeds losses by melting, evaporation, and calving. See also *ablation*.

ACID RAIN Any precipitation (snow as well as rain) that contains dissolved acids. Most rain is slightly acidic due to dissolved carbon dioxide. More strongly acidic rain also occurs due to atmospheric pollution, or sometimes from gases released by volcanic eruptions.

AEROSOL Tiny particles (about a millionth of a millimetre across) of dust or liquid suspended in the air.

AIR MASS A mass of air of uniform characteristics that may extend over thousands of miles.

ALBEDO The extent to which a part of the Earth's surface reflects incoming radiation from the Sun, usually expressed as a decimal fraction.

ALLUVIUM Sedimentary material deposited by rivers. Any particular accumulation of alluvium is called an **alluvial deposit**. An **alluvial fan** is a deposit laid down where a stream leaves a highland area and spreads out over a plain. **Alluvial soil** is soil derived from alluvium.

ANGIOSPERM A flowering plant (as distinct from a conifer, fern, moss, or other plant). Angiosperms also include many tree species. See also *coniferous*.

ANNUAL A plant that lives and dies within one year.

ANOXIA Lack of molecular oxygen (O_2), which many (but not all) organisms require for respiration.

ANTICLINE An arch-like, upwards fold of originally flat strata due to horizontal compression. See also *syncline, fold*.

ANTICYCLONE A weather system in which winds circle around an area of high pressure. See also *cyclone*.

AQUIFER A layer of porous rock that can hold and transmit water.

ARCHIPELAGO A group of islands forming a chain or cluster.

ARÊTE A narrow mountain ridge separating two adjacent cirques. See also *cirque*.

ASTEROID One of thousands of bodies of rocky material orbiting the Sun that are smaller in size than the planets.

ASTHENOSPHERE The layer of the mantle immediately below the rigid lithosphere. It is sufficiently non-rigid to flow slowly in a solid state and plays a key part in the movement of tectonic plates. See also *lithosphere, tectonic plate, mantle*.

ATOLL see *coral reef*.

AUREOLE The area around an igneous intrusion where thermal alteration (metamorphism) of country rock has taken place. See also *igneous rock, metamorphism, country rock*.

AURORA BOREALIS Flickering lights in the sky that are sometimes visible in northern polar regions. They are caused by the interaction between high-energy particles from the Sun and the Earth's magnetic field. Their southern hemisphere equivalent is called the **aurora australis**.

B

BACKWASH The movement of water down a beach after waves have broken. See also *swash*.

BAR A long, sandy deposit built up by sea or river action. An **offshore bar** is a coastal bar not attached to the land. A **baymouth bar** is a spit that has grown so it extends right across the mouth of a bay. A **longshore bar** lies between the high- and low-water marks, parallel to the shoreline. A **barrier bar** is a long bar parallel to the coastline. A **point bar** is a bar deposited by a river on the inside of a meander. See also *spit, meander*.

BARCHAN see *dune*.

BARRIER BAR see *bar*.

BARRIER ISLAND A long island of sediment parallel to a coastline. It is normally higher than a barrier bar. See also *bar*.

BASALT The Earth's most common volcanic rock, which usually originates as solidified lava. Basaltic lava can erupt on continents, but basalt also forms the oceanic crust. Basalt is glassy to fine-grained (composed of very small crystals). See also *igneous rock, flood basalt, crust*.

BATHOLITH A very large igneous intrusion, 100km (60 miles) or more across, which originates deep underground. The Earth's great batholiths are known to science only if exposed on the surface by weathering. See also *igneous rock*.

BATHYAL A term referring to ocean depths of about 200–2,000m (660–6,500ft). See also *abyssal*.

BAYMOUTH BAR see *bar*.

BEACH An accumulation of sand, shell debris, or larger particles along a shoreline. A **beach face** is the steeply sloping part of a beach below a berm. See also *berm*.

BEDDING The manner in which a sedimentary rock was originally laid down in layers. A **bedding plane** is any plane in the rock that is parallel to these layers. See also *sedimentary rock*.

BERGSCHRUND A deep crack formed at the back of a cirque glacier caused by the glacier moving away from the cirque wall. See also *cirque*.

BERM A ridge of shingle on a beach, usually marking the point of the highest high tides. See also *beach*.

BIODIVERSITY The total variety of living things, either on the Earth as a whole or in the region described.

BIOLUMINESCENCE The production of light by living organisms.

BIOME A biological community existing on a large scale and defined mainly by vegetation type (for example, rainforest). The extent of any particular biome is determined by climatic conditions.

BLACK SMOKER see *hydrothermal system*.

BLOCKFIELD An area of broken rocks, usually in a mountainous region.

BOG A peat-accumulating wetland that receives water mainly from rainfall. Bogs are acidic, extremely poor in nutrients, and most support an abundance of *Sphagnum* mosses. The soils are composed almost entirely of dead plant matter, and are waterlogged rather than completely covered by water. See also *fen, marsh*.

BOREAL Relating to or coming from the colder parts of the northern hemisphere, between the Arctic and temperate zones.

BOSS An igneous intrusion that is roughly circular in horizontal cross-section. See also *igneous rock*.

BRAIDED STREAM A stream or river where water flows in many shallow channels that constantly separate and rejoin.

BRECCIA A sedimentary rock made up of angular fragments of minerals and other rocks.

BROADLEAF Of trees: having broad leaves (such as oak and chestnut), as distinct from needle-like leaves. Broadleaved trees are mainly angiosperms rather than conifers, and often deciduous rather than evergreen. See also *angiosperm, coniferous, deciduous, evergreen*.

C

CAATINGA A thorny, dry, tropical woodland found in northeast Brazil.

CALCITE A common mineral form of calcium carbonate.

CALDERA A bowl-shaped volcanic depression larger than a crater, typically greater than 1km (0.6 miles) in diameter caused by the collapse of a volcano into its emptied magma chamber after it has been evacuated by a volcanic explosion.

CALVE Of a glacier: to create icebergs by shedding ice blocks into a sea or lake.

CANYON A deep valley, usually not as narrow as a gorge; also a deep, irregular passage in a cave system. See also *gorge, tube*.

CATCHMENT AREA The area within which all precipitation is drained by a single river system.

CERRADO A type of South American savanna dotted with small, gnarled trees. See also *savanna*.

CHLOROPHYLL The green pigment that plants require for photosynthesis. See also *photosynthesis*.

CHLOROPLAST A structure, found within the cells of green plants, in which chlorophyll is found and photosynthesis takes place. See also *photosynthesis*.

CINDER CONE see *volcano*.

CIRQUE A steep-sided, rounded hollow carved out by a glacier. Many glaciers have their origin in a mountain cirque, from which they flow to lower ground.

CLAST A fragment of rock, especially when incorporated into another newer rock. See also *grain*.

CLAY Mineral particles smaller than about 0.002mm (0.00008in) in diameter that are found in soils and other earthy deposits. A clay soil contains an abundance of clay particles and transmits water slowly.

CLEAVAGE The characteristic plane (or planes) along which a particular rock or mineral splits. See also *foliation*.

CLIMAX VEGETATION The vegetation that in time would naturally dominate any given site or region.

CLOUD CONDENSATION NUCLEUS A tiny particle in the air around which a raindrop or snow crystal may begin to form.

CLOUDFOREST A damp forest almost constantly under clouds, especially in highland regions.

CLOUD-SEEDING A method of creating rain by scattering tiny particles onto clouds.

COALESCENCE In meteorology, the fusion of tiny droplets within clouds until they are big enough to fall as rain.

COAST The boundary between land and sea. A **drowned coast** occurs where, over the centuries, the sea-level has risen relative to the land; its opposite is an **emergent coast**.

COLD DESERT A desert in high-altitude, high-latitude, or temperate regions that may become very cold during the winter months.

COMET A body composed of rock and ice that orbits the Sun. Vaporization of the ice produces the spectacular tail seen during close passage to the Sun.

CONDENSATION The conversion of a substance from the gaseous to the liquid state – for example, water vapour condensing to liquid water. See also *cloud condensation nucleus*.

CONFLUENCE A place where two rivers, streams, or glaciers meet.

CONIFEROUS Cone-bearing. Typical coniferous trees, such as pines and firs, have needle-like leaves and are usually evergreen. See also *evergreen*.

CONSERVATIVE BOUNDARY see *plate boundary*.

CONSTRUCTIVE BOUNDARY see *plate boundary*.

CONTINENTAL RISE The slightly sloping area around the edge of the deep sea floor where it abuts the continental slope.

CONTINENTAL SHELF The gently sloping, submerged portion of continental crust seaward of most continental coasts. See also *crust*.

CONTINENTAL SLOPE The sloping ocean bottom between the edge of the continental shelf and the continental rise.

CONVECTION The movement and circulation of fluids (gases, liquids, or hot and ductile rocks) in response to differences in temperature, which in turn cause density variations between different parts of the fluid.

CONVERGENCE In meteorology, the situation where two air masses are moving towards one another. (For another sense, see *plate boundary*.)

CONVERGENT BOUNDARY see *plate boundary*.

COOLING JOINT see *joint*.

CORAL Any one of various simple animals related to sea-anemones. They are often colonial and can secrete skeletons to support themselves. **Hard corals** (sometimes called true corals) eventually create reefs out of the calcium-carbonate skeletons they lay down.

CORAL REEF A structure in shallow tropical seas built up by the activity of coral animals and other organisms over many years. A **fringing reef** is attached to the shore with little or no water between the reef and shore. A **barrier reef** is parallel to the shore but separated from it by a lagoon. A reef that has grown on top of a sunken extinct volcano forms a circular island called an **atoll**.

CORE The innermost part of the Earth. It consists of a liquid outer core and a solid inner core, both made of nickel-iron. See also *mantle*, *crust*.

CORIOLIS EFFECT The tendency for winds and currents moving in a northerly or southerly direction to be deflected and move at an angle because of the effect of the Earth's rotation. The deflection is to the right in the northern hemisphere and to the left in the southern hemisphere.

CORRASION Erosion of rocks by scraping – for example by rock-laden glacial ice.

COUNTRY ROCK Existing rock into which a new body, such as an igneous intrusion, is emplaced. See also *igneous rock*.

CRATER A bowl-shaped depression through which an erupting volcano discharges gases, pyroclasts, and lava. The crater walls form by accumulation of ejected material. This term also refers to a circular depression in the landscape caused by a large meteorite impact.

CRUST The rocky outermost layer of the solid Earth. The continents and their margins are made of thicker but less dense **continental crust**, while thinner, denser **oceanic crust** underlies the deep ocean floors. See also *mantle*, *tectonic plate*.

CRYOTURBATION The churning up of the land surface by the action of ice below ground level.

CRYSTAL Any solid in which the individual atoms or molecules are arranged in a regular geometrical pattern. Most pure substances can form crystals. There are seven basic patterns of crystal growth, called **crystal systems**.

CURRENT In oceanography, a flow of ocean water. Both surface and deep-sea currents exist. Some are driven by the wind; others (**thermohaline currents**) by differences in temperature and salinity that create differences in density between water masses.

CYCLONE A pressure system in which air circulates around an area of low pressure. A **tropical cyclone** is another name for a hurricane or typhoon. See also *pressure system*, *hurricane*, *anticyclone*.

D

DECIDUOUS Of trees and shrubs: having leaves that fall at a particular time of year, such as winter or a dry season. See also *evergreen*.

DEEP-SEA FAN A fan-shaped deposit on the ocean floor built up by turbidity currents. See also *turbidity current*, *alluvial fan*.

DEEP-SEA TRENCH A canyon-like, linear depression in the ocean floor, the site of subduction of one tectonic plate below another. Trenches are the deepest regions of the oceans. See also *subduction*, *plate boundary*.

DEFORMATION The ductile flow or brittle fracture of existing rocks due to geological movements.

DELTA The area of gently sloping sediment built up by many rivers when they enter the sea or a lake. Its overall shape depends on factors such as the amount of sediment brought down by the river, and the currents, wave action, and tides that it meets. See also *estuary*.

DEPOSITION The laying down of material such as sand and gravel in new locations, usually by wind or moving water or ice.

DESERT PAVEMENT A rocky or stony surface layer found in many deserts. A **hammada** is a solid-rock surface with weathered rock fragments on top.

DESERT VARNISH A black or brown glossy coating sometimes found on rock surfaces in a desert that have been exposed to the atmosphere for long periods of time.

DESERTIFICATION The transformation of a formerly more fertile region into desert.

DESTRUCTIVE BOUNDARY see *plate boundary*.

DEW POINT The temperature at which, under given conditions, liquid water will start to condense out of the air.

DINOSAUR A member of a dominant group of reptiles that died out between 145–65 million years ago. Their closest living relatives are birds and crocodiles.

DIPTEROCARP A member of a family of tall, mainly evergreen trees native to Africa and south Asia.

DISTRIBUTARY A branch of a river that flows away from the main stream and does not reconnect with it later.

DIVERGENT BOUNDARY see *plate boundary*.

DOLINE A depression in the surface of a karst landscape. It often leads down to an underground drainage system. Also called a sinkhole. See also *karst*.

DOME VOLCANO see *volcano*.

DRAINAGE BASIN see *catchment area*.

DROWNED COAST see *coast*.

DRUMLIN A hill-sized, usually streamlined mound of debris left behind by a retreating glacier. See also *moraine*.

DRY FOREST A forest growing in an area with a predominantly dry climate.

DUNE A mound or hill of sand, either in a desert, a river bed, or by the shore of a sea or lake. There are several varieties of desert sand dunes. A **barchan** is a crescent-shaped dune. A **linear** or **seif dune** can run for long distances roughly parallel to the prevailing wind. **Crescentic dunes** form ridges with slightly wavy edges. **Parabolic dunes** have long, trailing arms, while **star dunes** have arms stretching in several directions.

DYKE A sheet of intrusive igneous rock at a steep angle to the surface. A large number of dykes in a given area is termed a **dyke swarm**. See also *country rock*, *sill*.

E

ECOSYSTEM The entirety of living and non-living features of a region and the interactions between them. Organisms include plants, animals, and micro-organisms; non-living features include light, water, nutrients, and the environment. An ecosystem can be exceedingly small or as large as the Earth itself.

EKMAN SPIRAL The tendency of deep-ocean currents to change direction as they rise to the surface. The term also refers to the tendency of winds lower in the atmosphere to blow at an angle compared with winds higher up. The causes of the Ekman spiral include frictional effects and the Coriolis effect.

EL NIÑO The phenomenon in which the normally strong currents of the equatorial Pacific weaken and warm water that has piled up in the western Pacific floats eastwards, making water in the eastern Pacific warmer than usual. It is part of a larger phenomenon that can trigger changes to weather patterns worldwide. See also *La Niña*.

EMERGENT Of a forest tree: growing taller than most other species of tree in the forest. Of a wetland plant: growing taller than the water surface.

EMERGENT COAST see *coast*.

ENDEMIC Of animals and plants: native to a particular region, and found nowhere else.

EPEIROGENESIS The raising or lowering of parts of the Earth's crust due to vertical movements only, rather than the sideways movements involved in orogenesis. See also *orogenesis*.

EPHEMERAL Appearing for only a short time. In deserts, both plant life and rivers are frequently ephemeral.

EPIPHYTE A plant, especially a non-parasitic one, that grows on another plant.

ERG A large expanse of sand dunes within a desert.

EROSION The processes by which rocks or soil are loosened and worn or scraped away from a land surface. The main agents of erosion are wind, water, and moving ice, and the sand grains and other rock particles that they carry. See also *transport*, *weathering*.

ERRATIC A rock that has been transported from its original location, usually carried by ice.

ERUPTION The discharge of lava, pyroclasts, gases, and other material from a volcano. **Hawaiian eruptions** involve large flows of very liquid lava but little explosive activity. **Strombolian eruptions** involve frequent ejections of incandescent clasts and gases, but without major explosions. **Surtseyan eruptions** take place in shallow water and are partly powered by the conversion of water to steam. **Vulcanian eruptions** involve a series of explosive events that feed significant eruption columns. **Plinian eruptions** involve massive explosions to form towering eruption columns, in which much of the volcanic cone may be destroyed. **Fissure eruptions** take place through long cracks in the ground rather than via a volcanic crater. See also *volcano*.

ESCARPMENT The steep slope at the edge of a plateau, or at the edge of an area of exposed, gently sloping strata. An escarpment is also called a scarp.

ESKER A long line of raised debris left behind by a glacier. Eskers are thought to mark the position of former meltwater channels. See also *meltwater*.

ESTUARY The broad, funnel-shaped stretch of water found where many large rivers meet the sea. Most present-day estuaries owe their form to the drowning of river valleys when sea-level rose at the end of the last ice age. The term is also used more broadly to include all bays and inlets where seawater and fresh water mix and muddy sediments are deposited.

EUKARYOTE Any living organism built out of a complex cell or cells containing nuclei (which are enclosed in a membrane). All complex animals and plants are eukaryotes. See also *prokaryote*.

EUTROPHICATION The enrichment of natural waters with extra nutrients, especially as a result of human action. It often has drastic deleterious effects on aquatic ecosystems.

EVAPORITE A chemical sedimentary deposit created by the progressive evaporation of salty water to form various minerals such as halite and gypsum.

EVERGREEN Having leaves all year round. See also *coniferous, deciduous*.

EXFOLIATION A weathering process that involves the splitting off of outer layers of rocks, like the layers of an onion.

F

FAULT A fracture where the rocks on either side have moved relative to one another. If the fault is at an angle to the vertical, and the overhanging rock has slid downwards, it is called a **normal fault**. If the overhanging rock has slid upwards (in relative terms) it is called a **reverse fault**. A **strike-slip fault** is one where movement is horizontal. A **transform fault** is a large-scale strike-slip fault associated with oceanic spreading.

FELSIC ROCK An igneous rock rich in silica. The name reflects the abundance of the mineral feldspar and the high silica content. See also *silica, igneous rock*.

FEN A peat-accumulating wetland that receives water mainly from groundwater seepage. Fens are typically alkaline and nutrient poor (although not extremely so). They support a variety of vegetation types including *Sphagnum* mosses, sedges, and conifer trees. The soils are composed almost entirely of dead plant matter, and they are sometimes completely covered by water.

FERREL CELL A large-scale circulation within the atmosphere, in which air rises at around 60° North or South and flows towards the Equator before descending at around 30°. See also *Hadley cell*.

FETCH The extent of open water across which a wind or water wave has travelled.

FIORD A former glacial valley on the coast that has become an inlet of the sea.

FISSURE ERUPTION see *eruption*.

FLASH POINT The point at which super-heated water changes to steam. See also *geyser*.

FLASH-FLOOD A sudden flood occurring after heavy rain.

FLOOD BASALT An extensive area of basalt resulting from massive volumes of lava erupting and flowing widely over the landscape in relatively short intervals of geological time. It is resistant to erosion and commonly forms extensive plateaus after its formation.

FLOODPLAIN A flat plain next to a river that is liable to be covered with water when the river floods. See also *alluvium*.

FLOWSTONE A smooth coating of younger limestone precipitated over surfaces in caves. See also *calcite*.

FOG Condensed droplets of water forming in the air at ground level. **Radiation fog** is fog caused by the ground surface radiating heat at night, becoming cooler and also cooling the air above it.

FOLD A geological structure in which originally flat-lying rocks appear to have been flexed and bent. In reality, the rocks behaved in a ductile manner and flowed into these shapes, like a warm caramel bar. They may bend upwards in the middle to form a ridge (anticline) or downwards to form a trough (syncline). A **symmetrical fold** has slopes that are the same steepness on either side of the vertical; an **asymmetrical fold** does not. A **recumbent fold** is a fold that is lying on its side. In an **overturned fold**, a syncline is partly tucked underneath a neighbouring anticline. See also *anticline, syncline*.

FOLIATION The arrangement of platy minerals in parallel bands in some deformed metamorphic rocks. See also *cleavage, lamination*.

FOSSIL The remains or traces of an organism that have been buried and often petrified (with its original tissues replaced by minerals). Some fossils, such as preserved footprints and coprolites (fossilized droppings), also record activities.

FOSSIL FUEL Any fuel such as coal or oil that is derived from the remains of once-living organisms that were deeply buried beneath the ground.

FRONT In meteorology, the forward-moving edge of an air mass. See also *air mass*.

FUMAROLE In volcanic regions, a small opening in the ground through which hot gases can escape.

FUNNEL A tube of whirling air descending from a cloud. It becomes a tornado when its lower end touches the ground. See also *tornado*.

G

GALAXY An aggregation of millions of stars, often formed into an immense spiral shape. The Solar System lies within the Milky Way Galaxy.

GEODE A hollow cavity found within a rock and lined with crystals.

GEOTHERMAL ENERGY Energy obtained by tapping the heat generated in the Earth's interior.

GEYSER A jet of boiling water and steam that rises at intervals from the ground. It is powered by hot rocks heating groundwater. See also *hot spring*.

GLACIER A mass of semi-permanent ice capable of flowing downhill. Glaciers come in many varieties. The largest are **ice-sheets**, such as the Antarctic ice-sheet. Similar, but slightly smaller, are **ice-caps**. A **valley glacier** is smaller and flows down a valley, eroding rock as it does so. An **outlet glacier** is one that flows down from an ice-cap or ice-sheet. A **piedmont glacier** spreads out from higher ground onto a broad plain. A **surge-type glacier** is one that periodically increases its speed much above normal. A **cirque glacier** does not spread beyond the mountain hollow (cirque) that it has carved out. In a **polythermal glacier**, a cold surface layer of ice overlies much warmer ice.

GORGE A narrow, deep valley, usually with vertical cliffs on either side. See also *canyon*.

GRABEN see *rift valley*.

GRAIN A term referring to the texture of a rock: rocks can be either fine- or coarse-grained. The term also refers to a single small particle (for example, of sand).

GREASE ICE see *sea-ice*.

GREENHOUSE EFFECT The tendency of the atmosphere to contribute to warming of the Earth, by letting through the Sun's radiation but absorbing some of it that is re-radiated by the Earth. A **greenhouse gas** (such as water vapour, carbon dioxide, or methane) is any gas that promotes this process, whether naturally or via human action.

GROUNDMASS The fine-grained material surrounding larger crystals or clasts. The term is most commonly applied to volcanic rocks and some heterogeneous sedimentary rocks. See also *matrix*.

GROUNDWATER Water occurring below the surface of the land and held between grains or in the interstices of rocks. The upper limit of such a groundwater zone is called the water-table. Water held in the soil is not usually counted as groundwater. See also *aquifer*.

GUST FRONT An area of strong winds that travels ahead of a line of storm clouds. See also *front*.

GUYOT A flat-topped seamount. See also *seamount*.

GYRE A large-scale circular movement of ocean currents.

H

HABITAT Any area that can support a particular group of living things.

HADLEY CELL A major element in the Earth's atmospheric circulation, in which warm air rises at the Equator and flows north and south at high level before sinking and flowing at the surface, mainly back to the Equator.

HAMMOCK A small area of vegetation growing on raised ground. Hammocks are common in the Florida Everglades.

HANGING VALLEY A valley, usually carved by a glacier, that enters high up the side of a larger valley.

HEADWATER The upper portion of any river or stream, close to its source.

HORN, GLACIAL A steep-sided mountain left behind after erosion by glaciers occupying cirques. See also *cirque*.

HOTSPOT A long-lived zone of volcanic activity thought to originate deep in the Earth's mantle. Tectonic plates passing over hotspots are marked by linear chains of volcanoes that become progressively older with increased distance from the hotspot. See also *mantle plume*.

HOT SPRING A bubbling up of hot water and steam from the ground, caused by hot rocks heating the groundwater beneath. See also *geyser*.

HUMUS A dark-coloured substance found in soils, derived from dead plants, micro-organisms, and animals.

HURRICANE A large-scale low-pressure system of tropical regions, involving powerful circulating winds and torrential rain. It is also termed a **tropical cyclone** and (especially in east Asia) a **typhoon**. Its energy comes from the latent heat of water that has evaporated from warm oceans and later condenses. See also *latent heat*.

HYDROCARBON A chemical compound of carbon and hydrogen. Petroleum is a complex mixture of hydrocarbons.

HYDROTHERMAL SYSTEM Any natural system involving the heating and circulation of underground water and steam, powered by nearby hot or molten rocks. A **hydrothermal vein** is a mineral vein laid down by past hydrothermal action. A **hydrothermal vent** is an outlet for heated water from a hydrothermal system, especially one at the bottom of an ocean. When the heated water is coloured with dark material, sulphides, and other minerals precipitated when the hot fluid comes into contact with cold seawater, the vent is known as a **black smoker**. See also *vein, geyser, hot spring*.

I

ICE LEAD A open channel formed in sea-ice.

ICEBERG A floating mass of ice derived from a glacier.

ICE-CAP see *glacier*.

ICE-FIELD A large expanse of ice at high altitude, partly hemmed in by mountains.

ICE-HEAVE The growth of ice within the soil in periglacial regions, leading to disruption of the land surface and the creation of ice wedges and pingos. See also *periglaciation, ice wedge, pingo*.

ICE-SHEET see *glacier*.

ICE-SHELF A large area of floating ice attached to land and originally derived from a glacier, especially from an ice-sheet.

ICE-STREAM A region of an ice-field or ice-sheet within which faster flow is taking place.

ICE WEDGE An irregular mass of ice growing within a soil layer in a periglacial region. See also *ice-heave*.

IGNEOUS ROCK Rock that originates from the solidification of molten magma. **Extrusive** (volcanic) igneous rocks have solidified on the Earth's surface after volcanic activity and commonly have small, hardly visible crystals. **Intrusive** (plutonic) igneous rocks have solidified below the surface, cooling slowly enough to allow larger crystals to form. A body of intrusive igneous rock is called an **igneous intrusion**.

INSELBERG An isolated, steep-sided hill rising up out of a flat plain.

INTERTROPICAL CONVERGENCE ZONE The region where the main air masses north and south of the Equator come into contact. See also *Hadley cell*.

INTRUSION see *igneous rock*.

INVERTEBRATE An animal without a backbone, such as an insect, snail, or worm.

IRRIGATION The artificial supply of water to agricultural crops.

ISLAND ARC, VOLCANIC A line of volcanic islands associated with an ocean–ocean subduction zone. See also *subduction*.

ISOBAR A line on a weather map that joins points with equal atmospheric pressure.

ISOSTASY The concept that all columns of rock on the Earth have the same weight at some depth in the mantle. Continents rise high above the sea floor because continental crust is less dense than oceanic crust.

JK

JET STREAM Any of several winds that blow for long distances high in the troposphere. See also *troposphere*.

JOINT A crack running through a rock. Unlike a fault, the rocks on either side of a joint remain in the same position with respect to each other. A **cooling joint** results from an igneous rock shrinking as it cools. See also *fault*.

KARST A characteristic landscape formed in regions built of water-soluble rocks, especially limestone. A **karst coast** occurs where limestone has been eroded and later inundated by the sea.

KATABATIC WIND A wind that blows downwards from a glacier or cold valley at night.

KETTLE LAKE A lake occupying a **kettle hole**, a depression left after an ice block from a former glacier melted.

KT BOUNDARY The boundary between the Cretaceous and Tertiary Periods. It dates to about 65 million years ago and coincides with the extinction of some dinosaurs and many other life-forms.

L

LA NIÑA A situation in which the waters of the eastern Pacific become unusually cold; the opposite of the El Niño phenomenon. See also *El Niño*.

LAGOON An area of sheltered seawater, almost cut off from the open ocean. The term includes both shallow coastal lagoons and the lagoons of atolls.

LAHAR A muddy flow of water mixed with volcanic ash and other volcanic debris. See also *mass movement*.

LAMINATION The occurrence of thin, distinct, and generally parallel layers within rocks.

LAPSE RATE A rate at which air temperature decreases with height. See also *latent heat*.

LATENT HEAT The heat that is input when a liquid such as water turns into vapour. It is released again when the vapour condenses.

LAVA Molten rock that has reached the Earth's surface. Basaltic **a'a lava** (45–52 per cent by weight of silica) forms a rough-textured rock when it cools. **Pahoehoe lava**, of similar basaltic composition, flows easily and creates a smooth or ropy-textured surface. Basaltic **pillow lava** is lava ejected underwater, forming pillow-shaped mounds of rock. More silica-rich and andesitic-dacitic lavas (more than 57 per cent by weight of silica) typically form **block lava**, jostling masses of angular blocks, some of them many metres across.

LEVEE A raised bank of a river that is higher than the surrounding active floodplain. Levees commonly mark former floodplains prior to major downcutting events (when the river rapidly erodes and lowers its bed).

LIGHTNING The visible flash that accompanies electrical discharges from storm clouds. Discharges within or between clouds are **sheet lightning**; those between clouds and the ground are **forked lightning**.

LITHOSPHERE The Earth's crust together with the rigid uppermost layer of the underlying mantle. Each of the Earth's tectonic plates is made of a section of lithosphere. See also *crust, mantle, asthenosphere, tectonic plate*.

LITTORAL Relating to the shoreline, especially between the high- and low-water marks. See also *tide*.

LONGSHORE BAR see *bar*.

LONGSHORE DRIFT A current that flows parallel to a shoreline, usually picking up and transporting sediment as it does so.

M

MAAR A wide volcano crater formed by explosive eruptions that have excavated into underlying bedrock, which is exposed in the crater walls.

MAGMA Molten rock rising from the interior of the Earth.

MAGMA CHAMBER A region just below the Earth's surface where magma (molten rock) has collected.

MAGMATIC DIFFERENTIATION The various processes by which magma changes composition, typically towards higher silica contents. The processes include gravitational separation of early formed low-silica minerals and assimilation of high-silica crustal rocks.

MANTLE The rocks lying between the Earth's crust and its core. It makes up 84 per cent of the Earth's volume. See also *crust, core*.

MANTLE PLUME A column of hot rocks rising through the mantle and crust, giving rise to a hotspot at the Earth's surface. See also *hotspot*.

MARSH A freshwater or saltwater wetland that is dominated by soft-stemmed plants such as grasses or reeds, but not by woody plants such as trees or shrubs. Marshes are characterized by frequent or continual flooding. See also *swamp, salt marsh*.

MASS MOVEMENT The movement of rocks, soil, or mud down a slope in response to gravity. See also *transport*.

MASSIF A well-defined mountainous region whose rocks and landforms tend to be similar across the region.

MASSIVE Of a rock: having a structure that does not show layering or other divisions into smaller segments.

MATRIX The mass of relatively fine-grained material that binds together larger particles in some heterogeneous sedimentary rocks and larger crystals in volcanic rocks. See also *groundmass*.

MEANDER A loop or bend in a river. Meandering rivers gradually change their course, as erosion occurs on the outside of the bend and deposition on the inside.

MELTWATER Water flowing within or from a glacier. A **meltwater channel** is a channel carved by meltwater running under or near a glacier.

MESA A tall, usually flat-topped outcrop of rock, especially in desert regions, left behind after the rest of the former land surface has been eroded. It is usually capped by a layer of resistant rock.

MESOSPHERE The layer of the Earth's atmosphere between the stratosphere and thermosphere, at an altitude of about 50–80km (30–50 miles).

METAL Any of numerous chemical elements that are typically hard, shiny, malleable in the solid state, and good conductors of heat and electricity; also any alloy (mixture) of such elements.

METAMORPHIC ROCK A rock that has been transformed underground by heat or pressure to a new texture or new set of minerals. For example, marble is metamorphosed limestone.

METAMORPHISM The processes by which rocks are transformed by heat, pressure, or chemical reactions underground. In **thermal metamorphism**, the agent is heat. **Dynamic metamorphism** involves differential stresses that can impart new textures and structures to the rock. **Regional metamorphism** affects broad areas the size of mountain belts. **Contact metamorphism** results from the effects of hot magma on surrounding rocks.

METASOMATIC ROCK A rock that has been transformed by hot fluids penetrating it and changing its bulk composition and mineral assemblage.

METEOR A small mass of rock from space that vaporizes completely as it falls through the Earth's atmosphere, glowing as it does so.

METEORITE A rock from space that has fallen to the Earth's surface without completely burning up.

METEOROID A potential meteor or meteorite before it has entered the Earth's atmosphere.

MICROCLIMATE The distinctive climate of a particular place, such as a narrow valley or hillside.

MID-OCEAN RIDGE Any of the submerged mountain ranges running across the floors of the major oceans (although not all occur exactly in mid-ocean). They are sites where two tectonic plates are spreading apart and material is rising up from the mantle to form new oceanic crust. Mid-ocean ridges vary widely in their spreading rates, from fast- to slow-spreading ridges. See also *plate boundary, tectonic plate*.

MINERAL Any solid, naturally occurring inorganic material in the Earth that has a characteristic crystal structure and well-defined chemical composition. Most rocks are mixtures of more than one mineral. See also *rock*.

MIRE A peat-accumulating wetland such as a bog or fen.

MONSOON A pattern of winds, especially in southern Asia, that blow from one direction for about half the year, and from the opposite direction for the other half. The term is also used to refer to the heavy rains carried by these winds at certain times of the year.

MONTANE Of a forest: a type of woodland found in mountainous areas that includes conifers and other species such as beech.

MORAINE An accumulation of rock debris resulting from glacial action. Active valley glaciers create **lateral moraines** at their edges, **medial moraines** where two glaciers merge, and **terminal moraines** at their tips. These features often remain after the glacier disappears. See also *till*.

N

NATIVE ELEMENT A chemical element that is found in its pure (uncombined) state in nature. Gold is always found native, other elements, such as sulphur and copper, sometimes occur in native form.

NEEDLE-LEAF A needle-shaped leaf, typical of pine trees and other conifers. See also *coniferous*.

NOCTILUCENT CLOUD A very high-level cloud of ice crystals or dust particles that has a shiny appearance at night.

NUNATAK A mountain-top that rises above an ice-sheet that is otherwise covering the land.

O

OASIS A fertile area within a desert, normally fed by a spring arising from an aquifer. See also *aquifer*.

OCCLUSION In meteorology, the situation where a moving mass of colder air catches up with a warmer air mass, pushing the latter away from the surface of the Earth. See also *front*.

OFFSHORE BAR see *bar*.

OOZE The fine sediment that covers much of the deep sea floor. The names of some kinds of ooze refer to the particular tiny organisms whose skeletons or remains dominate: for **globigerina ooze**, single-celled organisms (foraminifera) of the genus *Globigerina*; for **diatom ooze**, certain algae (diatoms); for **radiolarian ooze**, other single-celled organisms called radiolarians; and for **pteropod ooze**, the shells of certain free-swimming snail-relatives.

ORE A rock from which a metal can be profitably mined.

OROGENESIS The process of mountain building, resulting from pressures generated by the horizontal movement of tectonic plates. An **orogeny** is a particular episode of mountain building. See also *epeirogenesis*.

OROGRAPHIC LIFTING The rising of an air mass as it moves over mountains, often resulting in clouds being formed.

OUTLET GLACIER see *glacier*.

OXIDE A compound of oxygen with one or more chemical elements. Examples of oxides include ferrous oxide (FeO) and silicon dioxide (SiO$_2$).

PQ

PACK ICE see *sea-ice*.

PANCAKE ICE see *sea-ice*.

PEAT Dead plant material that accumulates in bogs, fens, and other wetland habitats, remaining largely undecomposed. Peat soils are composed almost entirely of plant matter, particularly *Sphagnum* mosses, with little mineral content. See also *bog*.

PEGMATITE A plutonic igneous rock made up of unusually large crystals. **Pegmatitic veins** are narrow sheets or lenses of such rock. They are sometimes the source of valuable ores. See also *vein*.

PENINSULA An area of land jutting out into the sea or a lake.

PERENNIAL A plant that lives for three or more years. See also *annual*.

PERIGLACIATION Any of various features peculiar to landscapes that are subject to very cold conditions, while not having a permanent ice cover. See also *permafrost*, *pingo*, *ice wedge*, *tundra*.

PERMAFROST Technically, land that remains frozen for at least two years. It is characteristic of glacial and many periglacial regions. In tundra, the top layer of the soil generally thaws in spring and summer, while permafrost may remain deeper down. See also *periglaciation*, *tundra*.

PHOTOSYNTHESIS The process by which green plants and some micro-organisms use the energy of sunlight in the presence of chlorphyll to convert water and carbon dioxide into food.

PHREATIC ERUPTION A type of volcanic eruption or geyser activity where groundwater is turned to steam by contact with hot rocks near the surface.

PHYTOPLANKTON The tiny, mostly single-celled plants (algae) that float near the surface of oceans and lakes and are the foundation of most aquatic food chains.

PIEDMONT GLACIER see *glacier*.

PILLOW LAVA see *lava*.

PINGO In periglacial areas, a hillock with a core of ice that has pushed up above the surrounding landscape.

PLACER DEPOSIT An accumulation of sediments deposited by running water that contains minerals that can be profitably mined.

PLANET A large astronomical body that orbits a star and, unlike a star, is not heated by thermonuclear reactions taking place within it.

PLANETESIMAL One of millions of rocky objects of variable size believed to have been present in the early history of the Solar System and which later came together to create the planets.

PLATE see *tectonic plate*.

PLATE BOUNDARY A boundary between two tectonic plates. The plates concerned can be diverging (**constructive boundary**), converging (**destructive boundary**), or sliding past one another (**conservative boundary**).

PLATEAU A large area of relatively flat land that stands topographically above its surroundings.

PLATY A term used to describe thin, flat crystals.

PLAYA A level plain in a desert basin, sometimes occupied by a temporary lake that fills and empties seasonally.

PLINIAN ERUPTION see *eruption*.

PLUTON A large body of igneous rock that solidifies slowly underground to form a coarse-grained (plutonic) rock such as granite. A mass of many hundreds of adjacent plutons is called a batholith. See also *batholith*.

PLUTONIC Relating to igneous processes or materials formed deep below the Earth's surface. The term is derived from Pluto, the Roman god of the underworld.

PODOCARP A member of a family of coniferous trees found mainly in the southern hemisphere.

POINT BAR see *bar*.

POLDER An area of low-lying land reclaimed from the sea.

POLYMORPH A substance that can exist in different mineral or crystalline forms, all sharing the same chemical composition. For example, pure carbon can exist as both diamond or graphite.

POLYNA A stretch of open water in an ice-covered sea.

POLYTHERMAL GLACIER see *glacier*.

PORPHYROBLAST A large crystal surrounded by smaller crystals found in some metamorphic rocks.

PRECIPITATE Any material that has come out of solution to form a solid deposit.

PRECIPITATION Water that reaches the Earth's surface from the atmosphere, including rain, snow, hail, and dew.

PRESSURE SYSTEM Any pattern of weather in which air circulates around an area of high or low pressure. The **pressure gradient** is the pressure difference between two given points. See also *cyclone*, *anticyclone*, *isobar*.

PREVAILING WIND The source direction of wind that tends to blow most commonly at a particular location.

PRIMARY MINERAL A mineral that derives from the cooling of molten igneous rock, without being altered subsequently. See also *secondary mineral*.

PROKARYOTE Any single-celled organism, such as a bacterium, whose cell has a simple structure that lacks a well-defined nucleus. See also *eukaryote*.

PUMICE A light-coloured, low-density volcanic rock containing innumerable bubbles formed by expanding gases, ejected during some volcanic eruptions.

P-WAVE see *seismic wave*.

PYROCLASTIC Consisting of, or containing, volcanic rock fragments. **Pyroclastic flows** are fast-moving, sometimes deadly clouds of hot gases and debris. See also *pumice, scoria, tuff*.

R

RADIATION A flow of high-energy particles or waves. **Electromagnetic radiation** consists of electromagnetic waves: listed from long-wavelength to short-wavelength forms, these include radio waves, microwaves, infra-red rays, visible light, ultraviolet light, X rays, and gamma rays. Short-wavelength electromagnetic radiation has the highest energy.

RADIATION FOG see *fog*.

RAINBOW A large-scale, prism-like light effect caused by the Sun's rays being refracted (bent) as they pass through raindrops. See also *refraction*.

RAIN SHADOW The occurrence of low rainfall downwind of a mountain range, caused by the air shedding its moisture as it passes over the mountains.

RAINFOREST A forest, usually tropical, with high rainfall, high humidity, and high temperatures all year round.

REEF see *coral reef*.

REFRACTION The tendency for waves of any kind to be bent when they pass from one medium to another of different properties. For example, light waves can be refracted by passage from air to water. The amount of refraction depends on wavelength.

REGOLITH A general term for all the materials that are not solid rock covering the surface of the Earth, Moon, and other planetary bodies . On Earth, it includes soil and debris from glaciers. The lunar regolith refers to the thick blanket of rock dust produced by meteorite impacts.

RELATIVE HUMIDITY The amount of water vapour in the atmosphere, relative to the total amount that the atmosphere can hold at that particular temperature. Above 100 per cent relative humidity, water vapour will tend to condense as liquid water. Warm air can hold more water vapour than cold air. See also *dew point*.

RESURGENCE The emergence of water from an underground aquifer at the surface as a spring.

RIA COAST A type of drowned coast indented by former river valleys, known as **rias**, that are now inlets of the sea. See also *coast*.

RIDGE OF HIGH PRESSURE A long, narrow area of high pressure extending out from an anticyclone. See also *anticyclone*.

RIFT VALLEY A large block of land that has dropped vertically downwards compared with the surrounding regions, as a result of horizontal extension and normal faulting. A rift valley is also called a graben. See also *fault*.

RIMSTONE A deposit of calcite around an underground pool in a cave. See also *calcite, flowstone*.

ROCK Any solid material made up of one or more minerals and occurring naturally on the Earth or other planetary bodies. See also *mineral*.

ROSSBY WAVE A wave that forms in a jet stream at temperate latitudes, giving rise to areas of high and low pressure. See also *jet stream, pressure system*.

S

SALINITY The concentration of dissolved salts in, for example, water or soil.

SALT MARSH A wetland that supports salt-tolerant plants that grow on flat coastal areas regularly inundated by the tides.

SARGASSUM A floating seaweed common in the Sargasso Sea in the North Atlantic.

SASTRUGI The sculpted appearance of some ice surfaces, caused by erosion from wind-blown ice crystals.

SAVANNA A general term for all tropical natural grasslands. Most savannas also have scattered trees.

SCARP see *escarpment*.

SCORIA A dark-coloured volcanic rock containing innumerable bubbles formed by expanding gases ejected during some basaltic volcanic eruptions. Scoria is also known as cinder. See also *pyroclastic*.

SEA ARCH A natural arch formed in a sea cliff by erosion.

SEA CAVE A cave eroded into a sea cliff by the action of the sea.

SEA ICE Ice that arises from seawater freezing. (It does not include icebergs, which originally come from land.) The sea freezes in several stages. At first, separate crystals form. These begin to join together, forming a thick, oily texture called **grease ice**. Thin slabs of ice called **pancake ice** may form. When the sea-ice forms a continuous sheet it is called **fast ice**. Winds and storms may later break this up into fragments called **pack ice**.

SEAMOUNT An undersea mountain, usually volcanic in origin. See also *guyot*.

SEA STACK A tall column of rock rising out of the sea near a coastline. It is a resistant remnant of a formerly higher land surface that has otherwise disappeared due to erosion.

SECONDARY MINERAL A mineral that has replaced a primary igneous mineral, one originally solidified from a molten state. See also *primary mineral*.

SEDIMENT Solid particles that have been transported by water, wind, volcanic processes, or mass movement, and later deposited.

SEDIMENTARY ROCK Rock formed when small particles are deposited – by wind, water, volcanic processes, or mass movement – and later harden.

SEISMIC WAVE A shock wave generated by an earthquake. **P-waves** can travel through both solid and liquid portions of the Earth's interior, **S-waves** only through the solid parts.

SEMI-DESERT A dry region that has enough precipitation to support some plant life.

SERAC A pinnacle of ice in a glacier.

SHIELD VOLCANO see *volcano*.

SILICA Silicon dioxide (SiO₂), the most common mineral form of which is quartz, a hard mineral that is the dominant component of sand.

SILICATE Any rock or mineral composed of groups of silicon and oxygen atoms in chemical combination with atoms of various metals. Silicate rocks make up most of the Earth's crust and mantle.

SILL A roughly horizontal, sheet-like igneous intrusion that usually forms when igneous rock forces its way between layers of existing sedimentary rocks. See also *dyke*.

SINKHOLE see *doline*.

SKIN FLOW Creeping movements of soil in periglacial regions following rapid thawing of the surface layers. See also *periglaciation*.

SOFAR CHANNEL Short for Sound Fixing and Ranging channel. Sound achieves a much longer range at particular depths in the ocean, typically at 1,000m (3,300ft). This layer allows scientists with underwater microphones to detect sounds thousands of kilometres away.

SOLAR BUDGET The overall flow of radiant energy from the Sun to the Earth, and its ultimate re-radiation into space. See also *radiation, greenhouse effect*.

SOLAR CONSTANT The amount of energy from the Sun that reaches a unit area at the top of the Earth's atmosphere. It is not truly constant, but nearly so.

SPECIFIC GRAVITY A measure of the density of a substance, in terms of its weight for a given volume compared to the same volume of a reference material, usually pure water.

SPIT A peninsula of sand or shingle projecting from a shore, usually where the coastline changes direction. It is created by longshore drift. See also *bar, tombolo, longshore drift*.

SPUR A mountain ridge cut off as a result of past glacial action or tectonic faulting.

STALACTITE A deposit of calcite hanging down from the roof of a cave or underground passage. See also *calcite*.

STALAGMITE A deposit of calcite rising up from the floor of a cave or underground passage. See also *calcite*.

STAR A self-luminous astronomical body, such as the Sun, that generates energy by nuclear reactions, mainly involving the conversion of hydrogen to helium.

STEPPE Temperate grassland habitats, especially in regions with hot, dry summers and cold winters.

STRATOSPHERE A layer of the Earth's atmosphere extending from the top of the troposphere, at 8–16km (5–10 miles), up to about 50km (30 miles). See also *troposphere, mesosphere*.

STRATOVOLCANO see *volcano*.

STRATUM (pl. STRATA) A layer of sedimentary rock.

SUBDUCTION The descent of an oceanic tectonic plate under another plate when two plates converge. Subduction zones can be classified as either ocean-ocean or ocean–continent depending upon the nature of the two converging plates. See also *deep-sea trench, plate boundary, tectonic plate, crust*.

SUBLITTORAL Below the low-tide mark.

SUBMONTANE Of a forest: a type of woodland found in lowland and hilly sites that consists mainly of deciduous, broadleaved trees.

SUCCESSION A gradual change with time from one community of plants to another in a particular location – for example, from grassland to forest.

SUCCULENT A plant having thick, juicy leaves or stems for storing water.

SURGE-TYPE GLACIER see *glacier*.

SWAMP A freshwater or saltwater wetland that is dominated by trees. See also *marsh*.

SWASH The movement of turbulent water up a beach when a wave breaks. See also *backwash*.

S-WAVE see *seismic wave*.

SYNCLINE A downwards fold of originally flat strata as a result of horizontal compression. See also *anticline, fold*.

T

TAIGA The coniferous forest (also called boreal forest) that covers much of Europe, Asia, and northern North America.

TECTONIC PLATE Any of the large rigid sections into which the Earth's lithosphere is divided. The relative motions of different plates leads to earthquakes, volcanic activity, continental drift, and mountain-building. See also *plate boundary, subduction, deep-sea trench, mid-ocean ridge, lithosphere*.

TEKTITE A glassy particle sometimes formed when a large meteorite strikes the Earth. Tektites originate when melted target rock is thrown great distances from the site of impact.

TEMPERATE Relating to the regions of the Earth between the tropics and the polar regions.

TERRACE A flat region in a river valley that is higher than the present floodplain. It represents a former floodplain created when the river ran at a higher level. See also *floodplain*.

THERMOHALINE see *current*.

THERMOPAUSE The upper edge of the thermosphere, about 640km (400 miles) above the surface.

THERMOSPHERE The layer of the Earth's atmosphere above the mesosphere. It extends over altitudes of about 80–640km (50–400 miles).

TIDAL BORE A single large wave sometimes created when a rising tide enters a narrowing channel such as an estuary.

TIDE The rise and fall (usually twice each day) of water on the shore caused by the gravitational pull of the Moon and Sun. The difference in level between high and low tide is called the **tidal range**, and tends to vary on a monthly basis: **spring tides** (when the effects of the Moon and Sun reinforce each other) produce the highest high tide and the lowest low tide; **neap tides** (when the effects of the Moon and Sun oppose each other) have the smallest tidal range.

TILL Solid material laid down or left behind by a glacier. It typically consists of rock fragments of many sizes. Till left behind by glaciers from the last ice age covers many regions today. See also *moraine*.

TOMBOLO A type of spit connecting a small island to the mainland. See also *spit*.

TORNADO A narrow, rapidly whirling tube-shaped column of air, which is often highly destructive.

TRANSPIRATION The process by which water is drawn through plants. The evaporation of water vapour from leaves causes more water to be drawn in through the roots to compensate.

TRANSPORT The conveying of weathered and eroded material to another location, for example by wind, water, or ice action. See also *weathering, erosion*.

TRAVERTINE A rock, mainly consisting of calcium carbonate, that is deposited around the edges of hot springs.

TREE-LINE The latitude or altitude above which conditions are too harsh for trees to grow in a particular location.

TRIBUTARY Any river or stream that flows into a larger river.

TROPICAL Relating to the warm regions of the Earth that lie between the Equator and the tropics of Cancer and Capricorn, at latitudes of 23.5° North and South, respectively.

TROPOPAUSE The boundary between the troposphere and the stratosphere. Air temperature starts to increase with height above the tropopause, which varies from about 16km (10 miles) at the Equator to 8km (5 miles) over the poles.

TROPOSPHERE The lowest, densest layer of the atmosphere, where most weather phenomena occur. The height of the upper limit of the troposphere (known as the tropopause) varies from the Equator to the poles. See also *tropopause*.

TROUGH In meteorology, a long, relatively narrow area of low pressure. See also *front*.

TSUNAMI A fast-moving, often destructive sea wave generated by earthquake activity; popularly but incorrectly known as a tidal wave. It rises in height rapidly as it reaches shallow water.

TUBE A tunnel-shaped passage within a cave system through which water flows or has flowed. See also *canyon*.

TUFF A rock made of fine-grained pyroclastic material produced by an explosive volcanic eruption. See also *pyroclastic*.

TUNDRA A treeless habitat of low-growing, cold-tolerant plants widespread in the far north of North America and Siberia.

TURBIDITY CURRENT A flow of sediment-containing water from the continental margin down onto the ocean floor. Sediment deposited by such a current is known as **turbidite**.

TYPHOON see *hurricane*.

UV

ULTRAVIOLET see *radiation*.

UNDERSTOREY The layer of smaller trees and shrubs growing beneath the main trees of a forest.

VALLEY FOG A type of radiation fog occurring in valleys. See also *fog*.

VALLEY GLACIER see *glacier*.

VEIN A thin, sheet-like body of rock penetrating through other rocks. See also *hydrothermal system*.

VENTIFACT A rock or pebble polished by wind-blown sand in a desert.

VERTICAL TRANSPORT The upwelling or downwelling of nutrient-rich water in the oceans.

VISCOSITY Resistance to flow in fluids. The higher the viscosity of a fluid, the more sluggishly it flows.

VOLATILE In volcanology: a term used to describe water, carbon dioxide, and other potentially gaseous compounds that are dissolved in molten rocks.

VOLCANO An opening in the Earth's crust where magma reaches the surface; also, a mountain that contains such an opening. A **shield volcano** has shallow slopes and is built from lava that flowed easily. A **stratovolcano** is steeper and built from alternate layers of ash and lava. A **dome volcano** is rounded, steep, and built from viscous lava. A **cinder cone** is built from scoria that has fallen from the explosion clouds of an eruption.

VULCANIAN ERUPTION see *eruption*.

WXYZ

WADI A usually waterless river valley in a desert.

WATER-TABLE The upper surface of the groundwater zone in places where it is not confined by impermeable rocks. Water soaking into the ground will tend to sink down until it reaches the water-table. See also *groundwater*.

WATERSHED The divide between two catchment areas.

WAVE A regular motion or disturbance that transfers energy. For a wave crossing the open ocean, the water itself does not move significantly except up and down as the wave passes. The high point of a wave is its **crest** and the low point its **trough**. For waves breaking on shores (**breakers**), water motion becomes more complex and chaotic (**turbulent**).

WAVE REFRACTION see *refraction*.

WAVELENGTH The distance between successive crests (or troughs) of a wave.

WEATHERING The alteration of rocks caused by their being exposed at or close to the Earth's surface. Usually the original rock eventually crumbles or becomes weakened. See also *erosion*.

XENOLITH A fragment of older rock incorporated within a younger igneous rock. See also *igneous rock*.

YARDANG A wind-sculpted ridge of rock in a desert.

INDEX

Page numbers in **bold** indicate feature profiles or extended treatments of a topic. Page numbers in *italic* indicate pages on which the topic is illustrated.

ACKNOWLEDGMENTS

Dorling Kindersley would like to thank the following people for their help in the preparation of this book: Douglas Palmer for suggestions for photo sources, comments on the Glossary, and general advice; Vanessa Hamilton for original design work and Rebecca Milner for design assistance; Cathy Meeus for editorial help; Gemma Casajuana and Mark Bracey for DTP support; Erin Richards for administrative support; Julia Lunn and Rob Stokes for additional cartography; Robyn Bissette and Ellen Nanney of the Smithsonian Institution; Dr. A.G. Smith and Lawrence Rush of Cambridge University for plotting maps of the Earth's past tectonic plates; Philip Eales, Andrew Wayne, and Kevin Tildsley of Planetary Visions Ltd; and Sean Mulshaw and Geoffrey Gilbert for advice on the selection of features.

Revised edition
Dorling Kindersley would like to thank: Carron Brown, Lili Bryant, Ruth O'Rourke Jones, Rohini Deb, Susmita Dey, Nandini Gupta, Neha Pande, and Rupa Rao for editorial assistance; Michael Yeowell, Alison Gardner, Adam Brackenbury, Thomas Morse, Anna Hall, and Upasana Sharma for design assistance; Simon Mumford for help with cartography and artwork; Rohan Sinha and Sudakshina Basu for project management at DK Delhi; and Sachin Gupta, Bimlesh Tiwary, and Anita Yadav for technical assistance.
Data for sizes of urban areas has been reproduced from the Demographia World Urban Areas survey.

Smithsonian Enterprises Carol LeBlanc, Senior Vice President; Brigid Ferraro, Director of Licensing; Ellen Nanney, Licensing Manager; and Kealy Wilson, Product Development Manager.

This book was produced in collaboration with the **Smithsonian** in Washington DC, USA, the world's largest museum and research complex. This renowned research centre is dedicated to public education, national service, and scholarship in the arts, sciences, and history.

PICTURE CREDITS
Dorling Kindersley would like to thank the following for their help with images: Romaine Werblow and Rob Nunn in the DK Picture Library; Giovanni Cafagna at Corbis; Tony Waltham at Geophotos; Caroline Thomas; and Mariana Sonnenberg.

Key: L = Left, R = Right, C = Centre, T = Top, B = Bottom, a = Above, b = Below.

Abbreviations
B&C: Bryan and Cherry Alexander Photography; **DK:** DK Picture Library www. dkimages.com; **FLPA:** FLPA – Images of Nature; **Geo:** Tony Waltham Geophotos; **Getty:** Getty Images; **RHPL:** Robert Harding Picture Library; **NG:** National Geographic Image Collection; **NHM:** The Natural History Museum, London; **OSF:** Oxford Scientific Films; **SI:** Smithsonian Institution; **SPL:** Science Photo Library; **Still:** Still Pictures; **WWI:** Woodfall Wild Images.

Sidebar Images (from top to bottom)
Earth - NASA: Hubble Space Telescope Center (PR96-27B); **Corbis:** NASA, L Clarke, Ken Straiton, Michael T Sedam; **DK.**
Land – Corbis: Darrell Gulin, Walter Hodges, Wolfgang Kaehler, Gary Braasch, José F Poblete, David Muench.
Oceans – Corbis: FLPA / Winifred Wisniewski, David Pu'u, Darrell Gulin, Stuart Westmorland, Jeffrey L Rotman, Robert Yin.
Atmosphere – Corbis: Stuart Westmorland, Paul A Souders, William James Warren, Matthias Kulka, Craig Tuttle, William A Bake.

1 Still: UNEP / D Stanfill; **Science Photo Library:** Visuals Unlimited, Inc. / Patrick Endres C. **2/3 Alamy Images:** Phil Degginger. **Getty:** Taxi / Bav. **4 Corbis:** Darrell Gulin TC. **4/5 Still:** Pascal Kobeh b. **5 alamy.com:** ImageState / Adam Jones TL; **Corbis:** William James Warren C; **Galaxy Contact:** Johnson Space Center (STS066-208-205) TCRb; **Getty:** Image Bank / Peter Cade TR. **8/9 Corbis:** Darrell Gulin. **10/11 SPL:** John Reader. **12 Geo:** by **University of Edinburgh, Grant Institute:** TRb. **12/13 Corbis:** Tom Bean B. **13 Corbis:** George HH Huey Ca; James L Amos TCL; **NG:** Louis Mazzatenta TCbR; **SPL:** James King-Holmes CRb. **14 SPL:** NASA BR; Patrice Loiex, Cern BL. **14/15 Corbis:** Roger Harris. **15 NASA:** Chandra X-Ray Observatory (MSFC-9905485) C; Hubble Space Telescope

Center (PR96-38B) CRa. **16 NHM:** C. **16/17 Corbis:** Ric Ergenbright. **17 Courtesy of the Archives, California Institute of Technology:** BR. NASA: Saturn Apollo Program (MSFC-690096) CL. **SPL:** Dr Kari Lounatmaa Cb. **18 Roger Buick:** Department of Earth and Space Sciences & Astrobiology Program, University of Washington Cb, BC; **Corbis:** Roger Garwood BL. **18/19 Corbis:** Ric Ergenbright. **19 Dr Peter Crimes:** BR; **Dr Bruce Runnegar:** Centre for Astrobiology, Institute of Geophysics, University of California. **20 alamy.com:** Stephen Frink Collection / Masa Ushioda BL; **Corbis:** Bettmann CR; Ric Ergenbright L; **DK:** Colin Keates BC. **20/21 FLPA:** I. West. **21 DK:** Royal Museum of Scotland / Harry Taylor CR; **NHM** / Harry Taylor CR. **22 British Antarctic Survey:** Pete Bucktrout C; **Corbis:** Jonthan Blair CbR; **FLPA:** I. West (main); **Geo:** CLb. **23 Corbis:** Douglas Peebles BC; Kevin Schafer BL; Layne Kennedy R (main); **DK:** Hunterian Museum C; Jon Hughes BR. **24 Corbis:** Layne Kennedy (main); Tom Bean BL; **DK:** Senekenberg Nature Museum / Andy Crawford C; **NHM:** BC. **25 Corbis:** Richard Cummins CR; Royalty-Free R (main). **26 alamy.com:** Ukraft C; **Nature Picture Library:** Jurgen Freund CR; **Corbis:** Jonathan Blair BCL; **DK:** Harry Taylor BCR. **26/27 Corbis:** Royalty-Free. **27 Corbis:** Gallo Images CR; Torleif Svensson BC; **SPL:** Geospace C. **28 Corbis:** Hulton-Deutsch Collection C; **DK:** BLR; Museum of London / Dave King CRb; Pitt Rivers Museum / Dave King Cra; **NHM:** BL; **SPL:** John Reader CLb, BC. **28/29 Corbis:** Royalty Free. **29 DK:** Gables CL **Dr Sandy Tudhope:** Institute of Geology and Geophysics, Edinburgh University. **30 NHM:** BL; **Geo:** BR. **30/31 Corbis:** Royalty-Free. **31 Corbis:** William Findlay BL; **DK:** Royal British Columbia Museum / Andrew Nelmerm CL. **32/33 OSF:** Olivier Grunewald. **34 Hutchison Library:** Patricia Goycolea CLb; **NASA:** NSSDC / Apollo 8 BLa. **35 Corbis:** Stuart Westmorland CbR; **SPL:** Alfred Pasieka BR. **37 DK:** Clive Streeter CLa; **DK:** CR. **38 Science Photo Library:** (tr); **Corbis:** Raymond Gehman CLb; **Dr Sally Gibson:** Department of Earth Sciences, University of Cambridge CL. **39 Corbis:** Roger Ressmeyer Ca. Computer tomography scan reproduced from Schmandt, B. and E. Humphreys. 2010. "Complex subduction and small-scale convection revealed by body-wave tomography of the western United States mantle." Earth and Planetary Science Letters, 297, 435-445, doi:10.1016/j.epsl.2010.06.047 and Trabant, C., A. R. Hutko, M. Bahavar, R. Karstens, T. Ahern and R. Aster (2012), Data products at the IRIS DMC: stepping-stones for research and other application, Seismological Research Letters, 83(6), 846:854. doi: 10.1785/0220 120032: BR. **40 Geo:** CLb; Stephen Bond BCRa; Philip James Corwin TC; **Corbis:** Guy Motil CLa; **Geo:** CbL, CbR. **41 alamy.com:** David Noton Photography / David Noton Ca; **Geo:** BCL; Worldwide Picture Library / John Fowler CLb; **Still:** Staffan Andersson TL; Tiziana and Gianni Baldizzone Cb; **SPL:** George Bernard BR; Geo TCbR. **42 Philip E Batson:** CLa; **Corbis:** Kevin Schafer BR. **43 DK:** diamond; Colin Keates hematite, rock crystal; Harry Taylor azurite, calcite, galena, halite, kaolinite, magnetite, milky quartz, muscovite, smokey quartz, talc; NHM / Colin Keates opal; NHM / Harry Taylor gold; **SI:** BC. **44 DK:** stibnite; Colin Keates gold, olivine; Harry Taylor anhydrite, apatite, borax, calcite, chromite, green fluorite, wulfenite; **Geo:** Harry Taylor B. **45 Corbis:** Robert Garvey TL. **DK:** Colin Keates burmese ruby crystal, cusioned mix-cut; Harry Taylor amethyst quartz, fluorite, sphalerite; **NHM:** CL. **OSF:** Nick Gordon CRa. **SPL:** TCL; Dr Jeremy Burgess CLa. **46 SI:** BL; **Dr AG Tindle:** Open University CL. **47 Geo:** BC. **48 Corbis:** Hubert Stadler Ca; **Landform Slides:** Ken Gardner BCL; **OSF:** Michael Fogden CbR; **SPL:** Tony Craddock TL; **Geo:** CRb. **48/49 Corbis:** Lester Lefkowitz T. **49 B&C:** Ann Hawthorne BCL; **SPL:** BRa; Martin Dohrn CRa; Mike McNamee TCR; **SI:** BCa. **50/51 Corbis:** Yann Arthus-Bertrand. **52 Corbis:** L Clarke CbL; Pat O'Hara BL; **SPL:** TRb. **52/53 Visible Earth:** Image Courtesy Jacques Descloitres, MODIS Land Rapid Response Team, NASA / GSFC B. **53 Corbis:** Roger Ressmeyer BR; **DK:** Peter Anderson CRb; **SPL:** Mehau Kulyk Cb. **54 Corbis:** Dewitt Jones

BC; Galen Rowell BCaL; **SPL:** Dr Ken MacDonald BL. **54/55 Corbis:** Yann Arthur-Bertrand B. **55 Corbis:** Hubert Stadler TCb; **Ontario Science Centre:** BR. **56 Corbis:** James Randklev TR; **Geo:** B. **57 alamy.com:** Jon Arnold Images / James Montgomery CaL; **Corbis:** David Muench CL; Paul A Souders TCR; Royalty-Free BR; Wolfganf Kaehler CbL; **SPL:** Adam Hart-Davis CRa. **58 Association of American Geographers:** CL; **Corbis:** David Muench Cb; Michael S Yamashita BR; Paul A Souders BL. **58/59 Corbis:** Royalty-Free C. **59 Corbis:** Galen Rowell TR; Jon Sparks BRa; Wolfgang Kaehler CRa; **Geo:** BCR. **60 Corbis:** Charles Krebs Photography CL; Lowell Georgia BC; Travel Ink / Derek M Allan TRb; **SPL:** William Ervin CL. **60/61 Corbis:** Yann Arthus-Bertrand B. **61 NASA:** Johnson Space Center (STS026-43-98) BCR; Johnson Space Center / Image courtesy of Earth Science and Image Analysis Laboratory (STS043-22-23) BCR; Johnson Space Center / Image courtesy of Earth Science and Image Analysis Laboratory (STS41D-32-14) BCL; **SPL:** Dr Juerg Alean CbR; **Geo:** TCb. **62 Corbis:** Hans Strand Ca; Lloyd Cluff BC; **Geo:** BL. **62/63 Corbis:** SP Gillette C. **63 Corbis:** Jon Sparks BC; ML Sinibaldi BRa; **DisasterMan Ltd:** Bill McGuire CL; **Geo:** TR, CaL. **64 Corbis:** David Lees C; Natalie Fobes BC. **65 Rex Features:** Sipa Press. **64/65 Getty images:** AFP / STR. **66 Corbis:** Roger Ressmeyer CbL; **DK:** Harry Taylor BR; **Getty:** Photodisc CLa; **Images Of Africa Photobank:** Vanesse Burger CL; **SPL:** Dr David King CL. **66/67 Corbis:** Yann Arthur-Bertrand C. **67 Corbis:** Roger Ressmeyer TC; Sygma / Duthei / Didier BCRa; **Department of Geology, University of Witwatersrand:** BCL. **68 Aurora & Quanta Productions Inc.:** Peter Essick CL; **Corbis:** Paul A Souders BL; Royalty-Free BR; **NASA:** Haughton-Mars Project 2002 TCL; Marshall Space Flight Center (MSFC-0201920) CR. **69 AirPhoto:** Jim Wark Ca; **The Barringer Crater Company:** BR; **Corbis:** NASA TC; Image courtesy of **Virgil L Sharpton, University of Alaska – Fairbanks / Lunar and Planetary Institute and NASA:** Cb; **SPL:** Prof Walter Alvarez BR. **70 Corbis:** Michael S Lewis Cb; **Landsat:** CL; **NASA:** Johnson Space Center (STS511-33-56A) BCL; **Stadt Noerdlingen:** TL. **71 Geological Survey of Western Australia:** BL; **Global Impact Studies Project:** TR; **NASA:** Johnson Space Center (STS41D-14-41-028) CRb; **Novosti (London):** CLA; **Skyscan:** photo by skycam.com.au BR; Geo Ca. **72 Corbis:** Lowell Georgia BCL; Natalie Fobes Cb; Ricki Rosen BLA; Science Pictures Limited CLa; **72/73 Getty:** Image Bank / Harald Sund C. **73 Corbis:** David Muench C; Galen Rowell CRa; Papilio / Bob Marsh BCR; **OSF:** Ben Osbourne CRb; **SPL:** David Parker C. **74 Corbis:** Tom Bean TCR; **DK:** Brian Cosgrove Collection CaL, TLb; **Getty:** Taxi / Andrew Mounter B. **75 Corbis:** Doug Wilson TCR; Sygma / Aim Patrice BRa; **Galaxy Contact:** CLa; **Getty:** Stone / David Muench CLb. **76 alamy.com:** Peter Bowater C; **Corbis:** Tony Roberts CLb. **77 Still:** UNEP / A Ishokon. **78/79 alamy.com:** ImageState / Adam Jones. **80/81 Corbis:** Roger Ressmeyer. **82 Corbis:** Bettmann CRa; Roger Ressmeyer BCL; **DK:** Joe Cornish CaL; **James Jackson:** Department of Earth Sciences, University of Cambridge B. **82/83 Corbis:** Yann Arthur-Bertrand B. **83 Martin Miller:** Department of Geological Sciences, University of Oregon TL; **SPL:** Fred McConnaughey TR; Massonnet et al / CNES BRa. **84 Corbis:** TCL; Bettmann CLb; Lloyd Cluff B; **School of Earth Sciences, Stanford University:** TRb. **85 Corbis:** BRa; Progressive Image / Bob Rowan TR **Martin Miller:** Department of Geological Sciences, University of Oregon C, BCR, CLa. **86 Reproduced by permission of the British Geological Survey** © NERC All Rights Reserved IPR/38-31c CL, BL; **SPL:** Robert Brook CL; **Art Directors & TRIP:** C Sanders BR; **WWI:** Patricia McDonald TR. **87 Agence France Presse:** Sergei Chirikov Ca; **FLPA:** Walter Rohdich Cb; **NASA:** Johnson Space Center (STS41G-34-6) TCR; **SOA Photo Agency:** Blue Box BR. **88 alamy.com:** ImageState / Georgette Douwma C; **Corbis:** Bettmann BC; Stephen Frink Ca; **DK:** NHM / Harry Taylor BL; **Images Of Africa Photobank:** David Keith Jones CL; **NG:** Chris Johns TR. **89 OSF:** NASA / Johnson Space Center (STS40-152-180). **90/91 Corbis:** Epa / David Wethey. **90 Corbis:** Michael S Yamashita. **91 Corbis:** Ocean TR; **NG:** Reza BCR; **SPL:** James Stevenson TRb. **92 Corbis:** Lloyd Cluff CLb; **Art Directors & TRIP:** TCb; M Fairman

BCL; **Visible Earth:** Image courtesy Jacques Descloitres, MODIS Rapid Response Team, NASA/GSFC TR. **93 Institute of Geological and Nuclear Sciences, New Zealand:** TC, CR, B. **94/95 Press Association Images:** AP Photo / Saitama Shimbun via kyodo News. **96 Corbis:** Galen Rowell TR, Yann Arthus-Bertrand C. **96/97 Corbis:** Galen Rowell B. **97 Corbis:** Galen Rowell TR; **Geo:** CRb; NASA BCR; Yann Arthus-Bertrand TR. **98 Corbis:** Hulton-Deutsch Collection CL; **Getty:** Stone / Joe Cornish BL; **Magnum:** Stuart Franklin TCLb; **SI:** CR. **99 Bruce Coleman Ltd:** Johnny Johnson TCL; **Corbis:** Galen Rowell Ca; Lester Lefkowitz B (main); **RHPL:** Patrick Endres BCL; Scott Darsney TCR; **Still:** Peter Arnold Inc / Alan Maichrowicz TR. **100 Corbis:** Ecoscene / Graham Neden CR; Galen Rowell C; Hubert Stadler CRa, CRb; Jonathan Blair BCL; Lynda Richardson TCL; NASA CLb; William Manning CLa. **101 AKG London:** Alte Nationalgalerie, Berlin TRb; **Corbis:** Brian Vikander BCR; **DK:** TL; **South American Pictures:** Kathy Jarvis B (main); **Still:** Alan Watson TCR. **102 Bruce Coleman Ltd:** Rob Jordan Cb; **Corbis:** James L Amos CRa; John Noble BR; **OSF:** Konrad Wothe / SAL CLa. **103 Corbis:** Jon Sparks Ca; Michael Busselle CL; Roger Ressmeyer BL; **FLPA:** BB Casals B (main); J&C Sohns TR; R Wilmshurst TRb. **104 Corbis:** Galen Rowell TCLb; Patrick Johns TCLa; Randy Wells BRa; Sandro Vannini BL; **P A Photos:** European Press Agency CbL; **SPL:** TR. **105 Getty:** Taxi / Pascal Tournaire. **106 Corbis:** A Alamary & E Vicens CLa; Bojan Brecelij TR; Natalie Fobes CbL; **NG:** John Eastcott and Yva Momatiuk BL; Randy Olsen CRa; Konstantin Mikhailov: BR. **107 Corbis:** Christine Osborne CaL; Richard Bickel CRa; Yann Arthus-Bertrand CLa, CbL; **FLPA:** Panda Photo CL; **NG:** Steve McCurry B. **108 Corbis:** CLa; Earl & Nazima Kowall CaL; Gallo Images / Roger de la Harpe TCR; **DK:** Frank Greenaway CbR; Ken Findlay TCRb; **FLPA:** Fritz Polking BR; **NPA Group:** CbL; **OSF:** JC Stevenson / AA BL. **109 alamy.com:** Michael Grant BL; **Corbis:** NASA BCL; **DK:** Gables CRa; **Getty:** Taxi / Walter Bibikow T; **RHPL:** Gavin Hellier Cb. **110 Corbis:** Bettmann BL; David Keaton TRb; Galen Rowell TCL; Howard Davies TCb. **110/111 Mountain Images:** Ian Evans B. **111 Corbis:** Ecoscene / Robert Weight TR; **NASA:** Johnson Space Center (STS41G-120-22) CL; **OSF:** Dinodia Picture Agency TCL. **112 Corbis:** Eric & David Hosking CRb; **DK:** Rob Reichenfeld CLa; **Getty:** Image Bank / John William Banagan TR; **NG:** Paul Chesley B; **WWI:** Joe Cornish CR. **113 British Antarctic Survey:** David Cantrill CRa; **Corbis:** Galen Rowell B, TCLb; **FLPA:** Eric & David Hosking TCR; **OSF:** Kim Westerskov Ca. **114 Corbis:** NASA CL. **114/115 Bruce Coleman Ltd:** Gerald S Cubitt C; **Corbis:** Gary Braasch Cb; Roger Ressmeyer CR; **DK:** Rob Reichenfeld C; **SI:** CRb; Ca; **Geo:** TCR, TRb. **116 Agence France Presse:** TC; **Corbis:** TRb; Yann Arthur-Bertrand CaL; **US Geological Survey:** JD Griggs B; **Geo:** Ca. **117 Agence France Presse:** Romeo Gacard CLa; **Corbis:** Sygma / Patrick Robert Cr; **Geo:** TR, CL. **118 Corbis:** David Muench BL; Terry W Eggers CRa; **NG:** Bates Littlehales BR; **Geo:** Cla, CRb. **119 Corbis:** Gary Braasch B (main); **RHPL:** Calvin W Hall CR; **NG:** James C Richardson TRb; **Gary Rosenquist:** B (inset); **SI:** TCb; **US Geological Survey:** TC. **120 Corbis:** BLa; Roger Ressmeyer TL, Ca, CRb, BR; **NG:** James Amos TRb. **121 Corbis:** Nik Wheeler BLa; Sygma / Chloe Harford BR; **NG:** Sarah Leen Ca, TCb; **Rex Features:** Sipa Press CRb; **SI:** Olger Aragon BC; William I Rose, Michigan Tech University, Department of Geological and Mining Engineering and Science CRa. **122 Corbis:** Galen Rowell BL; Jeremy Horner CL; **Rex Features:** Roger Ressmeyer CRa; **Rex Features:** Sipa Press TCb; **SI:** Oscar Gonzalez-Ferran, Departmento de Geologia y Geofisica, Universidad de Chile CRb; **US Geological Survey:** CLa. **123 Corbis:** Ric Ergenbright TR; Roger Ressmeyer CRa; **Magnum:** Patrick Zachmann BL; **Geo:** BR, TCL; **Mats Wibe-Lund:** CL. **124/125 Press Association Images:** AP Photo / Francisco Negroni. **126 Agence France Press:** TCR; **Corbis:** Roger Ressmeyer CL; **Getty:** Image Bank / Guido Alberto Rossi CbL; **Tom Pfeiffer:** B (inset). **x127 Still:** Otto Hahn. **128 Corbis:** Yann Arthur-Bertrand. **129 Corbis:** Michael S Yamashita CRa; Ric Ergenbright CbL; Roger Ressmeyer CRb. **130 Corbis:** Bettmann TR; Roger Ressmeyer CLa, BR, CL; **NG:** Sisse Brimberg CRb; **N.H.P.A.:** Kevin Schafer CLb.

131 Corbis: Ecoscene / Chinch Gryniewicz Cb; Torleif Svensson B; Yann Arthus-Bertrand CLa; Magnum: Bruno Barbey TR, CRa; NG: George F Mobley CRb. 132 alamy.com: RHPL BL; Corbis: Peter Turnley TC; Katz/FSP: Gamma CLa; NG: Chris Johns CRb; Medford Taylor BR; SI: Krafft Collection CRa. 133 Corbis: Yann Arthur-Bertrand Ca; NG: Steve Raymer TR; OSF: NASA BR; SI: Alexander Belousov BC. 134 Bruce Coleman Ltd: Orion Press Ca; Corbis: Michael S Yamashita CLa; Magnum: Chris Steele-Perkins CLa; SI: Liu Xiang, Changchun University of Science and Technology, Department of Geology BL; US Geological Survey: Jack Lockwood BR. 135 Corbis: Roger Ressmeyer CR; Saba / Alberto Garcia C; Katz/FSP: Van Cappellen / Rea TCR; SI: Chris Newhall, Department of Earth and Space Sciences, University of Washington BR; Rizal Dasoeki / Volcanological Survey of Indonesia CL. 136 Corbis: Dean Conger TC; Roger Ressmeyer C; Getty Images: DigitalGlobe TC; NG: Paul Chesley CR. Popperfoto: CRa; SI: Krafft Collection BL; Still: Alain Compost BR. 137 Corbis: Galen Rowell C; Hulton Archive/Getty: CRb; OSF: Doug Allan B; Tarnmy Peluso TCL; Tui de Roy TR. 138 Geo: BCL, Bla; PJ Fleisher: R; Martin Miller: Department of Geological Sciences, University of Oregon CbL. 139 Martin Miller: Department of Geological Sciences, University of Oregon Cb; PJ Fleisher: CRa; Dr Parvinder S Sethi: BCL; SPL: Alfred Pasieka TCL; Geo: CRb. 140 Jens C Andersen: Camborne School of Mines CLa; Corbis: Charles E Rotkin CL; Kelly Mooney Photography BL; Kurt Hollocher: Union College TC; Geological Survey of Canada: Dr Robert H Rainbird CRa. 141 Corbis: Bill Ross C; Galen Rowell TR; Phil Shermeister CRa; Robert Holmes BL. 142 AirPhoto: Jim Wark TL; Corbis: Charles O'Rear BRa; David Muench CRa; Jonathan Blair C; Still: Peter Arnold Inc / Robert MacKinlay BL. 143 alamy.com: Neil Cameron CRa, RHPL CLa; Art Directors & TRIP: F Bognar BC; Geo: Tim Fogg BRa; Reproduced by permission of the British Geological Survey © NERC All Rights Reserved IPR/39-5c BL. 144 Corbis: Yann Arthus Bertrand BL; DK: Joe Cornish CLa; Art Directors & TRIP: B Gadsby TCL; METI / ERSDAC: TR. 145 Getty: Photodisc Green CR; ImageState/Pictor: Premium Stock BL; Geo: BR; National Park Service: C. 146 Corbis: Jeff Vanuga CL; Kevin R Morris BL; Still: Peter Arnold Inc / John Keiffer TC; WWI: Mark Hamblin Ca. 146/147 Corbis: Raymond Gehman CL. Still: Peter Arnold Inc / John Keiffer TC; WWI: Mark Hamblin Ca. 147 Getty: Image Bank / Michael Melford CRa. 148 Corbis: Charles O'Rear BC; Dave G Houser BL; Nik Wheeler BR; Getty: Stone / Jack Dykinga Ca; NG: E.C. Kolb CLa. 149 Corbis: Macduff Everton TR; SPL: Klaus Guldbrandsen BC; Geo: BR; WWI: Andreas Leemann Ca. 150/151 Getty Images: National Geographic / Carsten Peter. 152 Corbis: Eye Ubiquitous / Mike Powles CaL; Michael Freeman CRa; Michael S Yamashita BL; Robert Holmes Cb, BR. 153 Getty: Stone / John Lamb C; Taxi / Travel Pix BL; Geo: CRb, BR, Waimangu Volcanic Valley Ltd, New Zealand: TR, TLb. 154 Corbis: Roger Ressmeyer. 155 Corbis: Bob Krist Cb. 156/157 Corbis: Yann Arthus-Bertrand. 158 Getty: Stone / Hans Strand BL. 158/159 Corbis: Lester Leftowitz C. 159 Getty: Image Bank / China Tourism Press Bca; RHPL: Simon Harris BR; Still: Peter Arnold Inc / Aldo Brando CRb; Louise Thomas: C; Geo: BR. 160 © 2002 Environment Agency, National Centre for Environmental Data & Surveillance: TR; NG: Paul Nicklen Cla; Philip Schermeister TCLb; Getty: Image Bank / China Tourism Press B. 161 Corbis: Nathan Benn CL; Getty: Image Bank / NASA Cb; Still: Peter Arnold Inc / Jim Wark TRb; Visible Earth: NASA / GSFC / JPL, MISR Team BRa. 162/163 Corbis: NASA. 164 Corbis: Charles E Rotkin BL; Lowell Georgia TR; Paul A Souders CLa; RHPL: Maurice Joseph CRb; FLPA: Steve McCutcheon TCL. 165 AirPhoto: Jim Wark TCL; Corbis: Richard Hamilton Smith CL; Still: Peter Arnold Inc / Alex S MacLean B; Telegraph Herald: CaR. 166 AirPhoto: Jim Wark TCL. Corbis: Annie Griffiths Belt C; Buddy Mays BC; Russ Finley Stock Photography: BL. 167 Aurora & Quanta Productions Inc.: Peter Essick B. 168 Getty: Image Bank / Jack Dykinga TR; Image Bank / Michael Melford TC; Stone / Donald Nausbaum B; Landsat: CR. 169 Corbis: Bettmann BC; James Marshall

R; DK: Cyril Laubscher CLb; WWI: David Woodfall BL. 170 Corbis: Yann Arthus-Bertrand BCLa, TCL; Getty: Stone / Will & Deni McIntyre TR; South American Pictures: Tony Morrison CL, CbL. 171 Still: Luiz C Marigo. 172 Corbis: Adam Woolfitt BR; Eye Ubiquitous / Tim Hawkins CaL; Getty: Image Bank / Daniel Barbier CR; Taxi / David Noton BL. 173 Corbis: Papilio / Pat Jerrold CbR; Getty: Image Bank / Werner Dieterich BC; RHPL: Michael Busselle BL; Magnum: Thomas Hoepker C; P A Photos: European Press Agency TRb. 174 Corbis: Joe McDonald BC; Lester Lefkowitz CL. 175 Still: Jim Wark. 176 Agence France Presse: Pavel Neubauer CL; Getty: Stone / Simeone Huber TR; Landsat: CRb; Russia and Eastern Images: Mark Wadlow BR. 177 DK: Peter Hiscock TC; Getty: Image Bank / NASA B; Images Of Africa Photobank: David Keith Jones TR; NG: David S Boyer CR; Chris Caldicott CL. 178 Aurora & Quanta Productions Inc.: Robert Caputo / IPN B, TCL; Corbis: Dave G Houser TR. 179 Corbis: CL; Ed Kashi BRa; Galen Rowell CR; Nik Wheeler B; NG: Chris Johns TR. 180 Corbis: Dean Conger B; How-Man Wong TC; Tom Nebbia TRb; Still: Dera CR; Mark Carwardine Ca. 181 Corbis: Liu Liqun BL; Michael Freeman CR; Michael S Yamashita BR; Photowood Inc TCL; RHPL: Gina Corrigan CL. 182 Getty: Taxi / Gavin Hellier B; RHPL: CL; NASA: Johnson Space Center (STS087-707-092) TR; Still: Andre Maslennikov TL; K McCullough CL. 183 Australian Portraits: David Hancock BR; Corbis: Rik Ergenbright CL; DK: Cyril Laubscher Bcg; The British Museum, London / Peter Hayman TRb; RHPL: TC. 184 Getty: Image Bank / Art Wolfe R; NG: Emory Kristof Ca; Geo: CR; SC Porter: University of Washington Cb. 185 DK: Dave King TR; Mike Grandmaison: BR; RHPL: Paolo Koch Ca; FLPA: GT Andlewartha BL. 186 Corbis: Visions of America / Joseph Sohm CLb; Getty: Stone / Vito Palmisano BL; NG: Medford Taylor TC; Raymond K Gehman CaR. 187 NG: Medford Taylor. 188 alamy.com: Masrdis CaL; Corbis: Scott T Smith BR; RHPL: S Grandadam CaR; Leland Howard: BL. 189 Corbis: Craig Lovell CL; Kevin Schafer TR; Ronan Soumar B; South American Pictures: Tony Morrison CL. 190 Still: Glen Christian. 191 Corbis: Ian Harwood / Ecoscene CbL; Greenpeace: Shailendra Yashwant CR; Still: Gilles Corniere TCbR. 192 DK: Paul Harris BC; Steve Shott CLA; FLPA: F Ardito / Panda TR; Art Directors & TRIP: O Semenenko BL; WWI: David Woodfall CRb. 193 Corbis: Blaine Harrington III TRb; Bo Zaunders B; Getty: Image Bank / Macduff Everton CR; Image Bank / Werner Dieterich TCL. 194 Corbis: Bernard and Catherine Desjeux TCb; Jonathan Blair BR; Images Of Africa Photobank: David Keith Jones CR, BR; OSF: Richard Packwood TR. 195 Corbis: Caroline Penn Ca; Getty: Image Bank / Guido Alberto Rossi BL; Images Of Africa Photobank: David Keith Jones CL; Friedrich von Hörsten BR. 196 Corbis: Galen Rowell BC; Hulton-Deutsch Collection TRb; DK: Jerry Young TC; NG: Barry Tessman BRa; Sarah Leen BL; OSF: Mark Deeble & Victoria Stone Ca. 197 Corbis: David Turnley TL, CR; Yann Arthur-Bertrand B. 198 Aurora & Quanta Productions Inc.: Evan Roberts BR; Corbis: Diego Lezama Orezzoli TR; Mark Garanger TCLb; NASA BL; OSF: Tony Bomford CaL. 199 Corbis: Galen Rowell BL; Ted Spiegel BR; RHPL: CCD Tokeley BC.; ImageState/Pictor: David South TR; NG: Reza Ca. 200 Corbis: CLb, TRb. 200/201 Tom Till Photography: B; 201 Paul Deakin: TCb; Geo: CRa, CR, CbR; Jenolan Caves Reserve Trust: TCL. 202 Corbis: Craig Lovell TR; David Muench CbL; Russ Finley Stock Photography: TCL; OSF: Rodger Jackman CL; Terra Galleria Photography: T Luong B. 203 Aurora & Quanta Productions Inc.: Stephen Alvarez C; Corbis: Bojan Brecelj CR; NG: Wes Skiles BL; OSF: David M Dennis TCR; Arthur Palmer: CL; Geo: BR. 204/205 Getty Images: National Geographic / Speleoresearch & Films / Carsten Peter. 206 Caving Club of Touraine: Jean-Luc Roch BC; RHPL: TRb. NG: Sisse Brimberg Ca; Geo: CLa, BL, BR. 207 Cango Caves: Steve Mouton BL, CbL, CL; Geo: TR, B, CaL. 208 Corbis: Robert Holmes CR; Getty: Image Bank / Nevada Wier TCL; OSF: Clive Bromhall CLb; Geo: TR, B. 209 Geo: CLa, CRa; Jenolan Caves Reserve Trust: TL; Geo: CR; Koonalda Caves: Peter Bell BL. 210/211 SPL: Bernhard Edmaier. 212 Corbis: David Muench BCL;

Marc Muench Ca; RHPL: Andrew Sanders BL. 212/213 Corbis: Tom Bean C. 213 Corbis: Phil Schermeister BCR; Getty: Image Bank / Darrell Gulin CLa; Greenpeace: BRaL,CRb; RHPL: Tony Waltham TR. 214 AirPhoto: Jim Wark B; Corbis: Geo: CL, CRR; Tom Lowell: University of Cincinnati CLL. 215 AirPhoto: Jim Wark CRa; Geo: TR, Cb, BLA, TCL. 216 Corbis: Tom Bean Ca, BR; RE Johnson Photography: CRb; Dan Stone: CLa; US Geological Survey: Rod March BL. 217 Anthony Arendt: Univerity of Alaska CR; Jamie Buscher: Department of Geological Sciences, Virginia Tech R; Corbis: Neil Rabinowitz CLa; Still: Peter Arnold Inc / Jim Wark B. 218 Alamy Images: Niebrugge Images TR; Corbis: Danny Lehman CL; David Muench CLa; David Samuel Robbins CRa; Jim Zuckerman BL; The Purcell Team BR. 219 Corbis: Tom Bean Ca; NASA: Goddard Space Flight Center / USGS EDC B; OSF: Peter Arnold Inc / Jim Wark TR. 220 B&C. 221 Jason E Box: Polar Research Center, Ohio State University CRa; Corbis: Staffan Widstrand Cb; Geo: BR. 222 Josh Beck: BL; Peter Burden: CLa; Simon Heyes, Last Frontier Ltd: BCL; NASA: Goddard Space Flight Center B; Still: Peter Arnold Inc / SJ Krasemann CRa; Nozomu Takeuchi: Research Institute for Humanity and Nature (RIHN), Kyoto TCbR. 223 Corbis: Eye Ubiquitous / James Davies CL; Yann Arthus-Bertrand TR; NG: Steve Winter BL; Freysteinn Sigmundsson: Nordic Volcanological Institute, Reykjavik BR; Still: Alan Watson TL. 224 Kim Holmén: Department of Meteology, Stockholm University Ca; Dr Miriam Jackson: Norwegian Water Resources & Energy Directorate Hydrology Department BR; Dr John Wood: Department of Geography and Earth Sciences, Brunel University TR; Joran Zahl Marken: Bca. 225 Corbis: Marc Garanger CaR; Julia K Davidson, www.flickr.com/photos/juliakathleendavidson: BL; Still: Peter Arnold Inc / Bill O'Connor BL; Peter Arnold Inc / Gordon Wiltsie TCLb; Peter Arnold Inc / Helmut Gritscher BR. 226 Corbis: NASA BC; Jamie McPherson: BL; Klaus E Schwartz: BR; Still: Theresa de Salis TC, CLa. 227 Corbis: Galen Rowell BL; Thomas E Dietz: International Society for Mountain Medicine CR; NG: Robby Model TL. 228 Science Photo Library: British Antarctic Survey BC; U.S. Geological Survey: Courtesy of GNP Archives TC; Karen Holzer CRa. 229 Corbis: Frans Lanting. 230 Corbis: Yann Arthus-Bertrand TCL. 230/231 Getty: Image Bank / Joseph van Os B. 231 Corbis: Galen Rowell TR; Hulton-Deutsch Collection TCL; SPL: JG Paren CR. 232 alamy.com: Stock Connection Inc / James Kay BC; Alamy Images: imagebroker / Michael Krabs BL; Robert Dinwiddie. Corbis: Paul A Souders TCR. Tom Lowell: University of Cincinnati BR; Still: Peter Arnold Inc / Walter H Hodge CLb; Ulrich Walthert Coast Photography, New Zealand: BL. 233 David Summers. 234/235 Corbis: Yann Arthus-Bertrand. 236 Corbis: Kevin Schafer CL; Scott T Smith CbL; DK: Linda Whitwarm C; Getty: PhotoDisc BL. 236/237 alamy.com: Geoffrey Morgan C. 237 Corbis: Ric Ergenbright CRa; Getty: Taxi / Josef Beck Cb; Geo: TCL, TCR. 238 Corbis: CaL; David Muench TLb; Gallo Images / Hein von Horsten BC; Jeremy Horner CaR; DK: Alistair Duncan BL; Frank Greenaway Cb; NG: Des and Jen Bartlett BCLa. 238/239 WWI: David Woodfall C. 239 Corbis: Ecoscene / Andrew Brown TCL; George HH Huey CRa; DK: Geoff Dann C. 240 DK: Dave King CRb; Getty: Stone / RGK Photography BC; Taxi / Alan Kearney BL; Jim Harding C. 240/241 Scott T Smith: T; 241 Agence France Presse: John Gurzinski / STR CRa; Corbis: B.S.P.I. BL; Marko Modic BR; DK: Frank Greenaway Cb. 242 D Donne Bryant Stock Picture Agency: LLC / David Ryan B; Corbis: Charles O'Rear CLa, CRa. SPL: CNES, Distribution Spot Image tcl. 243 FLPA: A Christiansen Cb; Royal Geographical Society Picture Library: BR; Still: Michael Gunther T. 244/245 Getty Images: Daniel J Bryant. 246 Still: M&C Denis-Huot C. 247 DK: Andy Crawford CaR; Frank Greenaway BR; Getty: Image Bank / Jean du Boisberranger BR; NG: Michael S Lewis CbL; Still: Cyril Ruoso CLa; © M.P.F.T: TR. 248 Magnum: Steve McCurry BLA. 249 Still: UNEP / Voltchev. 250 Corbis: Gallo Images / Peter Lillie Ca; Michael & Patricia Fogden CbL; Papilio / Robert Gill BL; Gerald Cubitt: BR; DK: Frank Greenaway TR. 251 DK: Colin Walton TC; RHPL: Gina Corrigan BR; Russia and Eastern Images:

Mark Wadlow CRa; Wax Visual Stock Photography: BL. 252 Nature Picture Library: Gertrud Neumann-Denzau TC; Corbis: Dean Conger BC; Steve Kaufman BL; Geo: CR. 253 Getty: Image bank / Art Wolfe. 254 Corbis: Australian Picture Library BC; Eric & David Hosking CLa; Gallo Images / 318 TR; WWI: Ted Meads CRa, BR. 255 Corbis: Gallo Images / 318 Cb; Michael & Patricia Fogden BL; DK: Cyril Laubscher CRa; WWI: Ted Mead TL, BR. 256/257 Magnum: Stuart Franklin. 258 DK: Matthew Wark CaL; Neil Fletcher & Matthew Ward CLb, CbL; Steve Gorton CaR; FLPA: David Hosking CL. Still: Roland Seitre BCR.258/259 Natural Image: Bob Gibbons C. 259 DK: Peter Chadwick CaR; FLPA: B Borrel Casals TCb; Chris Mattison CaL; Fritz Polking BRa; Still: Frank Vidal Cb. 260 Corbis: Ecoscene / Andrew Brown BR; Getty: Stone / Jane Gifford CL; Natural Image: Bob Gibbons B; Rex Features: Sipa Press TCL; World Wildlife Fund: MedPo / Pedro Regato CaL. 261 Corbis: Jonathan Blair BCL; Raymond Gehman BL, BC; DK: Eric Crichton TLb; Neil Fletcher CaL; Peter Anderson TCR; FLPA: M Moffett / Minden Pictures CL; Martin B Withers CaR; NASA: Johnson Space Center (STS41G-45-40) CRa; Art Directors & TRIP: W Jacobs CLb. 262 Corbis: Gunter Marx Photography CR, TRb; FLPA: Mark Newman B; OSF: Lon E Lauber TCL. 263 Corbis: Bob Rowan / Progressive Image CRb; Galen Rowell TRb; Marc Muench BC; Art Wolfe Ca; David Drain TC; Art Directors & TRIP: M Barlow BCR. 264 Corbis: David Muench TCL; Mark Muench CLa; BC; Jerry Young BL; OSF: CRA, CRb; WWI: Alan Watson BL. 265 Corbis: Brian Vikander CL; DK: Jerry Young TR; Pau D'Arco CR; South American Pictures: Tony Morrison TCR; Still: Juan Carlos Munoz TCL; WWI: David Woodfall B. 266 Corbis: Macduff Everton CLb; Wayne Bennett BC. 267 Corbis: Robert Semeniuk. 268 FLPA: Roger Tidman BC; T de Roy / Minden Pictures CR; Natural Image: Bob Gibbons BL, BR; South American Pictures: Tony Morrison TL; Still: Alan Watson B. 269 Corbis: Adrian Arbib T, Michael Busselle BCL; DK: Neil Fletcher BCL; Getty: Stone / Stephen Studd C; Natural Image: Bob Gibbons BR; Rex Features: Express CR, BR; OSF: Maria Stenzel BCL; OSF: Daniel Cox CbL, Russia and Eastern Images: Mark Wadlow TC; Still: Patrick Bertrand Ca; Roland Seitre R. 271 Corbis: Keren Su CR; Gerald Cubitt: BL, DK: Kim Taylor CL; Nigel Hicks: BR; OSF: Andrew Plumptre TR; Still: Michael Gunther TCL. 272 FLPA: Frans Lanting. 273 Associated Press AP: Yenni Kwok, Stringer bc; Getty: Stone / Manoj Shah TR; RHPL: Louise Murray BR; SPL: Geoff Tompkinson C. 274 Corbis: Hulton-Deutsch Collection BC; Paul A Souders CbR; Peter Johnson BR; DK: NHM / Frank Greenaway TCR; FLPA: Terry Whittaker CRa; Tim Rushforth BL. Still: Mark Edwards TR; World Wildlife Fund: Steve Nelson & Zovtaigi c/o World Wise Ecotourism Network CLa. 275 Corbis: FLPA / Pam Gardner CRa; Paul A Souders L; Yann Arthus-Bertrand Cb; N.H.P.A.: Dave Watts TR; Skyrail, Cairns, Australia: BR. 276/277 WWI: Ted Mead. 278 Corbis: David Muench BL; Ecoscene / Ian Harwood CaL; Nik Wheeler BC; NG: courtesy Moesgård Museum, Arhus, Denmark / Ira Block TRb. 279 alamy.com: Steve Bloom Images / Steve Bloom B; Corbis: FLPA / Fritz Polking CaL; DK: Frank Greenaway TLb; Geoff Dann TC; Kim Taylor & Jane Burton TR; Philip Dowell CaR; FLPA: Tony Hamblin Cb; Raymond Gehman CL, BL; DK: Karl Stone BR; Dave Liebman: TC; Virginia Museum of Natural History: Susan B Felkner TR. 281 AirPhoto: Jim Wark CbR; Corbis: David Muench BL; Kevin Fleming TR; Tony Arruza BC; NG: Farrell Greham T. 282 Corbis: Tom Brakefield CLa; FLPA: Jurgen & Christine Johns CRb; OSF: Chris Catton CRa; Niall Benvie BR; Still: Gunter Ziesler TCL; Roland Seitre TRb; WWI: M Powles BL. 283 Getty: Image Bank / Art Wolfe BL; FLPA: Terry Andrewartha TCL; Natural Image: Bob Gibbons CLA; OSF: John Cooke Cb; Roland Mayr TR; Still: Nigel Dickinson BRa; Peter Arnold Inc / Gunter Ziesler CRa. 284 Corbis: Wolfgang Kaehler TR; Yann Arthus-Bertrand CLA; FLPA: Minden Pictures / Frans Lanting B; Still: Paul Springett CRA. 285 Aurora & Quanta Productions Inc.: Robert Caputo / IPN CL; Australian Portraits: David Hancock BR; Corbis: Gallo Images / 318 TC; DK: Andrew Butler CR; Exmoor Zoo / Peter Cross

CbR; **NewsPhotos:** Chris Crerar BCL. **286/287 Still:** Fritz Polking. **288 Corbis:** Michael S Yamashita CL; Peter Johnson BCLa; Tom Bean CbL; **OSF:** Mills Tandy Ca; Rafi Ben-Shahar BCR; **South American Pictures:** Tony Morrison BL, TCb. **288/289 Corbis:** Tom Bean B. **289 Corbis:** D Robert & Lorri Franz CaR; Staffan Widstrand CR; W Perry Conway TRb; **DK:** Frank Greenaway TC; Jerry Young CaL; NHM / Frank Greenaway CLa. **290 Corbis:** David Muench B; Joe McDonald TCL; Tom Bean CR; **FLPA:** Daphne Kinzler CL; **OSF:** Scott Camazine CLL; **Still:** Roland Seitre TR. **291 Corbis:** CRb; Macduff Everton C; **DK:** Jerry Young TLb; **South American Pictures:** Mike Harding B; **Still:** Roland Seitre TRb. **292 Corbis:** Sygma TRb; Wolfgang Kaehler TC; **Art Directors & TRIP:** J Farmar CLa. **292/293 Corbis:** Brian A Vikander B; **293 DK:** Mike Dunning TL; **Images Of Africa Photobank:** David Keith Jones TRb; **FLPA:** Terry Andrewartha TC. **294 DK:** Jerry Young CL; **Russia and Eastern Images:** Mark Wadlow CRa; **Still:** Adrian Arbib B; Stephen Pern TCR. **295 Corbis:** O Alamany & E Vicens BR; **DK:** Geoff Dann BCL; **FLPA:** E&D Hosking C; **Natural Image:** Bob Gibbons TCb; **NG:** Thad Samuels Abell II Cb; **Still:** Mark Edwards TR. **296 AirPhoto:** Jim Wark B; **Geo:** CRa, C, CaR. **297 B&C:** TR, BL, BCR; **Corbis:** Tom Brakefield CL; **Hutchison Library:** Andrey Zvoznikov CRb; **NG:** Rich Reid CRa. **298/299 Getty:** Image Bank / Peter Cade. **300/301 Getty:** Stone / Arnulf Husmo. **302 Robert Dinwiddie:** CLb, CLLb; **DK:** Andreas Einseidel BCLa; Frank Greenaway TCbR; © **1999 MBARI:** CaR, CaL. **303 Corbis:** Brian A Vikander TRb; **OSF:** Chris McLaughlin BCL; **FLPA:** S Jonasson Ca; **Richard Lutz:** CLb; **Corbis:** Arctic-Images CR. **304/305 NG:** Image from Volcanoes of the Deep, a giant screen motion picture, produced for IMAX theaters by the Stephen Low Company in association with Rutgers University. Major funding for the project is provided by the National Science Foundation C. **305 Corbis:** Reuters / Handout / Japan Coast Guard TC; **NG:** Paul Chesley CL; **Visible Earth:** Provided by the SeaWiFS Project, NASA/Goddard Space Flight Center, and ORBIMAGE CL; NOAA: NSF TR. **306 Robert Dinwiddie:** CLa; **SPL:** ER Degginger CL. **307 Getty Images:** Spencer Platt CLa; **Press Association Images:** AP / Nathan Becker – Pacific Tsunami Warning Center TR. **308/309 Corbis:** Nippon News / Aflo / Mainichi. **309 OSF:** David Fox TRb; Howard Hall Ca; Joyce & Frank Burek / AA C; Neil Bromhall Cb. **310/311 Corbis:** Jonathan Blair B. **311 SPL:** Eric Grave CaR; Institute of Oceanographic Sciences / NERC CbR; Jan Hinsch CRa; Manfred Cage TCR; Sinclair Stammers TR. **312 Corbis:** Paul A Souders Ca; **SPL:** Geospace CRb. **313 Japanese National Tourist Organization:** T. **314 Corbis:** Bettmann TRb; Jeffrey L Rotman Cb; Robert Yin Ca; **Southampton Oceanography Centre:** Dr Alex Mustard BCL. **314/315 Corbis:** Jose Fuste Raga C; **316 Corbis:** Yann Arthus-Bertrand Cb; **FLPA:** Minden Pictures / Fred Bavendam Cb; **NASA:** Image courtesy of Earth Sciences and Image Analysis Laboratory, Johnson Space Center (STS046-77-31) TCb; **Southampton Oceanography Centre:** Dr Alex Mustard TCL. **316 Corbis:** George Lepp CRb; Paul A Souders BC; Wolfgang Kaehler BCa; **FLPA:** Fritz Polking Cb; **NG:** Maria Stenzel T; **OSF:** Ben Osborne BR; Doug Allan

Ca. **317 Corbis:** Rick Price BL; Wolfgang Kaehler BR, BCa. **318 Corbis:** Jon Hicks TR; Onne van der Wal CLa; Stuart Westmorland CL; **DK:** BLa; **FLPA:** Silvestris CLb. **319 B&C:** Wendy Else TL; **Corbis:** Gianni Dagli Orti TRb; Peter Johnson BRA; Stephen Frink CRa; **DK:** Frank Greenaway TCb; **OSF:** David Fleetham Cl. **320 B&C:** TCL; **Corbis:** Bettmann BL; **NG:** Emory Kristof TCb; Paul Nicklen CL; **NOAA:** CL. **321 Getty:** Stone / Hans Strand. **322 alamy.com:** F.R. CLa; **B&C:** BR; **Corbis:** Staffan Widstrand CRa; **NOAA:** V Juterzenka, Piepenbung, Schmid TCL; **Visible Earth:** Provided by the SeaWiFS Project, NASA/Goddard Space Flight Center, and ORBIMAGE BCL. **323 B&C:** TRb; **Corbis:** Bruce Burkhardt CR; Raymond Gehman BL; Wolfgang Kaehler BR; **Visible Earth:** Image courtesy Jacques Descloitres, MODIS Rapid Response Team, NASA/GSFC TCL. **324 Corbis:** Jonathan Blair. **325 Corbis:** Neil Rabinowitz TR; Richard Cummins BCL; **DK:** Frank Greenaway BRa; **NG:** Nick Caloyianis BR; **David Robinson:** Cb. **326 Corbis:** Kevin Schafer CLa; Raymond Gehman BL; The Purcell Team CRb; **Hulton Archive/Getty:** Stock Montage / Archive Photos TRb; **NG:** James P Blair BR; Norbert Rosing Ca. **327 Corbis:** B; Darren Gulin CLb; Kevin R Morris CRb; Lynda Richardson TR; Stephen Frink TC; Tony Arruzal Cb; **Henry Genthe:** Ca. **328 Still:** Fred Bavendam. **329 Corbis:** Phil Schermeister CRb; Stephen Frink Cb; **Getty:** Taxi / Ron Whitby CLa. **330 Corbis:** TRb; Gavriel Jecan TCL; Macduff Everton B; Stephen Frink CR; **NG:** Wes Skiles CL. **331 Gunnar Britse:** windpowerphotos.com CRb; **Corbis:** Chris Hellier BL; Nik Wheeler BR; Patrick Ward CRa; **Geological Survey of Denmark and Greenland:** Peter K Warna-Moors Cb; **Geo:** CLa, Ca; **Visible Earth:** Provided by the SeaWiFS Project, NASA/Goddard Space Flight Center, and ORBIMAGE TCR. **332 Agence France Presse:** TRb; **Corbis:** Jeffrey L Rotman TCL. **332/333 Getty:** Image Bank / Raymond Gehman B. **333 Corbis:** Jonathan Blair TRb; **Magnum:** Stuart Franklin TC; **NASA:** Johnson Space Center (STS41G-17-34-081) TL. **334 B&C:** CbR; **Corbis:** Brandon D Cole CbL; Charles & Josette Lenars BR. **334/335 NG:** Gilbert M Grosvenor T. **335 42 Degrees South:** Rob Walls BC. **336 Corbis:** Dean Conger BL; Lawson Wood R; **Robert Dinwiddie:** CLb; **Geo:** TC. **337 Corbis:** Ca; Bojan BreceIj CRa; Kevin R Morris CRb; Yann Arthus-Bertrand BR, TCL; **Karen Hissman:** CbL; **Images Of Africa Photobank:** Brian Charlesworth BL. **338 Corbis:** BC; Sygma / Haruyoshi Yamaguchi BL; Tim McKenna TC; **Robert Dinwiddie:** CL; **Professor Peter Franks:** University of California, San Diego CL; . **339 Corbis:** Amos Nachoum. **340 alamy.com:** RHPL CRb; **Corbis:** Annie Griffiths Belt BL; Natalie Fobes Ca, TRb; Ralph A Clevenger CL. **341 Corbis:** BL; Joel W Rogers CRa; Michael S Yamashita CLa; Rick Price TCL; Hosik Kim: TR; **Visible Earth:** Provided by the SeaWiFS Project, NASA/Goddard Space Flight Center, and ORBIMAGE BR. **342 Corbis:** Catherine Karnow Ca; Jeffrey L Rotman Cb; Nik Wheeler BL; **P A Photos:** European Press Agency BR; **Visible Earth:** Provided by the SeaWiFS Project, NASA/Goddard Space Flight Center, and ORBIMAGE CR; © **2003 Norbert Wu:** www.norbertwu.com CLa. **343 Corbis:** FLPA / Pam Gardner CRa; Stuart Westmorland BCL;

Yann Arthus-Bertrand BR; **Jezohare.com:** Ca; **NG:** Paul Chesley CLa. **344 Magnum:** Jean Gaumy. **345 Corbis:** Hans Georg Roth CRa; Margaret Courtney-Clarke Cb. **346 Corbis:** Peter Johnson CL; Yann Arthus-Bertrand TCL; **Getty:** Stone / Kim Westerskov B; **SPL:** Simon Fraser TRb. **347 British Antarctic Survey:** D Allan CbL. **Corbis:** Galen Rowell TR, CaL; Rick Price C; Wolfgang Kaehler CRb, BR; © **2003 Norbert Wu:** www.norbertwu.com BL. **348/349 Geo. 428 Associated Press AP:** Zhan Xiaoding CaR; **Corbis:** Brandon D Cole CaL; **Getty:** Stone / Natalie Fobes BC; Stone / Philip Long BCL. **350/351 Getty:** Stone / H Richard Johnston C. **351 Corbis:** B.S.P.I. TC; Barry Davies TCbL; Sygma / Frederick Astier CaR; **OSF:** Richard Packwood CRb; **Rex Features:** Timepix / G Davies CRA. **352 Corbis:** Catherine Karnow BCaR; Paul A Souders CaR; Yann Arthus-Bertrand BL, BR. w353 **Corbis:** NASA TCR; **Getty:** Image Bank / Peter Hendrie B; **Geo:** TRb. **354 Corbis:** John Heseltine BCa; Michael S Yamashita BCR; **DJ Sauchyn:** Prairie Research Collaborative C. **354/355 Corbis:** Dallas and John Heaton C. **355 Corbis:** Carol Havens BCa; Ecoscene / John Farmer TRb; Joel W Rogers Cb. **356 Corbis:** Otto Rogge. **357 Corbis:** Gallo Images / Martin Harvey BC; Joe McDonald Ca; **Getty:** Stone / Jeremy Walker BR. **358/359 Corbis:** William James Warren. **360/361 alamy.com:** IMAGINA / Atsushi Tsunoda. **362 Corbis:** Eye Ubiquitous / Bennett Dean BCL; **Getty:** Image Bank / Kevin Kelley C; **NG:** Thad Samuels Abell II CLb. **363 Corbis:** Ron Watts CR; **Tom Ekland:** CL; **Getty:** Image Bank / Guido Alberto Rossi C; **P A Photos:** European Press Agency BR. **SPL:** David Parker TCLb; **US Geological Survey:** AM Sarna-Wojcicki CRb; **Visible Earth:** Image courtesy Jacques Descloitres, MODIS Rapid Response Team, NASA/GSFC RC. **364 Corbis:** Grafton Marshall Smith CRa; **Transition Region and Coronal Explorer (TRACE)** — a mission of the Stanford-Lockheed Institute for Space Research, part of the NASA Small Explorer Program CRb. **365 Corbis:** Sygma / Herve Collart CL; **Getty:** Image Bank / Stephen Frink BC; Stone / Kim Blaxland TL; Stone / Kim Westerskov CR; Stone / Mark Muench BR. **366 SPL:** David Hay Jones. **367 DK:** NASA BCa; **Rex Features:** Brian Harris CRb. **368 Bridgeman Art Library, London / New York:** Giraudon. *Portrait of Gustave Gaspard Coriolis* (1792–1843) engraved by Zephirin Felix Jean Marius Belliard (b.1798) (litho), Academie des Sciences, Paris, France BL; **Corbis:** Stocktrek C. **369 alamy.com:** Geoffry Morgan CRb; **Corbis:** NASA TR; **National Trust Photographic Library:** Mike Howarth CRa; **Visible Earth:** Image courtesy GOES Project Science Office BCL. **370 Corbis:** Paul A Souders CL; **FLPA:** H Hoflinger TR; **Visible Earth:** Provided by the SeaWiFS Project, NASA/Goddard Space Flight Center, and ORBIMAGE BR; Image courtesy Liam Gurney, MODIS Atmosphere Team, University of Wisconsin – Madison CLa; Image courtesy Jacques Descloitres, MODIS Rapid Response Team, NASA/GSFC BCL. **371 Corbis:** Lowell Georgia TR; Sygma / Telegram Tribune / Jason Mellom CL; **P A Photos:** European Press Agency BCL. **372 Corbis:** Frank Lane Picture Agency / Ron Boardman CL; **SPL:** BR; Eye of Science Ca. **372/373 Magnum:** Steve McCurry **373 Corbis:** CRb; Jonathan Blair C; **Royal Swedish Academy of Sciences:** TR. **374 Corbis:** In Pictures / Richard Baker CL; **NASA:**

TC, TR; **Press Association Images:** AP TL. **374/375 Corbis:** Paul Souders B. **376 Corbis:** Hans Strand. **375 Alamy Images:** David Lock BR; **Corbis:** Jim Reed TR; **Getty Images:** AFP / HOANG DINH NAM CLa; LatinContent / Rodrigo Baleia TC; **Rough Guides:** Karen Trist BC. **376/377 Corbis:** Science Faction / digital version / US Air Force. **377 Corbis:** Douglas Faulkner Cb; **NG:** Michael S Lewis CRa; **Corbis:** Sygma / Kapoor Baldev CR; **Science Photo Library:** Nature's Images BC. **378/379 Corbis:** Tom Bean. **380 SPL:** BL. **380/381 Corbis:** A&J Verkaik B. **381 Corbis:** Richard Hamilton Smith CLa; **OSF:** Bill Pike / SAL TCR. **382 Corbis:** Paul A Souders TCR; Roger Tidman CLa; **Getty:** Image Bank / Pascal Perret CRa; **Ferdinand Valk:** CRb; **Visible Earth:** Image courtesy Jacques Descloitres, MODIS Rapid Response Team, NASA/GSFC TR. **383 Agence France Presse:** STR BCR; **Corbis:** Stocktrek CLa; **NASA:** Johnson Space Center (STS51I-37-83) TR. **384 Corbis:** Sygma / Diaro Listen CLb; **NASA:** Goddard Space Flight Center (GPN-2000-001331) Cb. **385 Popperfoto:** Reuters / Andrew Winning. **384/385 Corbis:** Reuters / Lucas Jackson (c). **386 Getty:** Stone / David Olsen BL; **OSF:** Warren Faidley TR. **386/387 Getty:** Taxi / Ron Chapple B. **387 Getty:** Photodisc Green CbR; **OSF:** Michael Leach C; **SPL:** Simon Fraser CaL; **Visible Earth:** Provided by the SeaWiFS Project, NASA/Goddard Space Flight Center, and ORBIMAGE TLb; Provided by the SeaWiFS Project, NASA/Goddard Space Flight Center, and ORBIMAGE BR. **388 Corbis:** Galen Rowell B; Wolfgang Kaehler TC; **Magnum:** Steve McCurry CRa; **NG:** George Grall TCbL; Medford Taylor C; Patricia Rasmussen; CbL; **SPL:** Astrid & Hanns-Frieder Michler CRb; National Center for Atmospheric Research CR. **389 Corbis:** Raymond Gehman CLa; The Purcell Team TCL; William A Bake Ca; **Royal Meteorological Society:** CLb; **Visible Earth:** NASA Goddard Space Flight Center Image by Reto Stöckli. Enhancements by Robert Simmon BC. **390 Corbis:** Bettmann TCRb; Darrell Gulin B; **NG:** Priitt Esilind CL. **391 Corbis:** Ecoscene / Nick Hawkes TC; Kit Kittle TR; **OSF:** Stan Osolinski CRa; **SPL:** Picture Researchers Inc BC. **392 AirPhoto:** Jim Wark CL; **Corbis:** Inge Yspeert BL; NASA CRb; **NASA:** Johnson Space Center (STS41B-41-2347) TC; Johnson Space Center (STS51G-46-5) CRa; **NG:** Chris Johns BCR; **SPL:** Peter Menzel CR. **393 Corbis:** Jim Zuckerman B; W Perry Conway TCR; **Gene E. Moore:** CLa, CRa, CaL, CaR.

Endpapers AirPhoto: Jim Wark.

Jacket pictures
Front jacket: **OSF:** Olivier Grunewald
Back jacket: **Still:** UNEP / R Bernardo
Front Flap: **Joe Cornish**

Additional illustrations
Centrepiece artworks on the following pages by **Planetary Visions Ltd:** 34–35, 36–37, 40–41, 302–303, 362–363, 364–365, 368–369.

All other images © Dorling Kindersley
For further information see: **www.dkimages.com.**